TREATISE ON SEDIMENTATION

TREATISE

ON

SEDIMENTATION

PREPARED UNDER THE AUSPICES OF THE COMMITTEE
ON SEDIMENTATION, DIVISION OF GEOLOGY
AND GEOGRAPHY, NATIONAL RESEARCH
COUNCIL OF THE NATIONAL
ACADEMY OF SCIENCES

BY

WILLIAM H. TWENHOFEL

*The University of Wisconsin, Department of Geology
and Geography, Madison, Wisconsin*

AND COLLABORATORS

*in two volumes,
volume two*

Second Edition, Completely Revised

DOVER PUBLICATIONS, INC.
NEW YORK

This new Dover edition, first published in 1961, is an unabridged and unaltered republication of the second (1932) edition of the work published by The Williams & Wilkins Company in 1926.

The work has previously appeared in one volume, but this Dover edition is published in two volumes.

Library of Congress Catalog Card Number: 62-255

Manufactured in the United States of America

Dover Publications, Inc.
180 Varick Street
New York 14, N. Y.

CONTENTS

Volume Two

CHAPTER VI

STRUCTURES, TEXTURES, AND COLORS OF SEDIMENTS

CHAPTER VII

ENVIRONMENTS OR REALMS OF SEDIMENTATION

CHAPTER VIII

FIELD AND LABORATORY STUDIES OF SEDIMENTS

ILLUSTRATIONS

Volume Two

GYPSUM, ROCK SALT, AND OTHER SALINE RESIDUES

GENERAL CONSIDERATIONS

The most important saline residues are rock salt, gypsum, and anhydrite. There are many others of importance, but few of them form rock masses. The chief process involved in the formation of these substances is the evaporation of water in which the constituent materials are contained in solution, although some, as gypsum, may be precipitated by chemical reactions without evaporation, and a few have resulted from the freezing of water. Some are formed through replacement of other substances, gypsum replacing limestone probably being the most common example, and some are developed through metamorphism of saline residues due to original precipitation.

The various substances may be divided into chlorides, sulphates, carbonates, nitrates, and borates. The important chlorides are rock salt ($NaCl$), sylvite (KCl), douglasite ($K_2FeCl_4 \cdot 2H_2O$), carnallite ($KMgCl_3 \cdot 6H_2O$), tachyhydrite ($2MgCl_2 \cdot CaCl_2 \cdot 12H_2O$), and bischofite ($MgCl_2 \cdot 6H_2O$). The sulphates are many. Those occurring in the Stassfurt region are anhydrite ($CaSO_4$), gypsum ($CaSO_4 \cdot 2H_2O$), glauberite ($CaSO_4 \cdot Na_2SO_4$), polyhalite ($CaSO_4 \cdot MgSO_4 \cdot K_2SO_4 \cdot 2H_2O$), krugite ($K_2SO_4 \cdot 4CaSO_4 \cdot MgSO_4 \cdot 2H_2O$), kieserite ($MgSO_4 \cdot H_2O$), epsomite ($MgSO_4 \cdot 7H_2O$), vanthoffite ($MgSO_4 \cdot 3Na_2SO_4$), bloedite (astrakanite) ($MgSO_4 \cdot Na_2SO_4 \cdot 4H_2O$), loewite ($MgSO_4 \cdot Na_2SO_4 \cdot 2\frac{1}{2}H_2O$), langbeinite ($2MgSO_4 \cdot K_2SO_4$), leonite ($MgSO_4 \cdot K_2SO_4 \cdot 4H_2O$), picromerite ($MgSO_4 \cdot K_2SO_4 \cdot 6H_2O$), aphthitalite ($K_3Na(SO_4)_3$), and kainite ($MgSO_4 \cdot KCl \cdot 3H_2O$). Celestite is also present. Other sulphates which are formed in the bitter lakes are thenardite (Na_2SO_4), hanksite ($9Na_2SO_4 \cdot 2Na_2CO_3 \cdot KCl$), and others of rare occurrence. The carbonates are calcite, aragonite, dolomite, thermonatrite ($Na_2CO_3 \cdot H_2O$), natron ($Na_2CO_3 \cdot 10H_2O$), trona ($Na_2CO_3 \cdot NaHCO_3 \cdot 2H_2O$), and gaylussite ($CaCO_3 \cdot Na_2CO_3 \cdot 5H_2O$). The nitrates are those of sodium and potassium. The borates are borax ($Na_2B_4O_7 \cdot 10H_2O$), colemanite ($Ca_2B_6O_{11} \cdot 5H_2O$), searlesite ($Na_2O \cdot B_2O_3 \cdot 4SiO_2 \cdot 2H_2O$), ulexite ($NaCaB_5O_9 \cdot 8H_2O$), and kernite[661] ($Na_2B_4O_7 \cdot 4H_2O$).

If pure, these various salts are transparent to white and gray in color. Not uncommonly, however, they contain other substances, as clay, iron oxide, organic matter, and then the colors become blue, red, and even black. Amorphous or microcrystalline gypsum and anhydrite are known as rock gypsum or alabaster, and this is the variety commonly occurring in thick beds. The macrocrystalline variety of gypsum, selenite, ordinarily occurs

[661] Schaller, W. T., Science, vol. 67, 1928, p. x.

as individual crystals in clays and as veins and bands in the clay beds associated with the rock gypsum. Crystals of selenite are also not uncommon in clayey strata containing some carbonaceous matter. Satin spar, a variety with fibrous structure, is commonly found in veins. Gypsite is an earthy form of gypsum.

In so far as these substances are the result of evaporation, they develop through evaporation of sea water, the waters of lakes and playas, or waters brought to the surface by springs or capillary action.

The average salinity of sea water is 35 permille or 35 grams of salts per liter of normal sea water. This is about 3.5 per cent of the water by weight. The salinity differs slightly in the different oceans, and there are decided differences in different parts of the same ocean, it being lowest in those parts receiving a large influx of fresh water and highest in confined bodies adjacent to dry lands. Krümmel shows for each ocean a low content in a belt adjacent to the equator, a rise toward each of the two Tropics, and a fall toward the polar regions.[662] The content is high in such waters as the Red Sea and such enclosed basins as the Dead Sea and Great Salt Lake, being in the former 992.15 permille at the surface and 259.98 permille at 300 meters depth, and in the latter ranging from 137.90 permille to 277.20 permille.[663]

The elements in sea water in percentages and parts per million are given in table 60.[664] Table 61 gives the content estimated as salts in percentages of total solids.[665] This table shows that sodium and magnesium chlorides constitute the major portion of the salts in solution. The following elements have been detected: Aluminum, barium, boron, cæsium, cobalt, copper, iron, lead, lithium, manganese, nickel, radium, rubidium, strontium, and zinc. Moberg states that the elements given in the second part "of the table bear a constant ratio to each other and the total salt" and Bigelow[666] is in accord in his statement that "Whether the sample be taken in the Atlantic, in the Pacific, or in the Indian Ocean, in high latitudes or in low, the total solutes are found to be about 54 per cent chlorine; about 31 per cent sodium; about 4 per cent magnesium, about 1 per cent potassium; 1 per cent calcium; and about 0.2 per cent bromine, with about 8 per cent of sulphate radicals, about 0.2 per cent of carbonate radicals." While it is not certain that the ratios of these elements have always been as they are at present, their present distribution in all seas in approximately the same

[662] Krümmel, O., Handbuch der Ozeanographie, 1907, p. 334.

[663] Clarke, F. W., Data of geochemistry, 1924, pp. 157, 171.

[664] Moberg, E. G., Letter of August 25, 1931.

[665] Grabau, A. W., Geology of the non-metallic mineral deposits, vol. 1, Principles of salt deposition, 1920, p. 51.

[666] Bigelow, H. W., Oceanography, 1931, p. 110.

ratios is strongly suggestive that such may always have been the case. It is not improbable that the total solid content of the sea has experienced considerable variation throughout geologic time.

The evaporation of sea or other salt waters precipitates the substances in solution in reverse order to solubility and extent of saturation, with various modifications arising from interactions of the various substances in

TABLE 60

ELEMENT	PER CENT		PART PER MILLION
O	85.8	} 96.5	858,000
H	10.7		107,000
Cl	1.94		19,400
Na	1.14		11,400
Mg	0.14		1,400
S	0.09	} 3.4	900
Ca	0.04		400
K	0.04		400
Br	0.007		70
C	0.003		30
F	0.00008		0.8
Si	0.00002		0.2
N	0.00002		0.2
I	0.000005		0.05
As	0.000001		0.01
P	0.000002		0.02
Ag	0.000001		0.01
Au			0.000,005

TABLE 61

SALT	PER CENT OF TOTAL SOLIDS	GRAMS PER LITER
NaCl	77.758	27.213
MgCl₂	10.878	3.807
MgSO₄	4.737	1.658
CaSO₄	3.600	1.260
K₂SO₄	2.465	0.863
CaCO₃*	0.345	0.123
MgBr₂	0.217	0.076
	100.000	

* Includes all traces of other salts.

solution to temperature, sunlight, and probably other factors. The problem has been investigated by Usiglio,[667] who evaporated sea water obtained in

[667] Usiglio, J., Analyse de l'eau de la Méditerranée sur les Côtes de France, Annales des Chim. et Phys., vol. 27, 1849, pp. 92–107; Études sur la composition de l'eau de la Méditerranée sur l'exploitation des sels qu'elle contient, Ibid., 1849, pp. 172–191; see also Clarke, F. W., Data of geochemistry, Bull. 770, U. S. Geol. Surv., 1924, p. 220.

the Mediterranean off Cette on the south coast of France, the water having an initial salinity of 38.45 permille. Preliminary analyses showed that the composition of the water with possible combinations was as given in table 62.

This experiment was conducted in duplicate, 5 liters of sea water being used in each case, one sample having been obtained 3000 meters from shore and about 1 meter beneath the surface, the other 5000 meters from shore and at the same depth. Each sample was evaporated in a large porcelain dish kept in a hot house with temperature maintained at 40°C., the air being kept dry by use of quicklime. From time to time the liquids were removed from the hot house, cooled to ordinary temperature of 21°C., the liquids decanted, and the precipitates filtered, dried, and weighed. The order of precipitation and quantities of the different precipitates are given in table 63, the weights being in grams per liter.

Evaporation of the last bitterns gave interesting and variable results: The fall of temperature from that of day to that of night precipitated additional magnesium sulphate, which with warming of the water to day temperatures partially redissolved. Further evaporation precipitated sodium chloride and magnesium sulphate; cooling led to precipitation of more magnesium sulphate; and still further evaporation formed a deposit of magnesium sulphate, the double sulphate of magnesium and potassium, sodium chloride, and magnesium chloride and bromide. Continued evaporation and decantation led in succession to the deposition of the double chloride of potassium and magnesium with which at times was associated the double sulphate of potassium and magnesium. The final precipitate was magnesium chloride ($MgCl_2 \cdot 6H_2O$). This gave an order of deposition of salts from the mother liquor as follows:

1. Night—epsomite—$MgSO_4 \cdot 7H_2O$
2. Day—hexahydrate—$MgSO_4 \cdot 6H_2O$; halite—NaCl; and rarely potash salts
3. Night—epsomite—$MgSO_4 \cdot 7H_2O$
4. Day—hexahydrate—$MgSO_4 \cdot 6H_2O$; schönite—$MgSO_4 \cdot K_2SO_4 \cdot 6H_2O$; halite—NaCl; bischofite—$MgCl_2 \cdot 6H_2O$; magnesium bromide—$MgBr_2$
5. Afternoon—carnallite—$MgCl_2 \cdot KCl \cdot 6H_2O$
6. Night—carnallite, schönite
7. Day—little deposition
8. Afternoon—carnallite
9. Night—carnallite, epsomite
10. Autumn, some months later, temperature 5° to 6°C., bischofite.

The results obtained by Usiglio show that evaporation of sea water produces precipitates, or evaporites,[668] in the following order: calcium carbonate and iron oxide, calcium sulphate with its precipitation overlapping that

[668] Berkey, C. P., The new petrology, Bull. 251, N. Y. State Mus., 1929, pp. 105–118.

TABLE 62

SALT	GRAMS IN 100 GRAMS SEA WATER	GRAMS PER LITER
Fe_2O_3	0.0003	0.003
$CaCO_3$	0.0114	0.117
$CaSO_4$	0.1357	1.392
$MgSO_4$	0.2477	2.541
$MgCl_2$	0.3219	3.302
KCl	0.0505	0.518
$NaBr$	0.0556	0.570
$NaCl$	2.9424	30.183
Water	96.2345	987.175
Totals	100.0000	1025.801
$CaSO_4 \cdot 2H_2O$	0.1716	1.76
$MgSO_4 \cdot 7H_2O$	0.5051	5.181

TABLE 63

VOLUME	Fe_2O_3	$CaCO_3$	$CaSO_4 \cdot 2H_2O$	$NaCl$	$MgSO_4$	$MgCl_3$	$NaBr$	KCl
1.000								
0.533	0.0030	0.0642						
0.316		Trace						
0.245		Trace						
0.190		0.0530	0.5600					
0.1445			0.5620					
0.131			0.1840					
0.112			0.1600					
0.095			0.0508	3.2614	0.0040	0.0078		
0.064			0.1476	9.6500	0.0130	0.0356		
0.039			0.0700	7.8960	0.0262	0.0434	0.0728	
0.0302			0.0144	2.6240	0.0174	0.0150	0.0358	
0.023				2.2720	0.0254	0.0240	0.0518	
0.0162				1.4040	0.5382	0.0274	0.0620	
Total.......	0.0030	0.1172	1.7488	27.1074	0.6242	0.1532	0.2224	
Salts in last bittern..................				2.5885	18.545	3.1640	0.3300	0.5339
Total solids.	0.0030	0.1172	1.7488	29.6959	2.4787	3.3172	0.5524	0.5339

of calcium carbonate, sodium chloride with precipitation beginning before completion of that of calcium sulphate and continuing to association with precipitates of other sulphates, chlorides, and bromides.

This theoretical succession of salt deposits does not always obtain. In many cases gypsum or anhydrite does not have underlying strata of calcium carbonate. There are also occurrences of rock salt without the calcium sulphate, although the latter usually occurs somewhere in the region in the same formation. Salts other than calcium carbonate, calcium sulphate, and sodium chloride are not commonly present in significant quantities.

Naturally these experiments did not extend over periods of time comparable to those responsible for natural deposits and hence did not imitate nature in that respect. It seems certain that the formation of the important deposits of saline residues required long periods of time, that extensive changes of temperature took place during their deposition, that there probably were considerable fluctuations in salinity due to occasional influx of fresh water, and that the deposits ultimately were subjected to high pressures and rise of temperature, consequent upon burial. Usiglio did not obtain kieserite, polyhalite, kainite, and anhydrite, the last possibly because the temperature maintained was not sufficiently high.

It should be noted that the order of precipitation shown in Usiglio's experiments does not permit the formation of pure sodium chloride, and that pure calcium sulphate forms over a very narrow range. According to Stieglitz[669] and Wilder,[670] all calcium sulphate deposits formed by evaporation of waters of seas and stream-fed lakes under existing atmospheric conditions with respect to carbon dioxide content must contain 0.9 per cent of calcium carbonate. Carbon dioxide probably has been in the atmosphere from the latter's beginning, but it seems quite certain that large fluctuations have existed. It is also probable that the quantities of lime and also of other salts in solution in the ocean have been subject to variations. The two factors may permit calcium sulphate deposits with an entirely different calcium carbonate content.

As a general proposition, it is probable that incomplete rather than complete evaporation of a salt-water body has been the rule, and that a concentration has not often been attained to bring about precipitation of the mother-liquor salts, or even of the sodium chloride, and that calcium sulphate is commonly the end product of evaporation. There seems to be a greater number of calcium sulphate deposits than of sodium chloride. Also, after deposition the salts of latest precipitation are so soluble that their subsequent re-solution is likely unless a covering of impervious material, as clay, compels their preservation. It is probable that large bodies very

[669] Stieglitz, J., The tidal and other problems, Publ. 107, Carnegie Inst. of Washington, 1909.

[670] Wilder, F. A., Some conclusions in regard to the origin of gypsum, Bull. Geol. Soc. Am., vol. 33, 1922, pp. 386–394.

rarely reached the mother-liquor stage of concentration. In small bodies the opportunities for the dissipation of the mother-liquor salts are so great that the chances of preservation are small.

Calcium sulphate exists in nature in the two forms of gypsum and anhydrite. It is not certain, however, that present forms are those of the times of deposition. Under surface conditions in pure water, anhydrite slowly changes into gypsum at almost any temperature.[671] Such is known to have occurred in the deposits of New York, Ontario, Nova Scotia, Kansas, and many other localities. On the other hand, if gypsum is buried sufficiently deeply, both the increase in pressure and the increase in temperature favor its dehydration and change to anhydrite. Van't Hoff and Weigert[672] found that when solutions of calcium sulphate are evaporated in open containers under atmospheric pressure, gypsum or anhydrite is deposited depending upon the temperature reached at saturation. Below 66°C. the precipitate is gypsum, above that temperature anhydrite. The presence of other salts in the solution lowers the boundary temperature for gypsum-anhydrite deposition, and if the other salt is sodium chloride, the critical temperature is 30°C.; and Vater[673] concludes that only with temperatures above this boundary can calcium sulphate separate as anhydrite. For concentrated solutions of sodium chloride Van't Hoff and Weigert found that anhydrite begins to form at 25°C.[674] and thus "from the beginning of rock salt deposition only anhydrite is to be reckoned with." Variations in temperature would give rise to alternations of gypsum and anhydrite.

As most saline residues seem to have originated under arid conditions, it seems probable that anhydrite was formed in hot desert regions with tropical and subtropical climates, and that the deposition of gypsum took place in the cooler deserts of temperate regions.

Van't Hoff and his associates studied the formation of salts occurring in saline residues as single substances in solution, their interactions when two or more were in solution, and the effects of temperature and other factors. At 20°C., 100 g. of water will dissolve 26.4 g. of NaCl or 25.6 g. KCl; at 50°C., 26.8 g. NaCl, or 30 g. KCl, showing very different increases in solubility with rise in temperature. If the two salts are placed in solution, 100 g. of

[671] Goldman, M. I., Petrography of salt dome cap rock, Bull. Am. Assoc. Pet. Geol., vol. 9, 1925, p. 77.

[672] Van't Hoff, J. H., and Weigert, F., Untersuchungen über die Bildungsverhältnisse der oceanischen Salzablagerungen, insbesondere des Stassfurter Salzlagers, Sitzb. k. Preuss. Akad. d. Wiss., vol. 23, 1901, pp. 1140–1148.

[673] Vater, H., Einige Versuche über die Bildung des marinen Anhydrites, Sitzb. k. Preuss. Akad. d. Wiss., 1900, pp. 265–295.

[674] Van't Hoff, J. H., and Weigert, F., op. cit.; Grabau, A. W., Principles of salt deposition, 1920, pp. 61–67, 178.

water at 20°C. will dissolve 20.3 g. NaCl and 10.2 g. KCl, but at 50°C. only 18.5 g. NaCl and an increase in KCl to 14.7 g. It is obvious that evaporation with rise of temperature would precipitate NaCl. This is an application of the Nernst law that the solubility of a salt decreases with the presence in the solution of a second salt with a common ion.[675] If a salt with no common ions is introduced into the solution, the solubility is increased in accordance with the Noyes generalization.[676] It is obvious also that in a solution so complex as sea water there would be different degrees of solubility as temperatures changed and different substances were precipitated. Each of the three cations, Na, K, and Mg, and also the Ca, can unite with each of the two anions of Cl and SO_4, so that many combinations are possible, and the single compounds might unite with each other to form

TABLE 64

DOUBLE SALTS	COMPOSITION	MOLS. IN 1000 MOLS. H_2O.						TEMPERATURE
		NaCl	KCl	MgCl$_2$	Na$_2$SO$_4$	K$_2$SO$_4$	MgSO$_4$	
								°C.
Carnallite..............	$MgCl_2 \cdot KCl \cdot 6H_2O$		6	89				25
Schönite...............	$MgSO_4 \cdot K_2SO_4 \cdot 6H_2O$					11	40	25
Glaserite...............	$3K_2SO_4 \cdot Na_2SO_4$	88	30		9			25
Kainite................	$MgSO_4 \cdot KCl \cdot 3H_2O$	11	12	61			12	25
Leonite................	$2MgSO_4 \cdot K_2SO_4 \cdot 4H_2O$	24	20	40			17	25
Astrakanite............	$Na_2SO_4 \cdot MgSO_4 \cdot 4H_2O$	75		2			27	25
Langbeinite............	$2MgSO_4 \cdot K_2SO_4 \ldots \ldots$	43	42	36			11	83
Loewite................	$2MgSO_4 \cdot 2Na_2SO_4 \cdot 5H_2O$..	53		34			12	83
Vanthoffite............	$MgSO_4 \cdot 3Na_2SO_4$	86		13			12	83

double salts, and as water is present each of these might unite with water to form hydrates. This last might be prevented in the presence of such dehydrating materials as $CaCl_2$ or $MgCl_2$.

Table 64 lists the double salts, occurring in the Stassfurt deposits, which have been shown by Van't Hoff and his associates to be capable of formation at the temperatures and from the solutions shown.

The temperature of 83°C. or 181.4°F. is too high to have extensive prevalence in surface waters, and extensive occurrence of langbeinite, loewite, and vanthoffite probably should be referred to changes subsequent to deposition.

With waters at 25°C., with composition in molecules per thousand mole-

[675] Nernst, W., Theoretische Chemie, 1926, p. 613.
[676] Noyes, A. A., Zeits. phys. Chem., Bd. 6, 1890, p. 241, and subsequent papers.

cules of water of 24 NaCl, 15.5 KCl, 40.7 $MgCl_2$, and 20 $MgSO_4$, the condition of saturation for these salts, the above students found the following listed salts and sodium chloride to separate on evaporation in the order listed.

1. Magnesium sulphate
2. Magnesium sulphate and kainite
3. Hexahydrate and kainite
4. Kieserite and kainite
5. Kieserite and carnallite
6. Kieserite, carnallite, and magnesium chloride

From sea waters of normal proportion at 25°C., containing in molecules 100 NaCl, 2.2 KCl, 7.8 $MgCl_2$, and 3.8 $MgSO_4$ to 1000 molecules H_2O, the salts of table 65 separated in the order and quantities shown. This is saturated for NaCl, but not for the other salts.

TABLE 65

	ROCK SALT	KIESERITE	KAINITE	CARNALLITE	BISCHOFITE
1	95.40				
2	4.42	1.05	2.02		
3	0.03	0.35		0.10	
4	0.15	0.38		0.08	7.62
Totals......	100.00	1.78	2.02	0.18	7.62

The relations of K_2 to Mg, and SO_4 to Mg, in salt deposits are different from what they are theoretically in sea water, as shown in the following figures:[677]

	K_2:Mg	SO_4:Mg
Sea water theoretically................................	1:10.9	1:3
Salt deposits...	1:4.33	1:1.57

A comparison of the relative proportions in terms of thickness of deposits of the different common salts possible in sea water compared to the same salts in the Stassfurt deposits is given in table 66.[678] The rock salt is taken as 100 meters. This table shows an increase in anhydrite above that which may be expected from direct evaporation of sea water, but decreases in magnesium and potash, both forming salts that are quite soluble and hence readily removed.

[677] D'Ans, J., Untersuchungen über die Salzsysteme ozeanischer Salzablagerungen, Kali, 1915, p. 268.
[678] Erdmann, E., Die Entstehung der Kalisalzlagerstätten, Zeits. Angew. Chemie, vol. 21, 1908, pp. 1685–1702.

The complete evaporation of the waters of an arm of the ocean or a salt lake would not produce a great thickness of salt over the entire area of deposition. At the base would be a thin band of calcium carbonate containing iron oxide; this would be succeeded upward by calcium sulphate, either in the form of gypsum or anhydrite; and the calcium sulphate would be overlain by rock salt succeeded by the salts of the last bitterns. The calcium sulphate would merge at the base with calcium carbonate and at the top with sodium chloride, and the latter toward the top would be associated with, and gradually pass into the salts of the last bitterns. After a sea water has evaporated to the extent of precipitating most of the calcium sulphate, some of the remainder of the latter may unite with sodium sulphate to form glauberite, as is now occurring in the Gulf of Kara Boghaz, and as this concentration increases, langbeinite may form. These two salts are

TABLE 66

	SEA WATER—THICKNESS OF KINDS OF SALTS FORMED FROM PRECIPITATES	STASSFURT DEPOSITS—THICKNESS OF KINDS OF SALTS PRESENT
	meters	*meters**
Anhydrite..............................	3.4	5.7
Rock salt...............................	100.0	100.0
Kieserite...............................	7.2	2.2
Carnallite..............................	14.0	4.7
Bischofite..............................	23.5	

* If the anhydrite beneath the rock and other salt beds is considered, this figure becomes 20.4.

both present in primary form in the anhydrite region of the older rock salt of the Stassfurt district. Each 1000 feet of average sea water would make a deposit about 15 feet thick, of which only 0.7 foot would be gypsum. To form a bed of gypsum with thickness of 10 feet would require the evaporation of sea water equivalent to a depth of around 14,000 feet. It may be considered impossible that a water body with depth of 14,000 feet ever reached the degree of concentration necessary to deposit calcium sulphate. But thicknesses of calcium sulphate of many hundreds of feet are known, hence it is obvious that their origin cannot be due to simple evaporation of an enclosed body of water, and exceptional conditions for their formation must have existed. Likewise, salt beds of such immense thickness exist that direct evaporation of a water body cannot be responsible for their origin.

Among the thick gypsum or anhydrite deposits of North America are the following: At Hillsborough, Nova Scotia, there is a formation of essentially pure gypsum and anhydrite with thickness of around 250 feet.[679] The calcium sulphate beds of New York range in thickness to about 75 feet and have been stated to lie entirely above the salt beds of the same region. This is very questionable in many instances and is certainly not true in some.[680] It was Dana's[681] opinion that the calcium sulphates of the Salina resulted from the alteration of limestone. This probably was the case for some, but there seem to be few facts supporting this hypothesis of origin for most of the New York calcium sulphate deposits. The salt and gypsum beds range through a thickness of 1000 to 1500 feet, with maximum thickness of rock salt exceeding 300 feet and with beds of pure or nearly pure rock salt ranging in thickness up to around 75 feet, and in a well at Watkins a bed of rock salt 265 feet thick has been recorded. The maximum thickness in Kansas of individual beds of calcium sulphate is about 60 feet; a somewhat greater thickness is given for Oklahoma.[682] Udden[683] has described a well core from western Texas which contains calcium sulphate through 1950 feet, of which 1164 feet represent an essentially continuous deposit of anhydrite. The entire calcium sulphate portion of the core is laminated, with the units averaging less than 2 mm. in thickness. These laminations may have seasonal significance, and this hypothesis has been suggested for similar lamination in other salt deposits. The rock-salt beds of the Permian basin of western Texas also have great thickness.

In general, the thickness of rock salt in the regions of its occurrence exceeds the thickness of the calcium sulphate in the same region. In some cases the latter may have a greater thickness than given in well logs, because of its being identified by drillers as limestone. Beds of carbonate may lie immediately or not far below those of calcium sulphate, but in many instances the underlying beds are shale and less often sandstone.

The salt beds of the geologic column are usually without fossils, and such is very commonly, but not always, the case in the associated strata. Organic matter has been found in salt beds, and in a few instances fossils seem to be

[679] Kramm, H. E., The Hillsborough gypsum district, Guide Book, no. 1, pt. ii, 13th Intern. Geol. Cong., Geol. Surv. Canada, 1913, p. 362.

[680] Hartnagel, C. A., Culmination and decline of the Salina sea, in Bull. 69, New York State Mus., 1903, pp. 1158, 1160; Alling, H. L., The geology and origin of the Silurian salt of New York State, Bull. 275, New York State Mus., 1928; Newland, D. H., Recent progress in the study of the Salina formation, Rept. Comm. on Sedimentation, Nat. Research Council, 1927–1928, pp. 36–43; Idem., The gypsum resources and gypsum industry of New York, Bull. 283, New York State Mus., 1929.

[681] Dana, J. D., Manual of geology, 4th ed., 1925, p. 554.

[682] Snider, L. C., The gypsum and salt of Oklahoma, Bull. 11, Oklahoma Geol. Surv., 1913, p. 28.

[683] Udden, J. A., Laminated anhydrite in Texas, Bull. Geol. Soc. Am., vol. 35, 1924, pp. 347–354.

abundant. The upper Eocene of the Paris Basin contains a 65-foot gypsum member which is said to contain bones of mammals, shells, and wood.[684]

TABLE 67
ANALYSES OF ROCK SALT

	1	2
NaCl.	97.51	82.71
MgCl$_2$.	0.10	
Na$_2$SO$_4$.	0.57	5.32
K$_2$SO$_4$.		8.43
CaSO$_4$.	1.51	
Na$_2$CO$_3$.		2.46
Fe$_2$O$_3$.	0.11	0.15
Insoluble.	0.20	
H$_2$O.		0.82
	100.00	99.89

1. Salt from Kingman, Kansas.
2. Salt from bed in Katwee Lake, north of Albert Edward Nyanza region in Central Africa.

TABLE 68
ANALYSES OF GYPSUM

	1	2
SO$_3$.	46.18	46.18
Cl.	Trace	0.03
Al$_2$O$_3$, Fe$_2$O$_3$.	0.10	0.08
CaO.	32.37	32.33
MgO.	Trace	0.05
Na$_2$O.		0.14
K$_2$O.	0.10	
H$_2$O.	20.94	20.96
Insoluble.	0.10	0.05
	99.79	99.82

1. Gypsum from Hillsborough, Nova Scotia.
2. Gypsum from Alabaster, Michigan.

Under the bar theory of origin of salt deposits (p. 496 *et seq.*) an abundance of fossils is to be expected. The fact that such is not commonly the case

[684] Snider, L. C., op. cit., p. 28.

suggests origin under conditions different from those postulated in that theory.

Tables 67 to 69 give analyses of rock salt, gypsum, and bittern from several localities.[685]

Important deposits of saline residues are those of Stassfurt, and the deposits of the Salina formation of New York and adjacent states; the gypsum, anhydrite, and salt deposits of the Permian of Kansas, Oklahoma, and Texas and the Permian and Triassic of the Great Plains country in general; the various salt deposits of the playas and extinct and shrinking lakes of California, Nevada, and other western states; the nitrate deposits of western South America; etc. These are considered in greater or less detail in succeeding paragraphs.

TABLE 69

ANALYSES OF BITTERN

	1	2
Cl	56.33	63.93
Br	0.94	1.16
I		Trace
SO$_4$	9.28	0.06
Na	22.23	10.24
K	2.58	5.27
Ca	0.38	11.26
Mg	7.56	8.08
	99.30	100.00
Salinity permille	318.20	325.67

1. Bittern from Leslie Salt Refining Work, San Mateo, Calif.
2. Bittern from maximum concentration, Syracuse, N. Y.

The section given below shows the succession of strata in a portion of the salt beds of the Salina basin of Kansas. There is great variation in thickness of the individual salt beds, but they are known to have a maximum thickness of about 275 feet. The section, which is typical, shows that shales and limestones are the common rocks separating the salt beds of this basin and that sandstone is rare.

[685] Clarke, F. W., op. cit., pp. 231–233.

Record of well at Lyons, Kansas[686]

	Feet
Soil and sandy loam	45
Sandstone	10
Clays and shale	55
Sandstones	88
Red sandy shale	56
Red clay	18
Soft limestone	3
Gypsum and limestone	9
Blue shale	4
Red and blue shale mixed with gypsum	292
Dark gray and reddish gray shales	213
Rock salt, reddish at bottom	13
Gray shale	8
Rock salt	10.5
Gray shale and salt mixed	3
Gray shale	4
Rock salt	9
Rock salt and shale	1.5
Rock salt	8.5
Gray shale	1.5
Rock salt	8.5
Shale	1
Rock salt	6.5
Rock salt and shale	11
Rock salt, crystal	4
Rock salt and shale	25.5
Dark red shale	6
Rock salt and rock	10
Rock salt	17
Rock, and salt and shale	40
Rock salt	2
Shale	1
Rock salt	9.5
Shale	0.5
Rock and salt and a little shale	10

The Permian basin of western Texas, the Michigan basin, and the Salina basin of New York would yield somewhat similar sections. A section from the Permian basin of western Texas would show a much greater development of calcium sulphate in some localities, a great development of limestone or dolomites in others, and some sections would show a great thickness of salt beds.

Probably the most extensively studied salt deposits are those of the Stassfurt region, and these likewise possess the most extensive known occurrences

[686] Haworth, E., Mineral resources of Kansas, 1896, Article on salt.

of the mother-liquor salts. The descending section of the Stassfurt region is as follows:[687]

10. Surface materials, variable thickness.

9. Shales, sandstones, and clays, variable thickness.

8. Younger rock salt, variable thickness, missing in places.

7. Anhydrite, usually present, 30 to 80 meters.

6. Salt clay, occasionally absent, average thickness 5 to 10 meters.

5. Carnallite zone, 15 to 40 meters thick. At one place a bed of rock salt lies between 5 and 6, and in parts of the region kainite overlies the carnallite, is in turn overlain by "sylvenite" or hartsalz, and that in turn by schönite.

4. Kieserite zone.

3. Polyhalite.

2. Older rock salt and anhydrite. The anhydrite is in layers whose average thickness is about 7 mm.; these layers separate salt units of 8 to 9 cm. thickness. These layers have been referred to seasonal deposition, but the validity of the interpretation is uncertain. Zones 2–4 have a thickness ranging from 150 to perhaps 1000 meters.

1. Anhydrite and gypsum.

A well drilled near Amsdorf gave the following descending section:[688]

	Meters
Sand and gravel	16.30
Clay and gravel	59.40
Red sandstone	88.00
Gypsum	48.30
Older rock salt	1076.90
Anhydrite	2.60
"Stinkstein"	3.50
"Stinkstein" with gypsum	7.00
Gypsum	1.30
Anhydrite with "Stinkstein"(*)	18.70
White, crystalline rock salt	15.00
Anhydrite	41.50
"Zechstein" and "Faule"	3.50
Kupferschiefer	0.54
Weisliegende*	0.46
Total	1383.00

* Stinkstein, Zechstein, Faule, and Weisliegende are German stratigraphic terms.

It was shown by Van't Hoff[689] and his associates that the evaporation of sea water would produce a sequence of salt deposits possible of arrangement

[687] Clarke, F. W., op. cit., p. 223.

[688] Arrhenius, S., and Lachmann, R., Die physikalisch-chemischen Bedingungen bei der Bildung der Salzlagerstätten und ihre Anwendung auf geologische Probleme, Geol. Rundschau, Bd. 3, 1912, p. 151.

[689] Van't Hoff, J. H., Zur Bildung der ozeanischen Ablagerungen, Bd. 2, 1909, p. 40.

into five zones, and several of these zones were further subdivided by Rinne.[690] The result is as follows:

Zones	Van't Hoff		Rinne	
E.	Rock salt with bischo-fite, carnallite, and kieserite	62 m.	Bischofite zone	Sodium chloride with bischofite, kieserite, and carnallite
D.	Rock salt with kieser-ite and carnallite	6 m.	Carnallite zone	Sodium chloride with kieserite and carnallite
C.	Rock salt with kieser-ite and kainite	24 m.	Kainite zone	Sodium chloride with kieserite, kainite, hexa-hydrate, kainite, rei-chardtite, kainite
B.	Rock salt with bloe-dite (astrakanite) or reichardtite	8 m.	K-containing MgSO₄ zone	Sodium chloride with rei-chardtite, leonite
			K-free MgSO₄ zone	Sodium chloride with reichardtite, bloedite (astrakanite)
A.	Rock salt		Polyhalite zone	Sodium chloride with polyhalite
			Anhydrite zone	Sodium chloride with anhydrite
			Gypsum zone	Sodium chloride with gypsum / Sodium chloride without gypsum

The succession in the Stassfurt deposits does not seem to be such as would arise from direct evaporation of sea water. Reference to the table on page 470 shows that there is considerably less magnesium chloride than evaporation of sea water would yield.[691] This, however, is readily explainable on the basis of the high solubility of this salt and its consequent easy removal. There is also too much anhydrite or gypsum. Likewise, the Stassfurt deposits are lacking in, or do not have in well developed form, zones B and E, and the sodium chloride in zone D is far greater than can

[690] Rinne, F., Die geothermischen Metamorphosen und die Dislokationen der deutschen Kalisalzlagerstätten, Fortschritte d. Min., etc., vol. 6, 1920, pp. 101–136 (p. 113).

[691] Erdmann, E., Die Entstehung der Kalisalzlagerstätten, Zeits. Angew. Chemie, vol. 21, 1908, pp. 1685–1702.

exist in a solution saturated in carnallite. Another difference is the presence in the Stassfurt deposit of salt minerals which are not formed on evaporation of sea water under temperature conditions normal to the earth's surface. According to Van't Hoff,[692] the salts listed below, all of which occur in the Stassfurt deposits, required for their formation temperatures as follows.

Glauberite, formed above 10°C. (40°F.)
Hexahydrate, formed above 13°C. (57.4°F.)
Thenardite, formed above 15.5°C. (61.9°F.)
Kieserite, formed above 18°C. (64.4°F.)
Langbeinite, formed above 37°C. (98.6°F.)
Loewite, formed above 43°C. (109.4°F.)
Vanthoffite, formed above 46°C. (114.8°F.)
Loewite with glaserite, formed above 57°C. (134.6°F.)
Loewite with vanthoffite, formed above 60°C. (140°F.)
Kieserite with sylvite, formed above 72°C. (161.6°F.)

It is improbable that several of these temperatures are likely in surface waters, although it is known that temperatures above 70°C. do occur in the deeper waters of some salt lakes.[693] Hence, it has been concluded that in many cases the salts are not in their original condition, but by reason of the pressure to which they have been subjected through burial beneath thick accumulations of sediments and crustal deformation, and of the increase in temperature consequent to burial and deformation, there has been recrystallization of the original minerals, resulting in the formation of new salts (designated metasalts by Grabau), so that the existing deposits may properly be said to have been metamorphosed.[694]

ENVIRONMENTAL CONDITIONS LEADING TO THE DEPOSITION OF SALINE RESIDUES

It is thought that the different varieties or types of saline residues result from the occurrence of the following conditions or environments: (1) deposition from springs through evaporation, freezing, or other changes; (2) deposition from ground water upon, or just beneath the surface; (3) mechanical deposition by wind and possibly by water; (4) evaporation of the

[692] Van't Hoff, J. H., Zeits. Electrochemie, vol. 2, 1905, p. 709.

[693] Grabau, A. W., Geology of non-metallic mineral deposits, vol. 1, Principles of salt deposition, 1920, p. 77.

[694] On this phase of salt deposits there should be consulted Rinne, F., Die geothermischen Metamorphosen und die Dislokationen der deutschen Kalisalzlagerstätten, Fortschritte d. Min. etc., vol. 6, 1920, pp. 101–136 (113); Arrhenius, S., and Lachmann, R., Die physikalisch-chemischen Bedingungen bei der Bildung der Salzlagerstätten, etc., Geol. Rundschau, Bd. 3, 1912, pp. 139–157; Lachmann, R., Ekzeme und Tektonic, Zentralbl. f. Min. etc., 1917, pp. 414–426, Jänecke, E., Die Entstehung der deutschen Kalisalzlager, 1915, pp. 66–97. Rinne gives an extensive bibliography, pp. 129–136.

waters of playas, lakes, and marginal or isolated parts of the ocean or large lakes; (5) replacement of other substances.

Deposits of Springs

The various constituents of saline residues are present in greater or less abundance in most rocks. Circulating waters acquire these to some degree and ultimately may deposit them in rocks adjacent to, or upon, the surface, the different substances forming combinations permitted by the conditions. The most common substance seems to be calcium carbonate, already described, but any of the saline residue salts listed as primary may be deposited; most common are gypsum and rock salt, each possibly containing other rarer salts, the deposition ordinarily taking place about those points where the waters reach the surface as springs. The waters may be divided on the basis of maximum substances in solution into chloride, sulphate, carbonate, siliceous, nitrate, phosphate, borate, and acid waters, but there is every possible gradation among these different types.[695]

The gypsum deposited about springs is composed of small irregular crystals and plates and is known as gypsite or gypsum earth. The material is very soft and in some instances powdery. As connoted by the term earth, there is considerable incorporation of clay, sand, organic matter, etc. Deposits of gypsum of this origin are limited in extent and thickness, a few acres in area and 15 feet in thickness being probable maxima.[696]

Spring deposits of sodium chloride occur in Alberta and Manitoba, one described by Kindle having been formed about a spring which derives its waters from Silurian and Devonian limestones, the deposit covering an area 40 by 15 feet with an average thickness of about 10 inches. The interesting feature connected with this deposit is the fact that the precipitation of the salt is not a consequence of evaporation, but of the winter freezing.[697] McConnell,[698] Wallace,[699] and Rutherford[700] have described salt deposits of similar origin in the same general region.

Springs in the Mason Valley of the Lahontan Basin deposit sodium sulphate on the surface over which the waters flow. The waters are of

[695] For analyses see Clarke, F. W., op. cit., pp. 184–202.

[696] Stone, R. W., etc., Gypsum deposits of the United States, Bull. 697, U. S. Geol. Surv., 1920, p. 24.

[697] Kindle, E. M., Separation of salt from saline water and mud, Bull. Geol. Soc. Am., vol. 29, 1918, pp. 471–488.

[698] McConnell, R. G., Ann. Rept. Geol. Surv. Canada, vol. 5, 1893, p. 35 D.

[699] Wallace, R. C., The corrosive action of brine in Manitoba, Jour. Geol., vol. 25, 1917, pp. 459–466.

[700] Rutherford, R. L., Corrosion by saline waters, Trans. Roy. Soc. Canada, vol. 18, 1924, pp. 31–37.

low salinity and have temperatures ranging from about the mean for the region to 162°F. A section of such a deposit is as follows:[701]

Sodium sulphate with sodium chloride and some calcium carbonate, forms a hard white crust.................................... 1–2 inches

Soft mealy, or clayey sodium sulphate, calcium carbonate, calcium sulphate, etc... 2–7 inches

Clear, transparent crystals of sodium sulphate with some earthy impurities...6–8 feet

Saline clay

Rather uncommon substances in spring deposits are the alums. Their deposition is local, and they are commonly derived either directly or indirectly from the oxidation of sulphides. They occur as incrustations and stalactites about springs, or other places where water issues from the ground. Alunite ($K_2O \cdot 3Al_2O_3 \cdot 4SO_3 \cdot 6H_2O$) and alunogen ($Al_2(SO_4)_3 \cdot 18H_2O$) are the substances most commonly formed, the latter together with halotrichite ($FeSO_4 \cdot Al_2(SO_4)_3 \cdot 24H_2O$) occurring in large quantities in Granite County, New Mexico.[702]

Surface and Subsurface Efflorescences of Salts

Efflorescences are due to the evaporation of ground water brought near or to the surface by capillary action. This takes place in arid and semi-arid regions, giving rise to deposits known in the United States as alkali, caliche, tepetate, and some of the so-called hardpan, in India as reh, and in Egypt as sabach—substances of the same general character. The deposits may be either on the surface, or just beneath it. Irrigation without subsurface drainage hastens accumulation, so that in parts of Montana, Wyoming, and elsewhere, small areas have been abandoned, or have had their productivity impaired through accumulations of alkali which in places cover the ground like a white shroud. The deposits may reach a foot to several feet in thickness, or they may be in the form of isolated concretionary particles, as for instance an occurrence in central Kansas at depths up to about 4 feet beneath the surface which is known as the "kiel" bed.

Possibly the most common surface efflorescent salt is calcium carbonate which, as noted on earlier pages, may reach a thickness up to around a half-dozen feet. Usually parts contain considerable impurity, because of the original materials of the surface, and frequently the structure is pisolitic or concretionary.

[701] Russell, I. C., Geological history of Lake Lahontan, Mon. 11, U. S. Geol. Surv., 1885, p. 48.

[702] Hayes, C. W., The Gila River alum deposits, Bull. 315, U. S. Geol. Surv., 1917, pp. 215–223.

Artificially dried muds studied by Kindle[703] showed that sodium chloride was precipitated in the muds and on the surface in three different forms: an upper layer, a lower layer, and in mud cracks and disseminated through the dry mud. The upper layer was pure white and consisted of minute frost-like crystals. The lower was formed of acicular crystals in vertical position and held a small quantity of clayey matter in the lower part. The salt in the mud cracks and in the dry mud was in the form of cubical crystals with hopper-like faces.

The materials forming the alkali and caliche may be any of the salts to which reference has been made, the most common being calcium, sodium, and potassium sulphates, calcium and sodium carbonates, and calcium and sodium chlorides. They differ with locality, the differences being due to the nature of the rock and soil through which the water has passed on its way to the surface and to the origin of the water. In the analyses of table 70 they are grouped as sulphate-chloride salts and carbonate salts. The nitrate salts constitute an additional group.

The analyses give the chemical composition of the alkali and the arrangement into compounds, but state nothing respecting the varieties of minerals which may be formed therefrom. The presence of water during formation permits a wide range in variety.

Surface salt deposits dominantly composed of sodium carbonate are known as black alkalies; those mostly composed of sodium sulphate are white alkalies. There are all gradations between the two.

Nitrate deposits occur as surface and near-surface efflorescences and as those of caverns and similar relations. The latter generally have been considered derived from bat guano, but it has been shown by Hess[704] that the nitrogen might have been acquired from the soils and rocks above the caves. Hess' arguments have, however, been opposed by Nichols.[705] The complete history of the surface and near-surface deposits of nitrates has not yet been unraveled in a way to meet general acceptance.

Nitrogen compounds are known to form under some conditions of decay of organic matter. Concentrated excrements of birds, bats, and other animals are common sources, and rookeries of birds are well known for their accumulations of guano. These generally are rich in phosphates. Certain bacteria, as those infesting the roots of many Leguminosæ, have ability to fix atmospheric nitrogen. Some nitrogen compounds are also said to form in connection with volcanic activity and through discharges of atmospheric electricity.

[703] Kindle, E. M., op. cit., 1918.

[704] Hess, W. H., The origin of nitrates in cavern earths, Jour. Geol., vol. 8, 1900, pp. 129–134.

[705] Nichols, H. W., Nitrates in cave earths, Jour. Geol., vol. 9, 1901, pp. 236–243.

Nitrate deposits of the caliche type are mostly composed of sodium nitrate with potassium nitrate. One or more of the nitrates of barium, calcium, and magnesium and certain double salts containing nitrogen are usually associated. The most important occurrence of nitrates is in western South America.

TABLE 70

SULPHATE-CHLORIDE SALTS*

	A	B	C	D
NaCl....................................	85.27	70.81	5.93	10.81
Na₂SO₄...................................	1.75	26.38	94.04	53.14
Na₂CO₃..................................	2.59			
K₂SO₄...................................		1.94		32.34
MgCl₂...................................				
CaSO₄...................................				3.71
H₂O.....................................	8.57			
Isol. res................................	1.82			
	100.00	99.13	99.97	100.00

CARBONATE SALTS

	E	F
Na₂CO₃..	65.72	32.58
NaHCO₃..		
Na₂SO₄..		25.28
NaCl..	3.98	14.75
NaNO₃...		19.78
Na₂B₄O₇.......................................	8.42	2.25
K₂SO₄...	20.23	3.95
MgSO₄...	1.65	
KCl...		
(NH₄)CO₃......................................		1.41
SiO₂..		
	100.00	100.00

* From Clarke, F. W., op. cit., pp. 237-238. A and B from Nevada, C from Arizona, D efflorescence on loess from Argentina, E and F from California.

Many hypotheses have been formulated to account for the nitrogen of South American deposits.[706] They have been postulated to have been

[706] Considerations of these various hypotheses are given by Clarke, F. W., Data of geochemistry, Bull. 770, U. S. Geol. Surv., 1924, pp. 254-260, Grabau, A. W., Principles of salt deposition, 1920, pp. 285-289; Penrose, R. A. F., jr., The nitrate deposits of Chili, Jour. Geol., vol. 18, 1910, pp. 1-32; Singewald, J. T., jr., and Miller, B. L., The genesis

derived from guano, from decomposition of great masses of algæ of lakes or
sea, from decomposition of organic matter in soil, from bacterial fixation of
atmospheric nitrogen, from mother liquors of salts deposited in the Andes,
from atmospheric electrical discharges, from volcanic materials and activity,
and from ammoniacal dust blown from the sea. The last stage in the formation of the Chilean nitrates seems to have been deposition following evaporation of ground water, although Sundt[707] has postulated origin in situ of some
of the deposits, the nitrogen having been derived from the atmosphere and
the sodium from decay of feldspathic porphyries.

The South American nitrates are best developed in northern Chili over the
extremely arid lands lying between the Andes and the Pacific Coastal ranges,
where they are associated with rock salt, the latter more extensive and on
the lower areas. The nitrates generally are on the western and deeper
margin of the desert plain between the mountains, where they are underlain
by Jurassic volcanics and recent débris. Typical positions are the lower

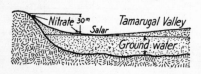 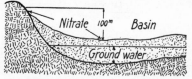

FIG. 62. IDEAL SECTIONS OF THE NITRATE DEPOSITS OF CHILI, (1) TARAPACÁ, (2)
AGUAS BLANCAS

The dotted areas represent gravel, the dashed volcanic rock. After Whitehead, W. L.,
The Chilean nitrate deposits, Econ. Geol., vol. 15, 1920, p. 207.

slopes of the hills rising out of the plain and the terraces or slopes around
the "salares," or salt flats, depressions in the desert plain characterized
principally by rock salt with which are smaller quantities of sodium sulphate and the chlorides and sulphates of calcium, magnesium, and potassium,
but no nitrates except on the Salar del Carmen in the Pampa Central.
The nitrate deposits range from a few to perhaps a hundred feet above a
"salar." Occasionally a deposit occurs over the bottom of a basin. All
gradations of nitrates and other salts seem to be present. Figure 62 shows
ideal relationships. The nitrate beds are known as "calitreras" and the

of the Chilean nitrate deposits, Econ. Geol., vol. 11, 1916, pp. 103–114; and with Sundt,
L., Econ. Geol., vol. 12, 1917, pp. 89–96; Miller, B. L., and Singewald, J. T., jr., The min-
eral deposits of South America, 1919; Whitehead, W. L., The Chilean nitrate deposits,
Econ. Geol., vol. 15, 1920, pp. 187–224. See also Singewald, J. T., jr. and Miller, B. L.,
Boletin de la Sociedad Nacional de Mineria, Nos. 244, 245, June, 1919.

[707] Sundt, L., op. cit., pp. 89–91.

crude nitrate as caliche. A general descending section of the nitrate deposits of the Tarapaca region is as follows:[708]

7. Gravel composed of small, polished, and angular rock fragments with little or no salt.
6. Sandy crystalline salt, dominantly sodium sulphate.
5. Hard, somewhat porous conglomerate of which the cement is sodium sulphate. This conglomerate is known as "panqueque."
4. Soft, white, fluffy sodium sulphate containing 10 to 15 per cent sodium chloride and traces of nitrate.
3. Sands and gravels cemented by salts containing less sulphate than 4, but more chloride and nitrate. This zone is known as "costra" and ranges in thickness to several feet.
2. Gravel cemented by salt with high nitrate content. This zone contains most of the minable ore and is known as caliche. The range in thickness is from a few inches to several feet. It usually forms a hard, compact bed which has a brown or buff color.
1. Fractured rock or gravel, uncemented, frequently containing high salt content, and then known as "congelo," otherwise known as "coba."

Below are stratified sands and gravels to various depths, or bed rock. Zones 4, 5, and 6 are known as "chucho" and range to several feet in thickness. Analyses of chucho, costra, and caliche are given in tables 71 and 72. It quite naturally follows that there is considerable variation.

As shown by the analyses, the nitrogen is mostly in the form of sodium nitrate. This generally occurs as a translucent mass, but it is also present as interlocking crystals, efflorescences, and some other forms. The pure nitrate is white, but impurities give many colors. The mined caliche usually contains 14 to 25 per cent sodium nitrate. Deposits approximating 50 per cent sodium nitrate are now seldom found in quantity.

Other nitrate deposits in South America are in Colombia, Bolivia, and Argentina. A deposit in Argentina lies within the Andes in a playa known as the Salinas Grandes. This deposit is 360 miles from the sea and at an elevation of 3500 meters, with the mountains around rising to 6000 meters. In the center of the playa, rock salt exists to a thickness of 20 to 30 cm. Around the borders of the salt are ulexite nodules, and other borax minerals are also present, suggesting contribution from volcanic sources. This playa is flooded in the spring time by waters from the mountains and is dry in summer. The deposit of one locality in Bolivia is also of interest, as it is composed of 60 per cent potassium nitrate and 30 per cent sodium borate ($Na_2B_4O_7$).

[708] Penrose, R. A. F., jr., op. cit., p. 14; Whitehead, W. L., op. cit., pp. 201–205.

TABLE 71
ANALYSES OF CHUCHO*

Soluble:		
CaO, MgO	14.3	15.3
K_2O	6.2	7.5
Na_2O	24.9	20.9
H_2SO_4	30.4	46.5
HNO_3	5.9	
Phosphoric acid	2.9	3.9
Iodic acid	0.3	
HCl	10.6	4.2
H_2O	4.7	2.1
	100.2	100.4
Insoluble	79.3	89.3

*Whitehead, W. L., op. cit., p. 202.

TABLE 72
ANALYSES OF COSTRA AND CALICHE*

	COSTRA*	CALICHE†
$NaNO_3$	13.6	22.73
KNO_3	1.3	1.65
NaCl	19.3	41.90
Na_2SO_4	6.7	0.94
$MgSO_4$	9.7	3.13
$CaSO_4$	2.7	4.80
$Na_2B_4O_7$		0.53
$NaIO_3$	0.1	0.07
NH_4 salts		Trace
Na_2CrO_4		Trace
H_2O	2.4	1.75
Insoluble	44.0	22.50
	99.8	100.00

The following minerals have been recognized in the caliche: anhydrite, gypsum, the-nardite, mirabilite, bloedite, epsomite, glauberite, halite, darapskite ($NaNO \cdot Na_2SO_4 \cdot H_2O$), nitroglauberite ($6NaNO_3 \cdot 2Na_2SO_4 \cdot 3H_2O$), lauterite ($CaI_2O_6$), and dietzeite ($7CaI_2O_6 \cdot 8CaCrO_4$).

*Semper and Michels, Die Salpeterindustrie Chiles, Zeits. f. Berg. Hütt.-Salinenw. vol. 52, Abh., 1904, p. 8.

†Penrose, R. A. F., Jr., p. 14. D. G. Buchanan, analyst.

There has been considerable difference of opinion respecting the conditions and processes of origin of the South American nitrate deposits, but present opinion seems to be practically unanimous in ascribing their deposition to ground-water action. The immediate factors responsible for their origin are the physiography and the extremely arid climate of the region, the latter leading to extreme evaporation and the former concentrating the underground and limited surface waters on the western edge of the desert basin. Singewald and Miller[709] assigned the nitrate deposits to "the accumulation, by means of evaporation, of the minute nitrate content of the underground waters of the region," the deposition of the salts representing "a sort of efflorescence." They point out that where the nitrate accumulates, the water table is not far from the surface, and they are of the opinion that capillarity brings some of the ground water thereto, where evaporation leads to deposition of the contained salts in the loose materials between the surface and the water table. The waters are thought to originate on the western slopes of the Andes, whence they drain through the materials of the desert basin to its deeper areas adjacent to the coastal ranges, there coming close to the surface and thus concentrating the contained salts in that portion of the desert. The nitrates are assumed to have been derived from the materials through which the ground water passed. Owing to the extremely deliquescent nature of the nitrates, they would tend to become concentrated in those parts of the western margin of the desert which are least moist, thus accounting for their occurrences in the lower portions of the sloping lands above the salars or salt flats.

Whitehead[710] questions the theory of Singewald and Miller and states that the depth of the water table and the nature of the overlying materials preclude capillarity from lifting the water so high and thus make the theory outlined above untenable. His theory differs chiefly from the above in that he holds that the waters of deposition are descending. The nitrate is derived from sources on steep slopes and hilltops and concentrated lower down on less steep slopes by dew, fog, and the occasional rains, the salts being stratified in accord with their solubilities. There is continuous removal from upper slopes and enrichment lower down and general migration of the entire deposit downward, so that finally the basin level may be reached. On first being taken into solution, descent is made to a surface less steeply inclined and thinly veneered with gravel, the first solutions to reach the upper gravel slopes being considered probably to be sodium nitrate because of the latter's deliquescent nature. These solutions penetrate the gravel, evaporate to some degree during the diurnal period of low humidity, and cement the materials penetrated. The occasional light rains dissolve the sulphates and chlorides left after removal of the nitrates, and these are carried

[709] Singewald, J. T., jr., and Miller, B. L., op. cit., 1916, pp. 107, 108.
[710] Whitehead, W. L., op. cit., 1920, pp. 210–216.

downward to lower slopes and deposited, possibly covering the previously deposited nitrate. The first deposits made on the upper gravel slopes are assumed to be thin beds composed of a mixture of sodium nitrate, sodium chloride, and sodium sulphate. The high humidity of cold nights may bring the relative humidity to 70 per cent, or that necessary to form a saturated solution of sodium nitrate. This sinks into the ground and moves downward on the slopes due to gravitation and capillarity. The succeeding low humidity and high temperature of day bring about deposition of the nitrate and of any sodium chloride and sodium sulphate in the solution. After this has been often repeated and the nitrate has been moved a considerable distance from the surface, a light rain may provide sufficient water to carry sodium chloride and sodium sulphate downward to be deposited in gravel above the nitrate. In this way the three characteristic zones of a nitrate deposit are formed: (1) the upper zone of the less soluble sodium sulphate, (2) the sodium chloride with sodium sulphate zone, and (3) the nitrate zone with its base at the greatest depth where porosity permits evaporation and deliquescence. Whitehead (pp. 216–222) favors the volcanic hypothesis as a source for the nitrogen.

The Whitehead explanation of the concentration of the nitrates seems reasonable, and if the ground-water level is as deep as stated by him and has always been so during the times of the accumulation of the nitrates, it does not seem that the explanation of Singewald and Miller is adequate.

Sodium nitrate occurs in the western United States under climatic conditions somewhat similar to those of Chili. In the Amargosa region of southeastern California it is found about 9 inches below the surface in a 5-inch layer of caliche which is mostly sodium chloride.[711] The nitrate content is, however, too low for commercial development.

Mechanical Deposits of Salts

Mechanical deposits of salts are composed mostly of gypsum and are usually of wind deposition, the particles having been derived from older gypsum deposits, from efflorescences of surface caliche, or other efflorescences about lakes and springs. Naturally, the deposits so far as they were derived from efflorescences would contain many salts besides gypsum, but if the region possesses any rainfall whatever, the more soluble would be leached out, leaving the gypsum fairly pure. Dunes of gypsum occur over an area of about 300 square miles in Otero County, New Mexico, the gypsum sand having been derived from older beds of gypsum within the region[712]

[711] Noble, L. F., Mansfield, G. R., etc., Nitrate deposits in the Amargosa region, southeastern California, Bull. 724, U. S. Geol. Surv., 1922.

[712] Herrick, C. L., The geology of the white sands of New Mexico, Jour. Geol., vol. 8, 1900, pp. 123–124.

(fig. 63). Similar sands on an apparently smaller scale are said to occur in Utah and Australia,[713] and small accumulations may be seen locally in any dry region possessing efflorescences on the surface or bedded deposits of gypsum. Wilder suggests that attention should be directed to this method of origin for some of the extensive gypsum deposits, and has described cross-laminated gypsum from Oklahoma which may have developed through wind deposition.[714]

FIG. 63. DUNES OF GYPSUM SANDS

Photograph of the dunes of gypsum sands near Alamogordo, New Mexico. The photograph was received from Professor Evan Just of the New Mexico School of Mines. The dunes are found over an area of about 10 by 30 miles.

Evaporation Deposits of Enclosed Basins

The saline residues of lakes depend on the waters of the regions, the nature of the country rock through which the waters flow, whatever their source, and the kinds of salts brought to the lakes by wind. In table 73 are given analyses of the waters of Great Salt Lake and some of its tributaries which illustrate the variations in the waters supplied and the result after concentration.[715]

The waters of enclosed basins show great quantitative as well as great qualitative variety in the substances in solution. This is shown by the analyses in table 74.

[713] Wilder, F. A., Some conclusions in regard to the origin of gypsum, Bull. Geol. Soc. Am., vol. 32, 1921, p. 389.
[714] Wilder, F. A., Gypsum, Mineral Industry, vol. 24, 1915, p. 371.
[715] Clarke, F. W., op. cit., Chap. V.

TABLE 73

	GREAT SALT LAKE, 1913	BEAR RIVER NEAR MOUTH	JORDAN RIVER NEAR SALT LAKE CITY	OGDEN RIVER, OGDEN, UTAH	WEBER RIVER NEAR MOUTH OF CANYON
Cl................	55.48	32.36	34.76	23.21	13.73
SO₄................	6.68	8.16	30.68	5.65	9.25
CO₃................	0.09	21.53	Trace	33.68	40.00
Na................	33.17	20.54	23.04	11.31	8.37
K................	1.66			4.16	4.19
Ca................	0.16	10.12	10.26	16.05	18.19
Mg................	2.76	4.76	1.26	5.94	6.27
Al₂O₃, Fe₂O₃....		2.53			
	100.00	100.00	100.00	100.00	100.00
Salinity permille........	203.49	0.637	1.09	0.444	0.455

TABLE 74

	SODA LAKE, NEV.	OWENS LAKE, CALIF.	BORAX LAKE, CALIF.	DEAD SEA 120 M. DEPTH	LAKE DOMO-SHAKOVO, SIBERIA	LAKE TEKIR-GHIOL, ROUMANIA
Cl................	36.51	24.82	32.27	67.66	3.71	60.53
Br................		0.04		1.98	Trace	0.18
SO₄................	10.36	9.93	0.13	0.22	63.62	0.67
CO₃................	13.78	24.55	22.47	Trace	0.08	Trace
PO₄................		0.11	0.02			
B₄O₇................	0.25	0.14	5.05			
NO₃................		0.45			0.07	
Li................		0.03				
Na................	36.63	38.09	38.10	10.20	30.61	34.78
K................	2.01	1.62	1.52	1.62	0.59	1.68
Ca................		0.02	0.03	1.51	0.58	0.28
Mg................	0.22	0.01	0.35	16.81	0.74	1.84
SiO₂................	0.24	0.14	0.01	Trace	Trace	0.01
Al₂O₃, Fe₂O₃....		0.04	0.01		Trace	0.03
As₂O₃................		0.05				
	100.00	100.00	100.00	100.00	100.00	100.00
Salinity permille........	113.7	213.7	76.56	245.73	145.5	70.877

These waters are thought to be fairly representative of those of enclosed basins. The content differs from year to year, with different seasons of the year, and also with depth.

The salts are precipitated from the waters of enclosed basins through evaporation, freezing, and changes of temperature, the type of mineral depending on the process responsible for the precipitation and the conditions prevailing at that time. The illustration given in connection with the deposits made about springs shows the effects of freezing. The experiments of Ochsenius, Van't Hoff, and others, and occurrences in nature prove that temperature is an important factor. Thus, in winter the sodium sulphate mineral, mirabilite, is deposited in heaps on the shores of Great Salt Lake and undergoes partial solution during the summer months. A similar condition obtains on the shores of the Gulf of Kara Boghaz.

Most lakes have periods of inflow of greater or less quantities of fresh water, during which time they receive quantitative and qualitative additions to the salts already in solution, have their waters diluted, and may receive suspended matter to be spread over the bottoms to greater or less thicknesses. During dry seasons deposits of salts may be made. Lakes whose waters have concentration as high as those of the Dead Sea have calcium carbonate and calcium sulphate precipitated near the mouth of each stream which enters, as the lake waters are already too highly concentrated to hold these salts. Thus, the Jordan precipitates calcium carbonate and calcium sulphate where it enters the Dead Sea.

Many basins of arid regions are without water during parts of the year or over terms of years. Of this character are Searles, Soda, and other lakes of California. These are under water only after big rainfall, and at other times are desert playas covered with white salt,[716] most of which in Soda Lake is sodium sulphate.

The deposits of Searles Lake[717] rival those of Stassfurt in chemical interest. During the Pleistocene epoch of glaciation this lake had a depth of 635 to 640 feet. During and for a short time after wet seasons the central part is flooded to a depth of a few inches; at other times it is dry. The "lake" consists of a "central area of firm, crusted salt," covering 11 to 12 square miles, surrounded by an area of salt-encrusted mud and sand which is bare of vegetation and composed of alluvium washed from the surrounding uplands, the whole impregnated with salts to a greater or less degree. These two areas constitute the "playa zone," containing about 60 square miles.

[716] Arnold, R., and Johnson, H. R., Sodium sulphate in Soda Lake, Carrizo Plain, San Luis Obispo County, California, Bull. 380, U. S. Geol. Surv., 1909, pp. 369–371; Gale, H. S., Sodium sulphate in the Carrizo Plains, San Luis Obispo County, California, Bull. 540–N, U. S. Geol. Surv., 1914, pp. 429–433.

[717] Gale, H. S., Salines in the Owens, Searles, and Panamint Basins, southeastern California, Bull. 580, U. S. Geol. Surv., 1914, pp. 265–312; see also Grabau, A. W., Principles of salt deposition, 1920, p. 283.

The playa zone passes gradually into the surrounding alluvial fan and kindred deposits, and these merge with the rocky slopes of the bordering mountain ranges.

The salt crust over the central area is mostly halite, which is so firm that it will support a wagon and team and even a heavy drilling rig. Drilling shows it to have a thickness ranging to over 100 feet and probably averaging 70 to 75 feet for the main part of the deposit. The salt contains more or less terrigenous sediment deposited by dust storms. There is more or less stratification, the layers differing in physical characteristics and also in chemical composition, the latter shown in table 75. The salts are immersed in more or less mother liquor, whose movement is possible because of a cellular structure of the deposit, the brine being estimated to exceed 25 per

TABLE 75

DEPTH IN FEET	INSOLUBLE SAND, ETC.	NaCl	Na_2SO_4	Na_2CO_3	$NaHCO_3$	NaB_4O_7	H_2O	TOTAL
0–18	0.2	79.7	7.6	3.2	0.0	Trace	3.3	94.0
18–12	1.4	44.0	30.5	14.8	2.5	1.0	5.8	100.0
25–30	1.4	47.3	28.1	10.6	0.0	2.0	10.6	100.0
30–35	3.0	42.7	17.1	19.1	5.9	2.0	10.2	100.0
35–50	1.4	43.5	22.3	9.5	2.5	5.5	15.3	100.0
50–65	Trace	82.8	10.6	3.2	0.8	Trace	2.6	100.0
65–79	Trace	19.0	7.3	40.3	18.5	0.5	14.4	100.0

cent of the volume. The hypothetical average composition of the anhydrous residue to the brine is as follows:

	Per cent
Sodium chloride	51.61
Sodium sulphate	19.22
Sodium carbonate	12.79
Sodium biborate ($Na_2B_4O_7$)	3.23
Potassium chloride	12.07
Sodium arsenate (Na_2AsO_4)	0.17
	99.09

The composition of the salts which the brine immerses is given in table 75, the samples having been acquired from a well drilled near the center of the main salt deposit. Other wells show different proportions of salts.

In general, the analyses of the salts from the different wells show a concentration of the carbonates and bicarbonates at the base of the deposit, particularly of the latter, and of sodium chloride at the top, and more or less continuous deposition of sulphate. The sequence and relations of the different salts are in accord with results obtained by Chatard[718] from evaporation of waters of Owens Lake, situated a short distance northwest of Searles Lake, and leave little doubt that the salts of the latter are the deposits of evaporation of the natural drainage waters of the region. However, there is one fact worthy of note, and that is, the mother liquors do not lie on the surface of the salts already precipitated, but rather thoroughly permeate them.

Minerals recognized in the Searles deposit are: halite, mirabilite, thenardite, trona, natron, borax, gypsum, anhydrite, glauberite, hanksite, northupite ($MgCO_3 \cdot Na_2CO_3 \cdot NCl$), pirssonite ($CaCO_3 \cdot Na_2CO_3 \cdot H_2O$), gaylussite, sulphohalite ($2Na_2SO_4 \cdot NaCl \cdot NaF$), tychite ($2MgCO_3 \cdot 2Na_2CO_3 \cdot Na_2SO_4$), searlesite, soda niter, dolomite, calcite, celestite, and colemanite.[719]

Death Valley seems to be an ancient lake bed of the same class as Searles Marsh. In the very lowest part of the valley is an area several miles across which is usually a smooth field of snowy white salt. This portion occasionally is flooded by water. A well bored in the southern part of this valley gave the following section:[720]

	Feet
Salt	0.5
Clay, light brown, soft, containing crystals	3.5
Salt, very hard	2.0
Mud, soft, brown, containing coarse crystals	11.0
Mud, soft, brown	0.5
Salt, in layers 1 inch thick	0.5
Mud, soft, brown	3.0
Mud, light brown, containing crystals	3.0
Mud, soft, brown, containing crystals	3.0
Salt, hard	2.5
Clay, tough, brown	0.5
Salt, hard	1.0
Mud, soft, brown, containing crystals	0.3
Salt, hard	0.7
Clay, dark, containing crystals	4.5
Salt, hard	1.5
Mud, black, containing crystals and 1 inch beds of hard salt	1.5
Salt, hard, black	2.0
Mud, black, containing crystals	1.5
Salt, hard	0.2
Clay, black, containing crystals	2.3

[718] Chatard, T. M., Natural soda: its occurrence and utilization, Bull. 60, U. S. Geol. Surv., 1890, pp. 59–67.

[719] Gale, H. S., Salines in the Owens, Searles, and Panamint Basins, southeastern California, Bull. 580, U. S. Geol. Surv., 1914, pp. 265–312; see also Grabau, A. W., Principles of salt deposition, 1920, p. 283.

[720] Gale, H. S., Prospecting for potash in Death Valley, California, Bull. 540, U. S. Geol. Surv., 1914, pp. 412–413.

Feet

Salt, hard, black..	0.5
Clay, light gray and black mixed, containing crystals.................	5.0
Salt, very hard...	1.5
Clay, dark, containing crystals..	0.5
Salt, hard...	0.5
Clay, tough, dark..	0.5
Salt, black, very hard...	15.5
Clay, dark blue, containing crystals..................................	1.0
Salt, very hard, black...	5.0
Clay, dark blue, containing crystals..................................	2.5
Salt, hard, black..	1.0
Clay, dark blue, containing crystals..................................	6.2
Salt, hard...	1.0
Clay, dark blue, containing crystals..................................	3.8
Salt, very hard..	1.5
Clay, dark blue, very tough, containing crystals......................	4.0
Clay, black, tough, containing crystals...............................	8.0
	104.0

This gives a total of 37.4 feet of salt out of a total of 104 feet.   The alternation of salt and mud or clay can hardly be seasonal and probably indicates irregular intervals of varied duration.   The crystals of salt in the clay may have formed there during deposition or subsequently.

In Funeral Mountain on the east side of Death Valley in Tertiary sediments there is a deposit of colemanite which outcrops for at least 25 miles. It is not a regular bed, but consists of irregular masses of colemanite through a thickness of 20 feet of clay.   The same region is reported to have a 60-foot bed of boracite.[721]

Among the deserts of central Asia is one in the basin of the Tarim River known as the Takla-Makan.   In this desert is the extensive salt plain of Lop in the lowest part of which is the contracted salt lake of Lop-Nor or Kara-Koshun.   The desert is surrounded by lofty mountains, has low precipitation, and great extremes of temperature.   The salt plain has a length of 200 miles and a width of about 50 miles at its broadest place.   The salt is very hard, and its surface is described by Huntington[722] as "resembling the choppiest sort of sea, with white caps a foot or two high, frozen solid." The salt deposit is that of an extinct lake.   After the salt became dry it broke up in the manner of mudcrack polygons into "pentagons" from 5 to 12 feet in diameter.   These cracks filled with dust into which capillary action brought salt from below.   The crystallization of this salt and perhaps other processes buckled the polygons and thus gave rise to the rough surface. Locally the surface of the salt plain is smooth, and in these places the salt

[721] Campbell, M. R., Bull. 213, U. S. Geol. Surv., 1902, p. 404.
[722] Huntington E., Pulse of Asia, 1907, Chapter XII and pp. 251–252.

rests on soft oozy mud which is evidently impregnated with bittern. The salt appears to have been brought into the extinct lake by streams draining the surrounding region.

In the early stages of a salt lake's history its water is likely to be inhabited by organisms, but when deposition of salt sets in, these begin to disappear and the final deposits are scanty in organic remains except as they are brought in by draining streams or blown in by wind, or as occasional terrestrial organisms become mired in the lake's muds.

As salt lakes are in desert regions, it frequently happens that the waters receive large quantities of dust from the atmosphere. This dust consists chiefly of the fine products of rock disintegration, but it may also contain matter derived from the efflorescences formed on the desert's surface. Some of these will go into solution unless the waters are already saturated therewith. The terrigenous material settles to the bottom and gives rise to a layer of clay, and the matter brought in suspension by streams gives rise to other beds of clay. There thus may be clays of two types of history in the deposits of salt lakes, one made during the dry season and the other during the season of rainfall. Data for differentiation have not been established, but the clay brought in by the streams should grade into more coarse materials toward the mouths of the streams, whereas that due to wind deposition should have uniform character and thickness over the entire basin.

As a lake grows smaller through evaporation, the waters become concentrated in the lower parts of its basin where the normal succession of deposits form. The more insoluble and first-precipitated substances will have more extensive distribution than the more soluble, whose deposition will be largely confined to the lower and probably more central area of the basin. However, many of the first-deposited salts may be redissolved and carried to the central basin to attain redeposition. Finally, evaporation would leave nothing except the mother liquor, and this, in accord with the conditions of the Searles Lake deposits, would permeate the already deposited salts, with its further evaporation retarded by the heat reflected back to the atmosphere from the whiteness of the surface salts. Drifting sands or dusts, on the other hand, might overwhelm the basin and bury the whole. The mother liquors might then travel to the surface by capillarity, to be evaporated and deposit their salts among the sands or dusts; and where the salts reached the surface, they might be scattered by winds.

From what has been stated in preceding paragraphs, it seems that the deposits of a desiccated salt lake would have lenticular form, with bordering salts less soluble than the central portion, and the latter mainly composed of rock salt, but containing a rather wide range of salt minerals. Muds of the character shown in the Death Valley section are likely to be present at various levels, particularly in the marginal portions.

In preceding paragraphs it has been assumed that the salts of salt lakes have been acquired from surrounding areas by the normal drainage of the region. It may be that this is not always the case. Holland[723] has offered an interesting and seemingly very valid explanation of the origin of the salts of some salt deposits made in the desert lake of Sambhar of the Rajputana Desert, northwestern India. He has proved that salt is carried as dust during the times of the southwest monsoon, the salt being derived from the Cutch region to the south and west. Analyses of the air showed that at least 3000 metric tons are carried over Sambhar Lake during one dry season and that 200,000 metric tons are annually carried into the Rajputana States. This salt dust is partly dropped over the desert and partly held in the atmosphere. During the rainy seasons it is washed from the atmosphere and from the surface of the desert and carried to the low places, where evaporation during each succeeding dry season leads to its deposition.

Grabau[724] has suggested that the Salina salt deposits of New York and adjacent regions developed in a body of water akin to a desert lake. He postulates the salts to have been contained in the Niagara limestones and to have come to the surface as efflorescences as the limestones decomposed and disintegrated under conditions of aridity then and there existing. These efflorescences were then washed, or blown, into the deeper portions of the Salina basin, where evaporation led to deposition of the salts contained in solution. The efflorescences are postulated to have been largely sodium chloride, and any calcium sulphate is supposed to have largely been left in the rocks of derivation, so that gypsum was not deposited except as scales and crystals in sands and muds. The products of the disintegration of the Niagara limestones are assumed to have occasionally been washed or blown into the basins in which the salt was deposited, and to have formed the beds of fine-grained limestone interstratified with the salt beds. This complex hypothesis accounts for deposition of salt without gypsum below (the gypsum at that time not believed to hold such stratigraphic relationship). But, as pointed out by Alling[725] and Newland,[726] the supposed relationship is doubtful and certainly incorrect in some cases, making several of Grabau's assumptions unnecessary. Few fossils occur in the salt and

[723] Holland, T. H., The origin of desert salt deposits, Proc. Liverpool Geol. Soc., vol. 11, pt. iii, 1912, pp. 227–250.

[724] Grabau, A. W., Comprehensive geology, pt. ii, 1920, pp. 340–343.

[725] Alling, H. L., The geology and origin of the Silurian salt of New York State, Bull. 275, New York State Mus. 1928, p. 75.

[726] Newland, D. H., Recent progress in the study of the Salina formation, Rept. Comm. Sedimentation, Nat. Research Council, 1928, pp. 36–43.

associated beds, and this has been construed into an argument that the Salina basin lacked connection with the sea, but this argument also fails of validity. Considerable gypsum, or anhydrite, lies above the sodium chloride. It was Dana's[727] view that the gypsum of the Salina basin resulted from the alteration of limestone, and Grabau[728] has concurred with him. However, there is considerable doubt that this is the correct interpretation, and neither Alling[729] nor Newland,[730] who have studied these deposits probably more thoroughly than earlier students, is in accord with this assumption. While not dissenting from the origin of local occurrences of calcium sulphate from limestone, each holds, particularly Newland, that the sulphate deposits are mainly of primary deposition.

Evaporation Deposits of Marine Waters

Evaporation deposits from sea water are made where arms or parts of the sea have been partially or completely cut off from the main body through crustal movement, or by the building of bars. The arm may receive additions of sea water regularly through an opening in, or seepage through, the barrier, occasionally through flooding over the barrier, or the separation may be so complete that no additions whatever are received.

Following Grabau,[731] water bodies containing sea water in which precipitation of salt may occur may be divided into the four classes of marginal salt pans, marine salinas, lagoonal deposits, and cut-off portions of the sea with complete or nearly complete separation.

MARGINAL SALT PANS. Salt pans exist near the mouth of the Indus in the Rann of Cutch, on the Red Sea coast, on the Nile Delta, on the Black Sea coast over the flat delta plains of the Danube and Dneiper regions, and on a small scale on many other coasts. The Rann of Cutch is the largest and is typical.

The Rann of Cutch is a low plain lying inland from, and on both sides of, the Island of Cutch south of the mouth of the Indus. The region is arid and the plain is mantled with sand plentifully impregnated with salt. The surface is always moist, and occasional pools of salt water are present. It has a width of about 60 miles, a length exceeding 180 miles, and an area of about 7000 square miles. The Rann merges laterally into the Put, the surface of which is flat and dry and which is margined by a sand-dune region known as the Thurr. The heights of the dunes range to nearly 400

[727] Dana, J. D., Manual of geology, 4th ed., 1895, p. 554.
[728] Grabau, A. W., Principles of salt deposition, 1920, p. 357.
[729] Alling, H. L., op. cit., p. 91.
[730] Newland, D. H., op. cit.
[731] Grabau, A. W., op. cit., pp. 116–122.

feet, and lakes locally lie between them.   There is no vegetation in the Rann and Put, apparently no life of any kind in the Rann, and no fresh water anywhere in the region.   During the times of the southwest monsoons the Rann is flooded to a maximum depth of about a meter; during the northeast monsoons this water flows back to the sea so far as it is possible; a part of it, however, soaks into the ground or is held in pools, but in either case the water ultimately evaporates and deposits crusts of salt.   These crusts average about 10 cm. in thickness, but may exceed a meter.

A salt pan on the Nile Delta near Alexandria receives from 7 to 14 cm. of large, intergrown crystals of well bedded salt each year, the salt deposits resting on a black slime filled with organic material.   When dry, the surface of the pan becomes broken up into polygons separated by ridges of salt from 5 to 30 mm. in height.   The brine of this pan contains small crustaceans of red color, and these color the salt.[732]

Deposits formed in a salt pan obviously cannot reach a great thickness so long as the original surface of the pan remains stationary with respect to sea level, but if sea level should gradually rise it would be possible for salt to accumulate to a thickness closely related to the extent of such rise.   This salt would consist of thin units, each deposited annually, and composed of calcium carbonate, calcium sulphate, sodium chloride, and other compounds. There would be essentially no development of mother-liquor salts.   Salts of this origin ought also to contain marine organisms, as the pans periodically receive waters directly from the sea.

MARINE SALINAS.   Marine salinas are those bodies of water adjacent to a sea coast which receive sea water by seepage through a separating sand or gravel barrier and have no or very slight inflow of fresh water.   Deposits appear to be possible only on arid coasts.   The best example is a sea-coast lake on the Island of Cyprus in the eastern Mediterranean[733] (figs. 64, 65). The basin has an area a little greater than 2 square miles, and its greatest depth is only about 3 feet.   The surface of the water in the lake averages 10 feet below sea level in summer and 7 feet below in winter.   The barrier is about 1.5 miles wide and consists of unconsolidated sands, clays, and shell matter resting on impervious clay.   Evaporation exceeds inflow during summer, and a crust of salt is formed over the bottom of the basin.   Another example of this type of basin is Lake Tekir-Ghiol in Roumania, which is separated from the Black Sea by a barrier about 1000 feet wide.   An analysis of the solid content of the waters of the lake is given on page 488.

[732] Grabau, A. W., Principles of salt deposition, 1920, pp. 120–121.   Walther, J., Das Gesetz der Wüstenbildung, 2nd ed., 1912, pp. 241–243; 4th ed., 1924, pp. 305–306.

[733] Bellamy, C. V., A description of the salt lake of Larnaca, Quart. Jour. Geol. Soc., vol. 56, 1900, pp. 745–758.

The deposits of marine salinas could contain marine fossils only in case waves passed over the barrier, as they might do in times of storm, or in case they were carried in by other animals.   A lake of this kind is probably

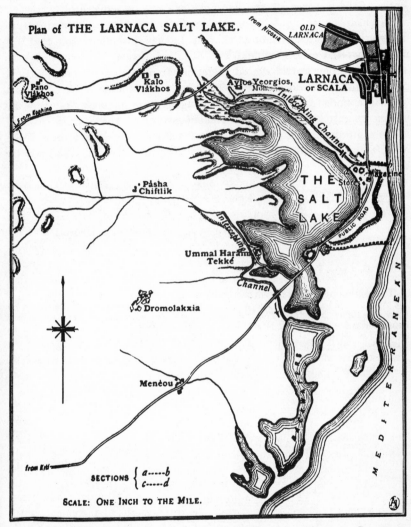

FIG. 64. OUTLINE MAP OF THE SALT LAKE OF LARNACA, ISLAND OF CYPRUS

The map shows the position of the lake with respect to the Mediterranean and the bar which separates the lake from the sea.   A cross section of bar is shown in figure 65.   The intercepting channels were constructed to decrease the inflow of fresh water and thus make the lake more valuable for the extraction of salt.   After Bellamy, C. V., Quart. Jour. Geol. Soc., vol. 56, 1900, pl. 39.

only an incident in the history of a coast, and the deposits could hardly be other than of small extent and thickness. Mother-liquor salts might be deposited, but the probabilities are not great. Deposits of this origin may occur in the geologic column, but none has been recognized.

LAGOONAL DEPOSITS. Lagoonal deposits are made in basins marginal to the sea into which a current flows from the main body to restore that lost in the lagoon through evaporation. The requirement for their origin is that evaporation should exceed accretions from streams or precipitation, thus requiring additions from the main body to maintain level. This is a not uncommon condition, and such lagoons precipitating salts are by no means rare. Thus, lagoons back of islands on the eastern coast of Mexico are depositing salts, although connections with the waters of the Gulf are not greatly restricted.[734] The lagoonal theory, as outlined by

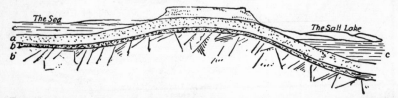

FIG. 65. CROSS SECTION OF THE BARRIER SEPARATING THE SALT LAKE OF LARNACA
FROM THE SEA

The upper portion of the barrier consists of sands, gravels, and shell matter, this forming the layer designated a and what is above. These sediments are succeeded downward by clays of various character. The beds containing shells, sands and gravels extend to a depth below the shore of the lake of about 10 feet. The level of the lake approximates about 7 feet below the level of the sea and the deepest part of the lake is estimated at about 10 feet below mean tide level. a = Permeable strata (sands and conglomerates). b = Impermeable stratum (clay). b' = Layer of watery matter. After Bellamy, C. V., Quart. Jour. Geol. Soc., vol. 56, 1900, pl. 39.

Ochsenius,[735] postulates an arm of a sea, or the ocean, connected with the main body by an opening sufficiently large to permit inflow of water, but not deep enough to permit circulation, so that water entering the arm largely remains there except as removed by evaporation. A region is required with climate sufficiently arid to prevent inflow of fresh water into the arm, or to decrease it to a quantity below that removed by evaporation, so that the level of the bay must be maintained by additions over the barrier. The barrier may be made by waves or result from crustal movement, but a barrier of the latter type might develop a basin of the character of a relic

[734] Baker, C. L., Depositional history of the Red Beds and saline residues of the Texas Permian, Bull. 2901, Univ. Texas, 1929, p. 27; Pan-Am. Geol., vol. 52, 1929, p. 346.

[735] Ochsenius, C., Die Bildung der Steinsalzlager und ihrer Mutterlaugensalze, Halle, 1877; Beiträge zur Erklärung der Bildung von Steinsalzlagern und ihrer Mutterlaugensalae, Acad. Nova Acta, vol. 40, 1878, pp. 121–166.

sea. The thickness of deposit in a lagoon would be measured by depth of water, a great depth favoring a thickness related thereto. As the inflowing current brings additions of salts, the salinity of the water constantly increases, and ultimately the concentration essential for the precipitation of calcium sulphate is reached. When this concentration exists throughout the lagoon, calcium sulphate is precipitated in maximum quantity in that portion of the lagoon adjacent to the entrance through the bar, and sodium chloride and other salts might be deposited over portions of the bottom remote from the bar. A long-time closure of the entrance to the lagoon might lead to deposition of all the sodium chloride, which would rest on deposits of calcium sulphate of considerable thickness adjacent to the bar, and on thin deposits of that salt in more distant parts of the lagoon, and it is possible that places might exist where no gypsum existed beneath the salt. Finally, mother-liquor salts might be deposited. Cutting of the bar would renew connection with the sea, and the cycle would be repeated. Depression of the locality of the lagoon with respect to sea level—hardly likely for a small area—would permit long existence of a lagoon and hence extensive accumulation which might be entirely gypsum adjacent to the entrance and at the base, mixed or dovetailing salt and gypsum farther from the entrance, and essentially pure sodium chloride in remoter parts of the lagoon.

Ochsenius gave the Gulf of Kara Bogaz (fig. 66) on the east side of the Caspian Sea as a modern illustration of the lagoon theory of salt deposition. The Caspian is a relic sea, as shown by the character of its fauna, and is a remnant of a once much larger body of water. Rivers have given it large additions of salts since its separation from its parent body, and there has been an excess of evaporation over inflow and precipitation, as its surface is below sea level. Nevertheless, its salinity is lower than that of the Mediterranean or the ocean. This arises from the fact that a current flows from the Caspian into Kara Bogaz, with the result that the Caspian has a position analogous to that of a lake with outlet. Analyses of the solid contents of the waters of the Caspian and the Gulf of Kara Bogaz are given in table 76.[736] The low calcium content in the Gulf is accounted for by the fact that neither calcium carbonate nor calcium sulphate can be held in solution, and both are precipitated shortly after entering the Gulf.

The barrier separating Kara Bogaz from the Caspian is wave-made and consists of two sand spits. The Gulf is about 95 miles long and about 80 miles wide; the depth is not over 15 meters. Its waters are estimated to have in solution 34,000,000,000 million metric tons of salt, and 350,000 tons are estimated to be brought into it daily.[737]

[736] Clarke, F. W., op. cit., p. 169.
[737] Grabau, A. W., Principles of salt deposition, 1920, footnotes p. 132.

Gypsum is deposited in quantity along the shores of the opening into the Gulf and for some distance beyond the opening. During the winter months the water is saturated with respect to sodium sulphate, but not the chloride,

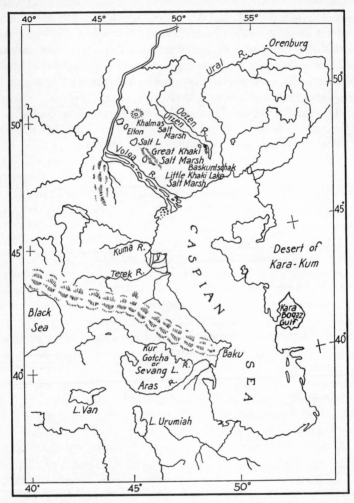

FIG. 66. OUTLINE MAP OF THE CASPIAN SEA AREA

The map shows the outlines and position of the Gulf of Kara Boghaz and the position and extent of the salt plains of southern Russia. After Grabau, A. W., Principles of salt deposition, 1920, p. 130.

and at that time deposits of glauberite are made in the shallow waters and toward the center, the area of such deposits being estimated at around 3500 square kilometers and the quantity of this salt at 1000 million metric tons. In summer the thickness averages about 1 foot, but it is thicker in winter. Rock salt is not deposited in the Gulf.

Many organisms are carried into the Gulf, where most of them stay to meet death, the only chance of escape existing for such of the nekton as are able to swim against the current. According to Andrussow,[738] the number of organisms thus killed is extremely large, and they can be found floating on the surface and piled along the shore, the greatest number being in fall and spring. Much organic matter must thus be incorporated in the salt which is being deposited, and it may be expected that fossils should be common, and even abundant, in salt deposits of lagoonal origin.

TABLE 76

	CASPIAN SEA	GULF OF KARABOGAZ
Cl.	41.78	50.26
Br.	0.05	0.08
SO₄.	23.78	15.57
CO₃.	0.93	0.13
Na.	24.49	25.51
K.	0.60	0.81
Ca.	2.60	0.57
Mg.	5.77	7.07
	100.00	100.00
Salinity permille.	12.67	163.96

A salt deposit which has been assigned to a lagoonal origin[739] was discovered in the building of the Suez Canal, where it passed through the Great Bitter Lake of Suez. The Canal exposed a deposit of salt 8 miles long and 4 miles broad with an average thickness of about 25 feet. In the center of the lake the thickness was about 60 feet. The deposit was composed of layers of rock salt and gypsum separated by layers of earthy matter and small crystals of gypsum. A thickness of 2.46 meters ($8\frac{2}{3}$ feet) had 42 layers of salt and gypsum, the latter ranging in thickness from 3 to 18 cm. Between the layers of salt and gypsum were clay layers a few millimeters in thickness, which, as a rule, contained abundant remains of organisms still living in the Red Sea. Separation of Great Bitter Lake from the Gulf of

[738] Andrussow, H., Der Adschi-darja oder Karabugaz Busen, Petermann's Mitth., Bd. 43, 1897, p. 29; Grabau, A. W., Principles of salt deposition, 1920, pp. 131–139.

[739] Grabau, A. W., op. cit., pp. 139–142.

Suez is thought to have occurred some time after 600 B. C., the separation being caused by the building of a bar which prior to its permanently reaching the surface was exposed at low tide and possibly during occasional storms. It is possible that it was during such a time of exposure that Moses and his followers crossed the Red Sea to escape Pharaoh and his hosts.   The occurrence of fossils in the clay layers points to decreased concentration and entrance of waters and sediments from the sea, and at the same time there would be removed mother liquors left from the salts already deposited. Such mother liquors at the time of cutting of the canal were found to be of far less quantity than was demanded by the salts already deposited.   It would seem that entrance of the sea in large volume would be a frequently recurring event in lagoonal history, and that a lagoonal deposit would not often reach the stage of mother-liquor salt deposition.   Walther[740] has suggested that the only chance mother liquors of lagoonal or other waters have to become evaporated would be brought about by burial beneath hot desert sands.   Capillarity might then bring the mother liquors to or toward the surface, and in the former case they might become dissipated by winds, perhaps to be later concentrated in depressions between dunes and buried there.

A possible Miocene example of a lagoonal salt deposit is that of Wieliczka in Galicia.   This is abundantly fossiliferous, carries no mother-liquor salts, and seems to have been formed in close association with the Miocene sea of southern Europe.[741]

A summary of the characteristics of salt deposits of lagoonal origin indicates that: (a) they are not likely to, but may, have large extent; (b) they are formed in close association with marine conditions; (c) they should contain marine fossils in abundance; and (d) they do not, as a rule, contain mother-liquor salts.

The facts that there are many salt deposits without underlying gypsum and many gypsum deposits without beds of limestones below, and that many salt and gypsum deposits do not contain fossils, led Branson to postulate the occurrence of two or more basins[742] in the first of which the marine or stream organisms were killed and their remains buried or destroyed and the calcite and perhaps the gypsum precipitated.   The waters attaining the second lagoon, after having deposited their calcium sulphate in the first lagoon, would deposit sodium chloride and other salts in succeeding lagoons. This hypothesis of a number of connecting lagoons marginal to a sea coast

[740] Walther, J., Das Gesetz der Wüstenbildung, 4th ed., 1924, pp. 311–312.

[741] Grabau, A. W., op. cit., 1920, p. 142.

[742] Branson, E. B., Origin of thick salt and gypsum deposits, Bull. Geol. Soc. Am., vol. 26, 1915, pp. 231–242.

or basins in an arid region requires a nice balance of conditions which probably did not often occur during earth history, and it is not likely that many very extensive deposits developed in this way. A modification of the theory will be considered in connection with the deposits of relic seas.

SALT DEPOSITS OF RELIC SEAS. Relic seas lie in large, deep basins which at one time had connection with a sea or the ocean and became separated therefrom through diastrophic, volcanic, or depositional processes. It is not likely that such separation has commonly been caused by volcanic processes, but each of the other two probably has produced relic seas. In the beginning of a relic sea's history as such, its waters were of the same character as those of the parent body, and for a long period of time, connection therewith through a continuously decreasing opening probably was maintained. Relic seas may contain either fresh or salt water, depending upon the rainfall and evaporation of the surrounding regions. If more water is lost by evaporation than is introduced by rainfall and flow of streams, the waters are salty, with a concentration determined by the aridity and other factors. After separation is complete, the surface of a salty relic sea will fall below sea level.

The Salton Sea of southern California is a relic sea severed from the Gulf of California by the building of the delta of the Colorado River. It is not, however, a good illustration of the condition thought to be essential for the development of extensive salt deposits, as the sea is close and the Colorado occasionally breaks into the basin to bring in fresh water. The Caspian Sea is a better illustration. This sea at one time was much larger and was reduced by evaporation to form the existing body of water. The level was lowered, and it now stands 84 feet below sea level. The abandoned part of its basin has over twenty-five hundred lakes and playas in which salts are being deposited and into which salts formerly deposited in the sediments around these lakes and playas are being washed. The salts formed during seasons of strong evaporation consist of sodium chloride and some of the bitter salts. During wet seasons the more soluble bitter salts are dissolved, and sodium chloride and calcium sulphate are left. The Caspian is less salty than the ocean, because of accessions of fresh water on the western side from the Volga and other rivers and the flow from the Caspian on the eastern side into the Gulf of Kara Bogaz. If the Caspian did not have this Gulf, was surrounded on all sides by arid conditions, had no contributing rivers of significance, was connected with the ocean by a narrow and shallow opening, and was subject to evaporation in excess of all contributions of fresh water, sea level would have to be maintained by additions through the opening from the ocean, and as concentration became great, calcium carbonate would be precipitated near the entrance, calcium sulphate farther therefrom, and sodium chloride would be deposited over the remoter parts of the basin.[743] Accessory basins to the Caspian, as isolated bays and sounds, might receive deposits of bitter salts. Ultimately separation from the parent body would lead to shrinkage and lowering of the waters, and these might become restricted to several areas in the lower parts of the basin, in each of which the concentration would be high and possibly different. Deposits made in higher parts of the basin would be subject to removal through action of occasional rainfall and ground water. Only the more soluble salts would be likely to be removed, whereas such salts as calcium sulphate would be left. Removal of the soluble salts would increase the concentration in the shrunken waters, and finally a very thick deposit of sodium chloride and possibly of mother-liquor salts would result. Ultimately a relic sea might almost completely disappear, to become a playa or group of playas into which briny waters would be brought during times of rainfall to deposit their salts above those previously made, so that beds of rock salt, gypsum, and anhydrite would come to hold an apparently abnormal place in the sequence.

A relic sea owing its origin to diastrophic action might be expected to change position to some degree, and after having attained concentration essential to sodium chloride precipitation, to have been moved by warping over areas not previously occupied, and this would lead to deposits of sodium chloride over such areas with no calcium sulphate below. Again, the basin might deepen during and after its restricted connection with the ocean, thus making accumulation possible to a thickness related to the extent of deepening.

Fossils would be present in the deposits of a relic sea while connection with the ocean existed, and about places of inflow of fresh water, but after a degree of concentration had been attained prohibitive to most organisms, the organic matter would not be likely to extend a very great distance beyond the entrances and the mouths of streams. Hence, fossils should not be common in salt deposits made at some distances from the openings and inlets.

As diastrophic processes do not always seem to move in the same direction, but to fluctuate, with longer or shorter swings about a mean—in this case sea level—it is possible that connection of a relic sea with the ocean might be one or more times renewed, thus permitting something of a cyclic arrangement of the salt and associated deposits.

A large relic sea would be subject to a variety of conditions, due to temperature, variations in salinity, local influx of fresh water, influx of sediments,

[743] The reader should consult Baker, C. L., Depositional history of the Red Beds and saline residues of the Texas Permian, Bull. Univ. Texas, no. 2901, 1929, pp. 28–32, 41–47.

variations in depth, etc., and these would produce variations in the order and time of precipitation and character of the salts deposited, leading to lateral variation in the salt beds and to their splitting due to introduction of a wedge of clastic sediments. If such seas were of great depth, density stratification would be likely to obtain as exists in the Dead Sea at the present time in which the salinity ranges from 19 per cent at the surface to 26 per cent at the depth of 1000 feet. This might lead to the deposition of one variety of salt in the deeper waters and others in those of less depth. A similar qualitative variation would be likely to take place in deep lakes.

It is believed that the general conditions of environment outlined in the preceding paragraphs of this topic serve to account for the extensive and thick salt deposits of the geologic column, and it does not seem possible to account for these by any of the other conditions described. Bodies of water as deep as the thickness of the salt and associated sediments are not required. The characters of the sediments do not permit assumption of great depth, and it is not necessary to assume that the depositing waters were deep at any time. Hundreds and even thousands of feet of evaporites in a vertical section, such as exists in the Permian basin of west Texas, of course signify that most of these accumulated below the profile of equilibrium determined by the conditions, but it seems probable that the accumulation took place in a subsiding basin in which the waters were shallow at all times.

Extensive and thick salt and gypsum formations are commonly stated to carry few fossils, and this is as it should be if these are the deposits of relic seas, but the reported absence rests partly on traditional ideas suggesting that fossils should not be present, on careless observation based in part on assumption of absence, on insufficient collecting and observation, and on actual absence, not necessarily because organisms were never present in the depositing waters, but possibly because of corrosion in the brines.

It is suggested that the great salt deposits of the Permian of both the western United States and Europe developed in basins of relic seas. In the United States during the Permian the region of Kansas and some of the adjacent states was more or less cut off from the ocean to the southwest by the various mountains across southern Oklahoma. It is known that gypsum and anhydrite were deposited over the eastern and southern margin of this basin in some instances before the deposition of sodium chloride and also contemporaneous with and subsequent thereto. The stage for the deposition of the mother-liquor salts does not seem to have been reached in Kansas and Oklahoma, but polyhalite and other potash minerals are known to have been deposited in the Permian basin of western Texas. This Texas basin is also thought to be of the character of a relic sea, but the place of its connection with the parent body is not yet established. Baker,[744] who has studied these Texas Permian strata, postulates an opening between the Glass and Guadaloupe mountains of Trans-Pecos Texas and possibly another farther north to connect with California waters. Into this relic sea were flowing fresh waters from rivers, thus keeping portions of the Permian basin of sufficiently low salinity to permit marine organisms to thrive, either generally over an area or in the surface waters in those places where low salinity permitted them to float over more saline waters beneath. The basin was large, thus making possible great variations in salinity and the deposition of different varieties of salts at different places. It either was very deep when the deposition of saline residues began, or subsided during deposition to permit accumulation of eight to ten thousand feet of strata. The surrounding region was not necessarily one of great aridity, but conditions over the basin were such that the quantity of water evaporated exceeded that supplied by precipitation and the inflowing streams, thus compelling contributions from the ocean.

Fossils are present in strata below, between, and over the salt beds. These relations suggest, in general, lessening of the salinity of the waters, for the fossils above and between the salt beds. In some localities sodium chloride beds are said to occur without underlying calcium sulphate. This has been explained for Kansas by Haworth[745] as due to warping of the basin by crustal movements so that concentrated waters flooded areas which previously had been exposed.

In Europe the Variscian (Hercynian) uplift toward the close of the Pennsylvanian raised high mountains across central Europe, which separated the northern basin from the Atlantic to the west and the Mediterranean to the south, making connection with the open sea over a somewhat devious and distant passage to the east. At the same time the Germanic basin became more or less dry or arid, with evaporation exceeding precipitation. It is postulated that a high concentration was attained before complete separation from the ocean took place, so that an abundance of mother-liquor salts was present in solution, a part of which ultimately became deposited in the deeper parts of the Permian basin.

In several parts of the world the rocks contain salt domes whose origin for a long time was a subject of considerable difference of opinion. At the present time it seems probable that the domes represent beds of salt which under the influence of pressure have flowed and risen in the form of domes or plugs into overlying beds, the latter being more or less arched by the

[744] Baker, C. L., Depositional history of the Red Beds and saline residues of the Texas Permian, Bull. Univ. Texas, no. 2901, 1929, pp. 9–72.
[745] Haworth, E., Mineral resources of Kansas, 1893, p. 89.

rising salt, or rising because of the pressure and thus inviting the salt to enter. Cause and effect are more or less interrelated, so that separation is difficult. The finding of fossil algæ in the Markham salt dome of Texas[746] proves that this dome was so formed, and, inferentially, all others. Hence, from the point of view of sedimentation, the salt domes involve nothing other than the formation of extensive and thick beds of salt.

Alteration Deposits of Salt

Gypsum is the most common salt which is formed to any significant extent through alteration, although considerable celestite and perhaps sulphur may also develop in this way. Wherever waters carrying sulphuric acid come into contact with limestone, the latter is changed to hydrated calcium sulphate. That this has gone on to a considerable extent seems demonstrated, and it is known to be occurring in some places at the present time, but it does not appear possible that bedded deposits of gypsum of wide distribution can thus be explained. The gypsum deposits of New York, where they lie above the salt beds, were postulated by Dana to have originated in this way, although this does not seem probable.[747] Wilder has also directed attention to gypsum deposits[748] which he inferred to have had this origin. It should not be difficult to differentiate such replacement deposits from those of other origin, as there should be many places where they show gradation to limestone, and they should contain patches of unreplaced limestone.

Potash, Soda, and Sodium Chloride of Organic Origin

That potash is present in many plants is attested by the lye or potash from the ashhoppers of American pioneer days. Certain plants contain considerable potash and iodine and others contain soda. For the sake of completeness these are considered in this connection.[749]

The giant kelp of the Pacific Coast is among the most important of the plants secreting potash and iodine. Analyses of the ash of three species of these kelps are given in table 77.

Potash is almost universally present in the ash of all vegetable matter. The ash of corn cobs has been found to contain as much as 20.13 per cent of water-soluble potash, as well as 4.01 per cent phosphoric acid; gooseberry

---

[746] De Golyer, E., Discovery of potash salts and fossil algæ in Texas salt dome, Bull. Am. Assoc. Pet. Geol., vol. 9, 1925, pp. 348–349.

[747] Dana, Manual of geology, 4th ed., 1895, p. 554.

[748] Wilder, F. A., Some conclusions in regard to the origin of gypsum, Bull. Geol. Soc. Am., vol. 32, 1921, p. 390.

[749] Cameron, F. K., Potash from kelps, Rept. No. 100, U. S. Dept. Agric., 1915; Bard, J. S., The economic value of Pacific Coast kelps, Bull. 249, Exper. Station, Coll. Agric. California, 1915; Grabau, A. W., Principles of salt deposition, 1920, pp. 91–105, 247–258.

canes may contain 13 per cent potash, and yellow banana stalks 49.40 per cent.[750]

On the Spanish coast lives a plant known as *Salsola kali* L. whose ash is high in soda, and plants of the same characteristics occur along beaches of the Canary Islands, the Argentine salt steppes, and many other parts of the world. The ash of the Spanish plants carries 14 to 20 per cent sodium carbonate.

Some plants secrete sodium chloride, such occurring in parts of Africa, where the plants are burned and the ash leached for the salt content.

It is improbable that these plants would give rise to deposits of any of the substances which they secrete, but they do place these substances in a state of concentration which might aid in forming a deposit, as is thought

TABLE 77

	MACROCYSTIS PYRIFERA	ALARIA FISTULOSA	NEREOCYSTIS LUÉTKEANA
Average of number of analyses	58.	15.	51.
Ash..	5.90	7.50	4.20
Total soluble salts.........................	30.00	24.40	46.90
K₂O.......................................	12.59	9.10	20.10
I..	1.57	Trace	0.13
N...		2.60	1.90
Range K₂O, per cent......................		2.90–13.10	6.58–31.62
Range N, per cent........................		2.10– 3.30	0.81– 3.06

to be the case for the potash in Nebraska lakes, which has been assigned primarily to leaching of ash produced by burning of dry vegetation in the surrounding region.[751]

SUMMARY

It has been shown that there are several environmental conditions permitting the formation of saline residues, but that most of them permit the formation of deposits of limited extent, purity, and thickness. Such are the salt deposits of springs, surface efflorescences, salt lakes, marginal salt pans, marine salinas, lagoons, and replacement of limestone. Deposits of each of these origins probably occur in the geologic column. The large

[750] Jenkins, E. H., Bull. 198, Connecticut Agric. Exper. Station, 1917, p. 47; Bateman, E., Chemical and metallurgical engineering, 1919, p. 616.

[751] Hicks, W. B., Potash resources of Nebraska, Bull. 715, U. S. Geol. Surv., 1921, pp. 137–138.

and thick deposits of salt and gypsum are thought to be best explained as due to arms of a sea or the ocean which retain restricted connections with the parent body for a long period of time and ultimately become a relic sea. The evaporites successive to calcium sulphate are determined by the character of the salts in solution in the beginning, by introduction of fresh water and new salts, by temperature, and other factors. After burial, there will probably be reorganization of the salts deposited and formation of new salts adapted to the pressures and temperatures of the depths of burial.

With such a variety of environments producing saline residues, it is obvious that each salt deposit constitutes a separate problem. Hence, careful studies of the salt and associated strata are essential for the solution of the origin of each salt deposit, and the environment of origin can not be determined until the stratigraphy and sediments are worked out in detail.

SEDIMENTARY PRODUCTS DOMINANTLY COMPOSED OF SILICA

The importance of silica in the formation of sedimentary rocks is strikingly obvious when it is recalled that the silica annually carried in "solution" to the sea by stream waters (319,170,000 metric tons) ranks second in quantitative importance to calcium carbonate (557,670,000 metric tons).[752] This silica is not accumulated in sea water, for analyses show mere traces. Silica-using organisms account for a small quantity, but where the remainder is precipitated, and how, have not yet been positively determined.

Sedimentary products[753] dominantly composed of silica are the radiolarian and diatom oozes, siliceous sponge deposits, siliceous sinters and other spring deposits of silica, and flint and chert. The oozes are largely composed of organic remains, and such is the case for deposits of which spicules of siliceous sponges are the dominant constituents. Sinters and other siliceous spring deposits result from evaporation, work of organisms, or changes in the condition of waters. The flints and cherts are water deposits, but the exact nature of the processes leading to their development has not yet been established.

SOURCES AND TRANSPORTATION OF SILICA

Silica is carried from the land to the places of deposition by atmosphere and water, the transportation being effected by all methods possible in these media. As transportation by traction and visible suspension results largely

[752] Clarke, F. W., Data of geochemistry, Bull 770, U. S. Geol. Surv., 1924, p. 138.
[753] In this consideration such sedimentary materials as sands and gravels are not included, although sands are largely silica and so are many gravels. These have been adequately considered in another connection.

in coarse and fine grained clastics, these are not considered in this connection. The silica transported in other forms is finely divided and colloidal and possibly in solution, although it seems probable that most of the silica stated by analyses to be in solution in stream waters is in the colloidal state[754] and not in true solution. Alkaline waters are more potent in removing silica from the original rocks than are those of other character, and Lovering found that magnesium bicarbonate and calcium bicarbonate are two of the best solvents of silica in nature.[755] Dienert[756] has stated that silica is carried in solution as alkaline silicate, and with this view Moore and Maynard are in agreement.[757] Studies by Wallace, Baker, and Ward[758] have shown that the "dissolved" silica in the waters of the Red River of the North "is colloidal to the extent that one sixth of the silica content can be separated by a centrifuge running at 40,000 revolutions per minute." Kahlenberg and Lincoln state that sodium silicate is completely hydrolyzed into colloidal silica and sodium hydroxide at a dilution of 1257 parts per million.[759] Bogue[760] found, however, that complete hydrolysis required much lower dilutions than those indicated by Kahlenberg and Lincoln. Moore and Maynard[761] conclude "that silica in solution in natural waters is transported as a true colloid provided the concentration does not exceed 25 parts per million, but if the concentration is higher it is possible for a part to be transported as alkaline silicate. The average silica content of the rivers and lakes of the world does not exceed 15 parts per million," so that essentially all of the silica in natural waters may be considered to be in the colloidal state.

Some silica may be contributed to the sea by lavas erupted on its floor or intruded into the sediments which form its floor, or by hot springs on the sea floor which are fed by magmatic waters. Appeal has been made to this source to explain the cherts of the Lake Superior iron formations,[762] the Lower Paleozoic cherts of Notre Dame Bay, Newfoundland,[763] the Devonian

[754] Clarke, F. W., Data of geochemistry, Bull. 770, U. S. Geol. Surv., 1924, p. 195.

[755] Lovering, T. S., The leaching of iron protores: solution and precipitation of silica in cold water, Econ. Geol., vol. 18, 1923, pp. 523–540.

[756] Dienert, M. F., Bull. Soc. Chem., vol. 13, 1913, pp. 381–394.

[757] Moore, E. S., and Maynard, J. E., Solution, transportation, and precipitation of iron and silica, Econ. Geol., vol. 24, 1929, p. 390.

[758] Wallace, R. C., Baker, W. F., and Ward, G., The Red River as an erosive agent, Proc. Trans. Roy. Soc. Canada, Sec. 4, 1926, p. 166.

[759] Kahlenberg, L., and Lincoln, A. T., Jour. Phys. Chem., vol. 2, 1898, p. 90.

[760] Bogue, R. H., Jour. Amer. Chem. Soc., vol. 42, 1920, p. 2575.

[761] Moore, E. S., and Maynard, J. E., op. cit., pp. 302–303.

[762] Van Hise, C. R., and Leith, C. K., Geology of the Lake Superior Region, Mon. 52, U. S. Geol. Surv., 1911, pp. 506–516.

[763] Sampson, E., The ferruginous chert formations of Notre Dame Bay, Newfoundland, Jour. Geol., vol. 31, 1923, pp. 571–598.

cherts of Cornwall, England,[764] the Franciscan cherts of California,[765] and cherts found elsewhere.

Table 78 shows analyses of waters carrying notable quantities of "dissolved" silica. From this table, it is apparent that the volcanic waters of the Iceland geyser are extremely high in silica both in relation to other

TABLE 78

ANALYSES OF NATURAL WATERS CONTAINING NOTABLE QUANTITIES OF SILICA

	A	B	C	D	E
Cl	1.27	13.52	6.34	2.31	6.94
Br, I	Trace				
SO₄	3.93	9.01	4.90	18.74	2.26
S		0.32			
CO₃	41.47	10.16	24.93	31.43	24.15
NO₃	0.23		0.43	0.99	
PO₄	0.03				
BO₂	0.64				
Na	2.38	19.71	10.09	} 8.93	4.24
K	0.80	1.88	1.87		4.76
Li	Trace				
NH₄	0.03	0.28			
Ca	23.54		8.50	15.44	14.69
Mg	2.56	0.08	2.59	7.50	1.40
Mn	0.17				
BaSr	Trace				
FeAl	0.10		Fe₂O₃ 2.88	0.33 {Fe₂O₃ Al₂O₃}	12.97
SiO₂	22.85	45.04	37.47	14.33	28.59
	100.00	100.00	100.00	100.00	100.00
Salinity permille	19.7	113.1	7.3	9.8	3.7

A. Big Iron Spring, Arkansas, Clarke, 196.
B. Great Geyser, Iceland, Clarke, 197.
C. Neuse River at Raleigh, North Carolina, composite of 20 samples, Clarke, 77.
D. Wisconsin River at Portage, Wisconsin, mean of 24 analyses, Clarke, 81.
E. Amazon River at Obidas, Clarke, 95.

substances and in quantity actually present, and quantitatively this figure does not seem to be exceeded by that of any river. The percentage range of

[764] Dewey, H., and Flett, J. S., On some British pillow lavas and the rocks associated with them, Geol. Mag., vol. 48, 1911, p. 202.

[765] Lawson, A. C., Sketch of the geology of the San Francisco Peninsula, 15th Ann. Rept. U. S. Geol. Surv., 1895, pp. 419–426; Davis, E. F., The radiolarian cherts of the Franciscan group, Univ. California Publ. Geol., vol. 11, no. 3, 1918, pp. 235–432.

silica of total solids in "solution" for stream waters of North America is from 0.82 per cent in the Genesee at Rochester, New York, to 39.70 per cent in the Okmulgee near Macon, Georgia. The average for North America is 8.60 per cent. The range for South America is from 3.24 per cent in the Colorado River of Argentina to 46.22 per cent in the Uruguay at Salto, and the average is 18.88 per cent. The European range is from 0.15 per cent in the Rhine at Cologne to 32.54 per cent in the Ilz, and the average is 8.70 per cent. The average for Asia is 9.51 per cent and for Africa 17.89 per cent. The high averages for tropical countries are noteworthy and may have some significance.[766] Studies of river waters have shown that rivers high in silica are also high in organic matter; as shown later, this seems to be caused by the organic matter serving as a stabilizer to prevent the silica from being precipitated.

The average per cent of silica of the solid matter in "solution" is 11.67, which for the world indicates that annually 319,170,000 metric tons of silica are carried to the sea by streams.[766] Some is also blown there by the winds, and there are additional contributions from volcanic activity. Ocean water contains mere traces of silica. Evidently the silica contributed by streams is precipitated almost immediately on arriving at the sea, where it becomes mingled with sediments of all kinds, thus entering into shales, limestones, etc. Sediments in process of deposition whose positions are not such as to receive direct contributions from land waters should be low in silica. References will be made to this generalization on later pages.

SILICEOUS DEPOSITS MADE BY SPONGES

Spicules of siliceous sponges are rather commonly distributed in deep-sea deposits, those of the Hexactinellid sponges prevailing in the sediments of deeper waters and Tetractinellid and Monactinellid spicules in those of shallower depths. Locally sponges may be so abundant that deposits are formed of which their spicules are the most important constituents. This, however, appears to be the case only over small parts of the bottom, and their contributions to most marine sediments are of the order of magnitude of 2 to 3 per cent or less. The spicules are composed of hydrous silica and organic matter and yield on analyses a content of water ranging from 7 to 13 per cent. The evidence indicates that many of the spicules pass into "solution" not long after the deaths of their builders.

Siliceous spicules of sponges have extensive distribution in the geologic column. They occur mostly isolated and appear to be most common in chert and flint—this possibly a matter of preservation—but rarely do they

[766] Clarke, F. W., Data of geochemistry, Bull. 770, U. S. Geol. Surv., 1924, pp. 11, 119, 139.

appear to constitute more than a minor part. They have been considered one of the sources for the silica of the cherts and flints.

GEYSERITE AND SILICEOUS SINTER

Geyserite and siliceous sinter are usually associated with hot springs. The silica deposits of springs yielding waters of surface temperatures are essentially insignificant, the silica usually occurring merely as an impurity in other materials. About many hot springs with alkaline waters the deposits are of considerable importance. The silica is a variety of opal which in geyserite has a water content ranging from 9 to 13 per cent. There seem

TABLE 79

	1	2	3	4
SiO_2...............................	93.60	72.25	88.26	49.83
Al_2O_3...............................	1.06	10.96	0.69	4.74
Fe_2O_3...............................	Trace	0.76	3.26	18.00
FeO...............................		0.31		
CaO...............................	0.50	0.74	0.29	
MgO...............................	Trace	0.10	Trace	
K_2O...............................		1.66	0.11	
Na_2O...............................		3.55	0.11	
$NaCl$...............................		0.36		
H_2O...............................	4.71	9.02	4.79	10.62
C...............................		0.20		
SO_3...............................		0.45	2.49	
As_2O_5...............................				17.37
	99.87	100.36	100.00	100.56

1. Opal deposit, Norris Basin, Yellowstone National Park.
2. Geyserite incrustation, Giant Group, Upper Basin, Yellowstone National Park
3. Deposit from Scribla Spring, Icelandic geysers.
4. Deposit from Constant geyser, Yellowstone National Park, containing scoradite ($FeAsO_4 \cdot 2H_2O$).

to be few distinctions between sinter and geyserite; the latter is said to be more porous, to be frequently fibrous, and to contain more water. According to Weed,[767] spring deposits of silica result from relief of pressure, cooling, chemical reactions, evaporation, and the work of algæ. Algæ precipitate the silica upon themselves in gelatinous form, commonly brilliantly colored—golden-yellow, red, pink, and other shades. The color varies with the temperature, being white in the hottest waters and greenish in the cooler

[767] Weed, W. H., 9th Ann. Rept., U. S. Geol. Surv., 1889, pp. 613–676: Am. Jour. Sci., vol. 37, 1889, p. 351.

ones. The exact processes of deposition are not fully understood. On the death of the algæ, the silica changes to a soft cheese-like texture, and the brilliant colors are lost. New silica may be deposited in the midst of this and it may harden into a solid mass, but ordinarily there is considerable porosity. Analyses of silica deposits of some springs are given in table 79.[768] These serve to show the great range in composition.

DIATOMITE AND DIATOM OOZE[769]

Diatoms live in essentially all waters. In the ocean they seem to have their greatest abundance in waters of low salinity, as those of the Antarctic and Arctic oceans, estuaries, and off the mouths of great rivers. They also occur in the fresh waters of the land. They obtain their silica from that in "solution," which in sea water is very small, averaging only one part of silica in 250,000 of water, a quantity apparently not competent to satisfy the requirements of the organism; and perhaps from siliceous matter in suspension.[770]

Diatom tests are composed of opal, of which the formula may be expressed as $SIO_2(H_2O)_x$. It is probably a hardened hydrogel consisting originally of the two phases of silica and water, the latter diffusing into the silica and forming a solid solution.[771]

Diatoms sometimes die in enormous numbers during the so-called epidemics. In the case studied on the Pacific Coast at Copalis Beach, Washington, these seem to have been induced by dilution of sea water caused by heavy rains, followed by westerly winds and clear, sunshiny weather.[772] At such times there should be rapid accumulation of diatom remains.

Diatom ooze is named after the presence of its characteristic organic constituent. Wet ooze has a yellow straw or cream color; when dried, the color has a bluish tinge from the incorporation of terrigenous matter. Material other than diatoms consists of radiolaria and foraminifera, shell fragments, and various percentages of inorganic matter. Calcium carbonate in the Challenger samples ranges from 2 per cent in a sample from 1975 fathoms to 36.34 per cent in 600 fathoms; the average is 22.96 per cent. The mineral particles are terrigenous and volcanic, ranging from 3 per

[768] Clarke, F. W., Data of geochemistry, Bull. 770, U. S. Geol. Surv., 1924, pp. 207–209.
[769] Murray, J., and Renard, A. F., Deep sea deposits, Challenger Rept., 1891, pp. 208–213, 281–283.
[770] Murray, J., and Irvine, R., On silica and the siliceous remains of organisms in modern seas, Proc. Roy. Soc. Edinburgh, vol. 18, 1891, pp. 229–250.
[771] Rogers, A. F., in Tolman, C. F., Econ. Geol., vol. 22, 1927, p. 457.
[772] Becking, L. B., Tolman, C. F., McMillan, H. C., Field, J., and Hashimoto, T., Preliminary statement regarding the diatom 'epidemics' at Copalis Beach, Washington, Econ. Geol., vol. 22, 1927, pp. 356–368.

per cent in a sample from 1950 fathoms to 25 per cent in one from 600 fathoms, with the average 15.60 per cent. As there is such a great extent of diatom deposits in polar seas, ice-transported particles of all sizes should be present.

The upper layers of diatom ooze are thin and watery, but below the surface it is dense, compact, and probably laminated.

The average mechanical composition of five samples of diatom ooze is as follows:

Pelagic foraminifera	18.21
Bottom-living foraminifera	1.60
Other calcareous organisms	3.15
Siliceous organisms	41.00
Minerals	15.60
Fine washings	20.44
	100.00

The following analysis gives the chemical composition of a diatom ooze from a depth of 1950 fathoms in the southern Indian Ocean:

SiO_2	67.92
Al_2O_3	0.55
Fe_2O_3	0.39
$CaCO_3$	19.29
$CaSO_4$	0.29
$Ca_3P_2O_8$	0.41
$MgCO_3$	1.13
Insoluble	4.72
Loss	5.30
	100.00

Diatom ooze as an extensive deposit is largely confined to a great belt in the south polar regions, mostly between the Antarctic circle and latitude 40° south, where it covers an estimated area of 10,880,000 square miles of ocean bottom. There is a small patch in the North Pacific with an estimated area of 40,000 square miles. In depth it occurs between 600 and 1975 fathoms with the average 1477 fathoms. However, there are no reasons for considering that diatom deposits may not form on bottoms of any depth not so great that the shells pass into "solution" before reaching bottom. Diatoms seem to be as abundant over shallow bottoms as deep, but their accumulations over shallow bottoms are not apparent because of the abundance of sediments or because of their dissipation by scavengers. The Copalis Beach diatom accumulations at the time of the epidemics of 1925 extended along the beach as a continuous ridge for 20 miles and had thickness from 4 to 6 inches,[773] and every fact indicates that the diatom deposits of the Upper Cretaceous and Tertiary of the Pacific Coast were accumulated in shallow water.[774]   Extensive deposits have been made in fresh water.

Diatomaceous deposits of the geologic column are commonly known as diatomaceous earths.   The term "earth" is, however, rarely applicable, as the materials are usually consolidated, and the most extensive deposits are firm and hard and often in extremely thick beds.   Diatomite is a better term for those which are well consolidated, and shales, sandstones and limestones containing considerable admixtures of diatoms may be qualified by use of the adjective diatomaceous.[775]

Diatoms are known in the geologic column from the Lias of the Jurassic to the present, but important deposits are not known to have been made until the Tertiary.   The Fairhaven diatomaceous earth of the Miocene of Maryland has a greenish colored member at the base which consists of more than 50 per cent diatom frustules.   The rock on weathering becomes white to buff colored and has a known maximum thickness of 55 feet.[776]   A similar deposit occurs near Richmond, Virginia.[777]   The Miocene Monterey shale of California is in parts largely composed of the frustules of diatoms,[778] and several other Pacific Coast formations from the Upper Cretaceous to Pliocene locally and horizontally contain diatomite.[775]

RADIOLARITE AND RADIOLARIAN OOZE[779]

Radiolarian ooze is named from the fact that an important part of it is composed of the tests of radiolaria, and a non-calcareous ooze containing 20 per cent or more of the tests of this organism and siliceous organisms other than diatoms is designated radiolarian.   As a distinct deposit it is confined to the deeper bottoms of the ocean, its distribution having a greater average depth than the red clay from which it differs in a much higher content of siliceous organisms, and into which it passes by gradual transitions.   The ooze at the top is thin and watery; below the surface it is dense and compact. The tests, as those of diatoms, are composed of opal.

Radiolaria are widely distributed in ocean waters and are generally considered to be more abundant in waters some distance from land.   It does

[773] Becking, L. B., etc., op. cit., 1927, p. 359.

[774] Tolman, C. F., Biogenesis of hydrocarbons by diatoms, Econ. Geol., vol. 22, 1927, pp. 454–474.

[775] Tolman, C. F., op. cit., 1927.

[776] Shattuck, G. B., Miocene volume, Maryland Geol. Surv., 1904, pp. lxiii–lxiv.

[777] Merrill, G. P., Ann. Rept. Smithsonian Inst. for 1899, 1901, p. 219.

[778] Arnold, R., and Anderson, R., Bull. 322, U. S. Geol. Surv., 1907, pp. 38–40.

[779] Murray, J., and Renard, A. F., Deep sea deposits, Challenger Rept., 1891, pp. 203–208, 283–284.

not seem that proof of this assumption has been produced, and there seem to be no good reasons why they are not as abundant in waters over shallow bottoms as over deep ones.   They belong exclusively to the plankton and appear to be most abundant in tropical waters, particularly in the western and central Pacific and eastern Indian oceans.   They are thought to obtain their silica from that in "solution" and perhaps from suspended matter containing silica.

The radiolarian content of oozes may range as high as 60 to 70 per cent and downward to around 10 per cent in the diatom and globigerina oozes and 2 per cent or less in marine deposits of terrigenous derivation.

Colors range from straw to red.   Fragments of pumice, augite, feldspar, hornblende, magnetite, palagonite, magnetic spherules, and other minerals and rocks are commonly present.   Manganese nodules occasionally are common and also shark teeth and other resistant parts of vertebrates. Fragments are mostly angular; some are more or less rounded; and the volcanic matter is in various stages of alteration.   The average mechanical composition of the Challenger samples of radiolarian ooze is as follows:

Pelagic foraminifera	3.11
Bottom-living foraminifera	0.11
Other calcareous organisms	0.79
Siliceous organisms	54.44
Minerals	1.67
Fine washings	39.88
	100.00

Chemically, radiolarian oozes are composed very largely of silica.   Calcium carbonate ranges from a mere trace to 20 per cent in a sample from 2550 fathoms, and the average in the Challenger samples is 4.01 per cent.   Analyses of two radiolarian oozes are given in table 80.

Radiolarian ooze is confined to the Pacific and Indian oceans, with an area of about 1,161,000 square miles in the Pacific and 1,129,000 square miles in the Indian.   It does not seem to have made any significant deposits in the Atlantic.   The range in depth of the Challenger samples is from 2350 fathoms to 4475 fathoms, with the average 2894 fathoms, 164 fathoms deeper than the average for red clay[780] and nearly twice as deep as the average for diatom ooze.   Although existing deposits of radiolarian ooze appear to be confined to deep bottoms, there seem to be no good reasons why such may not accumulate over shallow bottoms, as the tests are probably settling to such bottoms as rapidly as over deep ones, but are not apparent because of masking by other varieties of sediments.

[780] Murray, J., and Renard, A. F., Challenger Rept., Deep sea deposits, 1891, pp. 203–208, 283–284.

On cementation and consolidation, radiolarian ooze gives rise to radiolarite. This has not been commonly described from the geologic column, whether because of rareness or failure of recognition remains to be determined. A formation of radiolarite of late Devonian or Mississippian age with a thickness of 9000 feet occurs in New South Wales, Australia, in which radiolaria are present to the number of about one million to the cubic inch. These are not deep-sea sediments, as they contain abundant evidence of shallow-water deposition.[781] The Jurassic of the Austrian Alps contains a deposit of radiolarite consisting of red to green jasper-like layers alternating with dense, reddish or greenish gray layers of sandy and clayey marls, the entire deposit ranging in thickness from 10 to 25 meters, the increase in

TABLE 80

	2900 FATHOMS	2750 FATHOMS
SiO_2	59.77	56.02
Al_2O_3	12.94	10.52
Fe_2O_3	14.29	14.99
MnO_2	0.57	3.23
$CaCO_3$	2.54	3.89
$CaSO_4$	0.29	0.41
$Ca_3P_2O_8$	0.65	1.39
$MgCO_3$	2.46	1.50
CaO	1.85	0.39
MgO	0.34	0.25
Loss	4.30	7.41
	100.00	100.00

thickness being due to the non-radiolarite layers.[782] Wilckens[783] has described radiolarites from the Lower Carboniferous of the Rhine region and from Great Britain, and cherts containing radiolaria have been frequently reported, as those in the Mississippian of western England[784] and the Jurassic Franciscan series of California,[785] each seeming to have developed under

[781] David, T. W. E., and Pittman, E. F., On the Paleozoic radiolarian rocks of New South Wales, Quart. Jour. Geol. Soc., vol. 55, 1899, pp. 16–37.

[782] Hahn, F., Geologie der Kammerker-Sonntagshorngruppe, Jahrb. d. k.-k. geol. Reichsanstalt, Bd. 60, 1910, pp. 389–390, 415–416.

[783] Wilckens, O., Radiolarit im Culm der Attendorn-Elsper Doppelmulde, Monatsb. Zeits. d. deutsch. Gesell., 1908, pp. 354–356.

[784] Dixon, E. E. L., and Vaughan, A., The Carboniferous succession, in Gower, etc., Quart. Jour. Geol. Soc., vol. 67, 1911, pp. 477–571 (519–531).

[785] Davis, E. F., The radiolarian cherts of the Franciscan group, Univ. California Publ. Geol., vol. 11, No. 3, 1918, pp. 235–432. The Berkeley Hills, a detail of Coast Range Geology. Dept. Geol. Bull. 2, pp. 349–450.

shallow water conditions although a deep sea origin has by some been postulated.

CHERT AND FLINT

BY W. A. TARR AND W. H. TWENHOFEL

Chert and flint have a wide distribution in the geologic column. They have been studied for many years, but it is probable that less is known of the methods of their formation than of those of any other kind of common sedimentary rock. They were thought to be of igneous origin by Hutton; of organic origin by most students in the last half of the nineteenth century;

TABLE 81

	A	B	C
	per cent	*per cent*	*per cent*
SiO_2.....................................	98.17	99.47	95.50
Al_2O_3, Fe_2O_3.............................	0.83	0.29	2.05
FeO.......................................			0.15
CaO.......................................	0.05	0.09	0.49
MgO.......................................	0.01	0.05	
K_2O.......................................		0.07	
Na_2O......................................		0.15	Trace
Ignition...................................	0.78	0.12	1.43
	99.84	100.24	99.62

A. Chert, Belleville, Missouri, analysis by Schneider, A. E., Bull. 228, U. S. Geol. Surv.

B. Novaculite, Rockport, Arkansas, analysis by Brackett, R. N., Rept. Arkansas Geol. Surv., vol. 4, 1890, p. 167.

C. Chert, Upper Carboniferous of Ireland, analysis by Hardman, E. T., Sci. Trans. Roy. Dublin Soc., vol. 1, 1878, p. 85.

and, during the last one or two decades, the increasing tendency has been to ascribe their formation to chemical processes.

In the strict sense, *chert* includes those crypto-crystalline varieties of quartz which are white, gray, or other light colors. *Flint* includes the dark gray and black varieties of the same material. *Jasper* is a variety colored red by iron oxide.[786] *Novaculite* is a type of chert. Early investigators had variously interpreted it as a fine-grained sandstone or as a replacement of limestone or dolomite by silica, but the most recent study by Miser and

[786] Lees, C. M., The chert beds of Palestine, Proc. Geologists' Assoc., vol. 39, 1928, pp. 445–462 (447). States that chert has a splintery fracture and flint a conchoidal fracture, probably a local distinction.

Purdue[787] has shown that it is a chert.   Some novaculite contains detrital grains of quartz, however.   *Jasperoid* is a common name for a chert-like rock occurring in southwestern Missouri, and adjacent parts of the bordering states, in association with the zinc and lead ores.   It is stated to be somewhat more coarse-grained than average chert.[788]   *Jaspilite* is a form of metamorphic chert occurring in association with the Lake Superior iron formations.

Chert and flint are dominantly composed of silica.   The common impurities are small quantities of Al_2O_3, Fe_2O_3, $CaCO_3$, $MgCO_3$, FeS_2, and carbonaceous material.   The chemical composition of several representative cherts is given in table 81.

Some cherts carry considerable quantities of calcium carbonate, and some pass gradually into limestone.   Cherts from Kentucky have been shown to carry up to 3.5 per cent P_2O_5,[789] and many cherts contain considerable amounts of pyrite or marcasite.

The coloring matter of flint and chert may be uniformly distributed, or it may be aggregated into irregular patches, giving a mottled appearance. The mottling may take any conceivable form and distribution.   The coloring matter is commonly due to included organic matter, iron oxide, minute grains of disseminated pyrite, or, indirectly, to differences in porosity of the rock.   Chert and flint may be concentrically or horizontally banded.   In some, the banding occurs in small irregular patches, the banded areas lying at all angles to each other and being separated by sharp lines.   Concentrically banded flints and cherts are apt to have the inner bands of a darker color than those of the exterior.   As a rule, the banding appears to be wider laterally than above or below, and commonly wider above than below.   There is great variation in the width of the bands, some being paper-thin, and others an inch or more wide.   In most materials, the banding is due to differences in composition, but in some it arises from differences in texture and porosity. Color is usually more uniform in flint than in chert.

Typical chert and flint have dense textures, and vitreous to waxy lusters, but some are more or less granular with a dull luster.   Those with vitreous to waxy lusters have a conchoidal fracture and the hardness of quartz. Granular varieties break irregularly.

To the unaided eye, cherts and flints seem to be uniform in composition

[787] Miser, H. D., and Purdue, A. H., The geology of the DeQueen and Caddo Gap Quads., Arkansas, Bull. 808, U. S. Geol. Surv., 1929, pp. 49–50.   This reference includes a summary of the previous views and a good bibliography.

[788] Cox, G. H., Dean, R. S., and Gottschalk, V. H., Bull. 2, Univ. Missouri School of Mines and Metallurgy, vol. 3, 1916, p. 10.

[789] Kastle, J. H., Fraser, J. C. W., and Sullivan, G., Am. Chem. Soc., Vol. 20, 1898, p. 153.

and amorphous in character, but under a high-power microscope most flints and cherts, particularly those earlier than Tertiary in age, become fine mosaics of chalcedony and quartz, together with a few particles of clay, pyrite, hematite, limonite, calcite, dolomite, and carbonaceous matter. Opaline or amorphous silica is wanting or extremely rare in Mesozoic and older flints and cherts, but may be found in those of the Tertiary and later. Calcite, or silicified, fossils in perfect forms and in fragments are commonly present. The silica that has replaced the calcite of fossils is in the form of crystalline quartz of which the grains are characteristically larger than those of the chert. Minute circular areas of quartz and chalcedony are found in some cherts. Those of Notre Dame Bay,[790] Newfoundland, show globular masses which are microscopically banded with transparent silica and silica with hematite, suggesting that the banding arose through diffusion while the material of the globule was in the form of a colloid gel. The jasperoid of southwestern Missouri is composed "chiefly of a fine-grained xenomorphic aggregate of irregular, rounded, or wedge-shaped quartz grains, the diameters of which are usually 0.02 to 0.06 mm."[791] The flint of the chalk in England is an extremely fine-grained mosaic of chalcedony and quartz.[792] The cherts which are largely responsible for the Flint Hills of Kansas are also composed of a mosaic of tiny grains of chalcedony and quartz with some calcite and limonite. Amorphous silica does not appear to be present. Weathered chert consists mainly of chalcedony.

Chert and flint may or may not contain fossils, but, if present, they are similar to those of the strata in which the chert and flint developed. The fossils may occur throughout the material or be confined largely to the outer portions. They may be calcareous or siliceous, or partly both. The preservation of these fossils is commonly excellent, usually much better than that of the fossils in the enclosing rock, particularly if the rock is a dolomite.

Form and Mode of Occurrence of Chert and Flint

Chert and flint occur in the form of globular, ellipsoidal, discoidal, and irregularly shaped nodules or concretions; as lenses; beds; cavity fillings; and cement for other types of sediments. Nodules are rather generally confined to calcareous rocks.

Nodules usually have irregular shapes, and their surfaces are commonly mammillary. Their usual position is along, or parallel to, bedding planes. They may unite with each other along the plane, and nodules of one plane

[790] Sampson, E., The ferruginous chert formations of Notre Dame Bay, Newfoundland, Jour. Geol., vol. 31, 1923, pp. 571–598.

[791] Cox, Dean, and Gottschalk, op. cit., p. 12.

[792] Tarr, W. A., The origin of chert and flint, Univ. of Missouri Studies, vol. 1, 1926 pp. 8–10.

may connect with those of adjacent planes. Some nodules are isolated and irregularly distributed within beds, and these may unite with each other to form a somewhat labyrinthine and intricate network. In some occurrences, as those in the older Paleozoic of Missouri[793] and the Pennsylvanian of Kansas, the nodules within beds are so abundant and have become so united as to constitute most of the beds. Some nodules attain a length of 10 or 12 feet and a thickness of 2 to 4 feet. Small nodules (a foot or less in length) are most common. Lenticular nodules usually have their longer axes parallel to bedding planes. Nodules of irregular shapes very commonly have the longest axis at some angle to the bedding planes, and it may be perpendicular thereto. It seems probable, however, that the most common occurrence of nodules is along bedding planes, although the planes are not always evident. Nodules may contain more or less limestone as irregular patches, some of which are connected with the surrounding limestone. They commonly contain geodal cavities lined with crystals of quartz and more rarely those of other minerals.

There is usually a sharp contact between the nodule and the enclosing rock, shown best after weathering, but in some there is no definite boundary. The outer portion of a nodule may be more or less weathered, resulting in an increase in porosity in that portion and a bleaching in color. Not uncommonly, this weathered outer portion has a chalk-like aspect.

In some formations (Burlington limestone and lower formations of Missouri and perhaps elsewhere), chert nodules occur with cracks filled with veinlets of the surrounding limestone, showing that the nodules were solid enough to maintain a crack before the enclosing limestone was entirely hardened (Tarr).

Bedded and laminated cherts are widely distributed in the geologic column; four of the most notable American examples are the radiolarian cherts of the Franciscan group of California, the Lower Paleozoic cherts of Newfoundland,[794] the jaspilite and similar rocks of the Lake Superior region, and the Rex chert of Idaho.[795] The massive chert formation of North Flintshire, Wales,[796] is also an example of this type. The beds of these cherts range in thickness from less than an inch to 1 or 2 feet. The thickness of individual beds is commonly very uniform, and the beds are very persistent. Other formations contain chert or flint in thick beds, which, however, as

[793] Purdue, A. H. and Miser, H. D., Folio 202, U. S. Geol. Surv., 1916.

[794] Sampson, E., The ferruginous chert formations of Notre Dame Bay, Newfoundland, Jour. Geol., vol. 31, 1923, pp. 571–598.

[795] Mansfield, G. R., Prof. Paper 152, U. S. Geol. Surv., 1927, pp. 367–372; Econ. Geol., vol. 26, 1931, pp. 353–374.

[796] Sargent, H. C., The massive chert formation of North Flintshire, Geol. Mag., vol. 60, 1923, pp. 168–183.

individual units are not extensively persistent. Such are the chert beds of the Pennsylvanian-Permian formations, which are responsible for the Flint Hills of Kansas.

The chert of any horizon is usually distinct from that of adjacent horizons, both with respect to characteristics and separation, the chert of each horizon having the aspect of having been formed independently of that of the adjacent horizons. Within each horizon, the chert may have a wide distribution, with but slight variation in character. This is illustrated by the cherts of the Oneota dolomite of the upper Mississippi Valley; those of the Pennsylvanian limestone members of Kansas and Oklahoma; and the Carboniferous cherts of Ireland, England, Belgium, and elsewhere.

Chert and flint have been found on the interior of fossils. This introduction is supposed by some to have been by ground water, but may be more accurately explained as a filling of the fossil by the original silica while yet soft. Chert and flint also serve as cement for various clastic sediments, as illustrated by the French Cretaceous formation known as "gaize."[797] A conglomerate at the base of the Trinity formation of Texas is locally similarly cemented by "amorphous" silica. In the Lower Paleozoic of Notre Dame Bay, Newfoundland, the spaces between pillow lavas are filled with chert.[798] The jasperoid in the Tri-State area cements the original broken chert.

The Rocks Associated with Chert and Flint

Nodular chert and flint occur almost wholly in association with calcareous strata. The nodules in chalk are very commonly flint; those in dolomites and limestones are commonly chert. However, chert nodules occur in chalk and those of flint in limestone and dolomite. Bedded cherts and flints are in association with shales, limestone, and sandstone. Vein flints and cherts occur (such occurrences are rare) in any variety of rock.

Geologic Distribution

Chert and flint are probably present in the calcareous strata of every geologic period. Chert interbedded with other types of sediments occurs in the Pre-Cambrian formations of the Lake Superior and Hudson Bay regions and in Wyoming; the Ordovician of southern Scotland; the Lower Paleozoic of Newfoundland; the Devonian of Cornwall and eastern Australia; and the Franciscan of California. Cherts in limestones and dolomites are abundant in the Upper Cambrian of the Appalachian region, the Mississippi Valley, and the western part of the United States; the Ordovician Knox dolomite and Shenandoah limestone of the Appalachians, some of the

[797] Cayeux, L., Mém. Soc. Géol. du Nord, vol. 4, pt. ii, 1897.
[798] Sampson, E., op. cit., p. 577.

Ordovician limestones of the Mississippi Valley, Texas, New Mexico, and Arizona; the Niagara limestone of the upper Mississippi Valley and the Great Lakes region; the Lower Devonian of the Appalachians and the Mississippi Valley; the Mississippian of the Mississippi Valley and Europe; the Pennsylvanian of the Mississippi Valley and parts of the Rocky Mountains; and the Cretaceous of both Europe and America. Chert is so abundant in parts of the Pennsylvanian strata of Kansas as to cause an important physiographic feature, the Flint Hills, before mentioned.

A fact of interest in connection with the distribution of the nodular cherts is that the equivalents of containing strata in some other parts of the world do not carry chert. Thus, the Beekmantown and Chazy limestones and dolomites of the Mingan Islands and Newfoundland have little chert, although their equivalents in the Mississippi Valley are filled with it. The Silurian rocks of Gotland and Anticosti carry no cherts, but those of the Great Lakes region and upper Mississippi Valley have it in abundance. This distribution must be related to the paleogeography of the times; the depths of water; and the nature of the water bodies and their relations to the open sea, the land, and the streams draining therefrom. Bedded cherts may be associated with pillow and ellipsoidal lavas, and this association probably has some bearing on the origin of the siliceous sediments.

Origin and Time of Development of Chert and Flint

The theories relating to the origin of chert and flint must be concerned with the source of the silica; the processes and agents responsible for its concentration and precipitation; the environment in which deposition occurred; and the time relationships to the enclosing rock. There is wide diversity in the evaluation of these various elements by different students of the subject, one emphasizing one set of factors in the process and another emphasizing a different group. The factor which has been considered the least and yet which is of as much if not more significance than the others is the source of the silica. Especially is this factor of necessary consideration by those advocating a secondary origin of chert and flint.

SOURCE OF THE SILICA. The quantity of silica in the form of chert and flint occurring in sedimentary rocks is enormous. The amount can scarcely be estimated in such formations as the Rex chert, with a thickness of 60 to 110 feet over hundreds of square miles; the Lower Paleozoic formations of the Mississippi Valley; the Knox dolomite, a formation 3,500 to 4,000 feet thick and estimated to contain a total of 800 to 1,000 feet of chert; and the chalk of England and France. In explaining the origin of these formations, it is as essential to have an adequate source for this silica as it is to have a source for the material in the enclosing beds. The literature contains little information as to the source of the silica of chert and flint, the authors having apparently assumed that if silica was present it was derived just as were the materials of the enclosing limestone or other sedimentary rock. However safe this assumption may be for those students who advocate the chemical deposition of chert and flint directly on the sea floor, the supporter of a secondary origin is required to shift these enormous quantities of silica about in solid rock, and for him an adequate source of such amounts of silica is a real problem. The source of the silica should not be ignored, however, under any theory.

Davis[799] in his discussion of the radiolarian cherts of the Franciscan group in California discussed the source of the silica and ascribed it either to the lavas associated with the cherts or to reactions, due to the lavas, that formed silicates which altered to chert. Others have sought to explain the silica as having been derived from igneous rocks or magmas below the sea. Siliceous springs have been suggested as a source. Those believing in an organic source for the silica think that organisms secured it from the sea water, which had received it from the land or through the decomposition of silicates in the sea. That chert and flint do not occur more commonly is due to the fact that when muds were carried to the sea most of the (colloidal) silica was deposited with them, as is being done at present. The view that the silica was derived from the land during the process of weathering thus ascribes the same source to the silica as is accepted for the calcium carbonate in limestone and dolomite. The detailed chemical studies of Moore and Maynard (which will be described) give further support to this view of the source of the silica.

Aside from possible igneous sources in the sea, the logical source is the land. Clarke's[800] averages of the composition (believed to be more accurate than those of Sir John Murray) of the river waters of the world have revealed that the second most abundant material annually added in solution to the sea by rivers is silica. Silica furnishes 11.67 per cent and calcium 20.37 per cent of these materials added to the sea. This amounts to 319,-170,000 metric tons for silica and 557,670,000 metric tons for calcium. As there is essentially no silica in the sea water, this silica is deposited in some form. Tarr[801] pointed out that during a period of peneplanation when chemical denudation would be at a maximum much greater quantities of silica would be carried to the sea. During such a period of low-lying lands, the seaward movement of clastic materials would be restricted and the forma-

[799] Davis, E. F., The radiolarian cherts of the Franciscan group, Univ. of California Publ. Geol., vol. 11, 1918, pp. 235–432.

[800] Clarke, F. W., Data of geochemistry, Bull. 770, U. S. Geol. Surv., 1924, p. 119.

[801] Tarr, W. A., Origin of the chert in the Burlington, Am. Jour. Sci., vol. 44, 1917, pp. 409–452.

tion of carbonate rocks favored. Thus, the formation of limestone and of chert would be favored at the same time, which explains the common association of the two rocks. A study by Tarr of the paleogeography of the Paleozoic and Mesozoic periods supported this view that low-lying lands were associated with the abundant deposition of chert and limestone.

CAUSES OF PRECIPITATION OF SILICA. Essentially all silica is transported as a colloid. That transported as the aluminous silicate (clay) does not enter into our discussion. The clay is of significance in our present problem only if present in large quantities (as in muddy waters entering the ocean), whereupon the colloidal silica having been coagulated by the electrolytes of the sea water goes down with the clay. An unsettled question regarding the colloidal silica is whether it is transported as sodium silicate (the composition of common water glass). The general view held by chemists and most students of ground waters and streams is that the colloidal silica is not so transported, but also that it is probably not one of the specific silicic acids such as H_4SiO_4 or H_2SiO_3. It is much more probable that the colloidal silica in solution is far more dilute than these; for example, one part of SiO_2 to hundreds or even thousands of parts of water. A silicic acid gel containing one mol of silica to 300 mols of water is solid enough to be broken apart, but will coalesce again by flowing together. As further evidence concerning the character of colloidal silica, it may be noted that quartz can be ground extremely fine and then converted into colloidal silicic acid by boiling in hot water. The process of weathering favors the formation of the colloidal silica, as the alkalies unite much more readily with the carbonate, sulphate, or chloride acid radicals present in the ground water.

The colloidal silica particle has a sheath of water molecules about it, which favors its stability. Most of the colloidal silica transported by ground water in streams is a hydrophilic colloid and not very sensitive to electrolytes. Hydrophilic colloids adsorb much water (a fact in keeping with the large amount of water in a hydrosol solution), and it is this marked hydration that is an important factor in the stability of such sols.[802] A sol may be further stabilized by adsorbing an ion with its electric charge, thereby making it necessary to have a larger amount of the oppositely charged ion to neutralize it and so bring about coagulation. Another factor in the stabilization of a colloid is the presence of a so-called "protective colloid." Organic colloids are especially good as protective colloids. Authorities are not agreed as to whether this protective colloid forms a film about the other, or whether they adsorb each other. As some of these factors of stabilization are difficult to determine, it is not surprising that variable results are secured when silica sols are experimentally coagulated.

[802] Freundlich, H., Elements of colloidal chemistry, 1924, p. 149.

The coagulation of a sol may be accomplished by decreasing the hydration or, as is more common, by neutralizing the charge on the colloidal particles through the addition of electrolytes of the opposite charge (for a silica sol, this is usually a positive charge) to the solution. After neutralization, the coalescence of the particles follows, more or less rapidly, as a result of their colliding, and thus depends on their concentration and velocity. There is a wide variation in the neutralizing ability of univalent, bivalent, and trivalent ions. Ordinarily, ions of the higher valency are adsorbed more readily and are more effective in coagulating the particles; but the concentration, character of the charge, and rate at which the electrolyte is added influence the coagulating power of the ions and may even reverse the process.[803]

This discussion of sols in general, with some reference to the character of silica sols, will enable us to understand better the experimental data given below. Much more work on sols (especially silica sols) is needed, with known degrees of hydration and known adsorption of ions and influence of protective colloids.

Several workers have experimented with the precipitation of colloidal silica, but without concordant results. Their work, however, contributes much of value to the study of chert and flint. Tarr[804] conducted a short series of experiments, using artificial solutions of $NaCl$, $MgSO_4$, and K_2SO_4 in the proportions in which they occur in sea water, and the $NaCl$ and $MgSO_4$ separately. His sodium silicate solutions consisted of 27.07 parts of silica per million, and half, and twice that quantity. He obtained a heavy precipitate of gelatinous silica in each test, and therefore concluded that colloidal silica is coagulated through the neutralization of the negative charges on the colloidal silica particles by the positively charged ions of sodium, potassium, calcium, and magnesium.

Lovering's[805] experiments carried the work still further. He used natural sea water and obtained results not in agreement with Tarr's in that there was no precipitate with sodium silicate solutions containing 30 parts of silica per million (possibly due to the stabilizing effect of the organic matter in the natural sea water). He obtained precipitation, however, from sodium silicate solutions containing 490, 6,000, and 8,000 parts of silica per million. Lovering concluded that 1 cc. of sea water will precipitate 0.0155 grams of silica from a sodium silicate solution, providing the concentration is sufficiently high, that precipitation is never complete, and that none occurs in

[803] Bancroft, W. D., Applied colloid chemistry, 1921, pp. 212–259.

[804] Tarr, W. A., Origin of the chert in the Burlington limestone, Am. Jour. Sc., vol. 44, 1917, pp. 409–452. See also The origin of chert and flint, Univ. of Missouri Studies, vol. 1, no. 1, 1926, pp. 24–32.

[805] Lovering, T. S., The leaching of iron protores; solution and precipitation of silica in cold water, Econ. Geol., vol. 18, 1923, p. 537.

solutions containing less than 36 parts silica per million.   He also concluded that 275 parts silica per million may fail of precipitation in a slightly alkaline solution in the presence of a large quantity of electrolytes.

Moore and Maynard's[806] studies are the most complete to date, however. They used three types of solutions containing silica: (1) sodium silicate, (2) dialyzed sodium silicate, and (3) sodium silicate solutions mixed with hydrochloric acid and then dialyzed.   Each of the solutions, with the exception of the undialyzed sodium silicate, contained the silica in the colloidal form, and even in the sodium silicate the greater part was probably a colloid.   Moore and Maynard found that precipitation was a complex process and obtained variable results where uniformity was expected.   This variability, however, as pointed out above in the discussion of colloids, should be regarded as highly probable.

Moore and Maynard concluded from their experiments that calcium bicarbonate and sea salts are two of the best precipitants of colloidal silica from sodium silicate solutions, that sodium chloride and potassium sulphate are not so effective, and that time is an extremely important factor.   Magnesium sulphate produced no or little precipitation in sodium silicate solutions containing 30 parts of silica per million, faint precipitation in those with 60 parts per million, and greater effects with increasing concentration in silica up to the limit of the experiments of 480 parts per million.   Not all of the silica could be precipitated, the quantity remaining in solution increasing with the original concentration and ranging from 28 parts per million in the 30 parts per million silica concentrate to 104 parts per million silica in solutions containing 480 parts per million.   It seems quite certain that a part of the precipitate was magnesium silicate.   Sodium chloride and sea salt were the most effective precipitants of dialyzed sodium silicate solutions, and time was an important factor in precipitation though even then not all the silica was precipitated.   Magnesium sulphate gave little precipitate, as did also calcium bicarbonate.   A silica hydrosol prepared by dialyzing a mixture of sodium silicate and hydrochloric acid yielded after 75 days little precipitate with sea salt, sodium chloride, magnesium sulphate, magnesium bicarbonate, and calcium bicarbonate, showing that this type of silica is probably unimportant in the origin of chert and flint.   The magnesium bicarbonate and calcium bicarbonate tended to dissolve more silica from the walls of the container rather than to precipitate the colloidal silica already in solution, which agreed with the findings of Lovering that these two salts in nature are not precipitants but common solvents of silica.

Considerable has been written with respect to the precipitating ability

[806] Moore, E. S., and Maynard, J. E., Solution, transportation, and precipitation of iron and silica, Econ. Geol., vol. 24, 1929, pp. 403, et al.

of calcium and magnesium bicarbonate. Church[807] states that 1 mg. of powdered calcite would convert a 1-per cent silica solution into a gel within 10 minutes time. Cox, Dean, and Gottschalk[808] obtained no results on treatment of a dialyzed mixture of water glass and hydrochloric acid with calcium carbonate, but did obtain a strong precipitate with a calcium carbonate solution saturated with carbon dioxide. Lovering,[809] on the other hand, has shown that a dilute dialyzed solution similar to that used by Dean in the presence of calcium bicarbonate retains considerable silica in solution, and he concluded that magnesium and calcium bicarbonate rarely act as precipitants of silica in nature but that calcium bicarbonate will precipitate colloidal silica when the concentration is over 40,000 parts per million, a state of concentration so rare in nature as to be of no importance. Moore and Maynard have shown these salts to be ineffective precipitants in such solutions as ordinarily occur in nature and to become important only when the concentration is high, under which conditions carbon dioxide and calcium carbonate also function. The time factor is important. They explain the disagreements of earlier results on the basis of difference in degree of concentration of the silica solution.

As previously noted, sodium chloride is a poor precipitant of colloidal silica formed from dialyzing a mixture of sodium silicate and hydrochloric acid, and also ineffective in undialyzed sodium silicate solution, whereas it acts very effectively in dialyzed sodium silicate solutions with the same concentration in silica. Calcium bicarbonate is an efficient precipitant in undialyzed hydrosols (sodium silicate), but ineffective in dialyzed hydrosols. Explanation of these facts is difficult, but Moore and Maynard suggest that in some cases the silica may be in true solution, in others have become stabilized by adsorption of various ions, and in still others that the character of the solutions and electrolytes may have reversed the charge. Hardy[810] has stated that silica is positively charged in acid solution and negatively in alkaline or very feebly acid solutions, and thus under some conditions a given electrolyte would be effective as a precipitant and in others not. The real coagulating factors are the ability of the colloidal particles to adsorb ions, and the valency of the ions adsorbed. Ions of a higher valence are, in general, more readily adsorbed; but some substances may adsorb better those having lower valencies, which was possibly a

[807] Church, A. G., Jour. Chem. Soc., vol. 15, 1862, p. 107.

[808] Cox, G. H., Dean, R. S., and Gottschalk, V. H., Studies on the origin of Missouri cherts and zinc ores, Bull. 2, Univ. Missouri, School of Mines and Metallurgy, vol. 3, 1916, pp. 5–34; Dean, R. S., The formation of Missouri chert, Am. Jour. Sci., vol. 45, 1918, pp. 411–414.

[809] Lovering, T. S., op. cit., 1923, pp. 537–538.

[810] Hardy, W. W., Chemistry of colloids and some technical applications, 1915.

factor in some of Moore and Maynard's experiments though it is also evident that other stabilizing factors were present.

Many geologic formations contain deposits of iron and silica in such relationships that there must have been more or less simultaneous precipitation of these substances. On an earlier page, it was shown that electrolytes in sea water precipitate ferric oxide almost immediately. Above, it has been shown that silica also is precipitated, but more slowly. Taken separately, the two substances were found to be quite stable in the low concentrations present in land waters. On the other hand, mixing of solutions of ferric oxide and silica led to the immediate precipitation of the iron and a part of the silica,[811] which, according to Thomas and Johnson,[812] is due to removal of peptizing agents by chemical action between the two substances, with complete precipitation taking place under certain conditions of concentration. With concentrations of 20 parts per million of ferric oxide and 60 parts per million of silica, Moore and Maynard obtained precipitation of most of the iron and about half of the silica. With conditions as they exist in natural waters, evidently other substances must be present to make ferric oxide and silica stable in the presence of each other. Clarke[813] gives some data that have a bearing upon the stabilization of these two colloids. His data regarding the composition of river waters show that organic matter in solution made possible the transmission of a much larger quantity of silica and iron. He did not recognize, however, that it was the stabilizing effect of the organic matter that held the silica and ferric oxide in solution longer. Moore and Maynard found that peat solutions acted quite effectively as stabilizers. One cubic centimeter of peat solution containing 92.2 parts of organic matter per million served to stabilize 200 cc. containing 10 parts of ferric oxide per million and 30 parts of silica per million. This organic matter after mixing with the other solutions became 4.5 parts per million of the whole, making it obvious that natural waters the concentrations of which approximate or rarely exceed the above will have no difficulty in transporting silica and ferric oxide, providing organic matter is present to the extent of 4.5 parts per million. With greater quantities of organic matter, greater stability exists. On reaching the sea, the iron is rapidly precipitated by the electrolytes in solution, whereas the silica remains a longer time in solution. The quantity of organic matter in solution in the rivers of the world averages greater than 4.5 parts per million, an amount adequate to stabilize and transport all silica and ferric oxide carried by natural waters. The precipitation of ferric oxide first and silica later gives

[811] Moore, E. S. and Maynard, J. E., op. cit., 1929, pp. 512, and references.
[812] Thomas, A. W. and Johnson, L., Jour. Amer. Chem. Soc., vol. 45, 1923, p. 2532.
[813] Clarke, F. W., Data of geochemistry, Bull. 770, U. S. Geol. Surv., 1924, p. 110.

rise to a deposit of two bands. New inflows of silica and ferric oxide would form additional layers and thus give rise to a thinly banded siliceous and ferruginous deposit.[814]

The considerations outlined above show that after the carrying waters have come in contact with those of the sea the silica is in time precipitated, and that the delay in precipitation is due to the stabilizing effect of the organic matter, which prevents precipitation until a considerable saturation has been reached.

It should be emphasized that, in the experiments noted above, not all of the silica in a solution was precipitated; in fact, that the amount remaining greatly exceeds the amount present in the sea water of today. The longer the time of the experiment, the greater the precipitate obtained, though even so, much still remained in solution. There can be no doubt of the value of the experiments made by these men, as they point to possible and probable means of precipitation of colloidal silica. Tarr, however, has pointed out that the deposition of silica from sea water in the past and at present has been and is far more complete than the laboratory experiments show. This is shown by the scarcity of silica in the present sea water (one or two parts per million) and the surprisingly low content of silica of the carbonate rocks that enclose chert and flint. The silica content of these rocks is essentially the same as for carbonate rocks free from chert and flint. This points to a rapid and complete precipitation of all the silica of sea water once saturation is reached, and shows us that as an efficient laboratory the supposedly complex ocean still surpasses man's best efforts.

During periods of dominant limestone deposition, it is evident that rapid precipitation of silica occurred from time to time. It seems probable, moreover, that the process of inorganic deposition has remained essentially the same since rivers have been contributing silica to the sea, and that this method has accounted for most of the deposition of the silica, though some was deposited by other means and with other materials. Organisms account for a part, the amount varying with the life of the period. Radiolaria do not seem to have existed in Pre-Cambrian time, nor diatoms before the Jurassic, and it may be that there have been times when silica-secreting organisms did little work. These would have been times of greater concentration of silica in ocean waters.

Part of the precipitated silica settles to the bottom to mingle with other sediments, especially clays and silts. The deposition occurs mostly adjacent to the places of mingling of stream waters with each other, those of lakes, or those of the sea. Colloidal silica readily unites or is coagulated with

[814] Moore, E. S. and Maynard, J. E., op. cit., 1929, pp. 516–520.

muds and silts, hence during periods of mechanical erosion when these sediments were being brought in, most of the silica in the sea waters would be carried down by and deposited with these clastic materials. During times of low lands, with transportation of clay and silt (or sand) greatly reduced or entirely stopped, calcareous sediments would accumulate adjacent to the land. If the accumulation of these sediments was sufficiently slow, it would be possible for the silica to form a distinct deposit, or at any rate, at the places of its dominant precipitation to constitute a large part of the calcareous sediments deposited. As the material precipitated is a gel, under conditions of slow deposition of other sediments the small particles might aggregate and continue growth because of the attraction a large body has for small particles of the same material. Also, some silica would probably be directly acquired from the surrounding waters.

Reference was made above to a paleogeographical study of chert and flint made by one of the authors (Tarr). The maps made showed that the greatest deposition of chert and flint had occurred in those broad, shallow epicontinental seas that were likewise the sites of limestone, chalk, and dolomite deposition. Formations, such as those of the Ordovician, Devonian, Mississippian, Pennsylvanian, and Cretaceous, which are uniformly cherty or siliceous over widespread areas must have been deposited in such shallow epicontinental seas. Silica was evidently contributed to such a sea from various areas, and was then uniformly distributed throughout the sea in the same manner as was the material for the limestone or other carbonate rock being laid down. Undoubtedly, the two materials, having the same source (the land), transported in the same way (streams to the sea), were both carried far and wide to be deposited over the entire epicontinental sea floor.

It is probable that if the quantity of silica carried by any stream was great enough to be near the saturation point, or if it accumulated locally near the stream inlet, deposition might occur under localized conditions. Twenhofel regards the cherty Pennsylvanian formations of Kansas (largely marginal and containing some fresh-water deposits) as having been formed where fresh and salt waters mingled. This assumption is not applicable to the cherty limestones of the Pennsylvanian in Missouri. As Twenhofel has stated, there is no direct evidence that such localities are the seat of such deposition. The wide-spread chert-bearing horizons are more apt to have been the result of epicontinental sea conditions.

Some writers have maintained that as the process of weathering proceeds, liberated silica is carried downward and redeposited in cavities and veins, replacing fossils, or as chert and flint. Some have suggested that silicified surfaces might result from this process, but the soil scientists who have carefully analysed both soil and subsoil do not support this view. That silica is transported by the ground water is readily shown, and no doubt the quartz crystals of geodes and the quartz (not chert) replacing fossils have been formed in this manner, but that chert and flint were formed by this method is improbable if not impossible.   If this process of concentrating silica were at all common, geodes should be far more abundant than they are, as limestones, the world over, contain some siliceous material, all of which is freed when the limestone goes into solution.   Yet geodes are the exceptional feature of such rocks, and when present are more commonly lined with calcite or dolomite crystals than with quartz.

Silicified fossils have long been regarded as evidence in favor of the theory that chert and flint are formed by circulating ground waters.   The statement has been made that such silicified fossils are chert, but Tarr has never found such a one though for years he has been studying these features. Fossils replaced by quartz are not uncommon and such *occur in chert*. Replacement of fossils by chalcedony is possible, but those silicified fossils studied by Tarr contain little or no chalcedony.   The so-called "beekite" (which is nothing but chalcedony) found on the surface of fossils is the most common occurrence of such replacement.   Is it not probable that the fossils that were supposed to have been replaced by chert were actually replaced by chalcedony?   This could be determined because under the microscope chalcedony shows a typical fibrous character with a dark cross between crossed nicols, which chert and flint do not.

It should be noted that silicified fossils originally presented an opening above capillary size.   Many of the so-called silicified fossils are merely lined or covered with quartz crystals and not wholly replaced.   A fundamental chemical reason underlies this, which will be dealt with below in discussing more fully the possibilities of weathering.   A meager fauna in a limestone or dolomite formation, occurring only as silicified forms in residual chert (as in some of the Ozarkian formations), is frequently advanced by paleontologists as proof of the epigenetic origin of the chert during weathering.[815]   The few fossils found in these carbonate rocks are imperfect and poorly preserved, whereas those in the chert are much better preserved. Why a few of the fossils should remain in better condition until weathering occurred no one has explained.   The logical explanation of all this is that the fossils of the chert were imbedded in it and replaced by silica at the time of burial and thus before the formation was recrystallized, which process destroyed the other fossils of the rock.

Finally, the vast number of unconformities in carbonate and other rocks which have absolutely no evidence of silicification would seem to be adequate

[815] Dake, C. L., Geology of the Potosi and Edgehill Quadrangles, vol. 23 (second series), Missouri Bur. Geol. and Mines, 1930, pp. 129, 146, 166.

proof that a concentration of silica at weathered surfaces does not occur. If it did, the subsurface geologists would have made use of it in their work.

ENVIRONMENTS OF FORMATION. Where it has been possible to determine the environment of a deposit in which significant amounts of flint and chert occur, that environment has been determined as having been salt water. There is proof also that these waters were shallow and that the greatest development of chert and flint was in widespread epicontinental seas that were surrounded by low-lying lands, a condition favoring a maximum of chemical weathering. Proof of the saltiness of the waters in which such extensive deposits as those of the Lake Superior iron ores were formed is lacking, but there is no doubt that these waters were shallow and subject to land influences. Silica brought to the sea bottom from magmatic sources might give rise to chert or flint deposits at any depth and at any distance from land, and it may be that extensive deposits exist beneath the deep sea. Likewise, the organic siliceous oozes are deposited at great as well as at shallow depths, and if these can give rise to chert or flint deposits such chert or flint might thus have been formed at great depths. No chert or flint deposits of this type are known on the land, however. Twenhofel states that lake deposits of arid regions contain considerable chert or flint, which had probably been deposited in salt water through the same causes and in the same places of precipitation as were those deposits known to have been formed in the sea.

TIME RELATIONS OF CHERT AND FLINT TO THE ENCLOSING ROCK. The various suggestions relating to time relations of chert and flint to the enclosing rock may be tabulated as follows:[816]

A. Formed after the consolidation of the enclosing rock. Epigenetic origin.
B. Formed contemporaneously with the accumulation of the materials of the enclosing rock. Syngenetic origin.
C. Formed penecontemporaneously with the accumulation of the materials of the enclosing rock. Syngenetic origin.

(A) Chert and flint to be of epigenetic origin must either replace the original rock or fill cavities therein. Replacement is generally considered

[816] On the consideration of the time relationships of cherts to the enclosing rocks, consult (a) Brydone, R. M., The origin of flint, Geol. Mag., vol. 57, 1920, pp. 401–405; (b) Richardson, W. A., The relative age of concretions, Geol. Mag., vol. 58, 1921, pp. 114–124; (c) Sargent, H. C., The Lower Carboniferous cherts of Derbyshire, Geol. Mag., vol. 58, 1921, pp. 265–278; (d) Massive chert formations of North Flintshire, Geol. Mag., vol. 59, 1923, pp. 168–183; (e) Further studies in chert, Geol. Mag., vol. 66, 1929, pp. 399–413; (f) Tarr, W. A., Origin of the chert in the Burlington limestone, Am. Jour. Sci., vol. 44, 1917, pp. 409–452; (g) Twenhofel, W. H., The chert of the Wreford and Foraker limestones along the state line of Kansas and Oklahoma, Am. Jour. Sci., vol. 47, 1919, pp. 407–429. Other papers in which time relationships are considered may be found in bibliographies or footnote references of the articles noted above.

to be the more common method, and it is assumed that ground water introduces the silica in solution. Except that replacement took place after consolidation, no limits are placed upon the time relationships. Also, it may occur in rocks at the surface or at some distance beneath. Most of those holding the replacement theory have assumed that permeating ground waters carrying silica in solution have substituted it for some part of the rock entered. There are several serious objections to any general application of this theory. These are: (1) cherts do not commonly preserve original structural or textural features of the rocks assumed to have been replaced; (2) many structural and textural features end where the chert begins; (3) chert nodules are distributed with little relation to channels of underground water circulation, such as joints and bedding planes; (4) occurrence of chert nodules is common along horizontal planes which may be independent of bedding planes; (5) fossils are better preserved in chert nodules than in the enclosing rock; (6) some of the rocks associated with cherts possess relative impermeability, which would greatly curtail, if not actually prohibit the passage of silica-containing solutions through them; (7) colloidal silica is a solid particle and thus cannot migrate through a solid limestone or dolomite, and, as much chert and flint occur within a bed (as along the bedding plane), such migration would be essential if chert were epigenetic in origin; (8) no explanation of the position of a series of nodules or lenses within a massive bed is possible under the replacement theory; (9) an adequate source of the silica necessary for replacement is unknown; and (10) most carbonate rocks are impermeable by ground water save along divisional openings. Some of the facts just enumerated are also opposed to the view that very much chert and flint could result from the filling of cavities. Moreover, not much chert and flint have been found that have the forms or shapes that would result from cavity fillings.

There are two general regions in which epigenetic cherts and flints might form: (a) the zone of cementation below the water table, and (b) the zone of weathering above the water table.

(a) The formation of chert in the zone of cementation below ground-water level would be confined to divisional openings in rocks or to porous rocks such as sandstones. As noted above, there is no evidence that chert and flint are related to these openings. Neither are vein deposits of chert known. Sandstones form quartzites by being cemented with quartz and, rarely, with chalcedony which is probably then called "chert." The point is sometimes made that small calcareous areas within chert and flint represent unreplaced remnants of the surrounding rock. These areas are as readily explained as being due to the inclusion of calcareous materials in the chert during its accumulation, or as being the result of the aggregation of both the calcium carbonate in the gel and that which had migrated into it. The migration of such salts in gels is a common phenomenon.

The evidence against replacement afforded by well logs is very positive. Studies of hundreds of thousands of well logs prove that chert and flint are as widely distributed underground as are the formations in which they occur. Denial of this is made by some who explain chert as a product of weathering, but the evidence is so overwhelming as to be incontrovertible. Lee[817] gives positive proof of this widespread occurrence of chert by his sections and statements that beds (up to 10 feet thick) and nodules of chert are abundant in the Gasconade formation throughout its occurrence. Lee tries to explain and apply Ulrich's view of the origin of the chert, but is forced to conclude that the bedded and other cherts are "apparently unassociated with any of the phenomena of unconformity or surface weathering." Geologic sections accompanying hundreds of papers and reports furnish like evidence of the widespread distribution of the chert in a formation, and thus show that the authors of the reports do not regard the chert as a product of weathering.

A further argument against replacement is that a determination of the composition of various cherty formations has shown that the silica content of the enclosing rock is very low. An extremely cherty formation in Missouri, the Eminence, is stated by Dake[818] to contain 0.22 per cent of silica in a sample taken near its base and 0.28 per cent in one taken near its top. The chalk associated with the flint in England shows a similar low silica content, and many other examples could be cited. Now, either these rocks never contained silica or it has been completely removed. Evidently, they never contained it, for, as has been pointed out above, particles of colloidal silica cannot be moved through these dense fine-grained calcareous rocks. Moreover, even if the colloidal silica could be moved through the rock, it would not be necessary to assume that it had been, as any silica scattered through the rock could just as readily be explained as having been disseminated from the chert horizons. And finally, the scarcity of silica in a limestone or dolomite associated with chert is evidence of the complete chemical precipitation of the silica at intervals of time represented by the vertical spacing of the chert and flint horizons within the rock.

The statement is frequently made that cherty horizons are associated with unconformities. If a marked connection existed between peneplanation (with the resultant greater chemical denudation in the later stages) and an abundance of limestone and chert, then chert should be more abundant in

[817] Lee, W., Geology of the Rolla Quadrangle, Missouri Bur. Geol. and Mines, vol. 12, 1913, pp. 12–19.

[818] Dake, C. L., op. cit.

the upper part of a limestone bed. A preliminary study has shown this distribution to be fairly common, but the study is not complete and a positive statement cannot be made at present. That it is commonly true is indicated by such an assumption on the part of those advocating a secondary origin for chert. It is not always true, however, and hence cannot be used to prove that chert is secondary. Many exceptions to this distribution of chert are known, of which a recent citation from Woodward, who attempts to show that certain cherts of Virginia are secondary,[819] will be made. In one formation (the Becraft) described by Woodward, the chert is in the middle; and in another (the Keyser) it is near the base and near the top. The distribution in both of these formations thus furnishes evidence against Woodward's view.

Various writers have supported the replacement theory, but none have definitely proved that replacement has occurred or met the various criticisms mentioned above. Barton,[820] Sollas,[821] Van Hise,[822] Sellards,[823] and others have advocated replacement in some degree.

(b) Surface weathering of a formation has been advocated as the means of concentrating the contained silica, which is then assumed to have been deposited in the form of chert. Silica is present to a greater or less extent in most rocks, although the quantity in carbonate rocks is generally low. On the decomposition of the containing rocks, this silica is released and most of it becomes a part of the soil and is later removed with it during soil erosion.

A small portion of the silica released during weathering, however, is removed by the ground water, either as a colloid (the usual form) or as a silicate. Spring and well waters (typical ground waters) contain very small amounts of silica (even the springs at Hot Springs, Arkansas, contain only 47 parts of silica per million). Furthermore, it must be remembered that the studies of soils and soil solutions by the soil scientists have shown that there is little or no downward movement of silica, save in the tropics where lateritic soils develop. The valuable studies of these men have been overlooked in previous discussions of the origin of chert, and there can be no doubt as to the significance of their findings in the problem; for, if there is no downward movement of the silica produced by weathering (save where

[819] Woodward, H. P., Paleozoic cherts of West-Central Virginia, Jour. Geol., vol. 31, 1931, pp. 277–287.

[820] Barton, D. C., Notes on the Mississippian chert of the St. Louis area, Jour. Geol., vol. 26, 1913, pp. 361–374.

[821] Sollas, W. J., Age of the Earth, 1912, p. 152.

[822] Van Hise, C. R., Treatise on metamorphism, Mon. 47, U. S. Geol. Surv., 1904, p. 818. See also pp. 816–820; 847–853.

[823] Sellards, E. H., 1st Ann. Rept., Geol. Surv. Florida, 1908, p. 48.

lateritic soils are developing), the commonly accepted source for the silica of secondary chert is removed. That some silica is carried in ground water is not doubted, but the quantity is wholly inadequate to account for the chert and flint in limestones and dolomites, even if there were no other objections to their formation there. The small amount of silica carried, 1 to 10 or 15 parts per million, may in time line a geode or the inner cavity in a fossil, but even this requires a vast period of time. It should be noted, moreover, that rapid precipitation of silica favors the formation of a colloidal gel that would become chert or flint; slower deposition by moderately warm or cold solutions favors the formation of chalcedony, as found in ore veins near the surface; and very slow deposition by ground water favors the formation of quartz, such as that constituting the cement in sandstone and forming geode linings and the replaced portions of fossils.

A statement often made is that chert horizons are associated with the slope of the present land surface, and certainly if weathering gives rise to chert, such chert should parallel the erosion surface. If the underlying formation were horizontal, the chert horizon, on the slopes, should *cross the ends* of the formation. That this is not true is known by all, for the chert (whatever its form) conforms to the structure of the rocks associated with it. In fact, the structure of parts of the chalk in England was determined from the position of the flints. Numerous highway cuts throughout the United States have revealed the layers of chert in the residual clays continuing unchanged into and through hills of the solid rock. In such exposures, one can prove that the chert in the solid rock is absolutely continuous and identical with that of the weathered residual material. Weathering has liberated the chert formed syngenetically, not produced it.

The surface of an exposed fossiliferous limestone is commonly covered with fossils. In some formations, the embedded parts are calcareous and the exposed parts siliceous.[824] Silicification of this kind must not be confused, however, with the relative increase of silica in a rock after removal of the carbonates or other substances by solution.

According to Van Hise and Leith,[825] some of the Pre-Cambrian cherts of the Lake Superior region may be a consequence of the alteration of greenalite; the equation expressing the reaction follows:

$$4Fe(Mg)SiO_3 \cdot nH_2O + 20 = 2Fe_2O_3 \cdot nH_2O + 4SiO_2$$

This silica on release might be deposited at or near the place of alteration. Ulrich[826] seems to have been the first to suggest rock weathering as an

---

[824] Bassler, R. S., Proc. U. S. Nat. Mus., vol. 35, 1908, p. 135.

[825] Van Hise, C. R., and Leith, C. K., Geology of the Lake Superior region, Mon. 52, U. S. Geol. Surv., 1911, p. 530.

[826] Bain, H. F., and Ulrich, E. O., Bull. 267, U. S. Geol. Surv., 1905, pp. 27 and 30.

explanation for the origin of chert. He regarded the chert of the Lower Paleozoic in Missouri as being due to a concentration of the silica by ordinary chemical weathering, giving as his reason that the greater amount of chert on the gentle slopes proved that it was so formed. What Ulrich was really observing was the greater accumulation of *residual* chert on a gentle slope than on a steep slope. As Ulrich's deduction has been cited so often by advocates of this view, it will be well to evaluate it. If a horizontal limestone containing 15 per cent of chert underwent chemical denudation, it is evident that all the chert in the beds would be concentrated at the surface as the insoluble material of the limestone. This would be the maximum quantity of chert. Increasing slightly the slope of the eroded surface would increase the carrying power of the runoff, so that at first the smaller pieces of residual chert would be removed. As the slope was increased further, more and more fragments would be carried away until finally at a vertical cliff all the chert loosened by weathering (largely mechanical) would accumulate at its base as talus or be carried away by a stream. The solid floors of chert in some valleys in the Ozark area of Missouri and in the southern Appalachian area are evidence of the activity of the streams in mechanically removing the chert. Thus to ascribe the chert on the gentler slopes to the longer and slower processes of chemical weathering is not a safe assumption as the chert could have been (and probably was) originally present in the limestone. Tarr[827] studied in detail both of the formations described by Ulrich and found an abundance of drusy quartz and some chert in the Potosi formation and a far greater abundance of nodules, lenses, and beds of chert (some of the beds are nearly 10 feet thick as shown by well logs) in the Gasconade. The chert was visible in excellent vertical exposures and was also encountered in wells. Throughout the Ozark area, chert is abundant in exposures of the Gasconade and has been encountered in hundreds of well logs so the chert is evidently as widespread as the formation. Furthermore, fragments and pebbles of the chert from these formations occur in conglomerates above them.

B. Chert formed contemporaneously with the accumulation of the materials of the enclosing rock has been thought to result either from (1) *organic* or (2) *inorganic* precipitation of silica.

(1) Chert of *organic origin* is assumed to form from the shells of siliceous organisms which undergo partial solution. This and any other dissolved silica are assumed to cement the undissolved portions. That silica does undergo removal is proved by the replacement of siliceous shells by calcite. The fact that many cherts and flints contain the siliceous shells of organisms

---

[827] Tarr, W. A., The barite deposits of Missouri, Univ. of Missouri Studies, vol. III, No. 1, 1917.

has been considered evidence of their organic origin, but it remains to be proved whether such occurrences are genetic or merely incidental.

The radiolarian cherts of the Jurassic of California and the diatomaceous cherts of the Monterey shales of the same state have been stated to be of organic origin, but in the former it seems fairly certain that the radiolarian shells are incidental.[828]

Siliceous sponge spicules have long been regarded as the source of the silica in chert and flint. Hinde[829] has been the chief exponent of this view and has written extensively upon the subject. Tarr[830] made a careful study of the material Hinde had studied (in some cases having identical materials), and found that sponge spicules were consistently absent from most slides. The Upper Greensand on the Isle of Wight has several beds containing sponge spicules. Some cherts occur in them. These beds also contain glauconite and quartz grains. The chert has the characteristics of a chemically deposited bed, which includes the sponges, glauconite, and sand. This deposit might have been due to rapid precipitation near the mouth of a river where the fresh and salt water met. The high silica content of the waters made conditions favorable for the growth of sponges. The spicules are still amorphous or opaline silica. Sponge spicules are singularly absent from the chalk. The Rex chert of Idaho has local basal beds largely composed of spicules of siliceous sponges.[831] These spicules may be present because a siliceous sea water favored the growth of sponges, and hence their remains in the chert are incidental just as are fossils in a limestone.

The view of the organic origin of flint and chert was also supported by Van Hise,[832] Geikie,[833] de Lapparent,[834] Sollas,[835] Wallich,[836] and others. Nearly every supporter of the organic theory, however, has considered that there is more or less subsequent alteration and rearrangement of the silica, and that chert and flint may also be formed in other ways.

[828] Fairbanks, H. W., San Luis Folio, No. 101, U. S. Geol. Surv., 1904, p. 244; Davis, E. F., op. cit.

[829] Hinde, G. J., Sponges in the Lower and Upper Greensand of the south of England, Phil. Trans. Roy. Soc., vol. 176, pt. ii, 1885, p. 403; On the organic origin of the chert in the Carboniferous Limestone Series of Ireland and its similarity to that of corresponding strata of North Wales and Yorkshire, Geol. Mag., vol. 24, 1887, pp. 435–446; On the chert and siliceous schists of the Permo-Carboniferous strata of Spitzbergen, etc., Geol. Mag., vol. 25, 1888, pp. 241–251.

[830] Tarr, W. A., Origin of chert and flint, Univ. of Missouri Studies, vol. 1, no. 1, 1926, pp. 8–9.

[831] Mansfield, G. R., Prof. Paper 152, U. S. Geol. Surv., 1927, p. 368.

[832] Van Hise, C. R., Treatise on metamorphism, Mon. 47, U. S. Geol. Surv., 1904, p. 819.

[833] Geikie, A., Textbook of geology, vol. 1, 1903, p. 179.

[834] de Lapparent, A., Traité de géologie, vol. 2, 1906, p. 687.

[835] Sollas, W. J., Age of the earth, 1912, pp. 163–165.

[836] Wallich, G. C., A contribution to the physical history of the Cretaceous flints, Quart. Jour. Geol. Soc., vol. 36, 1880, pp. 68–92.

A modification of the theory as outlined above assumes that some of the organic silica after deposition ultimately became a gel, and in this condition collected in depressions on the sea or lake floor, thus giving rise to the lenticular shapes of the nodules.

(2) The *inorganic origin* of syngenetic chert was first proposed by Prestwich.[837] Jukes-Browne and Hill[838] rejected the idea because of the then current view that silica could not be precipitated from sea water except by organic agencies. Tarr explained the inorganic theory in detail and proved experimentally that it is possible for chert to develop in this way. As outlined by Tarr,[839] the theory is as follows: the silica contributed to the sea accumulates (the accumulation is made possible by the stabilization of the colloidal silica particles) until its concentration causes it to be precipitated as a gel, the particles of which on settling to the bottom are aggregated into globular and ellipsoidal masses following the ordinary tendency of gels to assume globular forms that eventually become nodules and lenses of chert or flint. If the quantity of silica is large enough and the rate of precipitation sufficiently rapid, a continuous layer or bed would be deposited. Successive periods of accumulation, concentration, and precipitation at varying intervals would give rise to successive layers of nodules, lenses, or beds.

After the silica gel has been aggregated into globular forms on the sea bottom, further growth is assumed to take place through direct additions of silica from the water, and nodules partially buried in muds may replace or displace the adjacent materials. Such an origin by replacement or displacement verges upon the penecontemporaneous type. If other sediments accumulate rapidly, the growth of nodules might continue only as protuberances. A slowing up in the rate of accumulation of surrounding materials might permit the expansion of the protuberance into another nodule above the first. Protuberances or other irregularities in the shape of nodules might be caused also by varying rates of growth of the nodules themselves due to variable amounts of silica available for growth. Nodules may not have attained full size before burial, but the absence of evident displacement adjacent to them and the assumed difficulty of the penetration of calcareous muds by siliceous solutions are thought to render it doubtful that much material was added to the nodules after burial. The addition of silica to a buried nodule with a consequent enclosing of calcareous material around it, the precipitation of silica and calcium carbonate together before burial, or the migration of calcium carbonate into the silica gel may explain the gradation of chert into limestone and also the abundance of calcite in parts of some chert nodules.

[837] Prestwich, J., Geology, chemical, physical, and stratigraphical, vol. 2, 1888, p. 322.
[838] Jukes-Browne, A. J. and Hill, W., Quart. Jour. Geol. Soc., vol. 45, 1889, p. 419.
[839] Tarr, W. A., op. cit., 1917; op. cit., 1926.

If the water containing the globular masses of silica gel was shallow enough (some chert nodules formed in shallow water, as they occur with oolites which are known shallow-water deposits), currents might roll the gel masses about, whereupon more material would be added to them and concentrically banded nodules would result. Concentric banding in chert nodules is commonly due also to different rates of growth in individual nodules; a slow rate of accumulation of silica resulting in a greater accumulation of organic matter in the same amount of silica, which would be evident as a darker band in the nodule. As the masses of gel hardened, some of them might crack and portions of the surrounding calcareous mud would penetrate the cracks. The cherts and flints that show faulting were broken while still a gel, for the parts are displaced and yet have reunited along these broken surfaces. This property of breaking and reuniting is characteristic of silica gels. Ultimately, the globular masses of gel were buried; and, due to the weight of the overburden, most of them were flattened into lenticular shapes. Subsequently, dehydration and crystallization (a slow process) changed the gel to chert and flint.

Organisms were buried in the precipitated silica by falling into it from above; growing on it as a part of the sea floor; being picked up by a nodule as it was rolled about; or being enclosed as a mass of the gel spread over them. They might be distributed throughout the silica mass or be confined to the outer portion. The common excellent preservation of fossils in cherts as compared with those in the enclosing rock shows that burial took place soon after the death of the organisms, thereby insuring their protection from scavenger animals, solution work, or wave action. Annelid borings in chert nodules in the Middle Cambrian are reported by Walcott.[840] These were undoubtedly made while the chert nodule was still soft, which proves that it was formed at the same time as the enclosing beds.

It is thought that peneplaned or base-leveled lands, that is, lands supplying little arenaceous or clayey sediments, are necessary for the syngenetic formation of flint and chert deposits of any magnitude and purity, since high and dissected lands would furnish too much mud and sand to the sites of deposition, and the precipitated silica would thus be disseminated throughout the clastics.

Silica that is brought to the sites of deposition by hot springs of magmatic or other origin might arrive in sufficient quantities to form entire beds, and the high temperature of the waters together with the presence of iron might lead to the formation of iron silicates (greenalite), or cherts high in iron salts. Doubt has been expressed as to the adequacy of springs or

---

[840] Walcott, C. D., Fossil medusæ, Mon. 30, U. S. Geol. Survey, 1898, pp. 17–21.

other magmatic sources to contribute a quantity of silica sufficiently large to form such great quantities of chert as those in the iron formations of the Lake Superior region.[841] Nevertheless, it certainly could be done if the conditions of supply were maintained long enough. Gruner[842] and Moore and Maynard,[843] in advocating an origin by direct chemical precipitation for the cherts of the Lake Superior region, have presented evidence indicating that the silica necessary for their formation could have been derived through the normal processes of weathering. Sargent has advocated a similar source for the silica of the chert (which he explains has been precipitated on the sea floor) in North Wales (Flintshire) and of the Lower Carboniferous in Derbyshire. Tarr and Twenhofel regard the great quantity of chert in the Boone formation of Missouri and Oklahoma and in several of the Pennsylvanian formations of Kansas as having originated syngenetically by direct precipitation in sea water and the silica as having been derived through normal weathering processes. Mansfield,[844] likewise, favors a peneplaned land surface as the source of the silica in the widespread bedded cherts of the Rex formation, which he regards as being due to chemical precipitation on the sea floor.

Various objections have been raised to the theory of the direct inorganic precipitation of silica to form nodular cherts. The more important objections and the replies thereto are as follows: (1) it is claimed that the arching of the beds shows growth of the nodules subsequent to the deposition of the enclosing beds. It has been proved, however, that such arching occurs also over any object on the sea floor. (2) Objection is made that the method of precipitation is inadequate, but experimental proof has shown that direct precipitation can occur, and the rapid disappearance of the silica on reaching the sea proves that it has occurred in the sea water. (3) It is claimed that the silicification of fossils shows that replacement does occur. The abundance of unreplaced calcareous fossils both within and without chert nodules shows, however, that even this sort of replacement is unusual. Moreover, the fact that calcareous fossils can be buried in the silica gel without being replaced is a strong argument against replacement. (4) It is said that the shapes of nodules are never due to rolling on the sea bottom. It is not thought, however, that the shape of nodules was due primarily to rolling, but only that their initial globular form (normally assumed by gels) was possibly accentuated by rolling. Rolling would prob-

[841] Gruner, J. W., The origin of sedimentary iron formations, etc., Econ. Geol., vol. 17, 1922, pp. 407–460.

[842] Gruner, J. W., op. cit., pp. 452–460.

[843] Moore, E. S., and Maynard, J. E., Econ. Geol., vol. 24, 1929, pp. 520–527.

[844] Mansfield, G. R., Econ. Geol., vol. 26, 1931, pp. 371–374.

ably not have taken place had not the original form been rounded. The association of chert nodules with formations that are cross laminated, with oolites, and with mud-cracked beds is ample proof, however, of shallow-water conditions which would permit the presence of currents to produce the rolling. (5) The objection is made that no chert in the initial stages of formation has ever been observed under natural conditions. This has not been possible because deep-sea studies have not been sufficiently extensive, and because physiographic conditions on the lands bordering existing shallow waters permit the entrance of great quantities of mud and sand which carry the silica down with them. The wide flats of calcareous muds adjacent to the Bahamas would be favorable sites for the formation of chert today if those flats were adjacent to a land mass that could furnish the silica.

The theory of a syngenetic origin for chert and flint by direct chemical precipitation on the sea floor explains the distribution of chert nodules and lenses along planes, their repetition along successive horizons, their generally lenticular shapes, the occurrence of widespread beds of chert, the occurrence of calcareous fossils and areas within chert, the irregular shape of the nodules, the gradation of the chert into the enclosing rock, and many other physical features of chert. The theory accounts for the widespread distribution of chert in a given formation, for its localization near shore and adjacent to possible deltas, for the source of the silica, and lastly furnishes a satisfactory method of precipitation.

(C) The third theory of the origin of chert and flint has been designated as proving. a syngenetic origin though it postulates their formation pene-contemporaneously with the deposition of the other sediments. According to this theory, the silica is first precipitated and deposited (supporters of the theory do not state by what agency precipitation is brought about) on the sea floor along with the materials of the enclosing rock, just as is advocated under the direct-chemical-precipitate theory just discussed. After the deposition of silica and calcium carbonate, however, the silica is supposed to go into solution and then to be reprecipitated and redeposited, displacing or replacing surrounding sediments as this takes place, and eventually to become the chert and flint nodules. Why this additional stage or process of solution following the initial chemical precipitation should take place, it would be hard to say, especially as the dissolved silica is then supposed to be again precipitated and deposited in like manner as before. This theory can in no way account for great bedded deposits like the Lake Superior cherts and even its advocates use it only in explaining the origin of nodules.

In England, this theory of origin has received the support of Jukes-Browne and Hill, who explain some of the cherts of the Cretaceous in this way.[845]

845 Jukes-Browne, A. J. and Hill, W., Quart. Jour. Geol. Soc. vol. 45, 1889, pp. 403–421.

Likewise, Hull and Hardman[846] explained the Carboniferous cherts of Ireland as a result of the replacement of unconsolidated sediments, and the Carboniferous cherts of Belgium have been assigned to the same origin by Renard.[847] In America, this theory of origin has received the support of Cleland,[848] Van Tuyl,[849] and others.

SUMMARY OF ORIGIN. The immense volume of silica carried by rivers annually to the sea and the great abundance of chert and flint in all the geologic systems show that this type of sedimentary deposit is of primary importance.

It is believed that the silica of chert and flint in the form of nodules, lenses, and beds was deposited directly from the sea water usually under conditions of a slow rate of accumulation. A certain amount of silica replacement of the calcium carbonate surrounding the soft nodules as they rested on the sea floor among the other accumulating sediments may have taken place, also. Likewise, it is possible that some chert and flint have been formed by replacement of consolidated rock by silica which was obtained through a leaching of the rock by ground water or through the process of weathering. The quantity so formed was probably not large, however,

Research Needed

More research upon the chert and flint problem is very advisable. Detailed investigations should be made of what happens to silica in "solution" in fresh waters when they mingle with sea waters. The sea bottoms at such places should be studied to learn the condition of the silica in the sediments as they are deposited. Studies of areas where calcareous deposits are accumulating should be made as these areas are promising sites for the deposition of silica. However, the worldwide high relief of the continents of the present day with the resultant mechanical rather than chemical erosion is unfavorable to an accumulation and precipitation of silica in the sea, as the silica carried seaward by the present streams is being deposited with the abundant argillaceous muds. Therefore, of course, present times are not favorable for observing chert in process of formation. From the field point of view, it is essential that more care be devoted to observation of the field relations of chert and flint nodules to the enclosing rocks. The recognition that chert and flint are present in a deposit bears little on the problem of their origin, but the relationships of the nodules to each other and the enclosing rock, the nature and character of the banding of the nodules and their other structures, the distribution and preservation of

---

[846] Hull, E. and Hardman, E. T., Sci. Trans. Roy. Dublin Soc., vol. 1, 1878, pp. 71–94.
[847] Renard, M. A., Bull. d. l'Acad. Royale de Belgique, 2 S., T. 46, 1878, pp. 471–498.
[848] Cleland, H. F., Geology, physical and historical, 1916, p. 77.
[849] Van Tuyl, F. V., The origin of chert, Am. Jour. Sci., vol. 45, 1918, pp. 449–456.

fossils in the nodules and their similarities and dissimilarities to those in the enclosing rocks, any changes in the nodules from center to periphery, the presence of nuclei, the relation of the nodules of one zone to those of others in the same vertical section, structures in the chert which are also in the enclosing rock; these are all characters of significance with respect to the problem of the origin of chert and flint.

PHOSPHATIC SEDIMENTS[850]

GENERAL

Phosphorus has wide and most abundant distribution in the igneous and crystalline rocks as a constituent of apatite. It is also present in the more rare monazite and xenotime, and there are occurrences in still rarer minerals. From these minerals of original occurrence it is released in decomposition, and being taken into solution is carried to the sea or other site of deposition. It is probably transported as phosphoric acid and as calcium phosphate. The latter is soluble in carbonated waters[851] and in swamp waters rich in organic matter; it is precipitated in the presence of calcium carbonate, and hence natural waters acting upon a deposit of the latter and calcium phosphate would remove the carbonate unless these waters contained substances increasing the solubility of the phosphate. Some phosphorus-containing material is probably carried as colloid.

There are many phosphatic minerals formed by sedimentary processes, the greatest numbers of which exist or are formed in guano. Most of these probably are rare in other sedimentary phosphate deposits, of which the composing minerals, however, are not always known. Collophanite ($Ca_3 \cdot P_2O_8 \cdot H_2O$) is known to be present and also dahllite ($Ca_6(PO_4)_4 \cdot CaCO_3 \cdot \frac{1}{2}H_2O$).

Phosphorus in solution is precipitated or taken out of solution largely through organic agencies; vertebrates, brachiopods, annelids, crustaceans, and a few others being important in this work. Some reacts with materials on the sea bottom, forming various phosphates. Phosphorus may also be precipitated through bacterial action, as it has been shown that some bacteria contain phosphorus in their tissues.[852]

[850] The manuscript for the first edition was prepared by Doctor Eliot Blackwelder, but the state of Doctor Blackwelder's health precluded his assistance in the preparation for the manuscript for the present edition. The material of the first edition has been freely used.

For a bibliography on phosphate deposits to 1888, see Penrose, R. A. F., jr., Bull. 46, U. S. Geol. Surv., 1888. Information to date of 1928 may be found in Les reserves mondiales en phosphates, 2 vols., many authors, and published as a part of the work of the Fourteenth International Geological Congress, Madrid, Spain, 1926.

[851] Müller, R., Jahrb. k. k. Reichsanstalt, vol. 27, Min. pet. Mitth., 1877, p. 25.

[852] Alilaire, M. E., Sur la présence du phosphorus dans la matière grasse des microbes, Compt. Rend., Paris Acad. Sci., vol. 145, 1907, pp. 1215–1217.

All varieties of sedimentary phosphatic deposits grade insensibly into each other, but for purposes of description, they may be placed in two classes, primary and secondary, with subdivisions as shown.

A. Primary
   Stratified marine phosphorites
   Nodules in clay, greensand, etc.
   Guano
B. Secondary
   Leached phosphatic deposits
   Phosphatized rocks
   Detrital deposits

Primary Phosphatic Deposits

STRATIFIED MARINE PHOSPHORITES. The stratified marine deposits of calcium phosphate are generally known as phosphorite. In composition, the purest approach apatite, but unlike that mineral they seem amorphous and exist in compact, powdery, oolitic, and concretionary or nodular forms. They are known in the Mississippian and Permian formations of the Rocky Mountains in the United States, the Devonian of Tennessee, the Tertiary of Tunis and Algiers, the Cretaceous at Taplow in England, and in other occurrences of greater or less importance. The range in the geologic column is from Cambrian to Pleistocene, and in quantity they outrank all other types of phosphatic deposits.

Deposits of bedded marine phosphorites extend over areas of thousands of square miles in formations of comparatively uniform thickness. Associated strata consist of black shales, cherts, limestones, dolomites, and sandstones. The phosphorite units range in thickness from a fraction of an inch to many feet, the range in those of southeastern Idaho being to about 30 feet for beds of good phosphate, but such units are accompanied by other beds of shales and limestone which contain more or less phosphate. Individual beds range in thickness from about 1/16 inch to 6 or 8 inches, most being less than 1 inch thick and the average maximum 2 to 3 inches. The bedding in the western United States phosphorites is described as regular and even, devoid of such features as mud cracks, ripple marks, rain impressions, current and rill marks, and cross lamination.[853] Beds of phosphatic shale and impure limestone are interstratified with the phosphorites, the separation in some instances being sharp and in others not. Streaks of shale occur in some of the phosphate beds, and streaks of phosphate and phosphatic nodules are present in shales and sandstones. Some beds of phosphate pass laterally into sandstone, and sandy streaks extend into phos-

[853] Mansfield, G. R., Prof. Paper 152, U. S. Geol. Surv., 1927, p. 361.

phate beds. These variations indicate shallow waters and nearness to the regions of supply of terrigenous materials. The reasons for the variations in quantity and nature of materials supplied remain to be determined.

The Rocky Mountain phosphorites, which more or less typify others, are characterized by gray, brown, or black colors, depending on hydrocarbon matter present; have a strong bituminous odor and, in some cases, oolitic texture; weathered fragments have a characteristic bluish-white bloom and commonly white reticulate markings. In some occurrences, as near Lander, Wyoming, a phosphorite bed is saturated with petroleum. The phosphatic beds are sparingly or not at all fossiliferous, a few discinoid brachiopods, gastropods and fish-bone fragments being the fossils commonly found, and all are phosphatized. The associated strata carry fossils in greater or less abundance, consisting of bryozoans, corals, brachiopods, mollusks and calcareous algæ.[854] The section which follows shows the detailed character of the phosphorite and associated strata of the Permian Phosphoria formation at a locality in southeast Idaho.[855]

Rock character		Thickness	
Shale, dark brown, not fetid	1 ft.	10	in.
Phosphatic rock, gray, oolitic, nodular, P_2O_5 36.3 per cent	1	0	
Shale, brown, finely oolitic		5	
Phosphatic rock, gray, coarsely oolitic, nodular, P_2O_5 36.7 per cent		$8\frac{1}{2}$	
Shale, brown, part finely oolitic		$2\frac{1}{2}$	
Clay, yellow, sandy, contains concretions		8	
Phosphate rock, brown, medium oolitic, P_2O_5 35.3 per cent		5	
Shale, dark brown, phosphatic		2	
Phosphatic rock, dark brown, medium oolitic, P_2O_5 29.4 per cent		5	
Phosphate rock, gray, coarsely oolitic, P_2O_5, 35.9 per cent	1	2	
Shale, dark brown to black, finely oolitic		3	
Phosphate rock, coarsely oolitic, P_2O_5 35.9 per cent		4	
Shale, brown, sandy		1	
Phosphate rock, medium oolitic		$1\frac{1}{2}$	
Shale, brown, finely oolitic		5	
Phosphate rock, black, medium oolitic		2	
Shale, brown, calcareous		4	
Phosphate rock, black, sandy, medium oolitic		1	
Shale, brown, oolitic in thin streaks		2	
Phosphate rock, gray, coarsely to finely oolitic, P_2O_5 33.2 per cent		11	

---

[854] Branson, C. C., Paleontology and stratigraphy of the Phosphoria formation, Univ. Missouri Studies, vol. 5, 1930, pp. 1–99. This paper contains a rather complete bibliography of the Rocky Mountain phosphates.

[855] Mansfield, G. R., op. cit., 1927, p. 77.

Rock character	Thickness	
	ft.	in.
Phosphate rock, shaly, gray, finely oolitic...................		3
Phosphate rock, brown, medium oolitic......................		4
Shale, brown, $1\frac{1}{4}$ inch streak near base oolitic...............		6
Phosphate rock, shaly in places, dark brown, coarsely to finely oolitic, P_2O_5 33.2 per cent...............................		9
Phosphate rock, gray, coarsely oolitic, $\frac{1}{2}$ inch shale near base, P_2O_5 37 per cent....................................	1	1
Limestone, drab, impure................................		5
Phosphate rock, medium to finely oolitic...................		3
Shale, brown..		9
Phosphate rock, dark gray, coarsely oolitic.................		2
Shale, brown..		3
Phosphate rock, thin shale partings, dark gray, coarsely oolitic, P_2O_5 30 per cent...		10
Limestone, lenticular......................................		10
Phosphatic rock, dark brown, medium to finely oolitic, P_2O_5 26.1, per cent...	9	8
Shale, black, in part finely oolitic...........................	3	
Shale, brown..	1	8
Shale, black, phosphatic, in part finely oolitic...............	6	6
Shale, brown, contains concretions..........................		10
Shale, rusty brown to yellow, contains concretions............	1	8
Shale, dark brown, phosphatic in places, contains concretions...	16	6
Pebbly or concretionary bed...............................		4
Shale, brown..	1	2
Shale, black to dark brown.................................		9
Pebbly or concretionary layer, phosphatic...................		3
Shale, black, slightly oolitic................................		7
Shale, contains pebbles or concretions.......................		6
Shale, brown..	3	4
Pebbly or concretionary bed...............................		4
Shale, brown..	2	3
Pebbly or concretionary bed, phosphatic?....................		6
Shale, brown, phosphatic...................................	2	6
Shale, black...		6
Clay..		10
Shale, brown..	1	0
Shale, black to light brown, slightly phosphatic..............	11	0
Limestone, contains some shale.............................	6	0
Shale, slightly phosphatic..................................	21	0
Shale, black, phosphatic....................................	5	6
Shale, brown..	1	0
Limestone, lenticular......................................		8
Shale, dark..	15	0
Phosphate rock..	3	0
Soil, black, fetid..	9	0
Shale, black, phosphatic, finely oolitic......................	5	6
Shale, brown, somewhat phosphatic.........................	15	0

Rock character	Thickness	
Limestone, dark gray..	3 ft.	0 in.
Phosphate rock, dark brown, medium oolitic, high grade and represents the thickest and richest bed....................	7	0
Shale, brown..	1	0
Limestone, white, not measured...........................		
	175	2½

The section shows the thickness of the individual beds and the nearly maximum thickness of the phosphate member. It will be noted that many of the beds are oolitic. These oolites are more or less spherical with many

TABLE 82

	1	2	3
Insoluble...............................	10.00	1.82	2.62
SiO_2.................................	0.00	0.30	0.46
Al_2O_3..............................	0.89	0.50	0.97
Fe_2O_3..............................	0.73	0.26	0.40
MgO...................................	0.28	0.22	0.35
CaO...................................	45.34	50.97	48.91
Na_2O................................	1.10	2.00	0.97
K_2O.................................	0.48	0.47	0.34
H_2O.................................	1.04	0.48	1.02
H_2O plus............................	1.14	0.57	1.34
CO_2.................................	6.00	1.72	2.42
P_2O_5...............................	27.32	36.35	33.61
SO_3.................................	1.59	2.98	2.16
F.....................................	0.60	0.40	0.40
Cl....................................	Trace	Trace	Trace
Organic matter.........................	Not determined	Not determined	Not determined
	96.51	99.04	95.97

1. Phosphate from main phosphate bed, 2½ miles east of Cokeville, Wyoming.
2. Dunnellon claim, Crawford mountains, Utah.
3. Preuss Range, 8 miles east of Georgetown, Idaho.
Analyses by Steiger, U. S. Geol. Surv.

more or less irregularly flattened. They have a roughly concentric structure and range from mere specks to ½ inch in diameter, and scattered nodules up to 2 inches in diameter occur locally. They are generally darker than the matrix, and a few possess a dark shiny coating. The color ranges from gray to black and is generally dark brown. Some beds contain pebbles derived from earlier formed oolitic phosphates of the Phosphoria formation.

Table 82 gives the chemical composition of some beds of the Rocky Mountain phosphorites.

The analyses show the high content of calcium phosphate. The insoluble matter consists mainly of silica with minor quantities of kaolin. The carbon dioxide may be united with some of the lime to form calcite, but it also may be united with lime and phosphoric acid. The mineral composition has not been worked out, but according to Schaller the best that can be said is that the oolites are composed of an amorphous mineral, probably collophanite, and some of them are surrounded by a thin coating of crystallized mineral which may be one or more of several phosphate minerals.[856]

In most localities the richer phosphorite beds consist of small roundish grains or pellets whose composition is as given above. The granules are not altogether like those of typical oolites of limestones. Many have concentric structure; radiate structure has not been observed. The zonal or concentric structure is best shown in the outer portions, but some show it throughout. Mansfield states that the phosphatic grains are true oolites.[857] Many of the particles, however, have little or no concentric structure, and in others the zonal structure is confined to the periphery, the entire particle or central portion in these cases being composed of speckled and more or less granular or amorphous brown material whose original nature has not been determined. It has been suggested by Blackwelder that these may represent excretory pellets of such animals as fishes and holothurians.[858] Some of the oolites show a nucleus, but in most such seems to be wanting. Small grains of quartz are irregularly distributed through some oolites and some particles.

In some beds the oolites or granules are mingled with fragments of vertebrates and invertebrates. Some of these were originally phosphatic; others carried no phosphate in the beginning, but subsequently became phosphatized. The phosphatic shells appear to consist largely of a crystalline material which is probably the hydrous calcium carbophosphate, dahllite. Most beds contain a greater or less admixture of angular particles of quartz of the size of sand and silt grains. Marcasite (and pyrite) is a rather common accessory mineral, as should be expected from the hydrocarbonaceous matter present. The matrix of the phosphorite in most of the beds has composition similar to that of the oolites, but in others it consists of calcite, dolomite, or even chert.

Much has been written relating to the origin of the marine stratified phosphorites, and the problem has been only partly solved. Their interlamination

[856] Mansfield, G. R., op. cit., p. 367.
[857] Mansfield, G. R., op. cit., p. 361.
[858] Blackwelder, E., Treatise on sedimentation, 1925, p. 396.

with marine limestones, shales, and sandstones, and the presence of marine fossils within them, are thought to prove deposition in a marine environment. The high content of hydrocarbonaceous matter and the occurrence of marcasite show that this environment was one of reducing conditions. The replacement of shell and other organic matter, originally calcareous or only slightly phosphatic, by phosphate proves diagenesis and not direct precipitation for these portions, this probably taking place while the sediments were in a soft condition. The depth of deposition is not definitely shown by the phosphoritic beds, but their general character and that of the associated strata suggest shallow waters.

The rather uncommon occurrence of stratified marine phosphorites indicates that special and uncommon conditions are required for their formation. The fact that phosphate and glauconite occur in association above unconformities suggests more or less common conditions for the formation of the two types of sediments.[859] The conditions, however, are not identical, as glauconite does not seem to be present in the purest beds of phosphorite, but it is a common associate of associated calcareous beds, and the abundant occurrences of glauconite are low in phosphate. Benthonic organisms are essentially absent from the phosphorites, but Mansfield[860] shows in several of his sections that much phosphatized fragmentary shell matter is present. The absence of many benthonic organisms indicates bottoms not favorable for their presence, and this is supported by the commonness of hydrocarbonaceous matter. Undoubtedly, therefore, anaërobic and reducing conditions prevailed over and within the bottom deposits. It is possible that the waters above were abundantly aërated and populated by an abundant planktonic and pelagic fauna whose excretory pellets and excretions of indigestible shell fragments fell to the bottom to become phosphatized and furnish nuclei for oolites.

A part of the phosphorus in the phosphorites may have been derived from shell matter. This was first shown in 1854 by Logan and Hunt,[861] who demonstrated that the shells of *Lingula* and certain other marine organisms contain relatively large quantities of calcium phosphate. Later work by Clarke and Wheeler[862] shows this in greater detail (see table, p. 25). However, as the phosphorites are not composed in any large part of phosphatic shells, it is not possible to refer their origin directly to this source. Davies[863] described the concretionary-like structures of phosphatic particles and

[859] Goldman, M. I., Basal glauconite and phosphate beds, Science, vol. 56, 1922, pp. 171–173.

[860] Mansfield, G. R., op. cit., plates 67–70.

[861] Logan, W. E., and Hunt, T. S., Am. Jour. Sci., vol. 17, 1854, p. 236.

[862] Clarke, F. W., and Wheeler, W. C., Prof. Paper 124, U. S. Geol. Surv., 1922.

[863] Davies, D. C., Geol. Mag., vol. 4, 1867, p. 257.

presented the evidence for origin in shallow waters not subject to strong agitation. Sollas[864] in 1872 stated that many phosphatic nodules are pseudomorphs after sponges, shells, and other objects. The chemistry of the putrefaction of organic material was discussed in 1872 by Hudleston,[865] who showed that ammoniacal and phosphatic solutions are formed and under certain conditions calcium phosphate is precipitated. Teall[866] in 1875 described the experimental formation of phosphorites and pointed out that a thin unit of phosphorite ordinarily is represented elsewhere by a thicker unit of chalk or limestone. Penning and Jukes-Browne[867] noted the association between collophane coatings and decaying organic matter in the basal portions of shark teeth and the interiors of shells.

Several elaborate theories to account for the stratified marine phosphorites, each supported by detailed arguments, had been presented before 1900. Each has its merits, but no one seems to satisfactorily cover the entire problem. Renard and Cornet[868] in 1891 concluded that the phosphates had been precipitated from colloidal solutions derived from decay of organic matter under special topographic conditions. Lasne[869] presented a most elaborate theory involving special physiographic and climatic conditions on land and sea and the formation of particles of phosphatic matter at first enmeshed in floating vegetable matter, these particles afterward settling to the bottom. Murray[870] ascribed precipitation of the phosphate to ammonium carbonate solutions due to decay of accumulations of organic matter, produced by wholesale destruction of marine populations brought about by changes in the physical conditions of the waters beyond the endurance capacity of the organisms, and accumulation beyond the ability of scavenger utilization. He later cited the wholesale destruction of the tile fish in 1883, when this fish was killed by hundreds of millions along the Atlantic coast of the United States. Similar destruction on a large scale has been described by Oldham[871] and Blanford,[872] the instance noted by the

[864] Sollas, W. J., Quart. Jour. Geol. Soc., vol. 28, 1872, pp. 63–70, 76–81.

[865] Hudleston, W. H., Quart. Jour. Geol. Soc., vol. 31, 1875, pp. 376–385.

[866] Teall, J. J. H., The Patton and Wicken phosphate deposits, Cambridge, 1875.

[867] Penning, W. H., and Jukes-Browne, A. J., Geology of the neighborhood of Cambridge, Mem. Geol. Surv. England and Wales, 1881.

[868] Renard, A. F., and Cornet, J., Recherches micrographiques sur la nature et l'origine des roches phosphatés, Bull. Acad. Roy. de Belgique, vol. 21, 1891, p. 126–160.

[869] Lasne, H., Origine des phosphates de chaux de la Somme, Paris, 1901; Sur les terrains phosphatés des environs de Doullens, Bull. Soc. Géol. France, vol. 18, 1889–90, pp. 441–491.

[870] Murray, J., Changes of temperature in the surface waters of the sea, Geog. Jour., vol. 12, 1898, pp. 129–131.

[871] Oldham, R. D., Report on the Indian earthquake of June 12, 1897, Mem. Geol. Surv. India, vol. 29, 1899, p. 80.

[872] Blanford, W. T., Discussion of paper by Cornet, F. L., On the phosphatic beds near Mons, Quart. Jour. Geol. Soc., vol. 42, 1886, pp. 325–339.

former taking place in certain Indian rivers and being caused by earthquake shock, and that cited by the latter occurring on the Indian Malabar coast and being due to the change in monsoons.

Explanations of the origin of the phosphorites of western United States have been made by Gale and Richards,[873] Blackwelder,[874] Breger,[875] Pardee,[876] and Mansfield.[877]

Blackwelder directs attention to necessary special conditions of currents, temperature, and other factors, causing wholesale destruction of organisms whose decomposition produced ammoniacal solutions which dissolved phosphatic materials from bones, shells, etc. This was then reprecipitated to form hydrous calcium carbophosphates, locally replacing carbonates and enriching calcium phosphate in originally phosphatic shells, and in the main forming the nodules of the enclosing paste which now cements the beds of phosphorite. In the first edition of the present work Blackwelder referred the original character of the spherical particles to excrements. Breger considers the phosphates and oily shales to have a common origin in a micro-organic ooze, ascribing the oolites to rolling or to foraminifera, while the phosphates are thought to have been taken from sea water by bacteria. Pardee appealed to low temperature, known to have existed in the Permian, to account for failure of decomposition and also to prevent escape of carbon dioxide formed from organic decay and derived from the atmosphere. The presence of the gas in abundance in the sea water dissolved such carbonates as were formed or transported to the region, and this permitted the phosphates to accumulate as insoluble residue of a far larger original precipitation. Mansfield at first considered the oolites as originally composed of calcium carbonate and to have been replaced by phosphate in colder waters. His latest statement relating to origin is as follows:[878]

[873] Gale, H. S., and Richards, R. W., Preliminary report on the phosphate deposits in southeastern Idaho and adjacent parts of Wyoming and Utah, Bull. 430, U. S. Geol. Surv., 1910, pp. 457–535.

[874] Blackwelder, E., Phosphate deposits east of Ogden, Utah, Bull. 430, U. S. Geol. Surv., 1910, pp. 536–551; The geologic rôle of phosphorus, Am. Jour. Sci., vol. 42, 1916, pp. 285–298; Origin of the Rocky Mountain phosphate deposits, Bull. Geol. Soc. Am., vol. 26, 1915, pp. 100–101 (Abstract). The geologic rôle of phosphorus, Am. Jour. Sci., vol. 42, 1916, pp. 285–298.

[875] Breger, C. L., Origin of the Lander oil and phosphate, Min. and Eng. World, vol. 35, 1917, p. 632.

[876] Pardee, J. T., The Garrison and Philipsburg phosphate fields, Bull. 640, U. S. Geol. Surv., 1917, pp. 225–228.

[877] Mansfield, G. R., Origin of the western phosphates of the United States, Am. Jour. Sci., vol. 46, 1918, pp. 591–598; Geography, geology, and mineral resources of part of southeastern Idaho; Prof. Paper 152, U. S. Geol. Surv., 1927, pp. 75–77, 187–188, 208–214, 361–366; Econ. Geol., vol. 26, 1931, pp. 353–374.

[878] Mansfield, G. R., op. cit., p. 366.

The phosphatic oolites, which constitute so large a proportion of the phosphate beds, were probably formed directly by biochemical and physical agencies from phosphatic solutions or colloids on the sea bottom. This material may have been supplied by some accidental wholesale destruction of animal life, but more probably it represents a slow gathering and concentration of phosphatic debris under conditions which largely excluded oxygen from the deeper waters and were thus unfavorable for forms of life that ordinarily inhabit the sea bottom and prevent the accumulation of organic debris. These conditions were induced by the considerable separation of the waters of the Phosphoria sea from the ocean and by the restriction in the circulation of its waters caused by this separation and by the supposedly smaller temperature differences which then existed between high and low latitudes. Generally cool temperatures with some climatic oscillations prevailed during the time of deposition of the phosphate. These conditions tended to favor the growth of plant and animal life in the shallower waters, while at the same time they reduced the activities of denitrifying bacteria, which curtail plant life and thus hinder the growth of animals dependent upon plants. Reduction of the activities of denitrifying bacteria may also have curtailed the precipitation of calcium carbonate, thus favoring the concentration of phosphatic solutions from which oolites might be formed. There was sufficient time for the postulated slow formation of the extensive phosphate deposits now found.

PHOSPHATIC NODULES. Nodules containing more or less calcium phosphate, much seemingly in the form of collophane, are of rather common occurrence in some dark clays, shales, and greensands. Dimensions range from a few millimeters to about 6 centimeters in diameter. Shapes are irregular. Each, in general, has a more or less phosphatized nucleus or central portion, as a coprolite, shell, fragment of bone, etc., surrounded by concentric crusts of collophane. Shell cavities may be filled with the same material. Several of these nodules may become cemented to each other and to other substances to form a crust over the ocean floor. Many nodules are perforated in various directions by the boring of marine organisms, and they form excellent bases upon which benthonic organisms, as barnacles, oysters, bryozoa, algæ, etc., build and ultimately leave their skeletal structures to become phosphatized and form part of a nodule. Colors range from brown to black, largely from hydrocarbonaceous matter with which they are permeated. The surface of a nodule has a glazed appearance and a brownish or greenish color.

Phosphatic nodules have been dredged from the bottom of the Atlantic Ocean southeast of the United States, from the Agulhas Bank south of Africa in depths of 398 to 1500 fathoms, where they occur in association with greensand, and in deep water south of the bank in depths of 1900 fathoms in association with globigerina ooze, and on other parts of the continental slopes. The usual depths range from 200 to 500 fathoms.

According to Murray and Murray and Hjort,[879] they occur chiefly along

[879] Murray, J., and Hjort, J., The depths of the ocean, 1912, p. 159

coasts of which the waters are subject to great and rapid changes of temperature, these causing large-scale destruction of marine organisms. Phosphatic nodules are known in the geologic column from the Devonian-Mississippian black shales of eastern and central United States, the Permian Phosphoria formation of the Rocky Mountains, the Lower Cretaceous greensand near Cambridge, England, and many other terranes.

The content of calcium phosphate in nodules shows considerable range, but is relatively low. Analyses of two nodules dredged by the Challenger expedition off the south coast of Africa from depths of 150 to 1900 fathoms are given in table 83.[880]

With respect to the origin of phosphatic nodules, Murray and Renard[881] and Murray[882] suggest that an abundance of decaying organic matter favors

TABLE 83

	150 FATHOMS	1900 FATHOMS
P_2O_5	19.96	23.54
CO_2	12.05	10.64
SO_3	1.37	1.39
SiO_2	1.36	2.56
CaO	39.41	40.95
MgO	0.67	0.83
Fe_2O_3	2.54	2.79
Al_2O_3	1.19	1.43
Loss		3.65
Insoluble residue	17.34	11.93
	95.89	99.71

precipitation of phosphate. The fact that the nodules on the present sea bottom are merely calcium-phosphate cemented portions of sediments in which they occur is considered proof that they were formed in situ and not mechanically transported to the places of occurrence. The source of the phosphorus is sought in part in tests and shells of organisms and other organic matter which are assumed to have been brought into solution or to have been placed in the colloidal state by the decomposition products developed because of abundant organic matter. Ultimately the phosphorus is precipitated as the phosphate, some particle of matter, a shell, piece of

[880] Murray, J., Report on the specimens of bottom deposits, Bull. Mus. Comp. Zool., vol. 12, 1885, pp. 41–43, 52–53. Murray, J. and Renard, A. F., Deep sea deposits, 1891, pp. 396–400.

[881] Murray, J., and Renard, A. F., op. cit., pp. 391–400.

[882] Murray, J., The Maltese Islands with special reference to their geological structure, Scottish Geog. Mag., vol. 6, 1890, p. 481.

bone, or other substance serving as a nucleus. If adjacent matter is not removed, it becomes cemented into the nodule.

It is evident that the nodular deposits have much in common and, indeed, intergrade with the bedded phosphorites already described, and the conditions of their origins are believed to be rather similar. There is reason to think that these conditions range from certain peculiar situations on the sea bottom to those of coastal swamps.

Bonney[883] in 1875 concluded that the phosphatic nodules have been produced by phosphatization of various objects in the presence of ammonium carbonate and a weak solution of phosphoric acid on a muddy sea bottom, and that the conditions necessary for this reaction are somewhat complex and seldom realized. Gosselet[884] states that calcareous nodules, shells, and fragments of bone become more or less phosphatized and cemented in a matrix of variable character. Thus, phosphatic material, more or less resistant, may be reworked by marine currents to form local conglomeratic bodies and basal conglomerates of younger formations.

GUANO. *Primary.* Primary or true guano consists of the excrements of birds and other animals, accumulating in situations dry enough to retard bacterial decay and suited to the needs of vast colonies of birds. These conditions are best realized on low islands in the arid belts of the trade winds, the islands on the west coast of Peru,[885] Christmas Island in the Indian Ocean, and Navassa Island in the Caribbean being examples. Sea birds congregate in vast numbers on such islands, largely because they there are free from the depredations of foxes and other carnivorous animals of the mainland. In time the surface becomes covered with a layer of excrement and remains of dead animals. The thickness is variable on the same island and, of course, on different islands, but not infrequently a thickness of 10 to 20 feet has been attained.

Comparatively fresh guano is a dry pulverulent mixture of various organic compounds: phosphates, nitrates, and carbonates of lime, ammonia, and other bases (see analyses in table 84). From the time of its deposition it undergoes slow internal changes favored by the high temperature and assisted by the occasional rains. These changes gradually cause the elimination of the more volatile and soluble compounds, such as ammonia, the loss of the original structure, and a hardening of the deposit. During these processes many new minerals are produced in the interstices of the mass; most of these are hydrous phosphates, nitrates, and oxalates that are pe-

[883] Bonney, T. G., Cambridgeshire Geology, 1875.

[884] Gosselet, J., Des conditions dans lesquelles s'est fait le dépôt du chaux de la Picardie, Compt. Rend., Paris Acad. Sci., T. 123, 1896, p. 290–292.

[885] Penrose, R. A. F., jr., The nitrate deposits of Chili, Jour. Geol., vol. 18, 1910, p. 118.

culiar to guano deposits. Continuance of these changes eventually converts the guano and its foundation into firm rock. These are described on later pages as secondary phosphatic deposits. It is scarcely possible to draw a line of demarkation between primary and secondary; and yet it seems worth while to make such distinction.

Some guano is made in caves by bats. The deposits are not extensive, and the transformations through which bat guano passes seem to differ little from those occurring on bird islands.

TABLE 84

	1	2
SiO_2	0.64	
$FePO_4$, $AlPO_4$	1.04	1.04
$Ca_3(PO_4)_2$	18.22	83.47
"Organic matter"	5.90	
$MgNH_4PO_4$	4.00	
$(NH_3)_3PO_4$	0.90	
$(NH_4)_2SO_4$	1.82	
Ammonium urate	12.74	
NH_4Cl	1.55	
Oxalic acid	13.60	
Uric acid	21.14	
Resin	1.11	
Fatty acid	1.60	
K_2SO_4	3.30	
NaCl	2.44	
$CaSO_4$		0.37
$CaFl_2$		3.29
$MgCO_3$		0.44
$CaCO_3$		3.75
CaO		2.59
Moisture		1.70
Organic matter and combined water		3.30

1. Unaltered guano from the arid Chincha Islands off the coast of Peru (Analysis by Karmrodt).

2. Stone guano from Nauru Island, near Java (Analysis by Elschner).

Note: Although these analyses are not wholly comparable, they indicate clearly the loss of organic and soluble components and the concentration of calcium phosphates in the altered material.

Secondary Phosphatic Deposits

LEACHED PHOSPHATIC DEPOSITS. On the less arid bird islands, rain water soaks more or less copiously down through primary guano deposits and does its usual work of solution, aided by the fermenting action of bacteria. The different constituents of guano dissolve at different rates. Thus, the nitrates, oxalates, and carbonates, and ammonium phosphates pass out in solution much more rapidly than the less soluble calcium phosphate. Collapse and recementation of the honeycombed mass proceed until the result is a brecciated solid rock much richer in lime phosphates than the original guano. The material is generally light gray or white. Much of it consists of banded crusts of agate-like appearance, but there is no definite stratification and generally no fossils except bird bones.

The deposits of Nauru Island in the Java Sea are of this type. The analyses given in table 84 illustrate the difference between the primary guano and the altered product, or "stone guano." "Stone guano" is much more abundant than primary guano, and nearly all so-called "guano deposits" consist either of stone guano or phosphatized coral limestone, or of both these types and their intergradations.

The same general processes affect phosphatic materials other than guano. Some limestones contain appreciable quantities of phosphoric acid, generally in the form of grains of collophane, either scattered through the rock or segregated in thin layers. Under suitable conditions, and especially where such rocks have been elevated and subjected to the solvent action of descending ground water, the calcium carbonate dissolves more rapidly than the calcium phosphate, and the latter accumulates. These residual accumulations may reach considerable thicknesses. Examples of this type are found in Kentucky, Tennessee,[886] Belgium, France, and elsewhere, and they are usually closely associated with the more important phosphatized limestones to be described later.

A somewhat different type of leaching may occur in standing bodies of water where anaërobic conditions prevail and carbon dioxide is so excessively abundant that the lime carbonate goes into solution. Such effects upon previously deposited bottom sediments containing phosphoric acid might result in a thin layer of phosphorite being left as the sole residue of what otherwise would have become a thick bed of limestone. No proved example of this type is known, but instances have been reported from the chalk of England, northern France and Belgium, and from Balmez in Spain.

PHOSPHATIZATION OF OTHER ROCKS. Under suitable conditions various rocks have been extensively phosphatized by solutions carrying phosphoric acid downward through cracks and pores. Thus, coral and other limestones underlying deposits of guano have in many places been completely phosphatized,[887] and most of the guano islands of the tropics have such deposits.

---

[886] Hayes, C. W., Origin and extent of the Tennessee white phosphates, Bull. 213, U. S. Geol. Surv., 1903, pp. 418–423; Eckel, E. C., The white phosphates of Decatur County, Tennessee, Ibid., pp. 424–426.

[887] Sandberger, F., Neues Jahrb. f. Min., etc., 1870, pp. 306–310.

A similar change has been obtained in laboratory experiments. So rapid is the process under favorable conditions that on certain of the coral islands of the Pacific Ocean pure coral limestone has been completely phosphatized to depths of 2 to 3 feet in twenty years by the solutions derived from overlying deposits of guano. Elsewhere, marl and chalk beds containing scattered grains of phosphatic matter appear to have supplied phosphorus to descending solutions which have caused the substitution of phosphate for carbonate in limestone beneath. This appears to have been the origin of the most widespread and important of the Florida and Carolina phosphatic deposits, as well as many in France, Germany, and other countries. Analogous deposits have been found in caverns in France and elsewhere, the phosphorus in these cases having been derived from accumulations of bat guano.

In some instances rocks less susceptible to change than limestone have been thus converted into phosphates, D'Invilliers[888] describing the phosphatization of andesitic lava on Navassa Island in the West Indies. In this instance vivianite and other phosphates of iron and alumina were produced, rather than the usual tricalcium phosphate minerals.

DETRITAL PHOSPHATIC DEPOSITS. Like all other rocks, the various phosphatic beds are subject to disintegration and rearrangement by the various processes of transportation. In rather rare instances such processes yield deposits of sand or gravel which consist largely of phosphatic particles. The so-called "River Pebble Phosphates" of Florida appear to be of this origin, whereas the "Land Pebble Phosphates" are older beds of river gravel on terraces of flood plains. In such formations differential solution results in the more rapid abstraction of any particles of calcium carbonate that may have been included.

At certain localities in the Rocky Mountains of the United States the basal beds of the Permian, which are unconformable on the underlying strata, consist of calcareous shell fragments and abundant phosphate grains and nodules in a more or less sandy cross-laminated matrix. The cement of these deposits is not phosphatic, and they generally contain unphosphatized calcareous shells. The facts indicate that the phosphatized particles are detrital and were brought to their positions from other sources. The Lower Cretaceous Greensand of England contains phosphatized Jurassic ammonites which have been bored into by marine animals, and somewhat similar occurrences have been described from the Cretaceous of France, the Cambrian of Wales and England, and other regions.

---

[888] D'Invilliers, E. V., Phosphate deposits of the Island of Navassa, Bull. Geol. Soc. Am., vol. 2, 1891, p. 75.

THE SEDIMENTARY CYCLE OF PHOSPHORUS[889]

The phosphorus liberated in the decomposition of rocks on land generally finds its way in solution to the sea, where it is soon uniformly diffused. Ordinarily this dissolved phosphorus slowly passes through an intricate series of transformations from solution to solid form and back again through the activities of organisms. Plants absorb small quantities to incorporate in the nuclei of their cells. Animals devour the plants and make a similar use of the phosphorus, the higher forms using phosphates in making their shells, bones, and teeth. On the death of an organism, its remains are devoured by scavengers and decomposed by bacteria, with the general result that the phosphorus is returned to the oceanic solution.

From time to time, phosphorus escapes from this apparently endless circulation and becomes fixed in the sedimentary deposits. One well known method is through the agency of birds in the formation of guano and the secondary products derived therefrom.

In most situations, both on land and in the sea, the work of scavengers and bacteria is so effective that all dead organic matter is returned to solution. There are, however, a few environments where this process is more or less suppressed and modified because of the deficiency of oxygen. Such conditions exist in bogs, deep lakes, cul-de-sac bays, and other places where there is little circulation. It may also prevail in the muds beneath bodies of still water. In such situations anaërobic bacteria decompose organic matter, with the formation of hydrocarbons, ammonia, hydrogen sulphide, and other compounds. There is obviously much variation in the physico-chemical conditions. Under some conditions, which are but imperfectly understood, the phosphoric acid in solution interacts with lime carbonate to form collophane and probably other mineral phosphates. The element thus becomes fixed in the form of nodules or continuous beds of phosphorite. The sediments that accumulate in such places are of black or dark colors by reason of the hydrocarbon content.[890]

[889] Blackwelder, E., The geologic rôle of phosphorus, Am. Jour. Sci., vol. 42, 1916, pp. 285–298.

[890] In addition to the articles to which reference is made in the text, the following may be consulted with profit: Andersson, J. G., Über Cambrische und Silurische phosphoritführende Gesteine aus Schweden, Bull. Geol. Inst. Upsala, vol. 2, 1896, pp. 133–239; Blayac, M., Description géologique de la région des phosphates du Dyr et du Kouif, près Tebessa, Ann. des Mines (9 ser.), vol. 6, 1894, p. 319; Carnot, M. A., Sur les variations observeés dans la composition des apatites, phosphorites et des phosphates sédimentaires, Ann. des Mines, 10, 1896, pp. 137–231; Cayeux, L., Introduction à l'étude pétrographique des roches sédimentaires, Mémoires pour servir à l'explication de la carte géologique détaillée de la France, 1916; Clarke, F. W., Data of geochemistry, Bull. 770, U. S. Geol. Surv., 1924; Collet, L. W., Les concrétions phosphatées de l'Agulhas Bank (Cape of Good Hope), Proc. Roy. Soc. Edinburgh, vol. 25, 1905, pp. 862–893; Credner, H., Die Phosphoritknollen

MANGANESE IN SEDIMENTS[891]

BY D. F. HEWETT

Manganese is a minor constituent in most sedimentary rocks. Like several other minor constituents such as phosphoric acid, barium, strontium, glauconite, etc., it is commonly present only to the extent of a small fraction of one per cent of most sediments, but here and there, the percentage rises considerably higher and in a few places nearly pure manganese oxides and carbonates form distinct beds that persist over large areas. By their rarity as well as their economic value, such occurrences assume uncommon interest.

The element manganese has numerous valences and therefore it forms numerous compounds with oxygen, chlorine, and sulphur, an unusually large part of which occur in nature. More than 200 minerals contain manganese as an essential element. The solubility of these minerals under natural conditions, as well as any influences that tend to change the valence of the element, play an important part in determining where and under what conditions the various manganese minerals decompose or are precipitated in sediments. The minerals that contain manganous oxide are more susceptible to solution than those which contain it in higher states of oxidation. Since most observations concerning manganiferous sediments have been made at or near the surface where the effects of weathering are widespread, many investigators appear to have been led unconsciously to assume an

des Leipziger Mitteloligocäns und die norddeutschen Phosphoritzonen, Abh. k. Sachs. Gesell. Wiss., Bd. 22, 1895, pp. 1–47; Davies, D. C., On a bed of phosphate of lime, northwest of Llanfyllin, North Wales, Geol. Mag., vol. 4, 1867, p. 257; Dugast, L., Les phosphates d'Algérie, Rev. Gén. des Sci. Pures et Appliquées, vol. 8, 1897, pp. 769–782; Elschener, C., Corallogene Phosphat-Inseln Austral-Oceaniens und ihre Producte, 1913; Fuchs, E., et de Launay, L., Traité des gîtes min. et mét., 1893; Lacroix, A., Minéralogie de la France, vol. 4, 1910, pp. 555–600; Matson, G. C., The phosphate deposits of Florida, Bull. 604, U. S. Geol. Surv., 1915; Matthew, W. D., On phosphatic nodules from the Cambrian of southern New Brunswick, Trans. New York Acad. Sci., vol. 12, 1893, pp. 108–120; Murray, J., and Philippi, E., Wiss. Ergebn. der deutschen tiefsee Exped., 10, Lief. 4, Jena, 1908; Penrose, R. A. F. jr., Nature and origin of deposits of phosphate of lime, Bull. 46, U. S. Geol. Surv., 1888; Reese, C. L., On the influence of swamp waters in the formation of phosphatic nodules of South Carolina, Am. Jour. Sci., vol. 43, 1892, p. 402; Richards, R. W., and Mansfield, G. R., Phosphate deposits of Georgetown, Idaho, Bull. 577, U. S. Geol. Surv., 1914; Rogers, A. F., Collophane, a much neglected mineral, Am. Jour. Sci., vol. 3, 1922, pp. 269–276; Sellards, E. H., Ann. Rept. Florida Geol. Surv., 1913; Shaler, N. S., On the phosphate beds of South Carolina, U. S. Coast Surv. Rept. for 1870, pp. 182–189; Smith, E. A., The phosphates and marls of the State, Report on the Geology of the Coastal Plain of Alabama, 1894, pp. 449–525; Stutzer, O., Lagerstätten der Nichterze, Berlin, 1911; Teall, J. J. H., Summary of phosphate deposits, Proc. Geologists' Assoc., vol. 16, 1900, p. 369; Thomas, P., Giséments des phosphates de chaux des hauts plateaux de Tunisie, Bull. Soc. Géol. France, vol. 19, 1891, p. 370.

[891] Published with the permission of the Director, U. S. Geological Survey.

abundance and wider distribution of manganese oxides than may be justified. In recent years, it has become quite certain that manganiferous carbonates are much more widespread in unweathered sediments than the
oxides.

MANGANESE IN IGNEOUS ROCKS, WATERS, AND ORGANISMS

Among 135 specimens of a wide variety of igneous rocks that are assuredly
not metamorphosed,[892] manganous oxide attains a maximum of 0.93 per
cent in a hypersthene gabbro from Minnesota. In most rocks, the percentage ranges from 0.05 to 0.15. In general, the percentage is highest in
the basic rocks rich in iron and lowest in the alkaline rocks. There is little,
however, to indicate that the chemical character of the rocks which surround
a basin of sedimentation is an important factor in determining the degree of
concentration of manganese in the nearby sediments.

Although there is an abundant record of the manganese content of river
waters, especially in Europe and North America where its deposition in city
supply systems has been cause for concern, there is surprisingly meagre
record of the amount present in waters from hot and cold springs, lakes, and
the seas. In a broad way, the manganese content attains its maximum of
about 117 parts per million in certain spring waters; it commonly ranges
from 0.5 to 5 parts per million in river waters in the temperate zone, and
while the amount in sea water has not yet been accurately determined, it
is assuredly much less than the amounts recorded in springs and rivers. One
may readily conclude from existing data that in the progress of water from
the sources of rivers to the seas, manganese oxide is steadily removed from
solution, although it is not definitely known whether the precipitation is
caused by organisms or by simple chemical reactions. In general, waters
that contain much manganese belong to the mixed carbonate type and it
has been widely asserted that manganese is transported in solution as the
bicarbonate. As the chemistry of manganese has many resemblances to
that of iron, it seems probable that manganese, like iron, is not carried as
bicarbonate in natural surface solutions high in organic matter as has been
widely assumed, but in all probability it is transported as manganese oxide
hydrosol, stabilized by organic colloids.[893]

Manganese seems to be present in most if not all living organisms, both
animal and plant, but it is not known that any but the lowest organisms,
such as bacteria and algæ, play an important part in determining the amount
of manganese in sediments. Many manganiferous sediments contain

[892] Clarke, F. W., Data of geochemistry, Bull. 770, U. S. Geol. Surv., 1924, pp. 437–473.
[893] Moore, E. S., and Maynard, J. E., Solution, transportation and precipitation of iron
and silica, Econ. Geol., vol. 24, 1929, pp. 272–303; 365–402; 506–527.

marine invertebrate fossils, but even where they are present there is no apparent relation between the quantity of manganese and the number of organisms.

Probably bacteria and algæ deserve most serious consideration as active agents in precipitating manganese from solution.[894]   As a result of considerable experimental work, it seems clear that several genera of bacteria common in soils and in oceanic muds, especially *Crenothrix*, *Leptothrix*, *Cladothrix*, and *Clanothrix*, precipitate manganese oxides from a number of manganese salts. It is also possible but not yet demonstrated that some bacteria precipitate manganese carbonate.   As to the extent to which manganese bacteria have played a part in depositing known deposits of manganese oxides and carbonates, opinions differ widely.   Vernadsky[895] asserts that bacteria are largely responsible for the change from manganous compounds to the higher manganese oxides and doubts that free atmospheric oxygen can oxidize such compounds at ordinary temperatures.   This is obviously an extreme position and ignores much laboratory work that has been done.   Some students of the work of algæ in depositing calcium carbonate look with favor upon the possibility that the spherical and concretionary forms of manganese oxides, such as those found in the beds of manganese oxide near Tschiaturi, Russia, may have been deposited by algæ.[896]   It has been found that certain algæ abstract manganese oxides from the waters of the Elbe Valley which contain 0.25 to 0.65 parts per million and the fact has been the basis of processes to remove manganese from the waters.[897]   Recent studies by D.

---

[894] It has been known for about 100 years that certain bacteria selectively precipitate iron oxides from solution, and nearly as long that similar organisms precipitate manganese oxides.   Consequently there is abundant literature on the subject, especially in German, Swedish, and French.   The literature is well summarized by W. Vernadsky, in "La Géochimie," Paris, 1924, in which there is a chapter entitled "Histoire géochimique du manganèse," pp. 74–110.   More important recent publications follow: Beijerinck, M. W., Oxidation of manganese carbonate by bacteria and fungi, Fol. Mikrobiol., 2, no. 2, 1913, Summarized in Zentr. Biochem. Biophys., vol. 16, 1913–1914, p. 277; Söhngen, M. L., Umwandlungen von Manganverbindungen unter dem Einfluss mikrobiologischer Prozesse, Zentr. f. Bakteriologie, Abt. ii, vol. 40, 1914, pp. 545–554; Naumann, E., Ueber die See- und Sumpferze von Süd- und Mittel-Schwedens (Swedish with German review), Sver. Geol. Undersökning, Årsbok 13, 1922; Thiel, G. A., Manganese precipitated by microorganisms, Econ. Geol., vol. 20, 1925, pp. 301–311; Perfiliew, B. W., Die Rolle der Mikroben in der Erzbildung, Verhandl. Intern. Ver. f. Limnologie, vol. 3, 1927; Butkevich, E. S., The formation of marine iron and manganese deposits and the rôle of microorganisms in the latter, Wiss. Meeresinst., Berlin, 3 (3), 1928, pp. 7–80; Zapffe, C., Deposition of manganese, Econ. Geol., vol. 26, 1931, pp. 799–832.   This article contains an excellent bibliography.

[895] Op. cit., pp. 98–99.

[896] White, David, personal communication.

[897] Vollmer, D., Die Entmangung des Grundwassers in Elbethal und die für Dresden ausgeführte Anlagen, Jour. Gasbel., vol. 57, 1914, pp. 956–959.

White of calcareous tufa deposited by algæ near Furnace Creek, West Virginia, indicate that in times of drought such algæ also deposit manganese oxide.[898]

MANGANESE IN SEDIMENTARY ROCKS

Manganese in Clastic and Carbonate Sediments

Sandstones and the coarser sediments ordinarily contain little manganese, and that little is commonly confined to the undecomposed fragments of the source rocks or minerals. Analyses show quantities that range from mere traces to about 1.5 per cent manganese oxide.

Glauconitic sands appear to contain little manganese but, curiously, beds of these sands not infrequently occur near beds of manganiferous carbonate. Similarly, phosphatic oolites contain little manganese but in several localities they occur near manganiferous sediments. The beds of oolitic and fossil hematite which have been laid down in a manner similar to coarse sediments uniformly contain a little manganese, the percentage ranging from 0.2 to 0.5. Greenalite contains little manganese.

Small quantities of manganese oxides are present in most fresh specimens of shales and slates. Analyses show a range from a trace to 5.87 per cent. The quantity rarely exceeds one per cent and the range is commonly from 0.05 to 0.30 per cent, amounts not differing greatly from the content in the original igneous rocks. The percentage in the black and green slates appears to be higher than in those that are red and gray. Although the manganese content of fine sediments is rather uniformly low, zones of such sediments in many places contain thin layers of carbonate minerals which are locally rich in manganese. In these places, the percentage of manganese appears to be related to the content of ferrous iron.

There are comparatively few good determinations of manganese in the carbonate rocks. Pure non-magnesian limestones rarely contain more than 0.1 per cent of manganese oxide and similar quantities are present in fresh-water marls, travertines and tufas. On the other hand, the magnesian limestones commonly contain more manganese and the quantity tends to increase with the content of ferrous carbonate. Carbonate rocks with less than one per cent ferrous oxide commonly contain less than 0.1 per cent of manganese oxide but where the ferrous oxide content exceeds 20 per cent, that of manganese oxide rarely is less than 0.7 per cent.

[898] Howe, M. A., The geologic importance of the lime-secreting algae, Prof. Paper 170, U.S. Geol. Surv. (in preparation).

Manganese Oxides in Sediments

Among the beds of pure manganese oxides interlaid with coarse sediment none are more important than those of the Caucasus region of Russia.[899] These have been extensively explored near Tschiaturi where in a sing. bed in an area of 130 square kilometers there are estimated to exist from 10 to 150 million tons of marketable manganese ore. This bed lies in marl sand transitional from the Eocene to the Oligocene. Similar beds at similar horizon are recorded sporadically in an area about 90 kilometers i diameter. Similar deposits are recorded in Oligocene beds in the Nikope district, Russia, and in Pliocene beds on the Island of Milos, Greece.

In the Tschiaturi district, the manganese oxides form oolites that mak up a large part of distinct lenses in medium-grained arkosic sandstone In the explored region, the thickness of the bed ranges from 6 to 14 feet bu the thickness of the separate lenses of manganese oxides ranges from 3 t 24 inches. Commonly, the aggregate thickness of these lenses is less tha half the thickness of the bed. The oolites appear to be psilomelane an pyrolusite and are largely flat ellipsoids whose larger diameters range fron 1 to 10 mm. and average about 3 mm. (figs. 67–68). Most of these oolite contain a nuclear grain of quartz or feldspar but little more foreign materia Some are angular and appear to be broken fragments of symmetrical oolites The oolites are imbedded in a matrix of arkosic material, the grains of which quartz, feldspars, and mica, largely range from 0.05 to 0.10 mm. in diameter The cement is calcium carbonate. Numerous perfect shark teeth and a few invertebrate fossils indicate a marine origin for the beds. As the oolite are rudely sorted into distinct layers and some are broken, it seems that the oolites were formed in another habitat and have been transported to thei present site. Furthermore, most oolites have shrunken away from thei matrix and it seems that they must have steadily lost water since they were formed in their original habitat. De la Sauce does not think that the oolite have an organic origin.

Some of the manganese deposits of Oriente Province, Cuba, closely resemble those of the Tschiaturi region, especially those at the Sultana, Isabelita, and Cauto mines near Cristo.[900] Beds of tuffaceous material in lower Eocene rocks contain disseminated round grains of manganese oxide

[899] Drake, F., The manganese ore mining industry of the Caucasus, Trans. Am. Inst. Min. and Met., vol. 28, 1898, pp. 191–208; Zeretelle, D., Manganese ore with special reference to Georgian ore, Dryden Press, London, 1925, p. 136; De la Sauce, W., Beiträge zur Kenntniss der Manganerzlagerstätte Tschiaturi in Kaukasus, Abhandl. zur prak. Geol., Halle, 1926, 87 pp. and 3 maps. Contains bibliography of 40 titles.

[900] Burchard, E. F., Manganese ore deposits of Cuba, Trans. Am. Inst. Min. Eng., vol. 63, 1919, pp. 67–75.

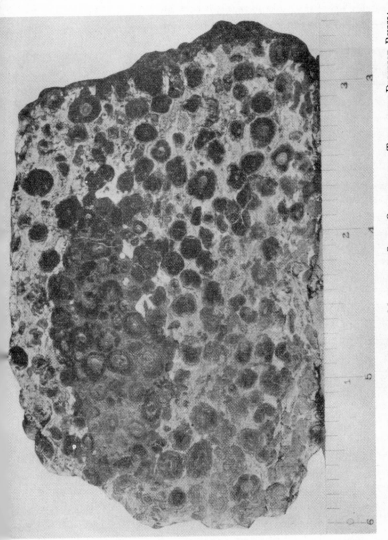

FIG. 67. A POLISHED SURFACE OF LOW-GRADE MANGANESE OXIDE ORE FROM THE TSCHIATURI DISTRICT, RUSSIA
The oolites are pyrolusite; the light matrix is composed of grains of quartz, feldspar, and mica in calcite. Secondary pyrolusite has replaced the matrix in the dark area. The scale indicates inches.

as much as 6 mm. in diameter.   The manganese content of beds as much as
20 feet thick ranges from 10 to 20 per cent.   Some beds contain considerable
glauconite.   At the Charco Redondo mine, there is a bed about 15 inches
thick made up of nearly pure manganese oxide in the form of small cauli-
flower-like growths which suggest the forms of algæ.

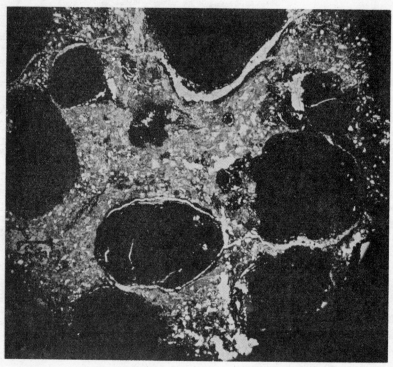

FIG. 68. MICROPHOTOGRAPH OF SOME MATERIAL SHOWN IN FIGURE 67
Note shrinkage cracks filled with calcite.   Ten times natural size

Near Las Vegas, Nevada,[901] there are several beds of nearly pure wad as
much as 36 feet thick included in latite tuffs of Pliocene age.   Also near
Cleveland, Idaho,[902] beds of nearly pure wad are found in fine sands and clays
laid down on the shore of a Pleistocene lake.   Near Artillery Peak and
Topock, Mojave County, Arizona,[903] wad impregnates latite tuff and ar-

[901] Hewett, D. F., and Webber, B. N., Bedded deposits of manganese oxides near Las
Vegas, Nevada, Bull. Univ. Nevada, vol. 25, no. 6, 1931, p. 17.

[902] Hewett, D. F., A manganese deposit of Pleistocene age in Bannock County, Idaho,
Bull. 795, U. S. Geol. Surv., 1928, pp. 211–221.

[903] Jones, E. L., and Ransome, F. L., Deposits of manganese in Arizona, Bull. 710–D,

kosic sandstone that occur in a group of tuffs and sandstone of mid-Tertiary age. The source of the manganese in these occurrences in Idaho, Nevada, and Arizona seems to be nearby hot springs and there is no evidence that organisms have caused deposition of the oxides.

In India and Brazil,[904] manganese deposits are widespread. In both countries there are outstanding deposits of manganese silicates, now weathered to oxides, in ancient gneisses and crystalline rocks, and in the same general regions, younger but pre-Paleozoic rocks contain stratified bodies of manganese oxides locally altered to silicates. In India, the beds of manganese oxides are associated with quartzites and limestones of the Dharwar series, and in the Miguel Burnier and Ouro Prieto districts, Brazil, such beds are associated with quartzites of the Piracicaba and Itabira formations. Since the oxides have been recrystallized, their original relations are obscure.

Manganese Carbonates in Sediments

To an increasing degree in recent years, data have been collected which show that thin zones of manganiferous carbonates and carbonate concretions are fairly common in fine-grained marine sediments. Although some accounts of such zones state that manganese oxides also accompany the carbonates, it is not yet certain that such oxides are not the product of recent weathering. Recalculation of analyses of material from several localities (Newfoundland, Wales) indicates the presence of rhodonite, the metasilicate of manganese. It seems probable that this mineral has formed during the process of incipient metamorphism after burial.

Near Trinity and Conception bays, Newfoundland,[905] a section made up largely of thin-bedded red and green shales contains thin layers of green jaspery carbonate of manganese as well as layers of calcium phosphate and baritic concretions. In the section on Manuels River there are four persistent and several lenticular layers of such carbonates which range from 0.2 to 0.7 feet thick. In the Brigus section, six beds with a total thickness of 4.5 feet contain appreciable manganese. Most of the manganese is present

---

U. S. Geol. Surv., 1920, pp. 143–149, 153–159; Wilson, E. D., and Butler, G. M., Manganese ore deposits of Arizona, Bull. 127, Univ. of Arizona, 1930, pp. 71–81.

[904] Fermor, L. L., Manganese ore deposits of India, Mem. Geol. Survey of India, vol. 37, 1909, p. 1294; Harder, E. C., Manganese ores of Russia, India, Brazil, and Chile, Bull. Am. Inst. Min. Eng., 1916, pp. 761–798.

[905] Dale, N. C., Cambrian manganese deposits of Conception and Trinity Bays, Newfoundland, Proc. Am. Philos. Soc., vol. 54, 1915, pp. 378–449. This article has an excellent bibliography.

as manganese carbonate, the content of which ranges from 10.23 to 44.3
per cent. In addition, the manganese dioxide content ranges from 2.3
to 28.93 per cent. Nearby, on Placentia Bay,[906] somewhat similar bed
include a layer which contains 84.6 per cent manganese carbonate.

FIG. 69. THINLY LAMINATED HIGH-GRADE MANGANESE CARBONATE
This sample is from a bed interlayered with Franciscan Chert (Jurassic), Buckeye
Mine, San Joaquin County, California. The scale indicates inches.

Similar beds of rather pure manganese carbonate are recorded in Cambrian grits and shales in Merionethshire,[907] Wales, and near Chevron, Belgium.[908] In the latter locality, the bed of carbonate, 3.9 feet thick, is
associated with layers of jasper; selected specimens contain as much as 84 per
cent $MnCO_3$.

[906] Hunt, T. S., Geol. Surv. Canada, 1857–58, pp. 204–205.
[907] Halse, E., The occurrence of manganese ore in the Cambrian rocks of Merionethshire,
Trans. N. Eng. Inst. Min. Eng., vol. 36, 1887, p. 103.
[908] DeWalque, G., Sur le rhodochrosite de Chevrons, Ann. Soc. Géol. de Belgique, vol.
11, 1883–1884, pp. lxiii–lxv.

Explorations of the manganese deposits that occur widely in the Franciscan (Jurassic) cherts of California have recently shown the presence of thinly laminated beds of gray, nearly pure manganese carbonate (see fig.

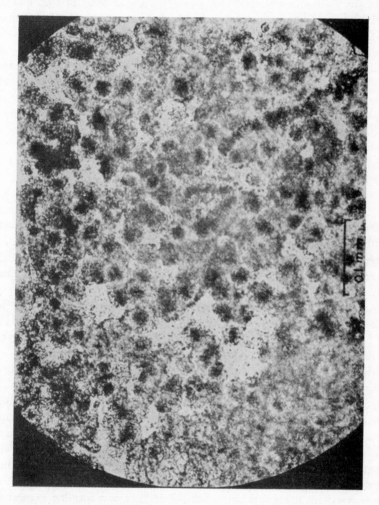

FIG. 70. MICROPHOTOGRAPH OF SOME MATERIAL SHOWN IN FIGURE 69
The manganese carbonate forms minute oolites. Magnified 200 diameters

69) from 2 to 6 feet thick. The separate laminæ range from 0.1 to 0.2 inch thick and are made up of minute spherules (figs. 69–70). Thin sections show sporadic foraminiferal remains. Near intrusive rocks such beds are

altered to hausmannite, hydrous manganese silicates (neotocite and bemen tite), and pink rhodochrosite.[909] The enclosing rocks, the thin-bedded chert that make up the Franciscan formation, have been studied by Davis.[91]

In the Batesville district,[911] Arkansas, the Cason shale of Upper Ordo vician age attains a maximum thickness of 12 feet. It is largely made up of thin, rather persistent layers of shale, fine sandstone, phosphate and nodules of iron-manganese carbonate. It overlies unconformably the Fernvale limestone which persistently contains small percentages of man ganese, and is generally overlain unconformably by the St. Clair limestone The nodules of iron manganese carbonate resemble concretions but are regarded by Ulrich as fossil algæ of the genus *Girvanella*. The unweathered nodules are pale greenish gray and the manganese is entirely in the form o carbonate. Where mined under cover and unoxidized, the nodular layers 3 to 8 feet thick, contain from 12 to 20 per cent manganese and 7 to 10 per cent iron.

Numerous mines on the Cuyuna Range, Minnesota,[912] explored below the oxidized ores, encounter cherty, manganese-bearing iron carbonate interlayered with shales and amphibolite rocks. Such carbonate rocks contain as much as 30 per cent iron and 5 per cent manganese which are largely, if not wholly, present as carbonates. These rocks are a part of the Deerwood iron-bearing member of the Virginia slate, probably of upper Huronian age.

An interesting zone of manganese-iron carbonate concretions has re cently been explored near Chamberlain, South Dakota. The zone of shale, 38 feet thick, lies 130 feet above the base of the Pierre shale (Upper Creta ceous) and 6 feet above a persistent sandstone layer. The nodules are flattened spheroids 3 to 8 inches in diameter, commonly show nuclei of shells (*Inoceramus*) and fragments of bones, and contain about 16 per cent man ganese and 10 per cent iron. They are not uniformly distributed through the 38-foot bed but are concentrated in narrow persistent layers. Exhaus tive tests indicate that 12 cubic yards of shale yield one ton of nodules. Close study of the nodules shows that the ratio of manganese to iron is twice as great in the center as in the peripheral zone. Furthermore, on exposure to weathering, the iron tends to oxidize in advance of the manganese. From these relations, it appears that when the nodules were forming, manganese

---

[909] The writer's observations.

[910] Davis, E. F., The radiolarian cherts of the Franciscan group, Univ. California, Dept. Geol. Publ., vol. 11, 1918, pp. 235–432.

[911] Miser, H. D., Deposits of manganese ore in the Batesville district, Arkansas, Bull. 734, U. S. Geol. Surv., 1922, pp. 23–28.

[912] Harder, E. C., and Johnston, A. W., Geology of east central Minnesota, Bull. 15, Minnesota Geol. Surv., 1918, p. 168.

which probably existed in the sediment as an oxide was more readily susceptible to reduction than iron. The relations confirm the theory announced many years ago by Dieulafait.[913]

In several parts of the eastern United States, bodies of manganese oxides in residual materials occur persistently over large areas at definite stratigraphic horizons in such a way as to indicate that the oxides are derived from nearby sources. Explorations to depths that commonly range from 200 to 400 feet below the nearby surface yield only the oxides similar to those near the surface but have not yet revealed the materials from which they may be derived. Such horizons are formed in Pre-Cambrian rocks in the Piedmont region from Lynchburg, Virginia, to Abbeville, South Carolina;[914] at the base of the Shady dolomite (Lower Cambrian) from southwestern Virginia to northeastern Alabama;[915] at the contact of the Holston marble with the Tellico sandstone (Lower Ordovician) of east Tennessee;[916] at the base of the Oriskany sandstone (Lower Devonian) in western Virginia;[917] and in the Fort Payne chert (Mississippian) of eastern Tennessee and northern Alabama.[918] The outcrops of two of these zones, the Shady and Oriskany, contain iron as well as manganese deposits but the other three yield only manganese. The manganese deposits at the lower two of these five zones, the Pre-Cambrian and Shady, occur in the transition zone from sandstones to limestones; the third lies largely in limestone near its contact with overlying sandstone; the fourth lies in shale and chert beds at the base of the Oriskany sandstone where it unconformably overlies limestone; and the fifth zone (Fort Payne) lies wholly in thin-bedded chert, much like the beds of manganese carbonate in the Franciscan cherts of California. For each of these areas, the conclusion is reached that the unweathered materials or sources of the manganese oxides are stratified layers of either rather pure manganese carbonate or concretionary zones of iron-manganese carbonate with little or no oxide. The conclusion is based upon the general lithologic resemblances to sections that contain carbonate layers in contrast with those which contain layers of oxides.

[913] Dieulafait, L., Application des lois de la thermochimie aux phénomènes géologiques; minérais de manganèse, Compt. Rend. Acad. Sci., Paris, vol. 101, 1885, pp. 609, 644, 676.

[914] Harder, E. C., Manganese deposits of the United States, Bull. 427, U. S. Geol. Surv., 1910, pp. 37–46.

[915] Stose, G. W., et al, Manganese deposits of the west foot of the Blue Ridge, Virginia, Bull. 17, Virginia Geol. Surv., 1919, p. 166; Hull, J. P. D., La Forge, L., and Crane, W. R., Manganese deposits of Georgia, Bull. 35, Geol. Surv. of Georgia, 1919, p. 295.

[916] Stose, G. W., and Schrader, F. C., Manganese deposits of east Tennessee, Bull. 737, U. S. Geol. Surv., 1923, pp. 29–31.

[917] Stose, G. W., and Miser, H. D., Manganese deposits of western Virginia, Bull. 23, Virginia Geol. Surv., 1922, p. 206.

[918] Stose, G. W., and Schrader, F. C., op. cit., p. 31.

The recent discovery of hauerite (bisulphide of manganese) in the ca rock of two salt domes in Matagorda and Galveston counties, Texas, interesting.[919] It is associated with anhydrite and probably represents a re arrangement of the manganese and sulphur present in the sediments rathe than an original constituent.

Manganese in Deep-sea Deposits

According to Murray and Renard, hydrates and oxides of manganese ar among the most widely distributed substances in marine deposits. Thes occur as (a) finely divided coloring matter in some deep-sea sediments; (b coatings over shells, bones, teeth, fragments of rock, etc.; and (c) nodule and concretions.

Some manganese is present in nearly every sample of deep-sea sediments Deep-sea clays are probably decomposition products of pumice, volcani glass, windblown dust, and other fine particles, and their reddish brown colo is due to the presence of oxides of iron and manganese. In some shallov places, such as the Clyde Sea,[920] the surface layer of the muds is reddis! whereas the underlying material is blue. The exposed surfaces of rock that rest upon the bottom are covered with manganese oxide but the part embedded in the mud are not coated.

In a broad way, the sediments of the ocean basins that are surrounded by basic rocks have a higher content of manganese than those surrounded by other types. Thus, in general, a given area of the bottom of the Pacifi Ocean contains more manganese oxide nodules than an equal area of the bottom under the Indian Ocean and much more than an equal area of the bottom under the Atlantic. Similarly, the red clays of the Pacific are darker and contain more manganese than those of the Indian Ocean, which in turn are darker than those of the Atlantic.

Manganese oxide nodules occur sporadically in all of the ocean basins. In shape, the nodules range from spherical and elliptical to irregular; the surfaces are commonly botryoidal or mammillary, much like those which characterize residual deposits. To a considerable extent, the shapes appear to depend upon the shapes of the nuclei which commonly are fragments of pumice or volcanic rock. Such nuclei are greatly altered and more or less replaced by manganese oxide. It is stated that the nodules of each locality

[919] Wolf, A. G., Hauerite in a salt-dome cap rock, Bull. Am. Assoc. Pet. Geol., vol. 10, 1926, pp. 531–532; Hanna, M. A., A second record of hauerite associated with Gulf Coast salt domes, Bull. Am. Assoc. Pet. Geol., vol. 13, 1929.

[920] Murray, J., and Irvine, R., On the chemical changes which take place in the composition of sea water associated with blue muds on the floor of the ocean, Trans. Roy. Soc. Edinburgh, vol. 37, 1893, pp. 431–508; On manganese oxide and manganese nodules in marine deposits, Ibid., vol. 38, 1894, pp. 721–742.

tend to have similar shapes and sizes. Nodules as much as 15 cm. in diameter have been recovered but the fragments dredged by the "Challenger" show that larger masses are present.

Typical analyses of some nodules are shown in table 85. Commonly, manganese oxide equals or exceeds iron oxide and these make up about 60 per cent of the weight. In the nodules from the ocean deeps, the manganese is largely in the state of MnO_2 but in those from littoral zones, it is largely Mn_2O_3; in both, the kernels are more highly oxidized than the surface layers.

Most of the information concerning manganese nodules here presented has been derived from the works listed below.[921]

TABLE 85

	1	2	3	4
SiO_2	6.00	18.97	28.30	15.00
Al_2O_3	3.50	2.45	3.25	2.00
Fe_2O_3	32.90	19.58	23.08	22.00
MnO_2	25.64	32.48	29.09	30.00
$CaCO_3$	3.15	3.07	2.58	3.00
$CaSO_4$	1.16	0.58	0.62	0.70
$Ca_3P_2O_8$	0.90	0.20	Trace	Trace
$MgCO_3$	1.51	1.72	3.40	1.50
Insoluble CaO and MgO	0.40	0.55	0.78	
Loss on ignition	24.84	20.40	8.90	15.00
	100.00	100.00	100.00	

1. Depth 1525 fathoms, southwest of Canary Islands.
2. Depth 2600 fathoms, southwest of Australia.
3. 3000 fathoms, south of Hawaiian Islands.
4. Approximate average of 40 analyses.

Recently it has been determined[922] that deep-sea nodules as well as those from streams are more radioactive than the average igneous and sedimentary rocks.

Nodules of manganese oxide are not uncommon in fresh-water lakes. In

[921] Buchanan, J. Y., On the composition of oceanic and littoral manganese nodules, Trans. Roy. Soc. Edinburgh, vol. 36, 1892, pp. 459–483; Murray, J. and Renard, A. F., Deep sea deposits, Challenger Rept., 1891; Murray, J. and Hjort, J., Depths of the ocean, 1912, pp. 149–190; Molengraaf, G. A. F., Manganese concretions in Mesozoic deep sea deposits of Borneo, Timor, and Rotti, Verslag, K. Akad. Wetensschappen, Amsterdam, vol. 23, 1915, pp. 1058–1073; Collet, L. W., Manganese in sediments, in Les dépôts marins, Paris, 1908.

[922] Iimori, S., Formation of the radioactive manganiferous deposits of Tanokami, Bull. Chem. Soc. Japan, vol. 2, 1927, pp. 270–273.

Lock Tyne of Scotland[923] the nodules have been found and in Zeller Sea, Austria,[924] nodules as much as 8 inches in diameter having the composition of those of the deep sea have been dredged from water about 20 meters deep.

STRATIGRAPHIC RELATIONS OF MANGANIFEROUS SEDIMENTS

The stratified rocks with which the bedded manganese oxides are associated show a wide range in lithology: limestones, marls, tuffs of diverse kinds, shales, and sandstones. Many recent bog deposits are as yet uncovered by other sediments.

On the other hand, certain lithologic associations are characteristic of the stratified manganese carbonates. First, they are commonly associated with beds of chert, glauconite, and calcium phosphate. Next, this assemblage of materials is commonly found in the fine-grained sediments, generally where they are transitional from coarse sandstones to massive limestones.

Not only do the manganiferous carbonates contain much more phosphoric acid than most sediments, but distinct beds of these carbonates and phosphatic nodules occur in close proximity, locally thick enough to be mined. This association is noteworthy in Arkansas (Ordovician), Virginia (Oriskany), and Newfoundland (Cambrian). Beds of chert are common near manganiferous carbonates in California (Calaveras and Franciscan formations) and in Oregon, in Minnesota (Cuyuna Range), in Tennessee and Alabama (Fort Payne chert), in western Virginia (Oriskany), in western Arkansas (novaculite), and Newfoundland. Chert is an accessory mineral in the manganese district of Grande County, Utah, and at the base of the Shady dolomite in the Appalachian region. On the other hand, little or no chert is known in the Batesville district (Arkansas), and in the many regions in New York, Pennsylvania, Maryland, Kentucky, Ohio, and South Dakota where manganiferous siderites are known. The associations suggest that the conditions which favor the deposition of beds of phosphate, chert, and glauconite also favor the deposition of manganiferous carbonates. Crystals of barite, apparently formed soon after the sediments were laid down, are common in Arkansas and Newfoundland.

In the second place, a relation between manganiferous carbonates and unconformities is suggested. In western Virginia, the manganiferous zone (carbonate?) overlies the first bed of sandstone of the Oriskany where it unconformably overlies the Helderberg limestone. In the Batesville district, the manganiferous Cason shale unconformably overlies the Fernvale

[923] Buchanan, J. Y., Proc. Roy. Soc. Edinburgh, vol. 8, 1890, p. 19.
[924] Lasch, H., Concretions of manganese ore from Zeller Sea, Tscher. Min. Pet. Mitt. vol. 40, 1930, pp. 294–296.

limestone. In the Blue Ridge region of Virginia, the manganese (carbonate?) bearing beds lie over a Lower Cambrian quartzite. The manganiferous carbonate of Newfoundland occurs in green and red shales that lie 100 feet or more above the basal Cambrian conglomerate. Such relations are recorded in Belgium, Germany, and Austria. On the other hand, the manganiferous iron carbonates of the "Coal Measures" of Pennsylvania, Ohio, and Kentucky and in the Cretaceous rocks of South Dakota have no recognized relation to unconformities.

SITES OF DEPOSITION OF MANGANESE DEPOSITS

If the beds of iron oxide which contain a little manganese (0.10 to 0.20 per cent) such as are found in the Clinton formation, be ignored, there is no convincing evidence that beds of manganese oxide have been deposited in North America during the Paleozoic or Mesozoic eras. Such beds are known in Tertiary and Quaternary rocks in both North America and Europe. The bedded oxides of Brazil and India are Pre-Cambrian. In some places the beds occur in marine strata (Tschiaturi, Nikopol, and Cuba); some are clearly interbedded with terrestrial deposits (Arizona, Nevada, Idaho) and the source of the manganese here appears to be nearby hot springs.

Beds of manganiferous carbonates commonly occur with strata which appear to have a marine origin. The associated strata, however, are not characterized by an abundance of fossils. In age they range from Pre-Cambrian to late Mesozoic. There is a meagre record that carbonates have been deposited in modern bogs. It is not always clear, however, whether the marine carbonates were deposited as such, or whether the contained manganese was deposited as oxides in sediments that contained organic matter and was later reduced and converted to the carbonate before being deeply buried. The beds of pure manganese carbonate (Franciscan formation) were probably deposited as such. On the other hand, most beds of impure carbonates are concretionary and bear evidence of solution and redeposition of the manganese (South Dakota).

Bedded manganiferous carbonates appear to have three types of stratigraphic relations, suggesting as many different environments: (1) In most places, they occur in fine-grained sediments which overlie coarser sediments which in turn rest on a surface of unconformity. Commonly they contain organic matter, fossil remnants, and a little pyrite. Under these conditions they appear to form part of the fine marine sediments laid down near the shores of shallow seas. (2) They occur in the alternating thin beds of coarse and fine sediments and marine limestones such as are common in the "Coal Measures" of the Appalachian region. In such places iron greatly exceeds manganese in the carbonates. (3) They occur in thin-bedded marine cherts with minor shale and limestone. Such carbonates rarely contain iron. They do not appear to be deposited in the midst of thick limestone sections, or in coarse sediments.

PROCESSES LEADING TO THE DEPOSITION OF MANGANESE MINERALS

Although it is known that manganese is rapidly removed from solution during the progress of surface waters from their sources in springs through small streams and rivers to the seas, little is known with assurance concerning the processes by which manganese accumulates in quantities above the average in sediments, either as oxides or carbonates. As in the case of iron, whose chemistry resembles that of manganese, there is no good evidence that excessive accumulations of either element in sedimentary deposits depend in any appreciable degree upon excessive percentages in the rocks that surround the basins in which the waters rise. The average igneous rock[925] contains 5.08 per cent iron and 0.125 per cent manganese, so that the ratio is about 40 to 1. Where there are sediments that are appreciably rich in either of these elements, the ratio of the two is generally widely different. Especially is this true in the case of the oxide-bearing sediments; many iron carbonate zones contain these elements in the ratio of about 40 to 1.[926]

To approach a satisfactory explanation of the accumulation of sedimentary zones of rich manganese oxides or carbonates, it seems necessary to explain (1) the earlier selective elimination of iron from the waters; (2) the selective deposition of the manganese minerals; and (3) the extraordinary local increase in manganese in thin stratigraphic zones. Experiments in the laboratory indicate that under several circumstances iron oxides tend to deposit more readily than, and therefore before, manganese oxides. Probably organisms play a large part in the early precipitation of iron as well as in the later selective precipitation of manganese, although some bacteria will precipitate either which may be available. No adequate explanation has yet been offered to account for such extraordinary local concentrations of pure manganese oxides as are known in the Caucasus region of Russia or of those of manganese carbonate in the Franciscan formation of California. They may be due to organisms but as yet nothing is known concerning the habitat under which the latter thrive.

SECONDARY MANGANESE DEPOSITS

Some of the oxides of manganese, especially pyrolusite and psilomelane, are highly stable in the zone of weathering under most climatic conditions,

[925] Clarke, F. W., Data of geochemistry, Bull. 770, U. S. Geol. Surv., 1929, p. 29.

[926] Penrose, R. A. F., jr., The chemical relations of iron and manganese in sedimentary rocks, Jour. Geol., vol. 1, 1893, pp. 356–370.

but most of the other manganese minerals are readily susceptible of solution. The common sulphides, carbonates, silicates, and phosphates are quickly oxidized under most conditions, especially those minerals in which manganese exists in the lowest state of oxidation. Although the presence of the bicarbonate probably has not been definitely proved in any natural

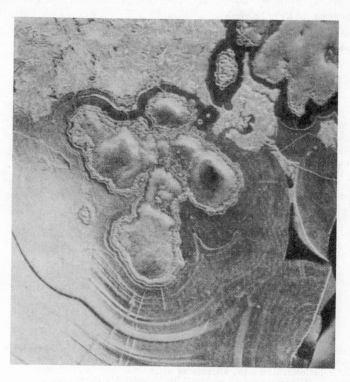

FIG. 71. POLISHED SURFACE OF CONCENTRICALLY BANDED DENSE PSILOMELANE AND ASSOCIATED CRYSTALLINE MANGANITE

Consists of soft structureless cores of pyrolusite or wad surrounded by banded psilomelane, the inner layers of which are highly crinkled and in cavities and crevices of which there is crystalline manganite (shown in upper left corner). From Cook Mine, near Walnut Grove, Alabama. Three times natural size. Photograph contributed by G. W. Stose, U. S. Geol. Surv.

waters, it has generally been assumed that manganese in solution exists in that combination. From recent work on the transport of iron in solution, it would appear that the manganese in waters that carry organic matter exists in the state of the hydrosol, stabilized by organic colloids. The first precipitate from solution seems to be flocculent hydrous oxide similar to wad and, in most places, it has the capacity of replacing a wide range of materials, such as clays, sandstone, shale, limestone, and most igneous rocks. Wad is not as stable as the other oxides, however, and if more manganese is brought in, psilomelane, manganite, and pyrolusite tend to form in the order given. As a consequence, in many places where manganese minerals are found, the surface zone contains coherent pyrolusite largely, which is succeeded in depth by loosely coherent psilomelane and manganite; the deepest zone shows only earthy wad (figs. 71–72). In the zone of oxidation, the least oxidized and most hydrous tend to form first; these give way successively to the most oxidized and least hydrous.

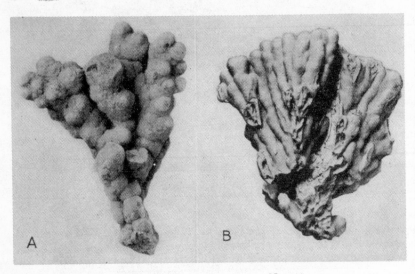

FIG. 72. FORMS OF PSILOMELANE NODULES

1. Irregularly branching, more or less botryoidal cluster. Mount Torry Mine, Virginia, twice natural size. Photograph contributed by G. W. Stose, U. S. Geol. Surv.
2. Radiate cluster of smooth rods, some of which are hollow, Dry Run Mine, Tennessee, natural size. Photograph contributed by G. W. Stose, U. S. Geol. Surv.

As the higher manganese oxides are very stable near the surface, they tend to accumulate on surfaces of planation. Consequently, in many parts of the world, workable bodies of oxides are found on peneplains.[927]

RESEARCH NEEDED

Careful detailed studies of stratigraphic sections containing manganiferous carbonates and oxides are greatly desired and these studies should be

[927] Hewett, D. F., Some manganese deposits in Virginia and Maryland, Bull. 640, U. S. Geol. Surv., 1916, pp. 43–47; Fermor, L. L., op. cit., pp. 370–389; Hummel, K., Über verschiedene Arten von Eisen-manganerzlagerstätten in Deutschland, Zeit. prak. Geol. vol. 35, 1927, pp. 17–21.

supplemented by chemical analyses of carefully selected specimens and by examination of thin sections. Glauconite and phosphatic layers should be sought nearby. Material from mine workings and drill cores remote from the effects of surface oxidation should be sought especially. Thin sections should be examined for traces of organisms which may have caused deposition of the manganese minerals. The work of Dale on the manganese deposits of Newfoundland may be taken as an example of desired investigations. This could have been improved only by closer search for glauconitic material and by a study of the paleogeographic relations of the beds.

There are also needed studies of the changes in manganese content of stream waters from their source to the seas. Further research into the activities of organisms that precipitate manganese is desired.

SEDIMENTARY DEPOSITS OF BARIUM MINERALS

Barium as a sediment is not of great quantitative importance. It is locally present in the waters of some wells, springs, and mines as an important part of the solids in solution. The quantity in surface waters is negligible, and it occurs in sea water in very small amounts. Pipes carrying waters from certain British coal mines are known to have become choked with deposits of which in some instances barium was the chief constituent, samples analyzed yielding 81.37 to 93.35 per cent $BaSO_4$.[928] The barium seems to be carried in solution as the chloride and bicarbonate.

Barium is not a common constituent of modern sediments, and such seems to have been the case through all of geologic time. It is stated to be present in small quantities in most marine deposits; some occurs in the manganese nodules of the deep sea;[929] and small, more or less spherical nodules containing 75 per cent $BaSO_4$ have been dredged from a depth of 675 fathoms[930] off the coast of Ceylon near Colombo. The barium in sediments is usually in the form of barite ($BaSO_4$), but it is also occasionally present as witherite ($BaCO_3$). In many cases the formation seems to have been epigenetic, and it was the conclusion of Greenwood[931] that such is its general origin. Barite occurs as incrustations about springs, as oolites and pisolites, as cement for sands, as concretions and crystal growths, and disseminated in sediments. It is not known to be confined to any particular environment.

Oolitic and pisolitic barite has been obtained from oil wells in the Batson and Saratoga oil fields under conditions which indicated that it had formed

[928] Clowes, F., Deposition of barium sulphate as a cementing material of sandstone, Proc. Roy. Soc. London, vol. 46, 1899, pp. 363–368; vol. 64, 1899, pp. 374–377.

[929] Murray, J., and Hjort, J., Depths of the ocean, 1912, p. 190.

[930] Jones, E. J., On some nodular stones obtained by trawling off Colombo in 675 fathoms of water, Jour. Asiatic Soc., Bengal, vol. 56, 1887, pp. 209–212.

[931] Greenwood, H. W., Proc. Liverpool Geol. Soc., vol. 12, 1920, pp. 335–361.

in the oil in the wells, as some of the particles are stated to have been of much larger diameters than the mesh in the screens of the wells. Some contained a core or nucleus which seemed to be pipe scale.[932]

Barite is deposited about some springs as incrustations, as described by Headden about Doughty Springs, Delta County, Colorado.[933] Similar deposits occur about a brine spring in a mine at Lautenthal in the Hartz Mountains,[934] the barium salts being precipitated by the mingling of the sulphate waters of the mine with the brine waters of the spring. Analyses of the dissolved content of the two waters, expressed as grams per liter, are given in table 86. Analyses of the deposits are given in table 87.

TABLE 86
ANALYSES OF SPRING AND MINE WATERS AT LAUTENTHAL

	SPRING WATER	MINE WATER
$BaCl_2$	0.318	
$SrCl_2$	0.899	
$CaCl_2$	10.120	1.515
$MgCl_2$	4.360	0.023
NaCl	68.168	4.533
KCl	0.450	
$MgSO_4$		0.652
$ZnSO_4$		0.015

TABLE 87
ANALYSES OF THE SPRING DEPOSITS AT LAUTENTHAL

	WHITE STALACTITES	BROWN STALACTITES	MUD	CRUSTS
$BaSO_4$	84.81	83.88	82.30	92.44
$SrSO_4$	12.04	8.64	13.40	4.32

Deposits of barite similar to those of Lauthental occur about certain springs in British coal mines,[935] the deposits also containing strontium. Barite occasionally serves as a cement for sandstones, as in parts of the Chester

[932] Wuestner, H., Pisolitic barite, Jour. Cincinnati Soc. Nat. Hist., vol. 20, 1906, pp. 530–533; Moore, E. S., Oolitic and pisolitic barite from the Saratoga oil field, Texas, Bull. Geol. Soc. Am., vol. 25, 1914, pp. 77–79; Moore, E. S., Additional note on the oolitic and pisolitic barite from the Saratoga oil field, Texas, Science, vol. 46, 1917, p. 342; Suman, J., The Saratoga oil field, Bull. Am. Assoc. Pet. Geol., vol. 9, 1925, p. 275; Barton, D. C., and Mason, S. L., Further note on barite pisolites from the Batson and Saratoga oil fields, Bull. Am. Assoc. Pet. Geol., vol. 9, 1925, pp. 1294–1295.

[933] Headden, W. P., Proc. Colorado Sci. Soc., vol. 81, 1905, p. 1.

[934] Lattermann, G., Jahrb. k. preuss. geol. Landesanstalt, 1888, p. 259.

[935] Dunn, J. T., Chem. News, vol. 35, 1877, p. 140; Richardson, T., Rept. Brit. Assoc., 1863, p. 54.

series of Indiana, the Triassic of England,[936] and this and other sandstones of continental Europe.[937]   Barite concretions are in the nature of crystalline growths, usually occurring in sandstone and to a less extent in sandy clays and shales.   The shapes are irregular, tabular, and rosette, the last not uncommonly known as petrified roses.   Barite in this form has been found in England, Russia, Egypt, Italy, and in the United States in Nebraska, Kansas, Oklahoma, and elsewhere.   Those described by Pogue from Egypt are nodules, rounded tablets, and involved intergrowths, with dimensions ranging to 70 mm. in diameter; they contain about 50 per cent barium sulphate cementing quartz sands.   The Russian occurrences have been described by Samoilov[938] and assigned to an organic origin.

An analysis of a sand barite rosette from Oklahoma is as follows:[939]

SiO_2	45.13
Al_2O_3	0.88
Fe_2O_3	0.96
H_2O	0.31
P_2O_5	Trace
SO_3	17.87
MnO	0.02
BaO	34.25
	99.42

Disks of barite have been described from the Lias of England by Richardson,[940] where they occur irregularly distributed along bedding planes, the disks having maximum diameter of 15 mm. and maximum thickness of 2 mm.   Both upper and lower surfaces were marked by radial furrows.   Each disk was found to be a single crystal flattened parallel to 001.   Somewhat similar disks, known as barite "dollars," occur in Nebraska.[941]

Barite is not uncommon as a crystal in geodes and the cavities of shells, and in these forms has been found in many parts of the world.   It is said to be common in ammonite shells of western Europe.[942]

[936] Clowes, F., op. cit., 1899; Greenwood, H. W., op. cit.; Nichols, H. W., Pub. no. 11, Field Columbian Museum, 1906, p. 31.

[937] Pogue, J. E., On sand-barites from Kharga, Egypt, U. S. Nat. Mus., vol. 38, 1910, pp. 17, et al.   Pogue lists the different localities with references to the papers where the occurrences are described.

[938] Samoilov, J. V., Mineralogical Mag., vol. 18, 1917, p. 87.

[939] Shead, A. C., Notes on barite in Oklahoma with chemical analyses of sand barite rosettes, Univ. Oklahoma Bulletin, n. ser., no. 271, 1923, p. 104.

[940] Richardson, W. A., Petrology of the shales-with-"beef," Quart. Jour. Geol. Soc., vol. 79, 1923, pp. 88–89.

[941] Burnett, J. B., Barite "dollars" from Franklin County, Nebraska, Nebraska Geol. Surv., vol. 7, pt. xv, 1916, pp. 105–111.

[942] Collet, L. W., Diffusion du baryum et strontium dans les terrains sédimentaires, etc., Compt. Rend., Acad. Sci., vol. 141, 1905, pp. 832–834; Martens, J. H. C., Barite and associated minerals in concretions in the Genesee shale, Am. Min., vol. 10, 1925, pp. 102–104.

The causes of precipitation of barite are known in a few cases. The de
posits in the mine spring at Lautenthal are precipitated by reaction of th
sulphate waters of the mine and the barium chloride waters of the spring
In other instances, as in British coal mines, it may have been precipitate
from barium bicarbonate waters consequent to loss of carbon dioxide or
these waters reaching the surface. This barium would be in the form o
witherite. Barite is also precipitated from waters carrying the bicarbonat
of barium at places of contact with gypsum, or oxidizing iron sulphide.[94]
Its occasional presence in limestone may be due to this latter reaction
Schulze[944] and Chevotiev[945] observed granules of barite in the bodies o
certain rhizopod protozoans, and thus it is probable that in some occurrence
barite is of organic origin.

SEDIMENTARY DEPOSITS OF STRONTIUM MINERALS

Strontium as a sedimentary product occurs as celestite ($SrSO_4$) and
strontianite ($SrCO_3$).   Both are rare, but celestite seems to be more common
than strontianite.

Strontium is found in ordinary surface waters as mere traces, but in some
springs it is present in comparatively large quantities, the mine spring a
Lautenthal in the Hartz Mountains[946] containing 0.899 grams of strontium
chloride per liter, nearly three times as great a quantity as the barium chlo
ride present.   Water from a gas well in Washington County, Pennsylvania
contained strontium to the extent of 1.31 per cent of the solid matter i
solution.   It is also found in small quantities in ocean waters.[947]

Strontium is carried in solution as the chloride, sulphate, and bicarbonate
and since the sulphate is more soluble than calcium carbonate, it may be
removed in solution from deposits of the latter.

Strontium is not detectable by ordinary methods in most recent marine
sediments.   Some manganese nodules contain the element in extremely
small quantities.[947]

The element is a deposit of certain springs, where it occurs as incrustations
in the form of celestite and less commonly as strontianite.   Common as
sociates are barite, as at the Lautenthal springs, sulphur, and gypsum.   It
is a characteristic deposit of certain of the springs of Sicily, where it is

[943] Dickson, C. W., School of Mines Quart., vol. 23, 1906, p. 366.

[944] Schulze, F. E., Wissenschaftliche Ergebnisse der deutschen Tiefsee-expedition auf
d. Dampfer "Valdivia," vol. 11, 1905, L. 1, p. 14.

[945] Referred to by Samoilov, op. cit., The original article is in Russian and was published in Petrograd in 1910.

[946] Lattermann, G., Jahrb. k. preuss. geol. Landesanstalt, 1888, p. 259.

[947] Clarke, F. W., Data of geochemistry, Bull. 770, U. S. Geol. Surv., 1924, pp. 124,
187, 589.

associated with sulphur and gypsum, the original source of the strontium being thought to be subterranean molten rock.

Both celestite and strontianite occur as disseminated crystals in other rocks and in cavities of various kinds. Crystals of celestite are disseminated through dolomite in Monroe County, Michigan, parts of the upper part of the dolomite containing 14 per cent celestite. Cavities in the lower part of the same rock contain celestite and considerable quantities of sulphur.[948] In Schoharie County, New York, celestite occurs in limestone in the form of pockets and thin layers, and in Oneida County of the same state both celestite and strontianite are found in geodes of the Clinton limestone, the latter in the outer part and the former within. The two minerals exist together in the rocks of Jefferson County, New York, and celestite is abundantly disseminated through a dolomitic limestone near Syracuse, New York.[949] A famous locality for celestite is Put-in Bay, Lake Erie, where a cave was found in 1897 whose ceiling, walls, and floor were covered with celestite crystals, and celestite is said to have been present for 22 feet beneath the floor.[949] Celestite is present in the Glen Rose limestone near Austin, Texas, in the form of nodules and pockets, with strontianite, epsomite, calcite, and aragonite as associated minerals. Some of the celestite nodules are stated to have weighed as much as 100 pounds. Celestite occurs at Cedar Cliff, Mineral County, West Virginia, filling cavities a yard in diameter and 3 to 7 inches high,[950] and as a cement for sands it is found in the Oriskany sandstone of western New York.[951] Strontianite deposits near Barstow, California, are in the form of beds and lenses interstratified with limestones and shales of lacustrine origin. The general relations suggest contemporaneous deposition with the associated sediments, but the detailed structures and textures of the strontianite seem best interpreted as due to replacement of limestone beds by cold (?) meteoric waters.[952] An extremely interesting occurrence of celestite lies on the south margin of the Avawatz Mountains in San Bernardino County, California, where the celestite with a maximum thickness of 75 to 80 feet is interstratified with beds of salt, gypsum, and clay of lacustrine deposition. The celestite contains

[948] Kraus, E. H., and Hunt, W. F., The occurrence of sulphur and celestite at Maybee, Michigan, Am. Jour. Sci., 4th ser., vol. 21, 1906, p. 237 et al.

[949] Kraus, E. H., The occurrence of celestite near Syracuse, New York, and its relation to the vermicular limestones of the Salina epoch, Am. Jour. Sci., vol. 18, 1904, pp. 30–39; Occurrence and distribution of celestite-bearing rocks, Ibid., vol. 19, 1905, pp. 286–293.

[950] Williams, G. H., Celestite from Mineral County, West Virginia, Am. Jour. Sci., vol. 39, 1890, pp. 183–188.

[951] Stone, M. H., An occurrence of Oriskany sandstone with celestite cement, Am. Jour. Sci., vol. 16, 1928, pp. 446–450.

[952] Knopf, A., Strontianite deposits near Barstow, California, Bull. 660, U. S. Geol. Surv., 1918, pp. 257–264.

more or less clastic material, gypsum, and iron and manganese oxides. Contemporaneity with the associated sediments is suggested, but replacement of carbonate beds is possible.[953] Celestite and barite occur together in a bituminous limestone of Transylvania.[954] The nummulitic limestone of Egypt contains celestite crystals which in some instances enclose fossils and in others fill the interiors of fossil shells.[955] This deposit has been considered by some as syngenetic with the associated sediments; others have held that the strontium was leached from overlying strata by ground water.[956]

Most of the strontium deposits which have been described seem to be of epigenetic origin, and only in the cases of deposition from spring waters is contemporaneity established. In a few instances doubt exists. The extreme rarity of strontium in solution renders it probable that contemporaneous deposits are rare and local.

Strontium in solution in natural waters is acquired from the rocks through which the waters circulate. Waters circulating through limestones would extract any strontium sulphate, leaving the calcium carbonate because of its greater relative insolubility. Precipitation might be accomplished where these waters reached cavities or the surface, or met other waters of differing content, leading to reaction and precipitation. This would take place where strontium chloride waters mingled with those containing sulphates. The bicarbonate of strontium is probably precipitated by loss of carbon dioxide. It is possible that some strontium is precipitated through the agency of life, as it has been detected in the shells of certain mollusks and corals,[957] and it is known to be present in the ash of some seaweeds.[958] An interesting bit of information in this respect is the brilliant discovery of Butschli that the shell of the radiolarian *Podactinelius* and the shells of the acantharian radiolarians, in general, are almost wholly composed of strontium sulphate.[959] Samoilov suggested an organic origin for the celestite which is stated to have extensive distribution in Turkestan.[960]

[953] Phalen, W. C., Celestite deposits in California and Arizona, Bull. 540, U. S. Geol. Surv., 1904, pp. 526–531.

[954] Koch, A., Neue Fundorte des Cölestin in Siebenbürgen, Tschermak's Min. pet. Mitth., vol. 4, 1877, pp. 317–320; Ein neues Cölestin- und Barytvorkommen in den Siebenbürgen, Ibid., vol. 9, 1888, pp. 416–422.

[955] Bauermann, M., and Foster, C., On the occurrence of celestite in the nummulitic limestone of Egypt, Proc. Geol. Soc. London, vol. 25, 1868, pp. 40–44.

[956] Andrée, K., Über den Cölestin in Mokattamkalk von Egypten, etc., Neues Jahrb. f. Min. etc., Beil.-Bd. 37, 1914, pp. 374–386. This paper reviews many of the then known occurrences of celestite, pp. 343–374.

[957] Vogel, O., Zeits. anorg. Chem,. vol. 5, 1894, p. 55.

[958] Dieulafait, L., Compt. Rend., Acad. Sci., Paris, vol. 84, 1877, p. 1303.

[959] Butschli, O., Chemische Natur der Skelettsubstance des Podactinelius und der Acantharia überhaupt, Naturwiss. Wochenschr., vol. 6, 1907, pp. 429–430. From Deutsch. Südpol. Exped., Bd. 9, Heft 4.

[960] Samoilov, J. V., Mineralogical Mag., vol. 18, 1917, pp. 87–98.

SEDIMENTARY DEPOSITS OF SULPHUR

Native sulphur of sedimentary origin is not uncommon in recent and ancient sediments, usually occurring as isolated particles, but sometimes present as beds, lenses, and bodies of various form. Many deposits of sulphur seem to be related to igneous processes, and the origin of some of the largest occurrences is unknown. Consideration is given only to those occurrences for which the evidence of sedimentary origin is strong.

The common associates of sulphur of sedimentary origin are gypsum, lime carbonate, and organic matter, the last usually in the form of black shale. It is precipitated from sulphates and hydrogen sulphide in solution, and from colloidal sulphur which is present in water under certain conditions; and it also forms one of the decomposition products of metallic sulphides.

ENVIRONMENTS AND AGENTS OF DEPOSITION OF NATIVE SULPHUR

Native sulphur seems to form and be deposited in four sedimentary environments: (1) the surface and the zone of weathering, through decomposition of metallic sulphides; (2) about springs; (3) in bodies or parts of bodies of water low in oxygen, so that reducing conditions and anaërobic bacteria prevail; and (4) in lakes into whose waters there are being brought volcanic gases containing sulphur.

The decomposition of metallic sulphides may yield sulphur as powdery efflorescences on the surface and as crystals in cracks and cavities. The latter may perhaps be exemplified by the native sulphur in some Michigan geodes. The former is excellently shown in south central Kansas over some portions of the exposed surfaces of the Cheyenne sandstones and the Kiowa shales, the two formations containing much pyrite from whose decomposition the sulphur is derived. The possibilities of sulphur of this environment assuming significant dimensions are rather limited.

Native sulphur, commonly associated with gypsum, calcite, and aragonite, is not uncommon about springs whose waters contain hydrogen sulphide, sulphates, and colloidal sulphur. The sulphates are supposed to be reduced by bacteria to hydrogen sulphide, and this oxidizes to water and sulphur. Sulphur may be carried as a colloid in waters which contain sulphur, sulphuric acid, and sodium sulphate in the relations of S 2.79–2.60, H_2SO_4 6.43–7.00, and $NaSO_4$ 3.75–3.92 per cent. If there are changes in the concentration of the salt, sulphur is precipitated.[961] It seems probable that deposits of this environment may be of the same order of magnitude as the spring deposits of other substances.

In the Trans-Pecos region of Texas are deposits of sulphur in Permian

---

[961] Hunt, W. F., The sulphur deposits of Sicily, Econ. Geol., vol. 10, 1915, pp. 545–546.

and Upper Carboniferous strata associated with gypsum and waters containing hydrogen sulphide of undetermined source. The sulphur and gypsum deposits are also associated with organic matter and limestones, and there are indications that some of the gypsum has been formed through alteration of limestones. The sulphur occurs as thin, amorphous films on gypsum and disseminated through it, one analysis by Steiger showing 18.36 per cent free sulphur. The fact that the sulphur is associated with gypsum and organic matter suggests a genetic relationship. Perhaps the sulphur was formed by reduction of gypsum,[962] and it is probable that sulphur is being deposited at the present time from the hydrogen sulphide escaping from the waters of springs in the same region.

Bodies of water deficient in oxygen below the surface become rich in hydrogen sulphide, which in some waters is so great as to make them unfit for marine organisms, as is the case in the Black Sea, which is habitable

TABLE 88

DEPTH	H_2S PER 100 LITERS
meters	*cc.*
213	0.33
427	2.22
2026	5.55
2528	6.55

to only 7 per cent of the depth.[963]   The quantity increases with depth as shown by table 88.[964]

The hydrogen sulphide occurring under these conditions is thought to be in part a decomposition product of the anaërobic bacterial decay of organic matter and in part a product of bacterial reduction of sulphates in solution. Oxidation of the hydrogen sulphide, for which bacteria are also probably in part responsible, leads to precipitation of sulphur. It is possible that sulphur deposits of this origin may attain significant proportions, but it is not known that such are accumulating to any extent at the present time.

It has been found that free sulphur is a common constituent of most samples of marine muds, the quantities ranging from 22 to 104 parts per

[962] Smith, E. A., Notes on native sulphur in Texas, Science, vol. 3, 1896, pp. 657–659; Skeats, E. M., Bull. 2, Univ. Texas Mineral Surv., 1902, pp. 29–42; Richardson, C. B., Bull. 9, Ibid., 1904, pp. 68–71.

[963] Hunt, W. F., op. cit., p. 569.

[964] Lebedinzeff, A., Travaux de la Société des Naturalistes à Odessa, vol. 16, 1891, Ref. by Hunt, W. F., op. cit., p. 569; also by Phalen, W. C., after Stutzer, O., The origin of sulphur deposits, Econ. Geol., vol. 7, 1912, p. 740.

00,000. Microscopical examination made of samples from Florida Bay, deposited in water less than a meter deep, showed minute grains of a yellow waxy substance having the properties of sulphur.[965] As most marine sediments are deposited under reducing conditions, it seems probable that bacterial activity in some way is connected with the occurrence of free sulphur in such sediments.

Sulphur is at present being deposited in certain lakes of some volcanic regions of Japan. The sulphur gases escape through crevices on the lake bottoms, and on contact with the water sulphur is deposited in the form of variously shaped grains of 0.2 to 3 mm. diameter. The grains are hollow and have kidney, fig, hemispherical, and spindle shapes. Although there are some features connected with the origin of this sulphur which are not sedimentary, its final deposition takes place through sedimentary processes.[966]

Sulphur is associated with some of the salt domes which are found in certain parts of the world. It is possible that this sulphur is the result of sedimentary processes, but the formation occurred at considerable depths and at temperatures probably higher than those normal to the surface.

SULPHUR DEPOSITS IN THE GEOLOGIC COLUMN

Small occurrences of native sulphur are known in the geologic column, particularly in the later systems. Large deposits are not uncommon in Tertiary rocks, but opinion is greatly divided with respect to the origin of many of these. For this reason the present discussion is limited to that occurrence which has perhaps been the most extensively investigated, and with respect to which the conclusion of a sedimentary origin has been reached by several students.

The most extensive deposits of sulphur for which a sedimentary origin seems probable are those of south central Sicily. Formerly these were considered of volcanic origin, but this view appears to have been abandoned with the working out of the geologic relationships.[967] These sulphur beds are interstratified with bituminous clays, gypsum, and limestone of Miocene and perhaps of lower Pliocene age, some of the associated strata being marine. The deposits are disconnected, and each appears to have a basin-like form. They are commonly underlain by tripoli formed of the tests of radiolaria

[965] Trask, P. D., and Wu, C. C., Free sulfur in recent sediments, Abstract, Bull. Geol. Soc. Am., vol. 41, 1930, pp. 89–90; Bull. Am. Assoc. Pet. Geol., vol. 14, 1930, pp. 1462–1463.

[966] Oinonye, Y. A., A peculiar process of sulphur deposition, Jour. Geol., vol. 24, 1916, pp. 806–808.

[967] Data relating to the sulphur deposits of Sicily have been largely derived from Hunt, W. F., op. cit., pp. 543–579; Stutzer, O., Transl. by Phalen, W. C., op. cit., pp. 732–743; and Sagui, C. L., The sulphur mines of Sicily, Econ. Geol., vol. 18, 1923, pp. 278–287.

and skeletal matter of sponges, and overlain by massive gypsum.   Crystals of celestite, aragonite, gypsum, and other minerals are associated with the sulphur.   The sulphur-bearing beds average 3 to 4 meters in thickness and range from 1 to 30 meters.   The character of the sequence is shown in the following section:[968]

	Meters
Bituminous shales	40
Sulphur-bearing layer	6
Bituminous shale	½
Sulphur-bearing layer	5
Bituminous shale	½
Sulphur-bearing layer	6
Tripoli and siliceous limestone	12–20

The sulphur-bearing layers consist of sulphur interlaminated with marly clay or limestone and gypsum.   Some bituminous matter is also present. The sulphur layers are less than an inch thick, whereas the separating units are about twice as thick.   Sulphur layers are known to extend distances exceeding 650 feet.[969]   Some are cross-laminated, and in one exposure a sulphur-bearing layer is unconformably overlain by shale, showing contemporaneous erosion.

The geologic relationships suggest that deposition took place in lagoons more or less disconnected with each other and the sea, the latter effecting entrance at times as indicated by the occurrence of marine fossils in some of the beds.   The gypsum is thought to have been deposited during times of high salinity brought about by excess of evaporation in the lagoons over inflow either from sea or land, such high salinity eliminating the sulphate-reducing bacteria held responsible for the formation of the sulphur.   It is known that the activities of some sulphate-reducing bacteria cease under such conditions, that of *Spirillum desulfuricum* ceasing when the concentration reaches 3 per cent and that of *Microspira æstuarii* almost ceasing when the concentration rises above 6 per cent.[970]   The bacteria reduce sulphates to sulphides, with hydrogen sulphide as an ultimate product.   This rises toward the surface and may oxidize to water and sulphur, bacteria assisting in, and perhaps being essential for, such oxidation.   The equations supposed to express the various reactions are as follows:

(1) $CaSO_4 + 2\ C$ (living micro-organisms) $= CaS + 2CO_2$
(2) $2CaS + 2H_2O = Ca(OH)_2 + Ca(SH)_2$
(3) $Ca(OH)_2 + Ca(SH)_2 + 2CO_2 = 2CaCO_3 + 2H_2S$
(4) $H_2S + O = H_2O + S.$

[968] Hunt, W. F., op. cit., p. 554.
[969] Stutzer, O., in Phalen, W. C., op. cit., pp. 735–736.
[970] Hunt, W. F., op. cit., p. 3.

The calcium hydrosulphide, coming in contact with sulphur settling from above, might react therewith to form a calcium polysulphide and liberate hydrogen sulphide as expressed in equation (5).[971] As this reaction is reversible, any hydrogen sulphide coming in contact with the polysulphide would precipitate free sulphur, so that at times a larger precipitation than ordinary might take place.

(5) $$Ca(SH)_2 + 4S = CaS_5 + H_2S$$

Other living bacteria which are concerned in processes like the above are *Proteus vulgaris, Bacterium mycoides, B. hydrosulfureum,* and *Vibrio hydrosulfureus.*[972]

The history of the Sicilian sulphur deposits is thought to have been somewhat as follows: During times of great bacterial activity there was large precipitation of pure sulphur. This precipitation was interrupted from time to time by the deposition of mud and calcium carbonate. Times of great evaporation or decreases in the quantities of water supplied to the basins produced concentration too high for bacterial activity, and at these times the products of concentration were deposited. Entrance of the sea brought in marine sediments.

Sagui[973] considers that the hydrogen sulphide was derived from an intrusion of basaltic lava from which it was washed by underground water and brought to the basins of deposition in springs. The gypsum is thought to have developed as a consequence of reactions between calcium carbonate, water, and sulphur.

SEDIMENTARY FELDSPAR

Feldspar occurs in sediments as fragments derived from pre-existing rocks and apparently as an original development. The former occurrences are well known and have been considered to some extent in connection with arkose, and it of course follows that detrital feldspar may be found in any variety of sedimentary rock. Feldspar as an authigenic mineral, however, is not so well known and has not received a great deal of consideration in America, the first American paper thereon having been published in 1917.[974] The literature was partly summarized in that paper, and a more complete summary with an excellent bibliography was published by Spencer in 1925.[975]

[971] Divers, E., and Shimidzu, T., Jour. Am. Chem. Soc., vol. 45, 1884, p. 283.

[972] Harder, E. C., Iron-depositing bacteria and their geologic relations, Prof. Paper 113, U. S. Geol. Surv., 1919, pp. 41–42.

[973] Sagui, C. L., op. cit., pp. 281–282.

[974] Daly, R. A., Low temperature formation of alkaline feldspars in limestones, Proc. Nat. Acad. Sci., vol. 3, 1917, pp. 659–665.

[975] Spencer, E., Albite and other authigenic minerals in limestone from Bengal, Mineralogical Mag., vol. 20, 1925, pp. 365–381.

Feldspar which bears all the evidence of being authigenic and a sedimentary product seems to be largely confined to calcareous sediments, but an occurrence in Triassic sandstones in northeast Ireland has been described by Reynolds,[976] and Van Hise cites occurrences in the Keweenawan sandstones of the Lake Superior region. The feldspar in most instances is albite, but in one instance the minerals were determined as microcline,[977] and in two instances as orthoclase.[978] The crystals are invariably small and mostly microscopic, but those studied by Spencer from the Cuddapah limestones of Bengal ranged to 10 mm. long. Others studied by Spezia[979] from a foraminiferal limestone of Argentea, Italy, ranged to 3 mm. long, those described by Foullon[980] from Eocene limestone of the Island of Rhodes ranged to the same length, and Issel[981] has described albite tablets from Eocene rocks of Pavia up to 11 mm. long. He considered them of hydrothermal origin, but it may be that such is not the case.

Feldspar of sedimentary origin has been reported from the Pre-Cambrian along the International Boundary between Montana and Alberta[982] and of the Lake Superior region, the Cuddapah (Pre-Cambrian?) system of India,[983] the Ordovician of New York,[984] the Carboniferous limestone near Moscow,[985] and Triassic, Jurassic, and Cretaceous rocks of various parts of Europe. It is not thought essential to describe all occurrences, but detail deemed sufficient for appreciations of characteristics and differences will be given.

The feldspar from the Pre-Cambrian of the International Boundary region

[976] Reynolds, D. L., Some new occurrences of authigenic feldspar, Geol. Mag., vol. 66, 1929, pp. 390–399.

[977] Grandjean, F., Propriétés optiques et genèse du feldspath néogène des sediments du bassin de Paris, Compt. Rend. Acad. Sci. Paris, vol. 148, 1909, pp. 723–725; Le feldspath néogène des terrains sédimentaires non métamorphiques, Bull. Soc. Franç. Min., vol. 32, 1909, pp. 103–133; Deuxième note sur le feldspath néogène des terrains sédimentaires non métamorphiques, Bull. Soc. Franç. Min., vol. 33, 1910, pp. 92–97.

[978] Daly, R. A., Mem. 38, Geol. Surv. Canada, 1912, pp. 50; op. cit., pp. 662–663; Cayeux, L., Existence de nombreux cristaux de feldspath orthose dans la craie du bassin de Paris. Preuves de leur genèse in situ, Compt. Rend. Acad. Sci. Paris, vol. 120, 1895, pp. 1068–1071.

[979] Spezia, G., Sul calcare albitifero dell' Argentea (Cuneo), Atti R. Accad. Sci. Torino, vol. 15, 1880, pp. 785–788.

[980] Foullon, H. B., Über Gesteine und Minerale von der Insel Rhodus, Sitzb. Akad. Wiss., Wien, Math.-Naturw. Cl., vol. 100, Abt. 1, 1891, pp. 144–176.

[981] Issel, A., Radiolaires fossiles contenues dans les cristaux d'albite, Compt. Rend. Acad. Sci. Paris, vol. 110, 1900, pp. 420–424; Il calcifira fossilifero di Rovegno in val de Trebbia, Ann. Mus. Civ. Storia Nat. Genova, vol. 9, 1890, pp. 91–119.

[982] Daly, R. A., op. cit., 1912.

[983] Spencer, E., op. cit.

[984] Singewald, J. T., jr. and Milton, C., Authigenic feldspar in limestone at Glen Falls, New York, Abstract, Bull. Geol. Soc. Am., vol. 40, 1929, p. 94.

[985] Grandjean, F., op. cit., 1909, 1910.

was described by Daly as occurring in the unmetamorphosed Waterton dolomite, of which some laminæ are filled with well-formed crystals of glass-clear orthoclase with diameters of 0.01 to 0.05 mm., and others contain clumps and isolated crystals of orthoclase. Some crystals of albite also seem to be present. A remarkable fact of this occurrence is that the feldspars in places compose 40 per cent of the rock. Van Hise[986] has described Keweenawan sandstones of the Lake Superior region whose cementation is said to be due largely to enlargement of fragments of both orthoclase and plagioclase, the later-deposited feldspar being in optical continuity with that of the old particles. The feldspars of the Cuddapah system described by Spencer[987] are of albite and occur in zones in a massive limestone (not dolomite), the boundaries of the zones not being very definite, but the zones extending vertically through 150 feet and traced along the strike for about three-fourths of a mile. The crystals usually are thinly scattered through the zones, but occasionally are crowded together. Solution of the limestone shows associated minerals to be quartz, mica, pyrite, tourmaline, rutile, sphene, zircon, and garnet, and it is suggested that some of the quartz, mica, tourmaline,[988] sphene, and rutile may be authigenic; the pyrite is quite certainly such. The albite crystals show Carlsbad twinning and have certain peculiarities not explained by that manner of twinning. Crystals range in dimensions to a little over a centimeter in their greatest length, but the cleanest and best developed usually are 1 to 2 mm. long, with the thickness ranging from about one-tenth to one-fifth of the length. Two analyses of crystals gave:

	(1) Per cent	(2) Per cent
SiO_2	66.95	67.10
Al_2O_3	19.72	19.95
Fe_2O_3	0.50	0.55
CaO	0.66	0.50
MgO	0.88	0.70
K_2O	0.52	0.60
Na_2O	9.95	10.30
Ignition	0.63	0.85
	99.81	100.55

Spencer considers that the perfection of the feldspar crystals precludes their being detrital, and she rejects the possibility of an anamorphic origin

[986] Van Hise, C. R., Enlargement of feldspar fragments in certain Keweenawan sandstones, Bull. 8, U. S. Geol. Surv., 1884, pp. 44–47.

[987] Spencer, E., op. cit., 1925.

[988] Wichmann, H., had previously reported authigenic tourmaline in sandstones, Neues Jahrb. f. Min., vol. 2, 1880, p. 294.

for them. The feldspar from the Ordovician limestones of New York was found in the insoluble residue of the limestones of which it was an abundant constituent. The crystals are euhedral. The sedimentary feldspars of the Triassic, Jurassic, and Cretaceous of the European Alpine region have been described by Heim,[989] Trumpy,[990] Kaufmann,[991] Lory,[992] Rose,[993] Drian,[994] de Stefani,[995] Spezia,[996] Lacroix,[997] Issel,[998] Grandjean, de Lapparent,[999] and others. Essentially all of these occurrences are in unanamorphosed, fine-grained, fossiliferous limestones. The feldspars are mostly albite, and in the case described by Heim small crystals of ankerite were also found. Pyrite and doubly terminating quartz crystals are associated. Kaufmann observed that the feldspars occur rather abundantly in nodular and geodic concretions. The crystals described by the above students are small but euhedral, with maximum lengths of about 0.2 mm., but commonly ranging between 0.05 and 0.08 mm. The feldspar crystals in the Triassic sandstones of northeast Ireland[1000] are stated not to resemble exactly any species recorded from igneous rock. Their optical properties are stated to be those of an orthoclase, but an excess of potash over soda allies them to microcline. Their specific gravity, 2.54, is lower than that recorded for any feldspar. Reynolds also described authigenic feldspar from the Keuper marl, the Dolomitic Conglomerate (base of Keuper), and the Magnesian Limestone (Permian), and Cayeux[1001] has described it from the Chalk of the Paris

[989] Heim, A., Beitrag geol. Karte Schweiz, vol. 20, 1916, pp. 514–567.

[990] Trumpy, D., Beitrag geol. Karte Schweiz, vol. 46, 1916, pp. 83–108.

[991] Kaufmann, F. J., Beitrag geol. Karte Schweiz, vol. 24, 1886, pp. 581–584.

[992] Lory, C., Bull. Soc. Géol. France, vol. 18, 1861, pp. 806–826; Ibid., vol. 23, 1866, pp. 480–497; Rev. Soc. Savantes, Sci. Math. Phys. Nat., Genève, vol. 2, 1868, pp. 235–239; Arch. Sci. Phys. Nat., Genève, vol. 16, 1886, pp. 237–239; Compt. Rend. Acad. Sci. Paris, vol. 105, 1887, pp. 99–101; Compt. Rend. Congr. Géol. Intern., 1891, pp. 86–103; Bull. Soc. Statist. Isère, vol. 14, 1890, p. 228.

[993] Rose, G., Über die Krystallform des Albits von dem Roc-tourne und des Albits in Allgemeinen, Pogg. Ann. Phys. Chem., vol. 125, 1865, pp. 457–468.

[994] Drian, A., Notice sur les cristaux d'albite renfermés dans les calcaires magnésiens des environs de Modane, Bull. Soc. Géol. France, vol. 18, 1861, pp. 804–805.

[995] de Stefani, C., Atti. Soc. Toscana Sci. Nat. Pisa, Proc. Verb., vol. 2, 1879, pp. 202–206.

[996] Spezia, G., op. cit.

[997] Lacroix, A., Bull. Soc. Franç. Min., vol. 11, 1888, pp. 70–71; Minéralogie de la France, vol. 2, 1896, pp. 158–168.

[998] Issel, A., op. cit.

[999] de Lapparent, J., Sur les cristaux de feldspaths développés dans les calcaires du Crétacé supérieur pyrénéen, Compt. Rend. Acad. Sci. Paris, vol. 167, 1918, pp. 784–786; Cristaux de feldspath et de quartz dans les calcaires du Trias moyen d'Alsace et de Lorraine, Ibid., vol. 71, 1920, pp. 862–865.

[1000] Reynolds, D. L., op. cit.

[1001] Cayeux, L., op. cit.

Basin, the feldspar being considered orthoclase. Grandjean[1002] also studied the authigenic feldspars of the Chalk and concluded they were microcline.

Tertiary authigenic feldspars have been described by Kaufmann[1003] and Termier[1004] from the Tertiary of the Alpine region and from the Eocene of the Island of Rhodes by Foullon.[1005] All of these occurrences are in limestones, and the crystals from the Paris Basin are small, averaging 0.04 to 0.05 mm. long. The crystals seem to be well formed and always occur singly. In the Island of Rhodes occurrence the enclosing limestone is fine-grained to dense, and the well formed crystals have maximum lengths of 2.5 to 3 mm. These crystals, first described in 1881, represent the earliest finds of macroscopic authigenic sedimentary feldspars.

There is general agreement among most of the students concerned that the feldspars described developed in the sediments, the evidence therefor being the euhedral shapes, the absence of any evidence of transportation, the impossibility of reference to anamorphism, and the relations to fossils. Thus, Lory found microscopic orthoclase within an ammonite shell; Drian, Spezia, and Spencer described carbonaceous matter scattered through albite crystals; and Issel found radiolaria enclosed within them (this last occurrence may be hydrothermal).

The conditions and processes of origin of the sedimentary feldspars are not known, but several observations which may bear on the environment of origin have been made. Cayeux noted that the feldspars of the Chalk of the Paris Basin do not occur in the same beds with glauconite; Spencer pointed out that the authigenic feldspars of the Cuddapah system are confined to the calcite limestones and are not found in the associated dolomite limestones; Lory directed attention to the common occurrence of doubly terminated quartz, pyrite, and bituminous matter in association with orthoclase, and idiomorphic quartz and mica with albite; Grandjean stated that limestones of lacustrine origin do not seem to contain authigenic feldspar; and de Lapparent found that the authigenic feldspars of the Flysch formation of the Alps were limited to the lower zone in limestones consisting of small granules, the granules being ascribed in part to algæ of the *Girvanella* type, suggesting that algæ may in some way be connected with feldspar formation.[1006] Other limestones of the Flysch in which algæ are not obvious do not seem to contain feldspar. To what extent the relationships are

---

[1002] Grandjean, F., op. cit.

[1003] Kaufmann, F.J., op. cit., p. 583.

[1004] Termier, P. cited by Daly, Proc. Nat. Acad. Sci., vol. 3, 1917, p. 665.

[1005] Foullon, H. B., op. cit.

[1006] de Lapparent, J., De l'elaboration de silice et de calcaires siliceux par les algues du groupe de Girvanella, Compt. Rend. Acad. Sci. Paris, vol. 167, 1918, pp. 999–1001.

causal is very uncertain. The connection with the absence of glauconit
may have some significance, but what it is cannot be stated. The occur
rence in the limestones but not the dolomites of the Cuddapah system ca
hardly have any significance, as feldspars are found in dolomites elsewhere
The absence of authigenic feldspars in lacustrine sediments suggests tha
the salts in solution in sea water may be essential for the formation. If tha
is the case, the presence or absence of this mineral would be a valuable cri
terion for differentiation of deposits of fresh and salt water. Whether an
weight can be placed on de Lapparent's suggestion is doubtful. That th
feldspar crystals in calcareous sediments grew in calcareous muds seem
certain. Foullon thought that the albite studied by him had grown during
slow deposition of the enclosing calcareous sediments, and Grandjean though
the crystals ceased to form after burial. On the other hand, Reynold
suggests that they may be formed by ground water long after consolidatio
of the enclosing rock. In most occurrences it is impossible that the rock
were ever subjected to a high temperature. Doelter has assumed that the
temperature of formation may have been as great as 100°C.[1007] (212°F.)
Daly suggests that it may have been as low as 70°C.[1008] (158°F.). Each o
these figures seems too high, and for some of the occurrences much lowe
temperatures must be assumed. The lowest temperature at which feldspar has been artificially formed is 300°C.[1009]

The facts that authigenic feldspars are usually associated with marine
limestones and that these limestones show evidence of originally having
contained much organic matter suggest that lime, salt water, and organic
matter are concerned in the formation.

MINERAL PRODUCTS OF EXTRA-TERRESTRIAL ORIGIN[1010]

In the deposits of the deeper waters of the sea, and very rarely in shallow-
water sediments, there occur particles which have been referred to extra-
terrestrial origin. A quart of red clay will yield from 20 to 30 small black
magnetic spherules which may or may not have metallic nuclei, and 5 or 6
brown spherules with crystalline structure. An equal quantity of globigerina ooze very rarely contains any of these substances, the more common
occurrence in red clays probably arising from slowness of accumulation of
these sediments.

The black magnetic spherules rarely exceed 0.2 mm. in diameter and have

[1007] Doelter, C., Handbuch der Mineralchemie, Dresden, Bd. 2, 2. Hälfte, 1915, p. 556.

[1008] Daly, R. A., op. cit., 1917, p. 664.

[1009] Chrustschoff, K., Compt. Rend. Acad. Sci., Paris, vol. 104, 1887, p. 602.

[1010] Murray, J. and Renard, A. F., Deep sea deposits, Challenger Rept., 1891, pp. 327–336.

exteriors composed of magnetite, and nuclei mostly of native iron or an iron alloy. Some are without nuclei. The surfaces are very smooth. The brown spherules, which resemble the chondrite variety of meteorite, contain silicon, have a color range from yellowish to brown, and possess a pronounced metallic luster said to be due to a finely laminated structure. The surfaces are striated and not smooth as in the black spherules. These brown spherules are also somewhat larger than the black ones, an average diameter being about 0.5 mm.

Perhaps the particles of moissonite recently identified in the rocks of the southern Mid-continent regions have their origins connected with the falls of meteorites.[1011]

ZEOLITES OF SEDIMENTARY ORIGIN

Only three zeolites: phillipsite, analcite, and apophyllite, occur in significant quantities as sediments. The first has rather wide distribution in certain marine deposits, and the other two are present in considerable abundance in parts of the Green River shales of Utah, Wyoming, and Colorado.

Phillipsite is a hydrous silicate of potassium and calcium, the formula in some cases (Dana) being $(K_2 \cdot Ca)Al_2Si_4O_{12} \cdot 4\frac{1}{2}H_2O$. It is found as free and isolated crystals in purely pelagic clays and oozes wherein it originates as a product of diagenesis. According to Murray and Renard,[1012] the decomposition of volcanic materials is responsible for its production.

Phillipsite has been found over extensive areas in sediments of the deep waters of the central parts of the Pacific and Indian oceans. The crystals are microscopic, as shown by the fact that certain arenaceous foraminifera use them in their tests. Some red clays are said to consist of 20 to 30 per cent crystals of phillipsite. A chemical analysis of phillipsite is as follows:

	Per cent
SiO_2	47.60
Al_2O_3	17.09
Fe_2O_3	5.92
MnO	0.43
CaO	3.20
MgO	1.24
K_2O	4.81
Na_2O	4.08
H_2O	9.15
Loss, organic matter	7.59
	101.11

[1011] Ohrenschall, R. D. and Milton, C., The occurrence of moissonite in sediments, Jour. Sed. Pet., vol. 1, 1931, pp. 96–99.

[1012] Murray, J., and Renard, A. F., Deep sea deposits, Challenger Rept., 1891, pp. 400–411.

Analcite has been described by Bradley[1013] from the Green River shales, wherein it occurs as thin, more or less persistent beds resembling sandstones, the individual particles consisting almost wholly of euhedral crystals with dimensions ranging to nearly 2 mm., all the crystals being clouded with dust-like inclusions. The matrix and analcite particle ratios vary from bed to bed, and in those places where the matrix is large the rock has a tuffaceous appearance and consists of chalcedony in which are embedded particles of minerals, strongly suggesting that the entire deposit originally was a volcanic ash. A few crystals of apophyllite, another zeolite, were seen. Analcite and apophyllite also occur as isolated crystals in many of the oil shale beds of the Green River formation, some beds consisting of 16 per cent by weight of analcite and others in excess of 1 per cent of apophyllite. Various volcanic minerals and a little volcanic glass are associated. Bradley explains the Green River zeolites as having formed in place on the bottom of the waters of deposition as a consequence of reactions between various salts dissolved in the waters and the dissolution products of falling volcanic ash. Strangely, no bentonite seems to be associated.

Zeolites have been described by Lacroix[1014] as resulting from the decomposition of granite and other rocks, chabasite, stilbite, and laumontite thus having formed under conditions of low temperature; and it has also been shown that zeolites form in soils.[1015]

MEERSCHAUM OR SEPIOLITE

As noted in the second title relating to analcite, several thin beds of meerschaum, or sepiolite, are also present in the Green River shales, interbedded with chocolate-brown oil shale containing an abundance of glauberite molds filled with calcite. These were seen by Bradley in Duchesne County, Colorado, no bed exceeding 1 cm. in thickness. Bradley related this sepiolite to deposition of magnesia and silica (the latter perhaps in form of a hydrated gel) from water. The composition as recalculated from analysis is as follows:

SiO_2	58.40
Al_2O_3	1.89
Fe_2O_3	0.42
MgO	26.58

[1013] Bradley, W. H., Zeolite beds in the Green River formation, Science, vol. 67, 1928, pp. 73–74; The occurrence and origin of analcite and meerschaum beds in the Green River formation of Utah, Colorado, and Wyoming, Prof. Paper 158, U. S. Geol. Surv., 1929, pp. 1–7.

[1014] Lacroix, A., Compt. Rend. Acad. Sci., Paris, vol. 123, 1896, pp. 761–764.

[1015] Burgess, P. A., and McGeorge, W. T., Zeolite formation in soils, Science, vol. 64, 1926, pp. 652–653.

CaO.. 0.69
TiO₂.. 0.10
H₂O.. 11.86

Except for an occurrence given by Dana in Utah, sepiolite has not been seen elsewhere in North America. It has been described from the Tertiary sediments of the Paris Basin and near Madrid, Spain, by Brongniart[1016] and from the Tertiary of southern France by De Serres.[1017] Dana[1018] cites further occurrences in Asia Minor, Moravia, and Morocco.

MISCELLANEOUS SEDIMENTARY PRODUCTS

There is a considerable variety of other substances which have a more or less rare development as sedimentary products. Only a few of these are considered, most being disregarded because of rarity or ignorance respecting occurrences, or of processes and environments to which origin is due.

Iron sulphates are deposited about some springs in small quantities, and mine waters carry zinc, lead, copper and other compounds and make deposits containing these substances in various places. Likewise, lead, zinc, copper and other deposits undergo secondary enrichment from the zone of weathering, the minerals deposited in the secondarily enriched zone usually being oxides or carbonates. Zinc sulphide deposits from mine waters are known in the Joplin district of Missouri[1019] and most geologists seem to be of the opinion that the lead and zinc deposits of the Tri-state district of Kansas, Missouri, and Oklahoma and southwestern Wisconsin were deposited by cold waters after having been dissolved from the surrounding limestones in which they had originally been deposited in widely disseminated condition by the ordinary processes of sedimentation.

Copper seems to have many of its compounds deposited by sedimentary processes. Veins of copper sulphides are oxidized and carbonated in the upper portions by meteoric waters, the compounds thus produced are taken into solution, and are carried downward to be deposited as cuprite (Cu_2O), tenorite (CuO), malachite ($Cu_2(OH)_2,CO_3$), and azurite ($Cu_3(OH)_2(CO_3)$). Even chalcocite (CuS) has been formed under ordinary sedimentary conditions, Winchell[1020] having treated cupriferous pyrite with dilute solutions

[1016] Brongniart, A., Le magnésite du bassin de Paris, Ann. des Mines, vol. 7, 1822, pp. 303–304.

[1017] De Serres, M., Mémoire sur les terraines d'eau douce, Jour. Physique, vol. 87, 1818, pp. 134–135.

[1018] Dana, E. S., A text-book of mineralogy, 1906, p. 480.

[1019] Robertson, J. D., On a new variety of zinc sulphide from Cherokee County, Kansas, Am. Jour. Sci., vol. 40, 1890, pp. 160–161; Iles, M. W. and Hawkins, J. D., Eng. and Min. Jour., vol. 49, 1890, p. 499.

[1020] Winchell, H. V., Synthesis of chalcocite and its genesis at Butte, Montana, Bull. Geol. Soc. Am., vol. 14, 1903, pp. 269–276.

of copper sulphate and sulphur dioxide and obtained films of cuprous sulphide. Bronze articles about some of the Swiss lake-dwellings have been found coated with chalcopyrite.[1021] The Permian Kupferschiefer of Germany contain copper minerals in wide distribution and the minerals are generally referred to deposition by sedimentary processes. The enclosing materials are dark shales which seem to have been deposited in shallow waters of such character as to be highly reducing. The copper minerals are chiefly bornite, chalcocite, and chalcopyrite. Native silver is also present in the ratio of about 1 part silver to 200 parts copper, and zinc and lead are common. The Kupferschiefer have been extensively worked for the copper which they contain. Most students have considered the copper minerals to be syngenetic with the enclosing shales, and the precipitation of the copper minerals by some has been referred to decaying organic matter, Thiel suggesting that bacteria may have been responsible.[1022]

Native copper in unanamorphosed sediments is found occasionally. Haworth and Bennett[1023] have described films of native copper near Enid, Oklahoma, existing under conditions where it must have been deposited by cold waters. Native copper has also been found as impregnations of fossil wood in the Permian of Texas.[1024] Lovering[1025] has described the occurrence of metallic copper in thin beds of black muck, full of organic remains and interstratified with sands and gravel, in a bog near Cooke, Montana. No copper occurs in the sands and gravels. The copper is in the form of extremely spongy masses which range from minute specks to lumps more than an inch in diameter. The copper is assumed to have been derived from sulphide copper lodes in the surrounding higher lands and to have been carried to the bog in solution as cupric salts, where it is thought to have been precipitated by micro-organisms living in the muck. Experiments showed that the micro-organisms were able to live in a 1/2500 solution of copper and to precipitate metallic copper from a copper sulphate solution whose concentration in copper ranged from 1/10,000 to 1/50,000. Three possible causes of precipitation were considered: adsorption by colloids, reduction of copper sulphate by waste products of the micro-organisms, and

[1021] Chuard, E., Compt. Rend., Acad. Sci. Paris, vol. 80, 1875, p. 1297.

[1022] Thiel, G. A., The influence of bacterial action in the deposition of the Kupferschiefer of Germany, Econ. Geol., vol. 21, 1926, pp. 299–300. For a review of the literature relating to the copper minerals in the Kupferschiefer, the reader should consult Trask, P. D., Origin of the ore of the Mansfeld Kupferschiefer, Germany. A review of current literature, Econ. Geol., vol. 20, 1925, pp. 746–761. Trask's paper gives a bibliography.

[1023] Haworth, E., and Bennett, J., Native copper near Enid, Oklahoma, Bull. Geol. Soc. Am., vol. 12, 1901, pp. 2–4.

[1024] Schmitz, E. J., Trans. Am. Inst. Min. Eng., vol. 26, 1896, p. 101.

[1025] Lovering, T. S., Organic precipitation of metallic copper, Bull. 795, U. S. Geol. Sur., 1928, pp. 45–52.

consumption of the sulphate by such organisms, with precipitation of native copper. Experiments seemed to demonstrate that the second method would account for the copper and that the first and third hypotheses were inadequate. Percy[1026] mentions a deposit of peat in Wales which has actually been worked as a copper ore, the ash of the peat containing 3 per cent of copper.

The circulation fluids of many mollusks and arthropods have a greenish color due to the presence of a copper protein known as hæmacyanin, and the decay of such organisms must lead to the deposition of some copper in sediments. Studies made by Galtsoff and Whipple[1027] show that the pigment which colors some oysters green is due to copper, not in the form of hæmacyanin or a copper proteinate of any kind, but in a highly disassociated unknown state. It was found that the "Copper content of normal oysters varies between 8.21 to 13.77 milligrams per 100 grams dry weight, or from 0.16 to 0.248 milligrams per oyster. Copper content of green oysters analyzed during the investigation varied between 121.71 and 271.91 milligrams per 100 grams dry weight, or from 1.24 to 5.12 milligrams per oyster." With such extensive utilization of copper by organisms—and there probably has been considerable range in its use throughout geologic time—it should not be difficult to account for the quantities found in some formations.

It has lately been stated that under some conditions waters of surface temperatures transport and deposit gold, the transportation and deposition not being in the form of clastic gold.[1028] It was found that the gold in sands and gravels in Brazil increased between the first and second workings and that the gold responsible for the increase was different from that present in the first working. The conditions limited the transportation to cold water. It was concluded that gold is attacked and removed by humic acids under conditions excluding oxygen, provided sufficient time is given. The conclusions are supported by experimental data and the field evidence indicates that concentration of gold is related to the plant growth above the containing sands and gravels. There is also presented in support of the conclusion the fact that the diamond-bearing conglomerates of Minas Geraes are partly cemented by gold deposited from solution. The experiments also showed chemical removal of palladium.

Leucoxene, a decomposition product of ilmenite, is a not uncommon substance in some sediments, but it does not seem to have been frequently

[1026] Percy, J., Metallurgy, vol. 1, 1875, p. 211.

[1027] Galtsoff, P. S. and Whipple, D. V., Oxygen consumption of normal and green oysters, Bull. Bureau Fisheries, vol. 46, 1930, pp. 489–508.

[1028] Friese, F. W., The transportation of gold by underground solutions, Econ. Geol., vol. 26, 1931, pp. 421–431.

identified in American sedimentary formations, only a single instance having come to the author's attention.[1029] However, studies made of Chester sandstones of southwestern Indiana show that the most common heavy minerals are leucoxene, rutile, and brookite. The leucoxene in part seems to have developed from the ilmenite, and crystals of rutile and brookite are present in the leucoxene and the associated sands, seeming to indicate that these minerals developed from the leucoxene after its deposition in the sandstones, the change having been effected under conditions of little pressure and low temperature.[1030]

[1029] Brown, L. S., The occurrence of leucoxene in some of the Permian Mid-Continent sediments, Am. Mineralogist, vol. 13, 1928, pp. 233–235.

[1030] McCartney, G., A petrographic study of the Chester sandstones of Indiana, Jour. Sed. Pet., vol. 1, 1931, pp. 82–90.

CHAPTER VI

STRUCTURES, TEXTURES AND COLORS OF SEDIMENTS

STRUCTURES OF SEDIMENTS AND THEIR ORIGINS

Structures of sediments include stratification, cross-lamination, unconformities, ripple mark, wave mark, rain prints and similar impressions, mud cracks, ice crystal impressions, clay galls, concretions, contemporaneous deformation, tracks and trails, and various features difficult of classification.

STRATIFICATION

Stratification, or arrangement in layers, is without doubt the most distinctive structural feature of sedimentary rocks. It is also a feature concerning which not a great deal with respect to origin is known. A *stratum* is defined as a layer which is separable along bedding planes from layers above and below, the separation arising from a break in deposition or a change in the character of the materials deposited.[1] The stratification is due to some change in the color, size, composition, etc., of the sediments deposited at a given place, or to some interruption in deposition, permitting a change to take place in the materials already deposited. According to some usage, the term "stratum" includes all continuous layers composed of the same kind of material; in this sense it carries the significance of a formation. A stratum may be stratified. If thin, these units are known as *laminæ*, or laminations, terms which have also been applied to thin strata. The upper limit of a lamination is indefinite, but may be placed at about one-half inch. In addition to laminæ, a stratum not uncommonly contains larger non-separable units which are indicated by changes of texture, organic content, concretions, etc. These may be termed *stratum layers*. Laminæ range from parallelism to high angles with bedding planes. The latter are considered under the topic of cross-lamination.

Stratification may be direct or indirect. Direct stratification takes place when physical and other changes bring different types of sediment to the sites of deposition. Indirect stratification results when sediments, after their initial deposition, are thrown into suspension by wave action and

---

[1] Walther, J., Einleitung in die Geologie, etc., 1894, pp. 620–621; see also Andrée, K. Wesen, Ursachen und Arten der Schichtung, Geol. Rundschau, Bd. 6, 1915, pp. 351–397

redeposited in layers based on differences in dimensions and specific gravities of particles.[2]

Regularity of stratification planes is more common in chemical and some organic sediments than in those of purely mechanical origin, but the latter may have considerable regularity of stratification planes.[3]

Many deposits do not show detailed stratification and it is probable that this in many cases is due to working over of the bottom materials by organisms which in their search for food bring about a more or less complete mixing of the materials and destroy any detailed stratification which may have been present.

Initial Inclination

Stratification approximates parallelism to the surface on which deposition takes place. This may be horizontal or inclined; in most instances it is probable that there is some inclination, as the present surfaces of deposition are "undulating. The deposit formed in any particular century has marked basins, monoclines, and anticlines that are not due to deformation after deposition."[4] The tendency is for the lower portions of a surface to receive thicker deposits, with the result that each successive stratum is deposited on a less inclined slope. This, however, is not always the case, and variations in deposition may make a new surface of greater irregularity than the old, and contemporaneous erosion of deposits may create extremely steep slopes. The steepest slope on and at which it seems possible for sediments to be deposited was given by Thoulet as 41°.[5] Walther states that sediments may be deposited in orderly sequence upon surfaces inclined as much as 30°.[6] Any agitation of the medium in which deposition takes place flattens the angle of deposition. Studies made on this problem by Miss M. B. Draper[7] gave results as follows:

The tendency is for larger grains to stand at slightly steeper angles under water than smaller grains.

Angular grains tend to stand at slightly steeper angles under water than rounded grains of the same size.

---

[2] Walther, J., Einleitung in die Geologie, etc., 1894, p. 631; Perry, N. W., The Cincinnati rocks, Am. Geol., vol. 4, 1889, pp. 326–336.

[3] A classification of stratification, based on the character and position of the units, has been proposed by Andrée. Andrée, K., Das Meer und seine geologische Tätigkeit, in Salomon (ed.), Grundzüge der Geologie, Bd. 1, 1924, p. 427.

[4] Shaw, E. W., Bull. Geol. Soc. Am., vol. 31, 1920, pp. 124–125.

[5] Thoulet, J., Ann. Chim. et Phys., vol. 12, 1887, pp. 33–64.

[6] Walther, J., op. cit., pp. 620–621; Andrée, K., op. cit., 1915, pp. 359–362.

[7] Draper, M. B., Maximum initial subaqueous dips of sediments, etc. Unpublished thesis, Univ. of Wisconsin, 1930.

The highest angle attained was 43 degrees with sands, mesh 8–14, mixed angular and subangular. The lowest maximum inclination was 33 degrees, with rounded grains, mesh 100–200. For medium sized sand grains, mesh 28–48, 35 degrees was found to be the maximum for rounded grains and 38 degrees for angular grains.

There is always a thinning of clay on the upper part of a slope regardless of the angle of inclination of the original slope on which the clay settled.

Clay will not accumulate on a slope of 30 degrees except as it adheres to the material already there.

Extremely steep slopes may be found on the outer or seaward sides of coral reefs. About some of the islands of the West Indies fault and volcanic slopes of 20° are not uncommon.[8] Some exceed 30°, and several exceed 40°. The steepest slopes formed by deposition are found in the smaller bodies of water where the absence of strong agitation limits wide spreading of material. At the mouth of the Aar where it empties into Lake Brienz the slope of the deposits is 30° near shore and 20° 300 meters from the shore.[9] The delta of the Dundelbach in Lake Lungern has a slope of 32° to 35°. These slopes are to be contrasted with those of the Mississippi and Rhine delta fronts, which average about 1° for the former and about 0.5° for the latter. The angle of deposition must also be considered in connection with the base level of deposition, as the finer materials are swept out over this surface and deposited in deeper water where the inclinations of the bottom are those of the continental slopes or the surface of previous deposits. As these deposits are made in waters which may be little agitated, initial inclinations may be large and are apt to be preserved. The sea bottom adjacent to a coast of submergence may have steep slopes and hence possibilities for high angles of initial inclination. It would seem that the gentlest initial inclinations should be made over the deep ocean bottom and extensive lowlands invaded by the sea. Very flat-lying deposits are also made on river flood plains, lake bottoms, playas, and in other shallow bodies of water.

River channels which are being aggraded are not infrequently filled with sediments which arch downward from bank to bank, giving a synclinal effect. It is not known to what order of magnitude these "synclines" may develop.

Many examples of high initial inclination are known from the geologic column. Mather has described initial inclination of 7° in limestones near Kingston, Ontario, the strata lapping against a granite knoll, and the beds thickening with distance from the knoll so that the higher beds approach horizontality.[10] Mississippian limestones in Allen County, Kentucky, are

[8] See United States hydrographic charts, particularly No. 2318.

[9] Thoulet, J., op. cit., p. 54.

[10] Mather, K. F., Surficial dip of marine limestones, etc., Econ. Geol., vol. 13, 1918, pp. 198–206.

stated to have initial inclinations up to 10°. Shaw has described examples of initial inclination in connection with coal beds and limestones of western Pennsylvania.[11] A coal bed in a mine south of Oakland, Indiana, dips 50 feet in a half mile, whereas an underlying coal bed in the same mine is essentially horizontal. Inclinations of 5° and 6° are common about the Silurian coral reefs of Gotland, Anticosti, and Wisconsin and the upward range is to as great as 40° or more. Very steep inclinations may be found in sand and gravel deposits. On the north side of the Baraboo Range there are places where the Cambrian sandstones and conglomerates dip to the north at angles as great as 15°. Dips up to 25° are not uncommon about the St. Francis Mountains of southeastern Missouri, and dips of 30° have been found in a few places, these dips occurring in rocks ranging from sandstones to dolomites.[12]

Thickness of Units of Stratification

The units of stratification range in thickness from paper-thin in some muds to many feet in these and other sediments. In general, the thickness of most units falls between 2 inches and 2 feet. As noted elsewhere, the thickness of units is not a measure of duration of deposition, as a paper-thin shale or a thin layer of sandstone may have taken a longer time to deposit than many feet of sandstone. Branson[13] has assumed that "extensive thin-bedded deposits could not form by means of subaerial agents, but only in rather quiet waters," but this is an assumption not to be accepted until proved by extensive studies of subaerial deposits in process of formation; and in the same category is his assumption that "it seems impossible that extensive ripple marks could form and be preserved in flowing waters of streams." The first assumption is doubtful, and the latter may be proved incorrect in several deposits.

Causes of Development of Stratification

Stratification appears to develop as a consequence of (1) seasonal changes, (2) weather changes, (3) variations in currents, (4) changes in climate, (5) rise of sea level, (6) deposition of colloidal sediments, (7) and growth of organisms. One of the more difficult problems confronting the sedimentationist is that relating to the origin of stratification, and few criteria have been established which make possible the determination of the origin of this structural feature and the environment in which it developed.

[11] Shaw, E. W., Anomalous dips, Econ. Geol., vol. 13, 1918, pp. 598–610.

[12] Bridge, J., and Dake, C. L., Initial dips peripheral to resurrected hills, Appendix 1, 55th Biennial Rept., Missouri Bureau Geol. and Mines, 1929, pp. 1–7.

[13] Branson, E. B., Triassic-Jurassic "Red Beds" of the Rocky Mountain region, Jour. Geol., vol. 35, 1927, pp. 625–626.

STRATIFICATION DUE TO SEASONAL CHANGES.   Seasonal changes may lead to stratification in the deposits of land waters and in those of marine waters directly affected by land conditions.   In most regions the rainy season is flood time; the lakes, flood plains, and deltas are then receiving their maximum accumulations.   The dry periods are times of low water when the main sites of deposition receive no deposits or thin deposits of fine material. It is probable, therefore, that stratification due to this cause would not develop in marine deposits except in the vicinity of the mouths of rivers.

Shaw has suggested that seasonal stratification is responsible for some of the laminations of the Mississippi Delta sediments.[14] Trowbridge dissents from this suggestion.[15] Gale[16] referred the banding of some of the Alsace potash deposits to seasonal deposition, a thin layer of sodium chloride being deposited in summer and a layer of sylvite of about equal thickness in winter. In this connection there should be mentioned the laminated anhydrite described by Udden from the Permian of Texas, in which the laminations average less than 2 mm. thick and extend essentially without interruption through over 1000 feet of anhydrite.   In 13 feet, 1737 laminations were measured.   They appear to be arranged in cycles.   The significance of the laminations,—whether they represent days, years, or other periods,—has not been determined.[17]

Raymond and Stetson[18] have described the occurrence of a jelly-like substance on the bottom of Massachusetts Bay whose origin, they suggest, is due to the decomposition of eel grass, a seasonal plant.   The production of this jelly would come during a limited part of each year, thus giving an annual deposit separated by the deposits of the other part of each year.

Aqueo-glacial deposits, particularly those of lakes, are stated to exhibit seasonal stratification to a marked degree.   The rapid melting of summer and the relatively high burden of suspended matter give a deposit of a certain degree of coarseness for a particular place.   The deposits of the succeeding winter at the same place are thinner and composed of finer grained materials, these commonly having darker colors than those deposited in summer.   The winter band is sharply separated from the summer band above, but grades into the summer band below.   Chemically the

[14] Shaw, E. W., The mud-lumps at the mouths of the Mississippi, Prof. Paper 85–B, U. S. Geol. Surv., 1913, p. 17.

[15] Trowbridge, A. C., Rept. of Comm. Sedimentation, Nat. Research Council, 1923, p. 58.

[16] Gale, H. S., The potash deposits of Alsace, Bull. 745B, U. S. Geol. Surv., 1921, p. 48.

[17] Udden, J. A., Laminated anhydrite from Texas, Bull. Geol. Soc. Am., vol. 35, 1924, pp. 347–354.

[18] Raymond, P. E., and Stetson, H. C., A new factor in the transportation and distribution of marine sediments, Science, vol. 73, 1931, pp. 105–106.

summer and winter bands are much alike except that the winter bands contain more ferric oxide, alumina, and potash and somewhat less lime. The winter bands of glacial lakes are assumed to have been deposited when the lakes were frozen over.

In Sweden De Geer,[19] in America De Geer, Antevs,[20] and others, and in Finland Sauramo[21] have used the occurrence of such laminations in estimating the time since glaciation. Sayles has interpreted the lamination in Permian glacial clays near Boston as due to this cause[22] and other laminated clays as suggestive of glaciation.[23] In Australia David and Süssmilch interpreted laminæ of Carboniferous glacial lake deposits as due to seasonal deposition.[24] Johnston's[25] studies of Lake Louise, Alberta, which is fed by Victoria Glacier, indicated a rate of deposition of one-sixth inch per annum. The study of the deposits showed four to six seasonal bands per inch, strongly suggesting that each band represents a year. The thickness of a varve varies, ranging from a few millimeters to several inches and perhaps a foot or more. The summer or winter portion of a varve may be laminated, this arising from variations in melting between day and night, variations in competency of waters reaching a place, and probably other causes.

Studies made by Fraser[26] indicate that the velocity of fall of particles less than 0.5 mm. in diameter decreases with decreasing temperature until a minimum is reached at 4°C., and the retardation of fall above the latter temperature becomes greater as the particles decrease in diameter. The result is a distinct grading, as may be seen in glacial varves. Unflocculated varved clay gave lamination when permitted to settle in fresh water just above freezing, but gave no lamination at 20°C. Experiments show that the maximum salinity permitting formation of varves in coarse clay seems

[19] De Geer, G., A geochronology of the last 12,000 years, Compt. rend., Congr. Géol. Internat., Sess. 11, Stockholm, 1910, 1912, pp. 241–253.

[20] Antevs, E., The recession of the last ice sheet in New England, Am. Geog. Soc., Research Ser., no. 11, 1922.

[21] Sauramo, M., Studies of the Quaternary varve sediments in southern Finland, Bull. Comm. Géol. Finlande, vol. 60, 1923, pp. 1–164.

[22] Sayles, R. W., Seasonal deposition of aqueoglacial sediments, Mem. Mus. Comp. Zool., vol. 47, no. 1, 1919; New interpretation of the Permo-Carboniferous varves at Squantum, Bull. Geol. Soc. Am., vol. 40, 1929, pp. 541–546; see also Wallace, R. C., Varve materials and banded rocks, Trans. Roy. Soc. Canada, vol. 21, 1927, sect. iv, pp. 109–118.

[23] Sayles, R. W., Possible tillite at Levis, Quebec. Abstract, Bull. Geol. Soc. Am., vol. 33, 1922, pp. 99–100.

[24] David, T. W. E., and Süssmilch, C. A., Proc. Roy. Soc. New South Wales, vol. 53, 1919–1920, p. 27.

[25] Johnston, W. A., Sedimentation in Lake Louise, Alberta, Am. Jour. Sci., vol. 4, 1922, pp. 376–386.

[26] Fraser, H. J., An experimental study of varve deposition, Trans. Roy. Soc. Canada, vol. 23, sect. iv, 1929, pp. 49–69; Kindle, E. M., Sedimentation in a glacial lake, Jour. Geol., vol. 38, 1930, pp. 81–87.

to be about one-fiftieth that of normal sea water, thus indicating that typical aqueo-glacial varves are fresh-water phenomena.

Varved gyttjas are composed of sediments consisting largely of organic matter, as animal remains, plants, excrements, etc.[27] Such are now said to be forming in the deeper waters of McKay Lake near Ottawa, the laminations being due to alternations of grayish-white, finely divided lime carbonate, and dark reddish organic matter with traces of lime carbonate,[28] the thickness of two laminæ being about 0.5 mm.

STRATIFICATION DUE TO WEATHER CHANGES. Stratification arising from weather changes would probably be developed wherever sediments are deposited in waters which are not extremely deep. A storm might affect all shallow-water sites of deposition in the region of occurrence, and a different type of sediments would be deposited during and immediately after the storm than before. Vast quantities of sediments might be swept seaward and deposited upon those portions of the bottom which are deeper than the temporary base level of deposition. These deposits would be different from those of the time before the storm.

STRATIFICATION DUE TO CLIMATIC CHANGES. Climatic changes are known to have occurred in many parts of the earth, and as the quantities, compositions, and colors of sediments to a large extent are controlled by climate, each climatic condition should be reflected to a greater or less degree in the stratification. It is probable, however, that climatic changes are never abrupt and require long intervals of time for consummation, thus rendering it essentially impossible that small-scale stratification units could result. Gilbert[29] has appealed to the astronomic cycle of the precession of the equinoxes as a cause of climatic change leading to the deposition of various units in the Colorado Cretaceous. The precessional period causes summer and winter to change places in each hemisphere. As a consequence, the climate might be warm and dry during one period of the reversal of the seasons and during the other moist and cool, with corresponding differences in the sediments derived from or deposited in the regions affected, but as the change takes place gradually it is difficult to see how stratification could be affected. The Bruckner cycle of 35 years might lead to stratification changes.

STRATIFICATION DUE TO VARIATIONS IN CURRENTS. Stratification due

[27] Antevs, E., Retreat of the last ice-sheet in eastern Canada, Mem. 146, Geol. Surv., Canada, 1925, p. 5; Lindquist, G., Notice on varved gyttjas, Geol. Fören. Förhandl., Stockholm, vol. 46, 1924, p. 193.

[28] Whittaker, E. J., Bottom deposits of McKay Lake, Ottawa [Ontario], Trans. Roy. Soc. Canada, vol. 16, 1922, pp. 141–157 (147).

[29] Gilbert, G. K., Sedimentary measurement of Cretaceous time, Jour. Geol., vol. 1895, pp. 121–127.

to variations in currents arises from changes in current direction and competency. Such changes may bring sediments which are different from those of previous deposition. The tides wash into bays, estuaries, etc., and sediment is thrown into suspension, of which much is redeposited over the surface whence it was derived, but parts are carried elsewhere. Stratification results in each locality. Johnston assigns some of the lamination in the Fraser River delta deposits to tidal deposition.[30]

STRATIFICATION RELATED TO RISE OF SEA LEVEL. Sea bottoms below the profile of equilibrium receive and retain deposits until built to that level. This is a temporary base level of deposition, and when it is reached no further permanent deposit is made over that part of the sea bottom. Any sediments brought to this bottom are shifted back and forth, the finer ultimately being carried to deeper waters. Each rise of sea level permits further deposition on the bottom to a thickness which approximates the rise of sea level, following which the top of the deposit becomes the surface over which sediment is shifted. The top of each stratum deposited under these conditions has a surface developed by current and wave wash, and two strata are separated from each other by a period of no deposition whose duration represents the time between two successive rises of sea level minus the time required to raise the bottom to the profile of equilibrium. This break in deposition, which may, and in many instances does, represent a much longer time than is required to deposit a stratum, has been designated a diastem.[31] It may have the time value of a disconformity. It is considered that rise of sea level may have been responsible for much of the stratification in the Ordovician over and around the Cincinnati Arch, the Ordovician and Silurian limestones of the Michigan Basin, the Ordovician and Silurian of Anticosti, and the Pennsylvanian of the Mid-Continent region. It must, however, be fully appreciated that much stratification of other origin is probably present in each of these regions.

To this cause may be assigned some of the rude stratification occurring in coral-reef rock. The corals build to or adjacent to the surface of the water, and when that level is reached, upward growth ceases until a rise of sea level again makes it possible.

STRATIFICATION DUE TO ORGANIC GROWTHS. Portions of the bottom of water bodies are thickly carpeted with the shells and tests of living organisms which from time to time may be brought to the verge of extinction by changes in the physical conditions, such as an influx of waters of different

[30] Johnston, W. A., The character of the stratification of the sediments in the recent delta of Fraser River, British Columbia, Canada, Jour. Geol., vol. 30, 1922, p. 123.

[31] Barrell, J., Rhythms and the measurement of geologic time, Bull. Geol. Soc. Am., vol. 28, 1917, p. 794.

emperature, too much material in suspension, a change in the chemical ontent of the water, etc. This leads to a break in accumulation and tratification. Changes in an environment may eliminate certain mem-ers of a fauna, or even an entire fauna, and at the same time create a new nvironment favorable to a different group of organisms. The deposits of ach environment might be expressed as a distinct bed.

STRATIFICATION OF COLLOIDAL SEDIMENTS. Very fine particles which re permitted to settle in still water arrange themselves in strata while still n suspension, each stratum being of approximately uniform opacity and he higher less so than those below.[32] Studies made by Mendenhall and Mason, using Cucuracha shale from the Panama Canal region, led to the ollowing conclusions.[33]

1. A lateral temperature gradient produces convection, and several dis-inct convection systems may develop in a mixture, the number depending on the magnitude of the lateral temperature gradient and the magnitude of he vertical density gradient arising from the settling of the particles.

2. The greater the vertical density gradient, the greater the number of strata produced by a given temperature gradient. If the temperature gradient for a given density gradient is too high, no strata result.

In most waters it is improbable that any stratification will arise from this cause, but possibly in very deep holes in lakes and the sea, the sediments may settle in the order of stratification in suspension, and paper-thin shales develop. However, it is considered improbable that any stratification known in the geologic column owes its origin to this cause.

If certain salts are introduced in a suspension of finely divided matter, a different type of stratification arises. Davis[34] prepared a suspension of finely divided clay in water containing a moderately strong content of sodium silicate. A solution of ammonium carbonate was carefully added so as to avoid serious mixing. Downward diffusion of the ammonium car-bonate resulted, with flocculation of silicic acid and the development of alternate bands or laminæ of fine clay and clear gelatinous silica. The laminæ were approximately equally spaced in any one experiment, but with slight variations in different experiments. Some laminæ, both clay and silica, thickened or thinned and terminated lenticularly. The experiment repeated with red shale and powdered crystalline quartz gave like results. Similar results might develop in the sediments of a sea or lake bottom composed of fine mud containing an abundance of organic matter.

[32] Barus, C., Bull. 36, U. S. Geol. Surv., 1886, pp. 15–20; Bull. 60, 1890, pp. 139–145.

[33] Mendenhall, C. E., and Mason, M., The stratified subsidence of fine particles, Proc. Nat. Acad. Sci., vol. 9, 1923, pp. 199–207; Theory of settling of fine particles, Rept. Comm. Sedimentation, Nat. Research Council, 1923, pp. 53–54.

[34] Davis, E. F., The Radiolarian cherts of the Franciscan group, Bull. 11, Univ. California Publ., Dept. Geol., no. 3, 1917, pp. 36, 399–402.

Concentric banding of the kind shown in cherts might arise in the same way. In the Liesegang experiments, glass plates coated with gelatine impregnated with potassium bichromate had a drop of silver nitrate placed upon them. A series of concentric rings formed around the drop, the rings being closely spaced adjacent to the drop and progressively wider apart with distance therefrom. Experiments by Stansfield[35] showed that under certain conditions it is possible to obtain equally spaced rings.

INFLUENCE OF TEMPERATURE ON LAMINATIONS. Work by Kindle[36] has shown that temperature is a factor producing lamination in fine sediments. The substance of his conclusions is as follows.

1. Lamination which resembles that generally assumed to be produced by seasonal deposition is developed by continuous and uninterrupted settling of fine sediments.

2. Temperature is an important factor in modifying the color and physical character of the laminations.

Rhythms in Stratification

Many geologic sections show something of a rhythmic arrangement in the strata, with the rhythms in some cases of several orders. In some sections strata of coarse materials alternate with finer through a greater or lesser sequence, and the alternations may fall into several units of a higher order. In other sections limestones alternate with shales and a group of strata in such arrangement alternate with beds of shale. Or there may be three different varieties of rock with arrangement in rhythmic order. Many chert and other concretionary structures exhibit rhythmic arrangement in their concentric laminæ. The factors responsible for the development of such rhythmic or cyclical arrangement are known in but few cases. Some rhythms no doubt are due to recurrences of chemical or organic conditions, others to recurrences of physical conditions, and still others to alternations of several conditions. The finding of rhythms by geologists seems at the present time to be a pleasant diversion. The first serious consideration of this problem was that of Barrell; others subsequently have made important and valuable contributions.[37] The conditions deemed important in producing rhythms are considered in the following paragraphs.

RHYTHMS DUE TO WEATHER CHANGES. Extensive falls of rain or snow

[35] Stansfield, J., Retarded diffusion and rhythmic precipitation, Am. Jour. Sci., vol. 43, 1917, p. 1.

[36] Kindle, E. M., Rept. Comm. Sedimentation, Nat. Research Council, 1924, pp. 40–42.

[37] Barrell, J., Rhythms and the measurement of geologic time, Bull. Geol. Soc. Am., vol. 28, 1917, pp. 745–904; Weller, J. M., Cyclical sedimentation of the Pennsylvanian Period and its significance, Jour. Geol., vol. 38, 1930, pp. 97–135; Richardson, W. A., Quart. Jour. Geol. Soc., vol. 79, 1923, pp. 96–97.

esult in flooded streams, and sediments of a certain degree of coarseness are brought to the flood plains and deltas. The subsiding waters lead to the deposition of finer sediments. Over fresh-water lake bottoms Kindle has shown that the sands settle first from suspension, and subsequently the fine muds. Each storm thus stirring up the bottom of a fresh-water lake makes a thin layer of material of a certain degree of coarseness succeeded by one of finer. In the sea and salt-water lakes the silts and colloids may flocculate and reach the bottom first, and the deposition of coarser material may follow.[38] During storms, sediments of temporary deposition on shallow bottoms may be swept into the deeper waters on the continental slopes in quantities larger than ordinary. These sediments may be coarser than those of previous deposition and may be succeeded by finer deposits laid down during the non-stormy periods. A rhythm thus begins with coarse materials in a relatively thick band and closes with a thinner band of fine material.

RHYTHMS DUE TO SEASONAL CHANGES. The spring and early summer seasons of many parts of North America and the world are the times of flood waters, and late summer and autumn the times of low waters. During the former the flood plains and deltas receive deposits of sediments of a certain coarseness; during the latter, no or thinner deposits of greater fineness, the rhythm thus beginning with coarser materials succeeded by finer. Each seasonal rhythm may also include several rhythms due to weather conditions. On bottoms deeper than the profile of equilibrium there is a maximum of deposition during those seasons of the year characterized by many storms and much rough weather. The intervening seasons of few storms are indicated by deposition of finer sediments of less thickness.

In glacio-fluvial and glacio-lacustrine deposits the times of warmth are the times of melting and abundance of waters; the periods of cold are those of little melting and little water. During the former the waters of the streams may be turbid, and the material deposited at any place has a certain coarseness; during the latter the streams and lakes may be ice-covered, the waters are clearer, and the deposits at the place are of finer grain. In very fine-grained sediments of this origin the smallest rhythm may be the annual one. In coarser sediments it might be possible to develop a rhythm each day, groups of diurnal rhythms forming the one of seasonal origin. Raymond and Stetson[39] record the occurrence of a jelly-like substance over parts of the bottom of Massachusetts Bay and, following Petersen,[40] sug-

[38] Kindle, E. M., Diagnostic characteristics of marine clastics, Bull. Geol. Soc. Am., vol. 28, 1917, pp. 907–908.

[39] Raymond, P. E., and Stetson, H. C., A new factor in the transportation and distribution of marine sediments, Science, vol. 73, 1931, pp. 105–106.

[40] Petersen, C. G. J., Rept. Danish Biol. Station, vol. 20, 1911.

gest that this represents decomposed eel grass, a seasonal plant. The seasonal growth would produce an annual deposit of "jelly" and thus give rise to a rhythm which might resemble a varve.

Stamp[41] has described rhythmic arrangement of laminated sediments in the Tertiary of Burma, which arrangement he assigns to "an annual variation in the volume and carrying capacity of the river or rivers which were sweeping sediment into the Burmese Gulf." The annual deposit is stated to consist of a double lamina, of which the coarser portion was deposited during the high-water or flood season, and the finer portion during the low-water season. While the above may be the correct explanation, it does not seem that other possible explanations have been eliminated. Rubey[42] has suggested that pairs of laminæ in the Cretaceous shales of the Black Hills region may represent seasonal deposition.

RHYTHMS DUE TO CLIMATIC CHANGES. The best known of the climatic and astronomic cycles are the 35-year cycle of Bruckner, the 21,000-year cycle of the precession of the equinoxes, and the 91,000-year cycle of minimum and maximum eccentricity. The repeated occurrence of glaciation during geologic time suggests others. It is not known what climatic cycles may do in sedimentation. It is possible that during one half of the cycle sediments of certain characteristics are deposited, and sediments of other characteristics during the other half. As mentioned before, Gilbert thought that the precessional cycle might have been responsible for the rhythmic arrangement of some of the units of the Cretaceous sediments of Colorado, wherein the sequence consists of 3,900 feet of shales and limestones, the latter constituting only a small part of the whole. The rhythms are best shown in the Benton, the base of the Niobrara, 90 feet above the base of the Niobrara, and at the top of the Niobrara. Each cycle is represented by from 18 inches to 3 feet of limestone and shale.[43]

Barrell has described ribboned slates at Slatedale, Pennsylvania, in which rhythms of great regularity are shown by thick bands of dark slates separated by thinner bands of light shales, the latter containing considerable sand. As the deposits have wide extent, are extremely fine, and contain an abundance of carbon, slowness of deposition is suggested. The sandy layers may indicate stirring up of the bottom and the washing away of the finer

---

[41] Stamp, L. D., Seasonal rhythm in the Tertiary sediments of Burma, Geol. Mag., vol. 62, 1925, pp. 515–528.

[42] Rubey, W. W., Lithologic studies of fine-grained Upper Cretaceous sedimentary rocks of the Black Hills Region, Prof. Paper, 165–A, U. S. Geol. Surv., 1930, pp. 40–44; Possible varves in marine Cretaceous shale in Wyoming, Abstract, Jour. Washington Acad. Sci., vol. 18, 1928, pp. 260–262.

[43] Gilbert, G. K., Sedimentary measurement of Cretaceous time, Jour. Geol., vol. 3, 1895, pp. 121–127.

materials.   Barrell suggested that each rhythm represented a period of years of quiet weather following one of storm, the duration of the cycle not being determinable.[44]

RHYTHMS DUE TO MOVEMENT OF SEA LEVEL.   A rise of sea level leads to an invasion of the sea over the land.   Sediments of a certain degree of coarseness are then deposited over a given place.   With progress inland the place receives finer materials and with still further progress only pelagic sediments may be deposited.   If the sea retreats before the bottom is built to the base level of deposition determined by the conditions, muds may be deposited over the pelagic sediments, and over these may be spread sands.   The cycle may exist in mixed continental and marine deposits, as those described by Udden[45] and Weller[46] from Illinois, the ascending sequence in the cycle consisting of (1) sandstones and sandy shales, (2) under clay, (3) coal, and (4) marine limestones and shales, the cycle having an unconformity at the base indicating, according to Weller, uplift and erosion followed by submergence.   The deposits seem to be those of the delta environment, and it is possible that the cycle does not always indicate uplift, but that in some cases periodical subsidence only took place.   Weller gives the following succession as that of a typical Illinois Pennsylvanian formation:

Marine
       8 Shale, containing ironstone bands in the upper part and thin limestone layers in the lower part.
       7 Limestone.
       6 Calcareous shale.
       5 Black shale
Continental
       4 Coal.
       3 Underclay, not uncommonly containing concretionary or bedded fresh-water limestone.
       2 Sandy and micaceous shale.
       1 Sandstone.
Unconformity.

The unconformity is not necessarily that of land erosion due to uplift. If the continental deposits are those of the delta environment, the unconformity may have been developed through the building of the delta over a bottom that had reached the base level of deposition for the conditions, and thus presented an eroded surface for the continental deposits, the channels

[44] Barrell, J., Rhythms and the measurement of geologic time, Bull. Geol. Soc. Am., vol. 28, 1917, pp. 803–804.
[45] Udden, J. A., Geology and mineral resources of the Peoria Quadrangle, Bull. 506, U. S. Geol. Surv., 1912, pp. 47–50.
[46] Weller, J. M., Cyclical sedimentation of the Pennsylvanian Period and its significance, Jour. Geol., vol. 38, 1930, pp. 97–135.

representing places where the extended streams cut into marine deposits. Where a considerable extent of marine deposits has been eroded, uplift seems to be implied. Moore[47] describes a cycle from the Mid-Continent Pennsylvanian which in ascending order when completely developed consists of (1)

limestone, yellowish brown, massive, locally irregular and impure, about 5 to 10 feet; (2) shale, clayey to calcareous, bluish, gray or yellowish, 5 to 15 feet or more; (3) limestone, blue, very hard, dense, brittle, a single massive bed weathering in angular blocks, thickness never more than 2 feet; (4) shale, dark bluish and black, fissile, clayey, the black zone always occurring at the base, 3 to 8 feet; (5) limestone, light gray, thin and unevenly bedded, in some cases chert-bearing, generally 10 to 20 feet thick.

The cyclic sequences are best developed in the Douglas and Shawnee groups of Kansas. The strata concerned seem to be mainly marine, but they are in close association with strata of the continental environment. They seem best interpreted as due to intermittent subsidence.

A rhythm due to movement of sea level may extend through hundreds and even thousands of feet and may include rhythms due to climatic, seasonal, and weather changes, as well as rhythms caused by minor movements of sea level. The large rhythms were designated circles of deposition by Newberry.[48] Cycles of sedimentation described by Stamp[49] in the Eocene of the London and Paris basins are defined as resulting from a transgressing sea and as beginning with a basal conglomerate, progressively younger landward, succeeded seawardly and vertically by sand and clays, and these last in some places by lacustrine, lagoonal, fluvial, and even by eolian deposits. Filling of the basin or retreat of the sea may lead to the deposition of coarse sediments at the summit of the succession. Advance of the sea for the second cycle would remove some of the materials of the preceding, giving rise to an unconformity or "ravinement,"[50] the period between two successive "ravinements" constituting a cycle of sedimentation, the deposits of which record a complete oscillation of a basin, "each oscillation including a positive phase of marine invasion and a negative phase of regression." Figure 73 shows cycles in the Hampshire basin. The Eocene deposits in the Hampshire Basin become more continental toward the west.

If an advance of the sea is pulsatory and the sea bottom is built to the profile of equilibrium before the beginning of each advance, rhythms of a

[47] Moore, R. C., Sedimentation cycles in the Pennsylvanian of the northern Mid-Continent region, Abstract, Bull. Geol. Soc. Am., vol. 41, 1931, pp. 51–52.

[48] Newberry, J. S., Circles of deposition in American sedimentary rocks, Proc. Am. Assoc. Adv. Sci., vol. 22, 1872, pp. 185–196.

[49] Stamp, L. D., On cycles of sedimentation in the Eocene strata of the Anglo-Franco-Belgian Basin, Geol. Mag., vol. 58, 1921, pp. 108–114, 146–157, 194–200.

[50] Stamp designates an unconformity of this origin a "ravinement."

minor order develop. The new rise of sea level brings the bottom below the profile of equilibrium, to which it is built during the time of stability, the bottom then receiving no permanent deposits until sea level rises again. The rhythm consists of various marine sediments succeeded by much washed sediments of indirect stratification. Calcareous sediments may be deposited in clearer but deeper waters, but as the coincidence of the bottom and the profile of equilibrium extends outward, these calcareous sediments become progressively covered on the landward margin with sands or muds, a rhythmic arrangement resulting.

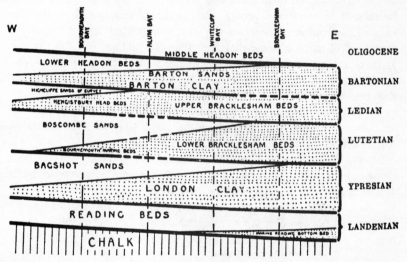

Fig. 73. Diagram of Cycles of Sedimentation in the Eocene of the Hampshire Basin, England

Marine strata are shown on the right, continental on the left. Each marine stratigraphic unit has its initial deposits and final deposits of more or less different character from those above the base and beneath the top. The lines bounding the marine units show the migrations of the shore. The vertical lines show the sections or geograms at the places indicated. Each cycle begins and terminates with a "ravinement." After Stamp, op. cit., 1921. Stamp also shows diagrams of cycles of sedimentation for the Paris, London, and Belgium basins.

SUMMARY. The rhythmic arrangement of sedimentary materials has been observed for more than a hundred years, and that it is a phenomenon of importance is obvious. It is thought, however, that caution is essential in its interpretation. Most sedimentary deposits are not easily studied in three dimensions. It is possible and even probable that if a group of sedimentary units were seen in three dimensions, their rhythmic arrangement would not be so obvious. On the other hand, wide observation is essential to establish such rhythms as those described by Stamp. At the present time it seems fashionable to discover rhythms, and the writer has the feeling that some of those which have been identified should be accepted with reserve.

CROSS-LAMINATION

Cross-lamination[51] (cross bedding, false bedding) is commonly present in sands and consists of their arrangement in parallel laminæ transverse to the planes of general stratification, the latter commonly truncating the upper edges of the laminæ. At the base the laminæ approach parallelism to the stratification planes, but this may not be very obvious and may not be present in coarse sediments. The tangential termination of the lower ends of the laminæ is known as the bottomset portion, and it ordinarily is composed of material somewhat finer than the inclined or foreset portion. If there are tangential terminations at the tops of the laminations, these are known as the topset portions. The angles of inclination may vary in direction and magnitude. According to Thoulet,[52] the angle of inclination never exceeds 41°. Cressey[53] found that the lee slopes of the dunes on the east shores of Lake Michigan have a maximum slope of 32°. An average high angle of inclination is around 20°. Cross-lamination inclinations are related to the quantity and coarseness of material and the rates of deposition, being steeper under conditions of rapid deposition and in coarse sediments. Initial angles of deposition may be reduced in compacting, although such reduction cannot be very great in sands. Length of foresets, or length of the inclined portion of a lamina, depends on quantity of material, rate of deposition, velocity of current, and other agitation of the medium of deposition. Large supplies and slow currents give steep foresets which are also long. Small supplies and slow currents yield short and steep foresets. Rapid currents and small supplies tend to give long and gently inclined foresets. Extremely long and steep foresets are very common in certain of the Cambrian sandstones of the upper Mississippi valley, some extending 50 or more feet at inclinations of 15° to 20°.

A variety designated festoon cross-lamination has been described by Knight[54] from the Casper and Fountain sandstones of Wyoming which is

[51] Gilbert, G. K., Ripple marks and cross-bedding, Bull. Geol. Soc. Am., vol. 10, 1899, pp. 135–139; Grabau, A. W., Types of cross-bedding and their stratigraphic significance, Science, vol. 25, 1907, pp. 295–296; Andrée, K., Wesen, Ursachen und Arten der Schichtung, Geol. Rundschau, Bd. 6, 1915, pp. 384–395.

[52] Thoulet, J., Ann. Chim. et Phys., vol. 12, 1887, pp. 33–64.

[53] Cressey, G. B., The Indiana sand dunes and shore lines of the Lake Michigan Basin, 1928, p. 38.

[54] Knight, S. H., Festoon cross-lamination, Abstract, Bull. Geol. Soc. Am., vol. 41, 1930, p. 86; The Fountain and the Casper formations of the Laramie Basin, Univ. Wyoming Publ. in Science, Geology, vol. 1, 1929, pp. 1–82 (56–74).

stated "to be the result of: (1) the erosion of plunging troughs having the shape of a quadrant of an elongate ellipsoid; (2) the filling of the troughs by sets of thin laminæ conforming in general to the shape of the trough floors; (3) the partial destruction of the filling laminæ by subsequent erosion, producing younger troughs" which in turn are filled by sets of thin laminæ. The direction of inclination of laminæ is controlled by the direction of plunge of the troughs within which they lie, and in any given trough there is some variation in direction. Inclinations range to 35°, most being between 10° and 25°. The troughs range in depth from 1 to 100 feet, in width from 5 to 1000 feet, and in length from 50 to several thousand feet. The average maximum slope of the sides of the troughs is between 10° and 15°, but may reach 25°. The upper end of a trough is closed, and the angle of inclination becomes or approaches zero at its lower end, where it may terminate at the closed end of another trough. The troughs have a rather constant plunge to the southwest. Many laminæ are stated to be intensely crumpled locally, due to slumping while deposition was in progress. The cross-lamination possesses some of the characteristics of eolian origin, but the constant direction of plunge to the troughs seems to preclude that origin. Knight refers the troughs to development in marine waters through agency of currents and waves produced by tides or storms.

Aside from significance as a sedimentary structure, cross-lamination is important in structural geology, as the truncation at the top of the foresets gives a nearly unfailing means for determination of the tops of beds. If there is no truncation of the upper parts of laminæ, each lamination is an S-shaped curve, but if truncation has occurred, there is a simple curve concave upward. This will aid in determination of position of strata.

Cross-lamination develops under four general conditions or environments not sharply separated from one another: building of deltas and alluvial fans, outward building of the bottom in seas and lakes to the position of the profile of equilibrium, movement of sandbars and dunes, and formation of ripple marks.

Cross-Lamination in Deltas and Alluvial Fans

The cross-lamination in deltas and alluvial fans may have extremely long foresets. The directions of inclinations fan out from the distributaries, the inclination directions extending through an arc of 180° or more. There may be a little cross-lamination in the opposite direction. Cross-lamination strictly due to delta building can be beautifully developed in laboratory experiment, and it probably takes place in small lakes to an almost equally perfect degree, but on large deltas and alluvial fans it is unlikely that cross-lamination due solely to the environment develops. Likewise, it should be noticed that cross-lamination due to sandbars and ripple mark forms in the delta and alluvial fan environments, this cross-lamination not being differentiable from that similarly formed elsewhere except that its distribution should indicate something of the environment.

Cross-Lamination Resulting from Outward Building of the Bottom in Seas and Lakes

The materials transported outward from shallow-water bottoms by waves and currents extend the shallows into deeper water, and where this has been seen in shallow water, cross-lamination in some cases develops, the directions of inclination being normal to the coast and toward the deeper water.

Cross-Lamination from Movement of Sandbars and Dunes

Sandbars move over bottoms of water as plateau-like areas with steep slopes on the advancing sides. They may range in height from less than an inch to 10 or more feet, most of them being a foot or less. The sand is rolled over the top, which usually undergoes some erosion. Reaching the edge of the plateau, the sands roll down the slope at the front. The direction of the front slope is usually not constant and the inclinations have a similar range in direction. The top surface approximates horizontality, and the bar may rest on a similar surface, but this under surface may have great irregularity due to variations in thickness of deposits and to contemporaneous erosion. These surfaces may be 20 or more feet apart, but more often they are a foot or less. The foresets thus vary in length depending upon the distances separating the bounding planes and the inclinations. Each bed thus formed has its cross-lamination in one direction, which may or may not be the same as that of the beds below and above. Cross-lamination formed in streams has a downstream component from which the direction of stream flow may be determined, but because of meandering the direction of this component may range through every point of the compass. Streams in which tidal action occurs may have cross-lamination with inclination upstream. Cross-lamination in the bars formed in standing bodies of water may have a different direction of inclination in every bed. The shore currents of a coast may have a prevailing, but not constant, direction, sometimes flowing directly opposite to that of the previous day or hour. On other days offshore or onshore currents may incline the lamination away or to the shores.

In general, cross-lamination formed through movement of bars is bounded by parallel planes, the two planes bounding a unit approximating the horizontal. However, either surface may be extremely irregular and very choppy, and violent waters lead to great irregularities in cross-laminations.

Waters of this character may be seen in rivers, estuaries, and over coastal shallow bottoms nearly everywhere.

Dune cross-lamination is developed through deposition on the lee sides at inclinations determined by the nature and quantity of the materials and the rates of deposition. The foresets are likely to be long and almost invariably truncated at the top. Due to the considerable range in direction of winds over short periods, there is great range in direction of inclination of the cross-lamination, and this range is increased because the lee side of

FIG. 74. A CRESCENT-SHAPED DUNE IN THE EASTERN PART OF THE STATE OF WASHINGTON

The lamination will be parallel, in general, to the steep face, but some may be developed on the windward slopes if it becomes necessary to build these to a level required by the competency of the wind.   Photograph made by Professor H. E. Culver.

a dune is so frequently irregular in its inclinations, and in the barchane variety of dune the inclinations may have a range through about 180° (fig. 74). The upper bounding plane of dune cross-lamination is inclined, and the lower may be, the cross-laminated unit thus being wedge-shaped in cross section (fig. 75). This and the great variation in direction in any cross-laminated unit seem the only characteristics which differentiate eolian from aqueous cross-lamination, and these are not always certain, as wedge-shaped units may under some conditions develop in water, and considerable variation in direction of inclination may develop under aqueous conditions.

Nevertheless, consistent inclination in any direction would seem to prove aqueous origin. There seem to be no differences in the range of inclination of the laminæ, and each seems to have the same range in length and shape of foresets as the latter are seen in cross section. However, the average

Fig. 75. Cross-lamination in the Mesozoic Red Sandstones near the Source of the Yen-shui, Northern Shensi Province, China

The lamination shown in the photograph has the characteristics developed by wind. Photograph by E. L. Estabrook, given to the author by F. C. Clapp.

length of foresets of eolian cross-lamination seems longer than in those of aqueous origin, the latter rarely exceeding 2 to 3 feet, the former commonly exceeding those figures, but ranging as high as that of any eolian origin.

Cross-Lamination Made by Ripple Mark

The foresets of cross-lamination made by ripple mark range in length from 3 to 5 inches for the average of those made in water. Ripples made in air have the foresets extremely short, probably less than an inch for most of them. The laminations are made on the lee sides of the asymmetrical ripples and their upper ends are truncated with ripple advance. The cross-lamination of the antidune of water traction is not apparent in those studied in the Sedimentation Laboratory of the University of Wisconsin. It is doubtful if such stand much chance of preservation. The direction of cross-lamination made in ripples records the directions of the currents, the inclinations in all cases except those of antidunes and rapid deposition being in the directions of current movement. As winds vary in direction through all points of the compass, it follows that the inclinations of laminations in wind ripples vary accordingly. Current ripples made in streams have the laminations inclined quite generally downstream, although inclination upstream may take place, particularly in streams affected by tides. Current ripples made in standing bodies of water have inclinations ranging in many directions, but as many currents parallel the shore, inclinations parallel thereto should be common.

Spurr has described an example of apparent cross-lamination in connection with current ripples which is thought to have developed wholly through deposition, no erosion occurring on the currentward side, each new lamination being deposited on the preceding so that the ripples maintained stationary position through several feet of sands. As the sands in the troughs of ripples are different from those on the crests, these different portions became superimposed over one another, and as the axial planes of current ripple marks are inclined upstream, there was thus given the appearance of upstream inclination of cross-lamination.[55] A similar occurrence has been seen in a delta kame near Madison, Wisconsin, and figure 76 shows an example from the Colorado River near the Boulder Dam project.

The cross-lamination in symmetrical or wave ripples is parallel to the surfaces of the ripples, and the inclinations may incline in opposite directions from the crests. Laminæ parallel to one side of a ripple are likely to terminate on the other side of the same ripple. Cross-lamination due to wave ripple is not particularly common.

[55] Spurr, J. E., False bedding in stratified drift deposits, Am. Geol., vol. 13, 1894, pp. 43–47.

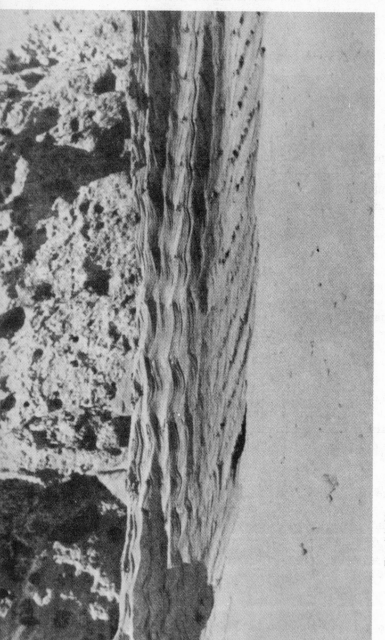

FIG. 76. SUPERIMPOSED CURRENT RIPPLE MARKS SHOWING FALSE CROSS-LAMINATION UP-CURRENT

The lower part of the picture shows a surface of deposition. Beyond this are small cliffs or slopes which show the deposit in the vertical dimension and the apparent dip in places of the cross-lamination up-current. The background of the picture shows the wall of Black Canyon. It should be noted that the cross-lamination of the ripples due to rapid deposition is both upstream and downstream. The ripples move to the left. Black Canyon of Colorado River near Boulder Dam. Photograph by Professor W. J. Mead.

UNCONFORMITIES

An unconformity represents a break in the geologic sequence and is a surface of erosion or non-deposition separating two groups of strata. If the strata below an unconformity are not parallel to those above, it is a nonconformity.[56] In general, a nonconformity indicates subaerial erosion preceded by deformation, but it is conceivable that such might also be developed beneath the water if the deformation was such as not to bring the bottom above the surface of the water, but near enough thereto to permit submarine erosion. Apparent nonconformities arise from variations in bedding inclination. An unconformity separating strata which are nearly parallel is a disconformity,[57] and represents a break in the geologic sequence of formation value. A diastem indicates a break of less magnitude than a disconformity and is represented elsewhere by a part of a formation.[58] It follows that there are diastems of many time values and all gradations between disconformities and diastems. A term used in Europe for a variety of disconformity is "ravinement," which is defined by Stamp[59] as "an irregular junction which marks a break in sedimentation. The break may be due to a period of denudation consequent on movement of masses of water, but not necessarily accompanied by earth-movements." Ravinements should be common in deltas and marine shallow-water deposits.

The absence of a break in a sequence implies, and is a consequence of, continuous deposition. Deposition in shallow waters probably is continuous for only brief intervals, and interruption seems to be the normal and usual fact, such interruption ranging from brief cessation of deposition to intervals of many years, and at the upper limit to erosion or the reverse of deposition.

The time value of an unconformity may range from that necessary to deposit a single formation, to such an enormous period of time as that represented by the unconformity between the Pre-Cambrian and Pleistocene. Nor is that the limit, as deposits of the far distant future may come to rest on a Pre-Cambrian surface to give an unconformity of far greater time magnitude. Every unconformity, either directly, or through another unconformity, has connection with the present land surface, and this surface on the oldest rocks may be compared to a low, wide-spreading plant with fan-like branches intercalated in all directions in the surrounding later sedimentary materials, eventually passing into diastems which presumably terminate

[56] Pirsson, L. V., and Schuchert, C., Text-book of geology, 1920, pt. i, p. 311.

[57] Grabau, A. W., Physical character and history of some New York formations, Science, vol. 22, 1905, p. 534.

[58] Barrell, J., Rhythms and the measurement of geologic time, Bull. Geol. Soc. Am., vol. 28, 1917, p. 794.

[59] Stamp, L. D., On cycles of sedimentation in the Eocene strata of the Anglo-Franco-Belgian basin, Geol. Mag., vol. 58, 1921, p. 109.

in the assumed continuous deposits of the deep sea, the unconformity having a different time value at different places.[60]

Disconformities are extremely difficult of determination, particularly after a surface has been brought to minor relief. There seem to be no criteria other than fossils to establish their magnitude. Many important ones long failed of determination, and it is probable that many still remain undiscovered.

Stephenson[61] lists several criteria which may be useful aids in recognition of disconformities. These are as follows:

1. A thin conglomerate composed of pebbles, bones, teeth, or other hard objects at the base of the overlying formation.

2. A thin layer of phosphatic nodules or phosphatic fossil casts of organisms.

3. A phosphatic layer which includes materials obviously derived from an older formation.

4. Sharp differences in lithology of the materials below and above the contact between two strata.

5. An uneven or undulating contact which cuts across the bedding planes.

6. Presence of distinctive faunal zones above and below a contact, which zones are elsewhere known to be separated by other strata of greater or less thickness.

7. Discordance of dip above and below a contact. Rarely determinable in disconformities.

8. Borings made by littoral organisms in strata below a contact, these borings filled with material like that composing the stratum above the contact. An additional criterion would be the occurrence in place of such littoral organisms as barnacles.

While important, only one of the above criteria is definite, as each feature may occur without indicating a disconformity. Number 8, after it had been proved that littoral organisms in place or their structures were present, would prove a disconformity. The best that may be said is that the existence of the features enumerated above suggests a disconformity or a diastem.

Unconformities are here considered from the points of view of occurrence between strata of (1) continental and (2) marine origin. Included with the latter are those unconformities separating marine strata above from rocks of other origin below.

[60] Blackwelder, E., The valuation of unconformities, Jour. Geol., vol. 17, 1909, pp. 289–299.

[61] Stephenson, L. W., Unconformities in Upper Cretaceous series of Texas, Bull. Am. Assoc. Pet. Geol., vol. 13, 1929, pp. 1323–1334.

Unconformities in Continental Sediments

Unconformities developed in continental deposits may occur in connection with fluvial, lacustrine, paludal, deltaic, glacial, and eolian sediments. Unconformities in fluvial, lacustrine, paludal, and deltaic sediments are considered under the head of fluvial sediments.

Unconformities in fluvial sediments may be examined from four points of view, as follows: (1) unconformities arising in channel deposits with the stream maintaining a constant position, (2) unconformities arising through the migrations of an aggrading stream over its deposits, (3) unconformities developed in the deposits of streams which alternately aggrade and degrade, and (4) unconformities developed through growth of alluvial fans and deltas.

1. Every stream scours and fills, the former occurring at flood time in the deeps and at low water on the shoals, the filling taking place in the opposite sense. In the deposits thus formed, a limited section might show unconformable relationships with relief as great as 50 or more feet, and if a section parallel to the course of a channel could be observed, the unconformity might be traced for long distances. As many unconformities would be present in such channel deposits, the correlation of those exposed in different sections would be difficult. The high initial dips might suggest nonconformity. The time interval represented by an unconformity developed in this manner usually is not long, and the magnitude of the break is that of a diastem.

2. A stream forming a flood plain of construction, or an alluvial fan, at one time or another occupies nearly every place on its flood plain. This is done by the migration of meanders and by the stream breaking through its natural levees and seeking the lower land of its back swamps. In the migration of the meanders, cutting is done on the convex side of the current and deposits are made on the concave side, these resting on a stream-eroded surface with irregularities inherent to the method of development. If a stream breaks through its levees, its new channel is cut in earlier deposits, and the fillings in this channel will have unconformable relationships to those beneath. As a flood plain or alluvial fan may contain river lakes and swamps, the unconformable relationships may be between lake, swamp, and river sediments below and river sediments above, or in the opposite sense. It is thought that an unconformity of this origin may have a relief as great as 50 feet and be traceable for many miles. The high initial dips might suggest a nonconformity. The interval may equal that of a disconformity or a diastem.

3. An aggrading stream ultimately reaches a stage where a profile of equilibrium is attained, and deposition ceases so far as raising the surface

is concerned, but the stream continues to migrate over the surface of its flood plain, and there may be gradual lowering of the surface. An increase in the supply of sediments, a downwarping of the flood plain, or a change in the climate of the flood plain to drier conditions may restore aggradation, and the deposits then made would lie unconformably on those below. The time interval represented by this disconformity may be long, and the high angles of initial dip may suggest nonconformity.

4. Alluvial-fan and kindred deposits by progressive overlap over the region on which they form develop an unconformity between themselves and the rocks beneath. The time interval may be very long and the relations those of nonconformity or disconformity.

The delta environment represents conditions similar to those of flood plains, but because of nearness to the sea another factor enters. A delta exists because of dominance of stream supply of sediments over wave and current disposition. Stream supply varies with climatic and topographic conditions at the sources. If these vary sufficiently widely and the stream at any time brings less sediments than the waves and currents are able to handle, the latter may remove a part of the materials at the delta front and develop a surface of erosion in so doing, and this may continue until the entire surface of the delta has been traversed. If the supply of sediment later rises above the disposing ability of the waves and currents, the delta advances and new deposits are made upon an eroded surface. A disconformity results. It may separate fluvial, paludal, and lacustrine deposits, and the time interval may be long. The advance of a delta over a marine bottom built or eroded to the profile of equilibrium places the delta sediments in disconformable relationships to the marine sediments beneath.

Glaciers advance and retreat, and each advance may erode the surface. During each retreat this surface receives glacial and aqueo-glacial deposits. A unconformity results which in some places appears as a disconformity and in others as a nonconformity. For an unconformity of this type of wide distribution the time interval may be long.

Winds frequently erode previous deposits, and subsequently they may make a deposit on the eroded surface, the breaks being in the nature of diastems.

Speaking generally, it needs to be emphasized that estimates of the time values of unconformities in continental deposits have little merit unless the estimates are strongly supported by fossil evidence of unquestioned character. The relief has little significance, as it may range from nothing to 50 or more feet in a limited exposure.

Unconformities Connected with Marine Sediments

Unconformities connected with marine sediments are arranged in five groups. These are not designated by name, but are discussed in succeeding paragraphs.

1. Rapid rise of sea level over a land of considerable relief advances a shore in landward direction, each successive deposit extending farther on the land and giving the marine progressive overlap of Grabau.[62] The submerged surface may be quickly brought beneath the level of the profile of equilibrium and thus experience little marine erosion. The relations may be those of nonconformity or disconformity; the relief of the surface may be great; and the time is quite certain to be long. Rapid rise of sea level over steep slopes favors the development of a basal conglomerate.

Such an unconformity has sediments nearest the original shore with characters determined by the conditions, and these would be followed seaward by others with characters of greater or less differences. With advance of the waters over the previous land surface, the shoreward and succeeding sediments follow, at the same time rising stratigraphically, being youngest in that part of the region marking the maximum progress of invasion. According to Hill,[63] the Edwards limestone of the Texas Comanche series and the Austin chalk of the Gulf series thus transgress time diagonally, the former being higher westward from Austin and the latter rising eastward from Texas. Stamp[64] has called attention to an interesting case in the Tertiary of Burma (fig. 77) in which "paleontological stages cross the lithological horizons" in a very marked way. It is not certain whether the paleontological stages or the lithological horizons represent definite time units. Cases of diagonal transgression of time should be the rule in overlap, but few have been noted.

2. Slow rise of sea level may permit a wave-cut surface on solid rock for a long distance from shore; the place of permanent deposition is also a long distance therefrom; thus the sediments are likely to be fine, and, ultimately, as the wave-eroded surface sinks below the level of the profile of equilibrium, it becomes covered with fine-grained terrigenous sediments or some type of pelagic sediments. A land surface in the late-maturity or old-age stage of the cycle of erosion would be likely to have a high water table and prob-

[62] Grabau, A. W., Principles of stratigraphy, 1913, p. 723.

[63] Hill, R. T., Two limestone formations of the Cretaceous of Texas which transgress time diagonally, Science, vol. 53, 1921, pp. 190–191.

[64] Stamp, L. D., Seasonal rhythm in the Tertiary sediments of Burma, Geol. Mag., vol. 62, 1925, pp. 515–528, fig. 2; The geology of the oil fields of Burma, Bull. Am. Assoc. Pet. Geol., vol. 11, 1927, pp. 557–579, fig. 6.

ably a shallow depth of decay, so that as the sea advanced over the land there would have been little undecomposed rock to remove, and the wave-cut profile would also be built on solid rock as above, the surfaces in either case having little relief. Unconformities of this character seem common in the geologic column, as shown by the rather general occurrences of undecomposed rock surfaces of little relief at the base of marine sequences. The relations may be disconformable or nonconformable, and basal conglomerates are not probable. The relief of the unconformity is dependent on the character of the original land surface and the rate of rise of sea level, being least for slow rise of sea level and low elevations. The time interval is long.

A modification of this type of unconformity exists in those cases where the rise of sea level is interrupted by times of stability. If these times of

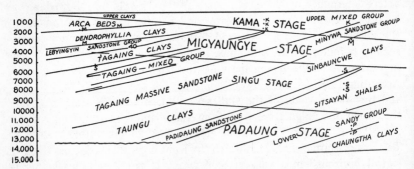

FIG. 77. NORTHWEST TO SOUTHEAST DIAGRAMMATIC SECTION OF THE UPPER PUGUAN REGION OF CENTRAL BURMA

About 30 miles are shown, the lithic units rising to the southeast, the faunal units to the northwest. The diagram shows the lack of coincidence of the faunal and lithic units, or their diachronous behavior. After Stamp, L. D., Bull. Am. Assoc. Pet. Geol., vol. 11, 1927, p. 566.

stability are longer than required to build the bottom at a given place to the level of the profile of equilibrium, the excess time will have no representation at this place other than a thin, much worked over deposit from which the finer materials have been removed. Remains of animals and plants that lived on this bottom while it was at the depth of the profile of equilibrium are not likely to be preserved, as solution, abrasion, and scavengers would have destroyed them. The unconformity of erosion on the submerged land surface thus merges seaward into a disconformity or diastem of non-deposition. It seems probable that many unconformities of this character occur, though they have rarely been recognized.

A somewhat similar condition obtains as a consequence of the marine cycle (fig. 3). In the early stages of the cycle the bottom receives certain quantities of sediments and may be built up to the profile of equilibrium determined by the conditions. As the cycle progresses toward completion, the quantity of sediments decreases and ultimately may become very small, determining a lower profile of equilibrium and making necessary the removal of some of the sediments previously deposited. A submarine erosion surface results on which rests a veneer of the coarser particles washed from the removed sediments.[65] The beginning of a new cycle covers this surface with sediments, and the unconformity over the submerged land thus passes into one developed beneath the sea. Every period of the past that witnessed stable conditions for a long time and was followed by submergence should have unconformities of this kind in its rocks.

3. Rapid falls of sea level bring parts of the bottoms above the profile of equilibrium, and sediments will be removed from such parts, leaving an eroded surface on which permanent deposits are not made until there is a rise of sea level or an increase in the supply of material. Such deposits, when made, hold disconformable relationships to those beneath. The disconformity or diastem is likely to have little relief, may represent a short or a long time, and as a rule is not indicated by a basal conglomerate, though the basal materials may be coarser than those which follow. Few remains of the organisms dwelling on the bottom during either the deposition or erosion of the missing strata will be present in the basal layer because of scavengers, solution, and wave action.

4. The profile of equilibrium established on any water body bottom is not entirely dependent on local conditions, but to a considerable extent is influenced by outside conditions. As the latter change, a lower or higher level may be established and the bottom may be eroded or receive deposits, a stratigraphic break occurring in the latter case.

5. Many stratigraphic breaks of greater or less extent develop in connection with coral reefs. The reef organisms build to the surface of the water, and upward growth then ceases, not to begin again until sea level rises with respect to the surface of the reef, but there may be more or less lateral growth. When sea level rises, the reef is again built to the surface and lateral growth repeated. Thus, extremely elusive breaks are created. The general situation is shown in the diagram of figure 27.

Unconformities in marine deposits generally have wider extent and denote longer time intervals than those in continental deposits. The latter, however, are not uncommonly the more impressive. The magnitude of an unconformity can be measured only by the duration of the lost interval, and the fossils in the enclosing rocks may afford the only clue to this duration. Neither the prominence of the unconformity nor the coarseness of the sediments which lie upon it is indicative of its importance or duration. Much

[65] Johnson, D. W., Shore processes and shoreline development, 1919, p. 256.

may be tcld from the metamorphism, intrusive effects, and deformation of the lower rocks as compared to those above, the differences being suggestive but not decisive of magnitude. A disconformity cannot be told from a diastem by the coarseness of the succeeding deposits. Fossils and the missing strata afford the only clues, and the former are not always reliable. It has been pointed out by Goldman[66] that unconformities are often indicated by glauconite for a foot or so above the break where it is associated with coarse clastics, and if glauconite exists elsewhere in the overlying formation, that adjacent to the break has more irregular surfaces, larger grains, and is of deeper color. Cayeux[67] much earlier suggested that there is a relation between phosphate beds and the movement of sea level, and that glauconite has similar relations. However, there is much glauconite bearing no relationship to unconformities, and the same is true of phosphate, and thus these criteria lose in value.

Every period of stability on a land must have seen many parts of the bottoms of the adjacent shallow waters brought to the position of the profile of equilibrium. Any submergence following such a period of stability led to the development of a disconformity, and such should be present in greater or less numbers in the rocks of those geologic periods which are traditionally described as having this or that continent in a base-leveled condition. Such great marine invasions as the Cambrian, Ordovician, Silurian, and Cretaceous must have led to the development of many diastems and disconformities recording times of no deposition or submarine erosion, and such should be expected and sought for.

RIPPLE MARK AND ITS INTERPRETATION

BY E. M. KINDLE[68] AND W. H. BUCHER

Beds of sand exposed either to wave action or to currents of air or water of the proper degree of intensity become covered by the flutings known as ripple marks. These may be seen on sand dunes, lake and sea beaches and bottoms, and on river beds. Parallelism of troughs and ridges characterizes the forms commonly called ripple marks, but a variety of irregularly shaped forms of water sculpture are properly included under this term.

Granular sediments with little or no cohesion between the composing particles are essential to ripple-mark formation in water. Ripple mark develops on all types of sands, but is more universal on siliceous sands because of their greater abundance. Mud, marl, and other cohesive sediments

---

[66] Goldman, M. I., Lithologic subsurface correlation of the "Bend Series" of North Central Texas, Prof. Paper 129, U. S. Geol. Surv., 1921, p. 4.

[67] Cayeux, L., Génèse des giséments de phosphates de chaux sédimentaires, Bull. Soc. Géol. France, vol. 5, 1905, pp. 750–753.

[68] Published with permission of the Director, Geological Survey of Canada.

are never ripple-marked by water; when dry and in the form of dust, they may be ripple-marked by wind.   It sometimes happens that a deposit of mud abruptly passes into one of sand; in such case ripple mark on the sand stops abruptly at the line of contact with the mud.   The limitation of ripple mark to granular sediments affords an important clue to the original texture of the materials of ripple-marked limestones.

A record of the work of air and water currents has been inscribed in terms of ripple mark on some of the oldest of the sedimentary rocks, and from a study of ripple mark much may be gleaned concerning the history of these older sediments.   Fossil ripple mark should indicate whether the material impressed by it was laid down under wave or current action, by water or by wind, and, if currents were present, their directions and within certain limits their velocities.   Where both fossils and ripple mark are preserved in the same beds, the correct interpretation of the latter may aid greatly in understanding the environmental conditions of the former.

It is evident that any trustworthy interpretation of the significance of fossil ripple mark must rest upon a detailed study of the conditions under which it is now being formed.   Such studies have shown that all examples of ripple mark can be classified into a few types which are the product of definite geologic agents.   A definite and distinctive type of ripple mark always results from water-current action on a sandy bottom, a different type from wave action, and still another type from the direct action of wind on sand or dust.   If these different types can be recognized by the geologist as examples of fossil ripple mark, their discrimination will in many cases afford important aid in determining the history of the formations with which he has to·deal.

In the study of ripple mark, both the experimental and observational methods have contributed in an important way to knowledge of the subject. Among those who by noteworthy experimental studies have contributed to the development of the physical theory of ripple mark are Hunt,[69] De Candolle,[70] Darwin,[71] Forel,[72] and Gilbert.[73]   A host of contributions from

[69] Hunt, A. R., On the formation of ripple mark, Proc. Roy. Soc. London, vol. 34, 1882, pp. 1–19.

[70] De Candolle, C., Rides formées à la surface du sable déposé au fond de l'eau, Arch. Sci. Phys. Nat., Genève, vol. 9, 1883, pp. 241–278.

[71] Darwin, G. H., On the formation of ripple mark in sand, Proc. Roy. Soc. London, vol. 36, 1883, pp. 18–43.

[72] Forel, F. A., La formation des rides du Leman, Bull. Soc. Vaudoise Sci. Naturelles, vol. 10, 1870, p. 518; Les rides de fond dans le golfe de Morgues, op. cit., vol. 15, 1878, pp. 66–68, 76–77; Les rides de fond étudiées dans le Lac Leman, Arch. Sci. Phys. Nat., Genève, vol. 10, 1883, pp. 39–72.

[73] Gilbert, G. K., Ripple-marks, Bull. Philos. Soc. Washington, vol. 2, 1880, pp. 61–62; Ripple-marks, Science, vol. 3, 1884, pp. 375–376; Ripple-marks and cross-bedding, Bull. Geol. Soc. Am., vol. 10, 1899, pp. 135–140; The transportation of debris by running water, Prof. Paper 86, U. S. Geol. Surv., 1914.

the descriptive or observational point of view which range in importance from brief notes to elaborately illustrated papers have been made by other geologists.   Only a few of these can be mentioned in the following historical sketch of the growth of knowledge concerning ripple mark.

Nomenclature

The phenomenon generally known as ripple mark has been described under various names, as ripple-drift, current-drift, current-mark, wave mark, and friction mark.   The first three terms have been pretty generally discarded.   Wave mark is now generally applied to the faint thread of sand, or swash mark, marking the upper limit of a wave on a beach.   Gilbert used the terms "dune" and "anti-dune" for migrating ripple ridges, but the pre-emption of the word dune for large eolian hills of sand makes its use for ripple mark confusing.   For the larger forms allied to ordinary ripple marks, sand waves, tidal sand ridges, and the recently coined names meta-ripples and para-ripples are among the terms which have been used.   Bucher[74] has defined the term "sedimentary ripples" so as to include all of these forms as well as beach cusps and longitudinal dunes.   These last two structures are not, however, included in the term ripple mark as here used.

Comparison and description of different types of ripple mark involve the use of certain terms which are defined as follows.

The *amplitude*[75] is the elevation of the ripple ridge above the trough.

The *wave length* is the distance from crest to crest of the ripple ridges.

The *ripple index* is the wave length divided by the amplitude.

Historical Sketch[76]

The data which are indispensable for an adequate interpretation of any given part of the geologic record naturally fall into three groups: (1) an accurate and exhaustive knowledge (description) of the forms constituting this record, their vertical range (in the stratigraphic sense) and areal distribution; (b) a quantitative knowledge of all factors which determine these forms and their horizontal distribution and vertical range in nature; (c) a

---

[74] Bucher, W. H., On ripples and related sedimentary surface forms and their paleogeographic interpretation, Am. Jour. Sci., vol. 47, 1919, pp. 207–208.

[75] In Kindle's paper (Recent and fossil ripple-mark, Mus. Bull. 25, Geol. Surv. Canada, 1917) amplitude is used to signify the distance from crest to crest.   This use is in conformity with a common dictionary definition in which width or breadth is indicated as the primary meaning of the word.   In one of his papers (The descriptive nomenclature of ripple-mark, Geol. Mag., vol. 41, 1904, pp. 410–418) Hunt has pointed out the objections to the use of amplitude in the sense of height.

[76] This is entirely the work of Professor Bucher.

quantitative knowledge of all factors which determine the preservation of these forms.

The following historical sketch will trace briefly the growth of information in each of these groups.

FORM, RANGE, AND DISTRIBUTION. In his "Geological Observer" Sir Henry De la Beche gave a classical account of modern and fossil ripples, clearly describing two fundamental types, the symmetrical (oscillation) and the asymmetrical (current) ripples.[77]

The difference between the sharp-crested positive and rounded form of the negative (mold) of the symmetrical ripples, although emphasized repeatedly in the following decades,[78] has only recently been recognized by geologists.[79]

De la Beche devoted a separate, though primitive, illustration to the "unequally distributed and variable formed elevations and depressions," recently called linguoid ripples by Bucher, which are common in fluvial and shallow-water sediments, but have only much later been described satisfactorily in geologic literature (Fuchs,[80] Cox and Dake,[81] Kindle,[82] and Bucher[83]). Their form was analyzed by Blasius.[84]

Similarly, the polygonal, cell-like pattern of interference ripples, described by Hitchcock[85] as "tadpole nests," although occasionally referred to and figured, has not generally been recognized as a necessary constituent of rippled sediments. Many negatives of these interference ripples in geological collections are still labelled "curiosa" or are classed with bodies of concretionary origin.

The valuable differences between current ripples of aquatic and eolian

[77] The geological observer, 1851, pp. 87, 113, and especially 506–509. The first edition which appeared in 1835 under the title "How to observe" is not accessible to the writer.

[78] Jukes, J. B., Manual of geology, 3rd ed., 1872, pp. 162–164; Fuchs, T., Studien über Fucoiden und Hieroglyphen, Denks. Akad. Wiss., Wien, vol. 62, 1895, p. 372, figs. 1–2; Van Hise, C. R., Principles of North American Pre-Cambrian geology, 16th Ann. Rept. U. S. Geol. Surv., pt. i, 1896, pp. 719–721.

[79] Very few textbooks refer to this difference. Some of the best use the negative to illustrate "ripple marks," as, e. g., Dana, J. D., Manual of geology, 1895, p. 95; Chamberlin and Salisbury, Geology, vol. 1, 1906, p. 371.

[80] Fuchs, T., op. cit.

[81] Cox, G. H., and Dake, C. L., Geologic criteria for determining the structural position of sedimentary beds, Bull. School of Mines, Univ. Missouri, vol. 2, 1916.

[82] Kindle, E. M., op. cit., 1917.

[83] Bucher, W. H., op. cit., 1919.

[84] Blasius, H., Über die Abhängigkeit der Formen der Riffeln und Geschiebebänke vom Gefälle, Zeits. f. Bauwesen, vol. 60, 1910, pp. 466–472.

[85] Hitchcock, E., Ichnology of Massachusetts, 1858, pp. 168–169; Kindle, E. M., An inquiry into the origin of *Batrachioides* the *antiquor* of the Lockport dolomite of New York, Geol. Mag., vol. 1, 1914, pp. 158–161.

origin, in the ratio of wave length to amplitude, was first observed by Cornish[86] and later independently by Kindle.[87]

Large ripples, the para-ripples of Bucher, with wave lengths measured by feet rather than inches, were described as early as 1838 from the Upper Ordovician of the Cincinnati Anticline.[88] Owing to their abundance in the Eden and Richmond divisions, they have frequently been referred to and described in publications on the local geology of Kentucky, Ohio, and Indiana. More recently, isolated occurrences have been described from the Silurian, Devonian, and Mississippian of eastern and central United States and from the Comanchean of Texas.

Ripples of similar dimensions, but generally of much more pronounced asymmetry, the meta-ripples of Bucher, abound on sand bars exposed after a flood and on tide-swept flats. They were repeatedly described and in one instance mapped in minute detail by engineers of the Mississippi River Survey.[89] The tidal meta-ripples, while mentioned in earlier writings on ripples, were not described adequately until 1901.[90]

Beautiful illustrations of modern and fossil ripples were given in the comprehensive paper published by Kindle in 1917, together with a wealth of observations. This paper represents the results of the first systematic extensive and intensive field studies made by a geologist since the days of Lyell and De la Beche.

Most formal observations on ripples have been made more or less casually without reference to their areal distribution. The greatest depth to which oscillation ripples actually can form early attracted attention. As early as 1841, the French engineer, Siau,[91] published an account of white ripples of coral sand separated by troughs filled with black grains of basalt which he observed at St. Gilles, near the westernmost point of the Island of Bourbon (Réunion) in the Indian Ocean, and by an ingenious method traced down to a depth of 188 m. (617 feet).

[86] Cornish, V., On snow waves and snow drifts in Canada, Geog. Jour., vol. 20, 1902' p. 105; On desert dunes bordering the Nile delta, Ibid., vol. 15, 1900, pp. 27–28.

[87] Kindle, E. M., Recent and fossil ripple mark, Mus. Bull. 25, Geol. Surv. Canada, 1917, p. 12.

[88] Locke, J., Geological Report, Geol. Surv. Ohio, 2nd Ann. Rept., 1838, p. 247, pl. 6.

[89] Suter, C. R., Rept. Chief Eng., U. S. A., vol. 2, 1875, p. 502; Johnston, J. B., Result of sand wave and sediment observations, Ibid., 1879, pp. 1963–1967; Ockerson, J. A., On a minute survey of a sandbar in Mississippi River, Ibid., 1884, p. 2571; Hider, A., Mississippi River Commission Rept., 1882, pp. 83–88.

[90] Cornish, V., Sand waves in tidal currents, Geog. Jour., vol. 18, 1901, pp. 170–202; On tidal sand ripples above low water mark, Rept. Brit. Assoc., 1900, pp. 733–734; On the formation of wave surfaces in sand, Scottish Geog. Mag., vol. 17, 1901, pp. 1–11; Waves of sand and snow, 1914, p. 278.

[91] Siau, M., Observations diverses faites en 1839 et 1840, pendant un voyage à l'Ile Bourbon, Compt. Rend., Acad. Sci. Paris, vol. 12, 1841, pp. 774–775; Action des vagues à de grandes profondeurs, Ann. Chim. et Phys., vol. 2, 1841, pp. 118 ff

In most similar observations at much lesser depths, little attempt has been made to describe the ripples with reference to the total configuration of the coast and the adjoining parts of the water body, that is, to understand them as an integral part of a definite dynamic and topographic system. As two notable exceptions we may quote Forel's classical investigations on Lake Geneva[92] and Cornish's studies on tidal meta-ripples.[93]

Forel showed that the depths to which oscillation ripples may form is limited by the size of the waves which, in turn, depends primarily on the size of the water body. He also noted that at any given locality the position of the ripples remains unchanged and corresponds to the orientation of the strongest waves on the lake surface which, in turn, depends primarily on the line of greatest fetch of the wind.

In the case of asymmetrical meta-ripples formed by the strong tidal currents of the British coast, Cornish showed that on the open sea-shore, as well as in the estuaries, they trend essentially at right angles to the shoreline.

Only two systematic areal studies of fossil ripples are known to the writer: one on the oscillation ripples of the Bedford and Berea formations of Ohio by Hyde[94] and the other on the large para-ripples of the Eden and Richmond series and the Brassfield formation of central Kentucky by Bucher.[95]

A later analysis of Hyde's observations by Bucher suggests that the remarkable uniform trend of the Bedford-Berea ripples is due to the action of monsoons. The para-ripples of the Ordovician and Silurian of Kentucky (and adjoining states), on the other hand, are considered as the product of tidal currents, more or less reinforced by wind drift.

QUANTITATIVE STUDIES OF FACTORS DETERMINING FORM AND DISTRIBUTION. The problem of the qualitative and quantitative character of the factors which determine the origin and form of ripples forced itself independently upon workers in widely separated fields of research outside the confines of geology, and their experiments and observations have furnished most of the data upon which our present understanding of the process of ripple formation is based.

The qualitative nature of the process was, however, already correctly recognized by such master observers as Lyell and De la Beche, who had no doubt that the "furrows and ridges" were "produced by the fric-

[92] Forel, F. A., op. cit., 1878, p. 66; op. cit., 1883; Le Leman, Lausanne, vol. 2, 1895, pp. 248 ff.

[93] Cornish, V., Sand waves in tidal currents, Geog. Jour., vol. 18, 1901, pp. 170–202.

[94] Hyde, J. E., The ripples of the Bedford and Berea formations of central Ohio, etc., Jour. Geol., vol. 19, 1911, pp. 257–269.

[95] Bucher, W. H., Large current-ripples as indicators of paleogeography, Proc. Nat. Acad., Sci., vol. 3, 1917, pp. 285–291; On ripples and related sedimentary forms and their paleogeographic interpretation, Am. Jour. Sci., vol. 47, 1919, pp. 149–210, 241–269.

tion . . . of currents over arenaceous accumulations"[96] and that "they are formed equally by currents of wind . . . and under water."[97] De la Beche also knew that oscillation ripples could be readily reproduced artificially in "sand . . . acted upon by agitating water above it in conveniently formed vessels of sufficient dimensions."[98]

In 1882 Hunt[99] published the results of his systematic experiments "On the formation of ripple mark," and a few months later De Candolle set forth the results of experiments in which he had studied from a broad point o view the rippling of the contact surfaces existing between a "viscous" substance, that is, one consisting of mobile particles with considerable friction (like viscous liquids, dust, sand), and a liquid of low viscosity, moving past each other.[100] In November of the same year G. H. Darwin[101] published his classical observations on artificial ripples in sand, and finally in the same year Forel[102] summarized his exquisite experimental and field observations on oscillation ripples.

Through this important group of papers, dealing almost exclusively with oscillation ripples, the laws determining their formation and existence were definitely established. The more important of these laws are as follows: Oscillation ripples owe their origin to an oscillatory movement of the water; they are stationary; their wave length grows with the velocity of the oscillatory movement and with the size of the sand grains; they can form and exist only within rather narrow limits of velocity; once formed they are unaffected by weaker oscillatory movements of the water.[103]

However, these papers placed undue importance upon oscillation ripples and upon waves as a cause of ripples. Hunt wrote "to prove that ripplemarks formed under water are, as a rule, completely independent of the rise and fall of tides, of tidal currents, of sea beaches; and that they have little in common with the current mark that owes its origin either to a continuous current of air or of water." De Candolle considered an "oscillatory" or "intermittent" movement of the water as indispensable to the formation of ripples, meaning by "intermittent" a current constant in direction but variable in velocity. Indirectly, at least, this assumption found the support of Darwin, who wrote: "I feel some doubt as to the view

[96] De la Beche, H. T., The geological observer, 1851, pp. 87, 113, 506–509.

[97] Lyell, C., Principles of geology, 11th ed., 1872, p. 342.

[98] De la Beche, H. T., op. cit., p. 508.

[99] Hunt, A. R., On the formation of ripple mark, Proc. Roy. Soc. London, vol. 34, 1882, pp. 1–8 ff.

[100] De Candolle, C., Rides formées à la surface du sable déposé au fond de l'eau, Arch. Sci. Phy. Nat., Genève, vol. 9, 1883, pp. 241–278.

[101] Darwin, G. H., op. cit., 1883.

[102] Forel, F. A., op. cit., 1878, p. 66; op. cit., 1883; op. cit., 1895.

[103] For a systematic discussion and additional facts see Bucher, op. cit., 1919, p. 192.

that a regular series of dunes may be formed by uniform current; at any rate, in my experiments the dunes were irregular and had no definite wave length." Current ripple mark thus assumed secondary importance, and its origin appeared to be linked with a mysterious factor responsible for the "intermittent" character or "pulsations" of the currents.

These pulsations still figure in Baschin's excellent paper[104] in which he viewed the sedimentary ripples as specific cases of the general law which treats the wave form as the necessary surface of equilibrium between two liquids moving at different velocities, or between a liquid and a sediment. The true value of this conception of current ripples as the necessary form of surface of contact separating the moving water and the sediment was not realized until, at the beginning of this century, systematic experiments on the transportation of sediment by running water were begun on a large scale.[105]

Quantitative experimental determinations of the factors involved in the formation and existence of current ripples were published by Hahmann.[106] His results show that, excepting the difference in form and behavior (traveling) which follow from the contrast between oscillatory and continuous current, the laws govering the formation of current ripples are identical with those of oscillation ripples. There can be no doubt that both are the result of the same process and that oscillation ripples are but a modification of current ripples, resulting from the rhythmic reversal of the current.

In the course of the hydraulic experiments to which reference has been made, the less common forms of rhomboid and linguoid ripples attracted attention and were studied in detail, the former by Engels, the latter by Blasius.

Reynolds[107] had observed the formation of current ripples while experimenting with artificial tidal currents in his model estuary. Without entering into an analysis of the physics of these ripples, he assumed from the ratio of this model to nature that real tidal currents should give rise to truly gi-

[104] Baschin, O., Die Entstehung wellenähnlicher Oberflächenformen, Zeits. Gesell. Erdkunde, vol. 34, 1899, pp. 408–421.

[105] Eger, Dix, and Seifert, Versuch über die Bettausbildung der Weserstrecke von Km. 303–306, Zeits. f. Bauwesen, vol. 56, 1904, pp. 323–344; Engels, H., Untersuchungen über die Bettausbildung gerader oder gekruemmter Fluss-strecken mit beweglicher Sohle, Ibid., vol. 55, 1905, pp. 663 ff.; Blasius, H., Über die Abhängigkeit der Formen der Riffeln und Geschiebebänke vom Gefälle, Ibid., vol. 60, 1910, pp. 466–472; Gilbert, G. K., The transportation of debris by running water, Prof. Paper 86, U. S. Geol. Surv., 1914.

[106] Hahmann, P., Die Bildung von Sanddünen bei gleichmässiger Strömung, Ann. Phys., 1912, pp. 637–676.   See also Bucher, op. cit., 1919, pp. 153–164.

[107] Reynolds, O., Reports of the Committee on the action of waves and currents, Rept. Brit. Assoc., 1887, pp. 555–562; 1889, pp. 328–343; 1890, pp. 512–534; 1891, pp. 386–404.

gantic ripples with a wave length of 80 to 100 feet. The same arbitrary
hypothetical enlargement of scale has led to the assumption that the large
subaerial dunes, which in regions of constant wind direction reach a remarkable degree of regularity in wave length and height, are merely full-grown
eolian current ripples.[108]

In all hydraulic experiments it soon became evident that above a certain
critical velocity current ripples in water cease to exist. Gilbert's[109] observations have clearly brought out the fundamental change in the relation
of the overlying fluid to the sediment which sets in when the ripples disappear. In his experiments with still higher velocities, the wave form re-
appeared, but was under radically different dynamic conditions, as direct
friction waves without the intercalation of vertical vortices. The probable
relation between these unstable "sand waves," which disappear when the
velocity drops below the critical value, and the larger forms of ripples (meta-
and para-ripples) was discussed by Bucher.[110]

Since a similar critical velocity in air currents destroys eolian current
ripples after they have reached a maximum size measured in centimeters,
the existence of regular current ripples of one to several meters' wave
length and of regular dunes of similar height and a uniform wave length of
several kilometers[111] presents a difficult problem. Its solution seems to be
contained in the observations of King,[112] which definitely established the
tendency of air currents to assume the form of stationary waves in the lee
of an obstacle. This leads to the assumption that for every obstacle of
given size and wind of a given average velocity "there exists a sinuous
surface which, when established, offers a minimum of friction. Whether the
surrounding surface be flat or consists itself of independent dunes, all
fortuitous changes in the distribution of the sand must gradually lead
toward the formation of this optimum surface,"[113] provided velocity and
direction of the wind remain unchanged for a sufficient length of time.

For the purpose of the geologist, the knowledge of the physical factors
determining the form and dimensions of ripples is of value only when translated into terms of geographical conditions. This translation has been
left almost entirely to the geologist, who only in the last two decades has
thoroughly realized the complexity of the task.

[108] Cornish, V., Progressive waves in rivers, Geog. Jour., vol. 29, 1907, pp. 23–31.
[109] Gilbert, G. K., op. cit., 1914.
[110] Bucher, W. H., op. cit., 1919, pp. 165–182.
[111] Hedin, S., Scientific results of a journey in Central Asia, see volumes 1 and 2 for
ripple mark, dune formation, etc., 1899–1902.
[112] King, W. J. H., The nature and formation of sand ripples and dunes, Geog. Jour.,
vol. 47, 1916, p. 189–209. It is interesting to note that Forel in his experiments on oscillation ripples observed that the presence of a linear obstacle of small height greatly
facilitated the formation of ripples.
[113] Bucher, W. H., op. cit., 1919, pp. 147–199, 201–202.

Two examples may serve to illustrate the uncertainty and errors that attach to most earlier reasoning about ripples.

Zimmermann[114] described small ripples from one of the layers of salt separated by very thin laminæ of anhydrite which were found in a drill core from the Zechstein at Schlitz in Hesse. Since this salt is part of the vast Permian deposits generally known as the Stassfurt salts, any definite information concerning the depth of the water body at any given locality would be of considerable interest. Zimmermann concluded that these ripples could have formed only under a very thin cover of water, perhaps but a few decimeters in depth, "else no ripples or at least none of such small size could have formed." Yet Siau had found ripples of similar dimension at a depth of 617 feet in the Indian Ocean.

The other extreme is represented by Gilbert,[115] who thought he had found oscillation ripples, 6 inches to 3 feet in height and 10 to 30 feet from crest to crest, in the Medina sandstone. He arrrived at the conclusion that these large ripples must have been produced through the action of waves no less than 60 feet high. The only point overlooked in this argument of far-reaching paleogeographical consequences vitiates its conclusions, namely, the existence of a critical current velocity, above which neither current nor oscillation ripples can form or exist.

The three comprehensive papers which have appeared since 1916[116] mark rapid strides forward toward an adequate understanding of the factors involved in the formation of the various forms of ripples.

Preservation of Ripple Mark

The question why one or the other type of ripples is not found in a certain sediment leads to this alternative: either they were not formed or were not preserved. For an adequate interpretation of the fossil sedimentary record, therefore, the factors which favor or prevent preservation are as important as those involved in the formation of ripples. They have barely been referred to, or not at all, in most of the earlier literature on ripple mark. The first attempt at a systematic discussion is contained in Bucher's paper of 1919.

[114] Zimmermann, E., Steinsaltz mit Wellenfurchen, etc. [Schlitz in Hessen], Zeits. d. Deut. geol. Gesell., vol. 60, Monatsb., 1908, p. 70.

[115] Gilbert, G. K., Ripple-marks and cross-bedding, Bull. Geol. Soc. Am., vol. 10, 1899, pp. 135–140; H. L. Fairchild showed that these are not ripples, see Beach structure in Medina sandstone, Am. Geol., vol. 28, 1901, pp. 9–14.

[116] Johnson, D. W., Contributions to the study of ripple-marks, Jour. Geol., vol. 24, 1916, pp. 809–819; Kindle, E. M., Recent and fossil ripple-mark, Mus. Bull. 25, Geol. Surv. Canada, 1917; Bucher, W. H., On ripples and related sedimentary forms and their paleogeographic interpretation, Am. Jour. Sci., vol. 47, 1919, pp. 149–210, 241–269.

Wind Ripple Mark

The ease with which every feature connected with the development of wind-made ripple mark can be observed makes it convenient to begin the study with the examination of eolian ripple mark. This finds its best development on the surfaces of sand dunes, but frequently may be seen on lake and sand beaches. Wind ripples also form in dusts and other fine materials.

Wind ripple mark is asymmetrical, the windward slope of slight inclination, the leeward steep.[117] The wave length and amplitude seem to vary little with wind velocity,[118] but they do vary somewhat with the size of the

FIG. 78. WIND RIPPLE MARK

The wind blew from left to right. Photograph by Doctor E. M. Kindle at a place west of Port Colborne, Ontario.

particles,[119] the largest wave lengths and the greater amplitudes being attained in the coarser sands. Both components vary within narrow limits, the majority of the former falling between 2 and 4 inches and the latter between 1/8 and 1/4 inch (fig. 78). Kindle records the occurrence of irregular ripples in coarse sands on the shores of Lake Erie with wave lengths up to 10 inches. The ripple index is relatively large.

[117] Lyell, C., The student's elements of geology, 6th ed., 1841, pp. 41–43. Lyell's description of the formation of wind ripple mark can hardly be improved upon.

[118] Kindle, E. M., op. cit., 1917, p. 10.

[119] Sokolow, N. A., Die Dünen, Bildung, Entwicklung und innerer Bau, German translation by Arzruni, A., 1894, p. 15.

Wine ripples approach parallelism, but commonly are not straight. They anastomose in broad net-like patterns and do not appear to have such extensive continuity as does water ripple mark.

The crests of wind ripple marks should contain coarser particles than occur in the troughs and on the slopes, but the distinction in many cases is difficult to make.

Figure 79a, which illustrates diagrammatically the mode of formation of wind ripple, will also show by comparison with figure 79b the essential difference between wind and water-current ripple mark. The height of the crest of the latter is always greater than the former when the wave lengths are approximately the same.

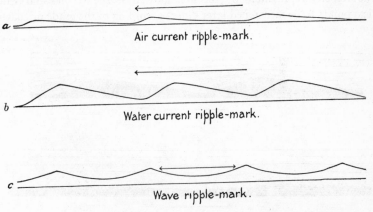

FIG. 79. DIAGRAMMATIC ILLUSTRATIONS OF TYPES OF RIPPLE MARK
Drawn by Doctor E. M. Kindle

WIND RIPPLE MARK ON SNOW. In cold climates wind ripple mark is sometimes formed on dry and granular snow. The cohesion of snow flakes or particles varies with the temperature and consequent moisture, so that ripple mark forms on snow only at temperatures considerably below the freezing point. With low temperature and the right type of powdery snow, a winter gale almost always develops over parts of a large level expanse of snow a type of asymmetric ripple with a highly variable wave length, which differs conspicuously from eolian sand ripple mark in having its steep face on the windward instead of the leeward side. Symmetrical ripple mark with a wave length of several inches sometimes forms on snow, but it is a relatively rare phenomenon. Obviously the shape of the ripples as reported in these observations is due to peculiar conditions inherent in the properties of snow which have not been analyzed so far.

Ripple Mark Formed by Water Currents

CRITICAL CURRENT VELOCITY. The surface of sand when exposed to a current of water is set in motion when the current reaches a velocity sufficient to drag some of the surface particles along with it, and at certain velocities ripple mark forms in the moving surface layer. Its development results through the operation of the general principle that a sinuous surface of contact between a moving fluid and a sediment offers a minimum of friction for certain velocities.

Below a certain velocity, a current is unable to move the débris forming its bed. The point at which, with increasing velocity, motion is started, is called the "first critical point" in the following discussion.[120]

The velocity represented by the first as well as the second and third critical points to be mentioned later differs according to the grade or coarse-

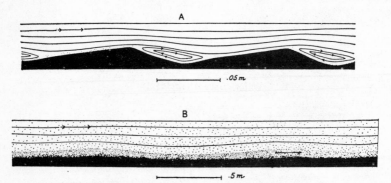

FIG. 80. DIAGRAMS CONTRASTING THE MOVEMENT OF SAND GRAINS AND CURRENT IN CURRENT RIPPLES (*A*) AND SAND WAVES (*B*)

Drawn by Doctor E. M. Kindle

ness of the débris. In each case, however, the critical point of current velocity is the velocity which is correlated with a radical change in the behavior of the sediments which are subjected to it.

The results of three series of determinations of the first critical point by Umpfenbach, Login, and Gilbert have been brought together by Bucher[121] and are given in table 89.

CURRENT RIPPLES. Shortly after the first critical point of the current is reached, current ripples develop consisting of numerous essentially parallel, long, narrow, more or less equidistant ridges trending at right angles to the

---

[120] It corresponds to the lower critical velocity of Lechalas and to the velocity competent for traction of Gilbert's nomenclature, Gilbert, op. cit., 1914, p. 194.

[121] Bucher, W. H., op. cit., 1919, p. 151.

current. These ridges are asymmetrical in profile, with a steep lee-side and a gentle stoss-side slope (figs. 81–83).

The lines of flow, as represented in figure 80, were first recognized and figured by Darwin,[122] who demonstrated the existence of a vortex on the lee-

TABLE 89

APPROXIMATE CURRENT VELOCITIES NECESSARY TO MOVE DÉBRIS OF DIFFERENT SIZES*

DESCRIPTION	MEAN DIAMETER	DEPTH	VELOCITY
	mm.	*m.*	*m./sec.*
Brick clay, allowed to settle from suspension (L)........................		(Shallow)	0.08 (s)
Fine loam and mud (U)................		(Shallow)	0.32 (s)
(Fine sand) (G).......................	0.4	0.13	0.26 (m)
(Sand) (G)............................	0.5	0.12	0.28 (m)
Fresh-water sand (L).................		(Shallow)	0.20 (s)*
(Sand) (G)...........................	0.7	0.2	0.34 (m)
Sea sand (L).........................		(Shallow)	0.34 (s)
Coarse sand (L)......................		(Shallow)	0.49 (s)
(Coarse sand) (G)....................	1.7	0.006	0.34 (m)
(Fine gravel) (G).....................	3.2	0.028	0.46 (m)
Rounded pebbles size of peas (L)........		(Shallow)	0.61 (s)
Very small pebbles (U)................		(Shallow)	0.65 (s)
(Fine gravel) (G).....................	4.9	0.033	0.65 (m)
(Fine gravel) (G).....................	7.0	0.066	0.86 (m)
Gravel (U)...........................	27.0	(Shallow)	0.97 (s)
Gravel (U)...........................	54.0	(Shallow)	1.62 (s)
Boulders (U).........................	171.0	(Shallow)	2.27 (s)
Boulders (U).........................	323.0	(Shallow)	3.25 (s)
Boulders (U).........................	409.0	(Shallow)	4.87 (s)
Boulders (U).........................	700–800	(Shallow)	11.69 (s)

* (U) = Umpfenbach, quoted from Penck, Morphologie der Erdoberfläche, vol. 1, 1894, p. 283.

(L) = Login, Proc. Roy. Soc. Edinburgh, vol. 3, 1857, p. 475.

(G) = Gilbert, G. K., Prof. Paper 86, U. S. Geol. Surv., the first three figures from table 9, p. 69, and the others from the averages on p. 71.

Also: (s) equals surface velocity and (m) mean velocity.

Login's and Gilbert's figures have been transformed from inches to the nearest millimeter and from feet to the nearest centimeter.

side by placing a drop of ink in the trough between two ripples. The action of this vortex causes small particles to creep upstream on the lee-side of a ripple.[123]

[122] Darwin, G. H., On the formation of ripple-mark in sand, Proc. Roy. Soc. London, vol. 36, 1883, pp. 18–43.

[123] Bertololy, E., Kräuselungsmarken und Dünen, Münchener Geog. Studien, 9. Stueck, 1900, p. 86.

FIG. 81. WATER-CURRENT RIPPLE MARK

These current ripple marks were made on sands of Nantasket Beach, Massachusetts. The currents which formed the ripples were quite regular and moved from right to left. It will be noted that the steeper slopes are on the side opposite to that from which the currents came. After Johnson, D. W., Shore processes and shoreline development, 1919, p. 495.

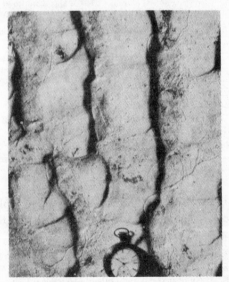

FIG. 82. WATER-CURRENT RIPPLE MARK WITH MOLLUSK AND WORM TRAILS

The current moved from left to right. Photograph by Doctor E. M. Kindle.

Current ripples travel downstream as the grains are rolled up the gentle slope and dropped into the vortex of the lee-side to be deposited there.[124] It should be noted that the ripple as such is absolutely rigid, while just the grains of the top layer roll along the surface, no grains being carried in suspension.

The gentler slopes of current ripple mark are invariably up-current. In shallow streams with relatively smooth bottoms, the ridges are essentially parallel and may extend with even and regular crests from bank to bank, some occasionally dying out, others uniting and new ones appearing. Irregularities on the bottom and bends in the stream produce irregularities in

Fig. 83. Large Water-Current Ripple Marks with Crests 10 to 15 Feet Apart
Below bridge over the Avon River, Windsor, Nova Scotia. Very much smaller current ripple marks are superimposed upon the larger. Photograph by Doctor E. M. Kindle.

wave length, amplitude, and direction. Most streams have local upstream currents, and such may develop ripple mark with reversed slopes. In bays and similar bodies of water the trends exhibit great variation, and the gentle slopes may be either seaward or landward.

As lamination is always developed on the lee-side of current ripple mark, it follows that in cases of parallel crests the cross-lamination is regular in direction of inclination, and that diversity of ripple-mark development leads to equal diversity in direction and inclination of cross-lamination.

The distribution of particles in current ripples is such that the coarsest are found in the troughs and the finest on the crests. This often is very

[124] Forel calls the stoss side, "face d'érosion," the lee-side, "face d'alluvion."

distinctly shown, and in cases of rapid deposition of sediments, successive crests and troughs may coincide so as to produce apparent cross-lamination in an up-current direction.[125]

REGRESSIVE SAND WAVES. With increasing current, a second critical point of current velocity is reached when current ripples disappear and the sand surface becomes a smooth sheet of sand.[126] This is due to the fact that the mechanical effect of the current is extended below the surface, destroying the immobility of the sand bed, which is the prerequisite of the existence of current ripples. Instead of the topmost grains rolling and skipping over a bed of sand, we find a whole layer of mixed sand and water in motion, grading insensibly into the motionless substratum. Above this layer of moving sand and water we find water with little sand in suspension, the transition being not gradual but abrupt.

After the "smooth phase" following the second critical point, a third critical point was reached in Gilbert's experiments at which the sand again assumed a waved surface. At this velocity, however, the waves of sand which Gilbert called "anti-dunes" traveled upstream. For Gilbert's term Bucher has substituted that of "regressive sand waves."[127] "This movement is accomplished by erosion on the downstream face and deposition on the upstream face."[128] Cornish found this reversed motion of the ripple mark occurring when the velocity attained about 2.2 feet per second.[129] Gilbert found the development of this phase to be connected with increase of load as well as with increased velocity.

The regressive sand waves differ in shape as well as in the direction of movement from current ripples. They have symmetrical profiles and gently rounded crests.

PROGRESSIVE SAND WAVES. In waters carrying large quantities of sediments of high velocity above the third critical point, ripples of gigantic proportions called sand waves are developed. Hider[130] describes them as "a series of ridges irregular in shape, transverse to the direction of the current, which in deeper water and the most rapid current under favorable conditions become more regular in shape and size approaching the form of waves." Gently rounded broad crests, often nearly symmetrical, characterize these sand waves. Observations made by McMath from a diving bell in the

[125] Spurr, J. E., False bedding in stratified drift deposits, Am. Geol., vol. 13, 1894, pp. 43–47, 201–206.

[126] Gilbert, G. K., op. cit., 1914, p. 32.

[127] Bucher, W. H., op. cit., 1919, p. 165.

[128] Gilbert, G. K., op. cit., 1914, p. 11.

[129] Cornish, V., Waves of sand and snow, 1914, p. 278.

[130] Hider, A., Mississippi River Commission Rept., 1882, pp. 83–88; Chief. Eng., U. S. A., Rept., 1883, p. 2199.

Mississippi River showed a flowing motion at a depth of 2 feet below the surface of the sand wave, the velocity diminishing downward.[131]

These sand waves travel downstream like current ripple. Their broad rounded crests, however, are in sharp contrast with the angular crests and steep lee slopes of current ripple. Hider's observations appear to indicate that reduction of velocity results in the transformation of these sand waves into the large ripples seen in tidal flats and the sand bars of many rivers and creeks, and the observations of Reynolds[132] seem to support this view. Bucher explains the transformation as follows:

As the velocity drops below the third critical point, the bodies of the waves settle and become rigid, a vortex forms on the lee side and now the weak current, like a wind on a dune, moves but the grains of the surface layer, rolling them up the weather slope and dropping them on the lee side. Since the angle of rest of ordinary materials differs greatly from the gentle slope of the sand-wave, this must undergo a fundamental change in form, from more or less symmetrical waves to strongly asymmetrical dunes.[133]

META-RIPPLES. Bucher has proposed to distinguish between the sand waves and the secondary forms derived from them by using for the latter the term meta-ripples.[134] Direct observation through the turbid waters producing these structures is extremely difficult owing to the depth and large suspended load of the water at the time the transformation is assumed to occur.

Whatever the nature of the transformation may be which takes place between the phase of maximum activity in giant ripple mark formation and the emergence of the huge sand waves left by ebbing tides in estuaries and falling flood waters in rivers, the terrace-like structures of each, with steep, usually seaward-facing[135] fronts, are distinctly asymmetric and similar in essential features; but the tidal sand waves have a greater range than those of the rivers in the size of the ripples, some of the tidal sand ridges rising 7 or 8 feet above the troughs at the mouth of the Avon River,[136] while upriver meta-ripples rarely rise more than 2 or 3 feet above their troughs.

"FULLS AND LOWS" CONTRASTED WITH META-RIPPLES. Meta-ripples with the scarp face modified by tidal action might be confused with structures commonly called "fulls and lows" on the English coast but having a very

[131] Gilbert, G. K., op. cit., p. 156.

[132] Reynolds, O., Reports of the Committee on the action of waves and currents, Rept. Brit. Assoc., 1889, p. 343.

[133] Bucher, W. H., op. cit., 1919, p. 181.

[134] Bucher, W. H., op. cit., 1919, p. 181.

[135] Cornish recorded large tidal ripples facing with the flood tide at Barmouth, N. Wales, and on the Goodwin Sands; Geog. Jour., vol. 18, 1901, pp. 171, 190.

[136] Kindle, E. M., Notes on the tidal phenomena of Bay of Fundy rivers, Jour. Geol., vol. 34, 1926, p. 645.

different origin from any kind of ripple mark.   On some sea coasts a series
of two or more low uniformly rounded sand ridges usually many yards in
width border the sea beach, trending parallel with it in the intertidal zone
or below it.   Three of these sand ridges uncovered at low tide and separated
by a wide depression $1\frac{1}{2}$ to $4\frac{1}{2}$ feet deep lay seaward of the shore beach at
Skegness, England, during the early summer of 1928.   Similar underwater
structures border Point Pelee, the long sand spit extending into Lake Erie
from the north shore.   These "fulls" appear to be produced by breakers
and the resulting undertow currents during heavy storms.   They probably
shift their positions only in stormy periods.

PARA-RIPPLES.   Para-ripples, the large ripples found in many limestones,
are considered by Bucher to be the result of current action.   They vary
from strongly asymmetrical to completely symmetrical and are ascribed
to current rather than wave action chiefly on the evidence of lack of assortment of the materials composing them.   They differ from meta-ripples
chiefly in the greater number of symmetrical ripples and in the smaller index
of the asymmetrical forms.   It may be that they represent meta-ripples
modified by wave action or by tidal currents reversed so as to have lost
the original asymmetry.

Wave Ripple Mark

FORMATION.   Wave ripple mark is a function of wave action.   The agitation of the bottom resulting from the oscillatory movement of water produced by wave action throws the granular sediment into ripple ridges which
coincide in direction with the trend of the waves.   Ripple mark thus produced is characterized by the perfect symmetry of the ridges, which contrast sharply with the current ripples ordinarily seen on river bars and tide
flats (fig. 84).   Double or triple crests are sometimes developed in wave or
oscillation ripple mark,[137] and a subordinate lower crest occupies the middle
of the rather wide trough in one type of wave ripple mark.   These Cornish
suggests may be the result of a "settling of the sand."

Gilbert has formulated the essential elements of the theory of their formation as follows:

The ordinary ripple-mark of beaches and rock faces is produced by the to-and-fro
motion of the water occasioned by the passage of wind waves.   During the passage of a
wave each particle of water near the surface rises, moves forward, descends and moves
back describing an orbit which is approximately circular.   The orbital motion is communi-
cated downward, with gradually diminishing amplitude.   Unless the water is deep the
orbits below the surface are ellipses, the longer axes being horizontal, and close to the

[137] Cornish, V., Sand waves in tidal currents, Geog. Jour., vol. 18, 1901, pp. 193–194,
fig. 25.

bottom the ellipses are nearly flat, so that the water merely swings forward and back.   It is in this oscillating current, periodically reversed, that the sand-ripples are formed.   A prominence occasions vortices alternately on its two sides, and is thereby developed in a symmetric way with equal slopes and a sharp apex.   There is a strong tendency to produce a mole laterally into a ridge, the space between ridges is definitely limited by the interference of vortices and in time there results a regular pattern of parallel ridges, equally spaced.   It has been found experimentally that by varying the amplitude of the water oscillation and also by varying its frequency the size of the resulting ripples can be controlled; but the precise laws of control have not been demonstrated.   Evidently the frequency of the natural oscillation equals the frequence of the wind waves, and its amplitude is a function of the size of the waves and the depth of the water; so that a relation will ultimately be established between wave-size, wave-period and water-depth as condiions and ripple-size as a result.[138]

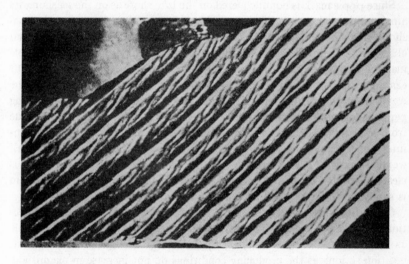

FIG. 84. WAVE RIPPLE MARK

This sandstone slab shows ripple marks which were made on an ancient sea bottom many millions of years ago.   A second, somewhat later and smaller series of wave ripples began to form in the troughs of the larger ones.   After G. K. Gilbert, U. S. Geol. Surv.

Darwin describes the first appearance of artificially formed oscillation ripples as follows:

When a very small quantity of sand is sprinkled in and the rocking begins, the sand dances backwards and forwards on the bottom, the grains rolling as they go.   Very shortly the sand begins to aggregate into irregular little flocculent masses, the appearance being something like that of curdling milk.   The position of the masses is, I believe, solely determined by the friction of the sand on the bottom, and as soon as a grain sticks, it

[138] Gilbert, G. K., Ripple-marks and cross-bedding, Bull. Geol. Soc. Am., vol. 10, 1899, pp. 137–138.

thereby increases the friction at that place. The aggregations gradually become elongated and rearrange themselves. . . . Some of the elongated patches disappear, and others fuse together and form ridges, the ridges become straighter, and finally a regular ripple mark is formed.[139]

They form equally well in oscillating currents produced in a vessel rotated alternately in opposite directions, where there is no evidence of stationary waves, or on the bottoms of water bodies agitated by waves, where the same reversal of current takes place.

OCCURRENCE. Oscillation ripples may be seen under the shallow water of most ponds and lakes. They also occur on tidal flats where the currents are not strong enough to produce current ripple.

Since ripple mark is not uncovered on the lake shore as on the seashore, its almost universal occurrence on suitable bottoms a few feet or yards from shore in water of moderate depth might never be suspected by the casual observer. Where the shoreline slopes abruptly under the water, ripple mark is not formed up to the very edge of the beach. A two-mile walk, for example, along the sandy beach of Lake Ontario near Wellington when the waves are forming ripple mark would enable one to see ripple marks along perhaps not more than 100 yards of this distance. But observations made from a small boat on this shore in water 4 to 10 feet deep would show an un-interrupted stretch of ripple-marked bottom. A water glass or a small wooden box with glass bottom will enable the observer, where the water is clear, to see the wide distribution of wave ripple mark wherever the bottom is sandy.

Oscillation ripples are stationary. They cannot advance in either direction, owing to the formation of vortices alternately on either side of the ripple as the current is reversed. Thus, the crests and troughs hold a constant position so long as the producing conditions do not increase in magnitude, in accordance with the Forel generalization[140] that "Ripples once formed do not experience a change in spacing as a result of diminishing amplitude of oscillation of the water." In the Joggins section of Nova Scotia Kindle[141] has observed symmetrical ripple mark directly superimposed throughout a 6-inch bed, and Gilbert records the occurrence of ripple mark holding the same position during the accumulation of 2 feet of sediments.[142]

The preservation of typical oscillation ripples under a thick layer of coarse

[139] Darwin, G. H., On the formation of ripple marks in sand, Proc. Roy. Soc. London, vol. 36, 1883, p. 23.

[140] Forel, F. A., Les rides de fond étudiées dans le Lac Leman, Arch. Sci. Phys. Nat., Genève, vol. 10, 1883, pp. 39–72; Transl. by Johnson, D. W., Shore processes and shore-line development, 1919, p. 512.

[141] Kindle, E. M., op. cit., 1917, p. 27.

[142] Gilbert, G. K., Bull. Philos. Soc. Washington, vol. 2, 1874–1878, pp. 61–62.

sand, as is frequently seen in many sandstone formations, offers a more difficult problem than the preservation of current ripples, as the very existence of oscillation ripples excludes the possibility of any current erosion in the vicinity of the sedimentary surface. However, the close relations sometimes observed between oscillation ripples and superposed non-rippled sandstone will be understood by geologists who are familiar with the surprisingly firm sand of certain sea beaches. At Skegness, England, for example, part of the sand beach is so firm that the sport of sailing over it in rubber-tired vehicles has developed, while adjacent to this beach are others where deep footprints are made in walking over the sand. The experienced student of ripple mark will discover in his wading observations beautifully developed oscillation ripple mark with the sand "set" so firmly that the ripples make unpleasant walking for bare feet and leave little if any trace of foot prints. Such ripple marks would survive the passage of sand-bearing currents, and speedy burial might result without damage to their form. A storm may throw a large quantity of sediment into suspension at one locality, while at another not far distant locality, its only effect on the bottom would be the production of oscillation ripples. The wind drift set up by the storm may also carry much sediment in the upper levels of the water from the former to the latter locality.

Classification of Ripple Mark

The simple forms of ripple mark are the product of either currents or waves acting alone. The successive or simultaneous action of these two agencies gives rise to complex forms. The relationships of the several kinds of ripple mark to the current and wave conditions producing them are concisely indicated in table 90.

COMPLEX FORMS OF CURRENT RIPPLE MARK. The simple types of ripple mark produced by air and water currents and waves have been described in some detail in preceding sections, and their relations are sufficiently indicated in table 90.

In this connection only those forms of ripple mark will be considered which result from combinations of simple forms or the complex operation of casual factors which in some cases do not readily admit of analysis.

LINGUOID RIPPLES. One of the modifications of the simple normal type of current ripple shows a highly irregular pattern with a wide range in the variety of forms. The tongue-like outline of the unit forms of many examples of the pattern led Bucher[143] to give it the name of linguoid. Negatives of these markings resemble small mud flows. Blasius has produced

[143] Bucher, W. H., op. cit., 1919, p. 164.

this form of ripple mark experimentally, transforming regular current mark into it.[144] For illustrations see Kindle.[145]

TABLE 90
CLASSIFICATION OF SUBAQUEOUS RIPPLE MARK

CONDITION OF WATER	TYPE OF RIPPLE MARK
I. Simple currents	

1. Current velocity between first and second critical points, with no sediment in suspension. A part of the fluid moving in horizontal vortices which are set up as grains shift on the surface of the sediment otherwise at rest.	Current ripples (asymmetrical):
	  a. Normal
	  b. Rhomboid
	  c. Linguoid

2. Velocity between second and third critical points with conditions of ripple destruction.	Smooth sheet of sand

3. Velocity at third critical point and higher, with much sediment in suspension. Regressive sand waves at lower, and progressive sand waves at higher, velocities.	Sand waves (symmetrical), (exist only while current lasts)
	  a. Regressive sand waves
	  b. Progressive sand waves

4. Falling velocities of high range, causing transformations of the unstable sand waves.	a. Meta-ripples (asymmetrical) b. Para-ripples (symmetrical and asymmetrical)
II. Oscillating currents, due to wave action.	Oscillation ripples (symmetrical)

III. Currents of different direction, acting successively or simultaneously, causing actual or potential sets of ripples to interfere.	1. One set forming after the completion of the other
	  a. The second set consisting of oscillation ripples. Oscillation cross ripples.
	  b. The second set consisting of current ripples. Current cross ripples.
	2. The two sets forming simultaneously. Compound ripples.

RHOMBOID RIPPLE MARK. A rare form of ripple mark called rhomboid[146] shows a reticular pattern strikingly resembling that of the scales of a ganoid

[144] Blasius, H., op. cit., 1910.
[145] Kindle, E. M., op. cit., 1917.
[146] Bucher, W. H., op. cit., 1919, p. 153.

fish. These seem first to have been noted by Williamson, who described them as resembling "the overlapping scale leaves of some cycadean stem[147]" (see p. 671).

Engels[148] found in his experiments that the first effect of transportation by a uniform current was the formation of small rhomboidal, scale-like tongues of sand. Each tongue has one acute angle pointing downstream, formed by two steep lee sides, while the other, pointing upstream, is formed by the gentle slope extending into the reëntrant angle of the lee sides of two tongues of the following alternating row. In Engels' experiments, with increasing velocity of the current, common current ripples took their place.

The rarity of this type[149] in nature is indicated by the fact that the authors have seen only two examples of it. The examples figured were found by Kindle[150] near the tip of a miniature spit on the shore of Lake Erie, assumed at the time to be the product of small cross waves. In the light of Engels' experiments, however, it seems probable that it was the product of the currents which produced the small bar. The location near the middle of a somewhat crescent-shaped bay would have favored the translation of waves entering the bay into localized currents impinging on each other at the point of the bar and forming an undertow or backwash current (fig. 85).

CURRENT CROSS RIPPLES. Cross ripples may also result from the intersection of a current with a pre-existing set of ripples, if the action of the current is sufficiently weak and of short duration. As there is no oscillation of the current, there is no reason for a transformation into the hexagonal pattern. The two sets of ripples may intersect at any angle (fig. 86).

MODIFICATION OR TRANSFORMATION OF TYPES. Ripple mark developed by current action frequently is modified by wave action. If the wind should blow at right angles to the course of a stream in which current mark is forming, or transverse to the direction of a tidal current, the ripple mark resulting from these currents will be crossed transversely by ripple mark which trends at right angles to the course of the wind. If the waves are the product of a moderate breeze and are of small size, the current ripple mark will be marked on its gentle slopes only by a miniature ripple-mark pattern which will be broken or interrupted by the troughs of the current ripples. The size or prominence of these superimposed ripples will depend on the strength of the waves producing them. Under the

---

[147] Williamson, W. C., On some undescribed tracks of invertebrate animals from the Yoredale rocks, and some inorganic phenomena, produced on tidal shores, simulating plant remains, Mems. Manchester Lit. and Philos. Soc., vol. 10, 1887, pp. 19–29.

[148] Engels, H., op. cit.

[149] Johnson, D. W., Shore processes and shoreline development, 1919, p. 517. Johnson suggests that this peculiar pattern is the work of a single backwash current, and he terms it backwash mark.

[150] Kindle, E. M., op. cit., 1917, pl. 19B.

influence of a strong wind they will develop to the extent of breaking across the current ripple pattern and producing a knobby surface. The ripple mark superimposed on the current mark by wave action is always of the asymmetrical type (fig. 87).

FIG. 85. PLASTER CAST OF IMBRICATED WAVE MARKINGS FORMED AT THE MARGIN OF THE BEACH BY WAVES CROSSING A MINIATURE SPIT

Beach of Lake Erie at Port Colborne, Ontario. Markings of this character are formed in the wave zone on beaches of fine sand with every retreat of waves. The watch is on the upper side of the beach. Photograph by Doctor E. M. Kindle.

FIG. 86. TIDAL-CURRENT RIPPLE MARK WITH SUPERIMPOSED SMALL PATTERN AT RIGHT
ANGLES

The latter was formed at a late stage of ebb tide when current direction was at right
angles to the earlier current.   Photograph by Doctor E. M. Kindle.

FIG. 87. CURRENT RIPPLE MARK MODIFIED BY WAVE ACTION

These asymmetrical or current ripple marks were made on the sands of the Avon River,
Nova Scotia, just below the town of Windsor. They were later modified by waves
moving oblique to the direction of the current, the finer sculpturing being the work of the
waves.   Photograph by Doctor E. M. Kindle.

Meta-ripples may be reshaped by waves acting in the same direction as the preceding current; their surface material is assorted and a sharp crest[151] placed in the center of the originally broad, round ridges.

Small current and oscillation ripples are in this way transformed one into the other, and nothing remains to indicate the change. Oscillation ripples are extremely sensitive even to very gentle current action.[152]

INTERFERENCE OR CROSS RIPPLES. A special form of compound rippling, to which the terms "interference ripples" or "cross ripples" should be limited, consists of polygonal, usually more or less irregular pits, arranged side by side like stones in a mosaic. Two fundamental types can be distinguished, the "rectangular" and the "hexagonal," which usually occur together and rarely show their pure form. Both consist of parallel ridges connected by crossbars. In the hexagonal type the crests of the parallel ridges zigzag, forming obtuse angles which in adjoining crests face in opposite directions, with crossbars connecting the spaces on alternate sides of each ridge. The rectangular type consists of two sets of ridges intersecting at right angles.[153]

Interference ripples come into existence whenever there is a sharp change in the direction of the wind so that the formation of wave ripple mark is continued at an angle to the original trend. This can be shown by simple experiment. The common occurrence of interference ripples in small ponds is thus accounted for.

Interference ripples seem to develop as a result of ordinary waves breaking up into two sets of oscillations crossing each other. Favorable conditions are furnished about the ends of bars, stranded logs, the angles of piers, and in small ponds. Ripple mark of this character is very common in shallow ponds and ordinarily may be seen by hundreds in the small ponds made by steam-shovel mining in the coal fields of southern Indiana. Originally they were considered tadpole nests, Hitchcock distinguishing two types, those of the Connecticut Valley sandstone being named *Batrachoides nidificans* and those of the Niagara limestone *B. antiquor*[154] (fig. 88).

COMPOUND RIPPLES.[155] A great variety of forms of complex rippling owe their origin to the simultaneous interference of wave-oscillation with current

[151] Analogous to that shown on a sand ridge of different origin on the beach of Lake Ontario, see Fairchild, H. L., Beach structure in Medina sandstone, Am. Geol., vol. 28, 1901, fig. 10, pl. 5.

[152] Kindle, E. M., op. cit., 1917, p. 31.

[153] For illustration of the rectangular type, see Kindle, E. M., op. cit., 1917, pl. 23, Fig. C; of the hexagonal type, figs. 8 and 17.

[154] Kindle, E. M., Origin of "Batrachoides the Antiquor," Geol. Mag., vol. 51, 1914, pp. 158–161.

[155] For illustrations, see Kindle, E. M., op. cit., 1917, pls. 14, 28, 29. See also p. 174, the effect of a gale on tidal meta-ripples.

action.   All seem to be characterized by a systematic breaking or offsetting of the crests of the current-ripples.   A systematic discussion of these forms, to which the term "compound ripples" might well be applied, is impossible at the present time, since practically no observations are available of the factors entering into their formation, or even of the forms themselves.

FIG. 88. "TADPOLE NESTS" (TOP) AND INTERFERENCE RIPPLE (BOTTOM)
Photograph by Doctor E. M. Kindle

Vertical Range of Ripple Mark

The discussions. of ripple marks found in many texts and treatises on general geology treat them as shallow-water features, and this inadequate and inaccurate conception is reflected in the casual references to ripple mark in numerous geological papers.

In considering the maximum depth at which ripple mark may occur it is important to discuss separately the two classes of subaqueous ripple marks which have been described. The wave ripple mark will certainly be developed on sandy beds at any depth to which the effective oscillatory movement of waves extends. In the case of current ripple mark, the only factors essential to its formation are current action and suitable bottom material. There are no reasons why both of these may not be found at any depth known in epicontinental waters.

CURRENT RIPPLE MARK. The vertical range of current ripple is coincident with that of currents strong enough to move sand or silty deposits. There is now on record an abundance of data showing that current action is an occasional, if not a common, phenomenon of the sea bottom at considerable depths. In the Skagerrak, for instance, "the tidal currents are scarcely noticeable in the upper water layers, whereas they have been met with there down at the very bottom at such great depths as 200 m." Measurements made on the "Michael Sars" are interesting in this connection. On the edge of the continental slope, about 80 km. northwest of Aalesund on the Norwegian coast[156] in the open ocean, not in any channel, the Atlantic current was found running, on the average, parallel with the continental slope, at times with a velocity of 0.215 m. per second at a depth of 250 m. The lowest velocity observed was 0.059 m. per second. "This velocity is so great that the water would move grains of sand, and wash them away from the bottom, which at this place was rocky."[157] A velocity of 0.214 m. per second is sufficient to move sand, according to the observations of Forbes quoted by Nansen,[158] and consequently to produce ripple mark. Nansen concludes that the continental slope off the Norwegian coast "where it is sufficiently steep and exposed to the open ocean is swept by currents sufficiently rapid to wash clayey deposits and mud down into depths of 600 or 700 m."[159]

Verrill[160] has noted evidence of currents strong enough to move sand on the continental shelf off the New England coast at depths of 65 to 150 fathoms. South of the Azores Hjort[161] found considerable tidal currents down as deep as 800 meters.

[156] Report Norwegian Fishery and Marine Investigations, vol. 2, no. 1, 1909, p. 79.
[157] Helland-Hansen, B., and Nansen, F., The Norwegian Sea, Rept. Norwegian Fishery and Marine Investigations, vol. 2, no. 2, 1909, p. 155; also table on page 778.
[158] Nansen, F., The bathymetrical features of the North Polar seas, The Norwegian North Polar Expedition, vol. 4, No. 13, 1904, p. 139.
[159] Nansen, F., op. cit., p. 144.
[160] Verrill, A. E., Marine faunas off the New England Coast, Am. Jour. Sci., vol. 24, 1882, p. 449.
[161] Hjort, J., The "Michael Sars" North Atlantic Deep-Sea Expedition, Geog. Jour., vol. 37, 1911, pp. 349–377.

It is clear from the abundant evidence of current action in deep water that current ripple mark may be formed at great depths, and that it probably is formed on favorable areas at all depths within the limits of the continental shelf.

WAVE RIPPLE MARK.   Oscillation ripple mark has a much more restricted bathymetric range than current ripple.   There can be no doubt, however, that oscillation ripples form at considerable depths.   There is reliable evidence, according to Hunt, "that at depths of about 40 fathoms in the English channel and of 50 fathoms on the Banks of Newfoundland, there is not only motion at the bottom, but strong motion, far exceeding the gentle oscillation of the water that is sufficient to ripple a sandy sea bed."[162]   We have the testimony of Wharton[163] that fine mud and sand may be moved to a depth of 80 fathoms by wave action, and that there is evidence of the chafing of cables to a depth of 260 fathoms.

The observations of Siau[164] appear to indicate that ripple mark formed by wave action occurs at a depth of 188 meters near St. Gilles, Island of Bourbon (Réunion) in the Indian Ocean.

Nansen[165] has cited a number of records of wave action at considerable depths, among which are the following: "Aimé has proved by experiments that the waves with a height of 1.5 m. may cause considerable horizontal oscillations (70 to 80 cm.) at a depth of 14 m., and in the road of Algier, 1 kilometer from the shore, he could prove the occurrence of appreciable oscillatory motion at a depth of 40 m."[166]   Cialdi states that in 1831 during the diving work on H. M. S. "Thetis" which had been wrecked at Cape Frio on the Brazilian coast, the diving bell at depths of 18 to 20 m., always during strong wind and not seldom in comparatively calm weather, was subject to violent horizontal oscillations of 1.5 m. amplitude, which made the work very dangerous to the divers.[167]   Herman Fol states from his own experience that in the Mediterranean the task of the diver becomes very difficult, and when a "swell" is on, "an irresistible force makes him oscillate like a pendulum."   "This see-saw motion of the water is felt nearly as much at 30 m. as at 10 m. of depth."   Cialdi asserts that the movements of waves may disturb fine sand on the bottom at a depth of 40

[162] Hunt, A. R., Proc. Roy. Soc. London, vol. 34, 1883, p. 15.

[163] Wharton, W. J. L., Foundations of coral atolls, Nature, vol. 55, 1897.

[164] Siau, M., De l'action des vagues à de grandes profondeurs, Compt. Rend., Acad. Sci., Paris, vol. 12, 1841, pp. 770–776.

[165] Norwegian North Polar Expedition, vol. 4, 1904, p. 137.

[166] Aimé, Ann. Chim. et Phys., Ser. d, vol. 5, 1842, pp. 417, et seq., quoted by Krümmel, O., Handbuch der Ozeanographie, 2nd ed., vol. 2, 1907, pp. 30–32.

[167] Cialdi, Sul moto ondoso del mare, 2nd ed., Rome, para. 776, 1866, quoted by Krümmel, O., Handbuch der Ozeanographie, 2nd ed., vol. 2, 1907, p. 91.

m. in the English Channel, 50 m. in the Mediterranean, and 200 m. in the open ocean.[168]

The following observations pertain to wave length and amplitude. (a) When first appearing, oscillation ripples show a wave length which is half that of their full development.[169] (b) The wave length increases with the velocity of the current, that is, amplitude over period of the oscillation. De Candolle's and Darwin's experiments have shown that the increment of wave length is proportional to the increment of velocity. This law, of course, holds good only between two critical points of velocity, between which oscillation ripples, like current ripples, can exist. It cannot be reversed—that is, the wave length does not decrease with the velocity.

Darwin noted that "when once a fairly regular ripple mark is established, a wide variability of amplitude in the oscillation is consistent with its maintenance or increase." Forel demonstrated that any oscillation weaker than that which produced the ripple will not affect its orientation, even if its direction diverges from the original up to 45°.[170] This explains his observation that at the same locality, in the Bay of Morges, near the center of the north shore of Lake Geneva, the oscillation ripples never changed their direction during three months of observation, although waves reach the bay from all directions between east, south, and west. Their orientation corresponded to waves from the south, the direction of the strongest winds. At the shore they swung into parallelism with the shoreline.[171]

Since the amplitude of the oscillation at the bottom of the water body is a function of the height of the water wave above, this must bear a definite relation to the wave length of the ripples. It is not impossible that this relation one day will be utilized for a direct determination of the decrease of the wave amplitude with depth. At present, practically no data comparing amplitude of water waves and wave length of ripples are available, and a collection of such data would represent a distinct contribution to the study of ripples.[172] A number of measurements of wave length and amplitude have been compiled by Bucher.[173]

Forel's experiments and observations have shown conclusively that the

[168] Cialdi, op. cit., chap. 3. Quoted by A. Geikie (Text book of geology, 1882, p. 423) from Delesse, A., Lithologie des mers de France, 1872, p. 111.

[169] Darwin, G. H., op. cit., 1884, p. 23.

[170] Forel, F. A., op. cit., 1895, p. 263.

[171] Forel, F. A., op. cit., 1895, p. 270.

[172] The only observation of this kind that has come to notice is that by Stuchlik, H., which shows the wave length of the ripple equalling one-half of the amplitude of the wave under the conditions given in his Table V. Cf. Gilbert's statement (Ripple marks and cross bedding, Bull. Geol. Soc. Am., vol. 10, 1899, p. 138) "that at the most the ripple marks are only half as broad as the waves rolling above them are high."

[173] Bucher, W. H., op. cit., 1919, p. 197.

wave length diminishes with increasing depth of water.   It should be noted however, that with relatively strong waves "for moderate depths the size of ripples is not very sensitive to variation of water depth," as observed by Gilbert on the bed of Lake Ontario.[174]

Experimental data led Ayrton to conclude that both amplitude and wave length are greater for wave ripple mark made in storms than in calm weather, and that the slopes on the shore side are steeper than those on the water side.[175] With both of these generalizations the observations of Kindle[176] are at variance.

In a series of observations[177] made along the shore of Lake Ontario near Wellington, Ontario, Kindle found a regular increase of the wave length with depth.   He found in water:

> Less than $\frac{1}{2}$ foot deep, ripples 1 to 2 inches long
> Less than $1\frac{1}{4}$ feet deep, ripples 2 to 4 inches long
> Less than $2\frac{1}{2}$ feet deep, ripples $3\frac{1}{2}$ to 4 inches long
> Less than 10   feet deep, ripples 4 to 6 inches long
> Less than 11   feet deep, ripples $4\frac{1}{2}$ inches long
> Less than 20   feet deep, ripples 4 to 5 inches long

This directs attention to a factor which is of some importance in connection with the interpretation of fossil ripples.   The waves which produced a velocity sufficient to form ripples of 4 to 5 inches wave length at a depth of 20 feet, had, of course, a higher orbital velocity at the depth of 2 feet. This velocity ought to have produced ripples of larger wave length, since 5 inches (12.7 cm.) probably was not the greatest wave length possible on the sediment in question.   According to Forel's observations, such large ripples, if ever formed, would persist, and hence their general absence is good evidence that they never formed.   We are, therefore, led to the conclusion that above a certain minimum depth a given bottom oscillation of a water wave will not produce ripples.   This is probably due to the abnormal conditions of flow resulting from the "breaking" of the wave.   Moreover, in shallower water, only smaller waves will produce ripples of smaller wave length.   Consequently, along a gently sloping shore we should theoretically expect to find at first a rather rapid increase of the wave length of the persisting ripples to a certain depth, and then a very gradual decrease down to very small size.   Small ripple marks may thus form in both shallow and deep waters, and their occurrences are, therefore, no indication of depth.

[174] Gilbert, G. K., op. cit., 1899, p. 138.
[175] Ayrton, H., The origin and growth of ripple mark, Proc. Roy. Soc. London, ser. A vol. 84, 1910, pp. 285–310.
[176] Kindle, E. M. op. cit., 1917, p. 28.
[177] Kindle, E. M., op. cit., 1917, p. 29.

On the other hand, wave ripple mark with large amplitude and wave length certainly cannot form in very shallow waters for the reason that large waves cannot develop to form them.[178]

Ripple mark observed by Kindle on the west side of Point Pelee, Lake Erie, displayed in two adjacent belts sharply contrasted wave lengths where the water depth ranged only from 18 inches to 26 inches. The near-shore belt in this case showed a wave length of 6 inches to 8 inches across a zone 7 or 8 feet wide which was followed by ripple marks spaced at 3 inches to 4 inches and extending lakeward an undetermined distance. These two sets of oscillation ripples in water of the same depth, one having a wave length twice that of the other, indicate the operation of factors other than depth in some situations which cannot at present be evaluated.

Ripple Mark on Calcareous Sediments

With few exceptions, the published observations on ripple mark of recent deposits relate to quartz sand. In subtropical and equatorial latitudes, calcareous sand frequently entirely supplants quartz sand on the beaches and in offshore waters. The specific gravities of the two kinds of sand are essentially the same, and they appear to react to wave and current action in much the same way.

The waters adjacent to Providence Island in the Bahamas afford good opportunities to see ripple mark on calcareous sand at localities easily accessible from the city of Nassau. The channel between Hay Island and Providence Island, with a depth of $1\frac{1}{2}$ to 3 fathoms, furnishes conditions favorable to the development of tidal currents of varying velocities between Nassau and the coral reefs 4 miles east, where the currents are strong enough to keep the limestone bottom swept clean of calcareous sand.

Between the reefs and west of the east end of the island considerable stretches of the bottom are covered with white "sand" consisting largely of coarse shell fragments. This "sand" is marked by ordinary current ripple mark of short wave length. Over the easterly part of the white sand bottom, where the currents probably have their maximum strength, the bottom is covered with sand waves or meta-ripples. These have a wave length estimated at from 15 to 20 feet and an amplitude of 6 to 8 inches.[179]

The waters of Biscayne Bay, Florida, furnish a considerable area of white calcareous sand bottom under water sufficiently shallow (12 to 18 feet) to permit careful inspection from a glass-bottomed boat. Asymmetric ripple mark with rather long wave length was observed near Cape Florida. A short distance from the steamer landing on the west side of the Cape,

---

[178] Johnson, D. W., Shore processes and shoreline development, 1919, p. 512.

[179] These observations were made by Doctor Kindle on December 13, 1920.

parallel ridges of the sand-wave type were seen spaced 25 to 50 feet apart. In the deeper water, highly irregular bottom features occur somewhat comparable in complexity of pattern to the flat-topped sand ridges at Annisquam, Massachusetts, illustrated by Kindle.[180]

Fossil ripple mark is met with less frequently in limestones than in sandstones, but it is by no means a rare phenomenon. Small ripples are quite common in the Richmond formation of Ohio and Kentucky, and occur not infrequently in the Eden formation. They are also common in the Monroe formation of Adams and Highland counties, Ohio. Ripple mark of unmistakable current-ripple type, with a wave length of $1\frac{1}{4}$ inches and an amplitude of 1/8 inch, is represented in the Canadian Geological Survey collections by a specimen from the Upper Devonian limestone of the Hay River section, Northwest Territory, collected by E. J. Whittaker. Miller[181] states that small ripple marks with a wave length of 1 to 2 inches and an amplitude of $\frac{1}{2}$ inch occur at several horizons in the Pamelia, Lowville, and Trenton. Most of the ripple mark in limestone reported in geological literature, however, has a wave length of from 1 foot to nearly 7 feet. The numerous examples of Paleozoic ripple mark described by Prosser include both symmetrical and asymmetrical ripples, but all are forms with long wave length, generally from 20 to 36 inches. In several cases they are described as "clearly asymmetrical,"[182] or with "slopes steeper to the west than to the east," thus leaving no question as to their current origin. In other cases Prosser found "no difference in the slope," and Udden[183] notes limestone ripples with large wave lengths which are "slightly unsymmetrical." Bucher[184] has brought together measurements of a number of limestone ripples with large wave lengths which are "nearly symmetrical" (para-ripples), and he raised the question whether the formation of such large ripple mark is possible by wave action.[185] It may be that the para-ripples represent meta-ripples sufficiently modified by wave action or reversed tidal currents to have lost their original asymmetry.

Interpretation of Fossil Ripple Mark[186]

USE IN DISCRIMINATING BETWEEN UPPER AND LOWER SURFACES OF STRATA. Oscillation ripples are strictly symmetrical and generally have

---

[180] Kindle, E. M., op. cit., 1917, pl. 45.

[181] Miller, W. J., Geology of the Port Leyden Quadrangle, Lewis County, N. Y., Bull., 135, N. Y. State Mus., 1910, p. 36.

[182] Prosser, C. S., Ripple marks in Ohio limestones, Jour. Geol., vol. 24, 1916, p. 459.

[183] Udden, J. A., Notes on ripple marks, Jour. Geol., vol. 24, 1916, p. 125.

[184] Bucher, W. H., op. cit., 1919, p. 260.

[185] Bucher, W. H., op. cit., 1919, pp. 262–263.

[186] The work of Professor Bucher except for part of first paragraph.

sharp angular crests separated by wide rounded troughs which may show a low ridge in the center. The negatives of such ripples correspondingly show broad rounded crests (possibly with a narrow median groove) separated by sharply cut V-shaped troughs. These characteristics, when fully developed and well preserved, afford certain and easy criteria for the determination of the original order of superposition of strata. It frequently happens, however, that both the crests and troughs of oscillation ripple mark are rounded as in figure 4 A of Kindle's[187] ripple-mark profiles. In such cases determination of order of superposition from ripple-mark profile is impossible. But in the more normal examples with wide troughs and angular crests (figs. B and C), ripple mark yields unequivocal evidence as to order of superposition of beds.

PALEOGEOGRAPHIC INTERPRETATION. Each ripple offers some positive information concerning the physical conditions under which it was formed. In reasoning from the data contained in sedimentary rocks back to the highly complex conditions to which they owe their existence, this information is always valuable and often of crucial significance. The basic inferences that can be drawn from ripples may be tabulated, as follows:

1. Ripples of large wave length (measured in feet). ("Meta-ripples," highly asymmetrical, and "Para-ripples," less asymmetrical and even symmetrical.) Originate only through *currents of relatively high velocities.*[188]

    (a) If the wave length of such large ripples varies greatly from point to point on the same surface, and if the individual rippled layers cannot be traced for any great distance, the velocity of the current that produced the ripples must have varied greatly from point to point and must have been limited to a relatively small area, as is the case in river (or estuary) channels.

    (b) If, on the other hand, the wave length of such large ripples is remarkably uniform on any given surface, and if such a rippled layer can be traced for relatively great distances (say over several square miles), conditions necessary for this formation are probably found only in arms of the sea agitated by tidal currents.[189]

2. Asymmetrical ripples of small wave length (measured in inches) merely indicate the existence of currents of lower velocity than 1.

    (a) A ratio of amplitude to wave length of 1:4 to 1:10 is characteristic of water-formed ripples.

---

[187] Kindle, E. M., Recent and fossil ripple mark, Mus. Bull. No. 25, Geol. Surv. Canada, 1917, fig. 4.

[188] For quantitative data concerning all forms of ripples, see Bucher, W. H., 1919.

[189] It seems improbable that wind-drift in land-locked bodies of water can obtain sufficient strength to reach the bottom velocities necessary for the production of such large ripples. No such case has been recorded. Wind-drift, however, is capable of strengthening or weakening tidal currents.

(b) A ratio of amplitude to wave length of 1:20 to 1:50 (or over) is characteristic of wind-formed ripples.

(c) Linguoid current ripples form only under subsiding water of vanishing
depth, that is, on flood plains and tidal flats.

3. Symmetrical (oscillation) ripples (always of small wave length measured in inches),
both of simple and polygonal interference pattern, form only under water in
the absence of currents at the time of their formation.

4. Ripples of any kind may be absent from a given formation, either because they
were not formed during the deposition of the sediments, or because they were
not preserved.   Ripples do not form:

(a) Where the required current or oscillatory motion is lacking or does not
touch the bottom with sufficient strength;

(b) Where the sediment is too coarse or too fine to form ripples;

(c) Where vegetation (for instance, water weeds) prevents uniform action of
the currents on the sedimentary surface.

Ripples are not preserved:

(d) Where conditions favoring the rapid covering of the ripples are absent.

The use of the basic data in paleogeographic interpretation is illustrated
by the following two examples.   In the cases chosen, reasoning from the
observation on ripples alone leads to remarkably definite results, which can
always be tested by independent lines of reasoning based on other characters of sediments.   It is from the convergence of such independent lines
of thought that we derive the degree of probability approaching certainty
which is our aim.   In these examples we shall limit ourselves to the observations on ripples, referring by numbers and letters to the preceding tabu-
lation.

Example 1. Fossiliferous limestone layers alternating with shales; para-
ripples on many layers, some traceable over large areas; small current ripples common; oscillation ripples present, but relatively rare (Richmond
group of Ohio, Kentucky, and Indiana).

These are sediments laid down in an arm of the sea in free communication with the ocean and agitated by tidal currents (1, b); deep enough to
allow sufficient sediment to be thrown into suspension to cover the ripples
when the agitation of the water has ceased (4, d); shallow enough to allow
waves to act on the bottom during periods of slack water (3); the depth
depending on the size of the waves which, in turn, is determined largely by
the "fetch" of the wind, that is, the size of the water body.

Since the time of slack water between tides is relatively short, oscillation
ripples are relatively rare.

Example 2.   Unfossiliferous fine-grained sandstones interstratified with
more or less shaly portions; oscillation ripples abundant, all other types
absent; most ripples of nearly the same strike (N.53°W.), which remains

constant over an area 115 miles long and 20 miles wide. (Bedford and Berea formations at the base of the Mississippian section of eastern and central Ohio.)[190]

Formed in a body of water not in free communication with the ocean, that is, in a land-locked arm of a sea or a lake, as shown by the complete absence of currents; the parallelism of the ripples indicates that in one direction larger waves formed than in all others, either because the shape of the water body gave the wind sufficient fetch only in one direction, or because strong winds blew practically in one direction only (or two co-linear directions) as, for instance, in the case of monsoons.

In the case of the Bedford-Berea ripples, a widespread unconformity between the Bedford and Berea formations to the north, which is absent in the south, seems to indicate that the trend of the ripples was independent of changes in the form and size of the water body. It seems probable, therefore, that their parallelism is due to the dominance of one wind direction over all other, that is, probably to monsoon winds.[191]

CURRENT MARKS

Current mark is a term which may be applied to irregular structures on bottoms showing current-erosion effects. A current mark which is common on some tidal mud flats uncovered at low tide is made by the aggregation of the retiring waters into channels, with the result that the surface becomes eroded into rectangular, triangular, etc., high places separated by these channels. Such were observed in splendid development in Ellis Bay on Anticosti Island, the elevations being 4 to 5 inches high and 2 to 70 feet across. After becoming covered by succeeding sediments, the channel fillings in some instances resemble casts of logs.

Another type of current mark is made on the lee side of an obstruction where the force of the water is intensified and it erodes a small depression. This is commonly seen on a beach where the returning water erodes on the lee side of a shell or pebble (fig. 89).

[190] Hyde, J. E., The ripples of the Bedford and Berea formations of central and southern Ohio with notes on the paleogeography of that epoch, Jour. Geol., vol. 19, 1911, pp. 257–269.

[191] Other important references relating to ripple mark are the following: Brown, A. P., The formation of ripple-marks, tracks, and trails, Proc. Acad. Nat. Sci., Philadelphia, vol. 63, 1911, pp. 536–547; Dodge, R. E., Continental phenomena illustrated by ripple marks, Science, vol. 23, 1894, pp. 38–39; Hunt, A. R, Description of oscillation ripples, Proc. Roy. Soc. Dublin, vol. 4, 1884, pp. 261–262; The new question of ripple mark, Geol. Mag., vol. 41, 1904, pp. 619–621; Jagger, T. A., Some conditions of ripple-mark, Am. Geol., vol. 13, 1904, pp. 199–201; Lemoine, P., Les ripple-marks, Nature, 1917, pp. 204–206.

MISCELLANEOUS STRUCTURES MADE BY WAVES

Swash Mark

Waves breaking on a gently sloping beach lead to a part of the water gliding up the slope as a thin sheet.   This is known as the swash.[192]   Its line of farthest advance is the place of total loss of beach-directed energy,

FIG. 89. CURRENT MARK

The sea is in the background.   The obstruction to which the mark is due is visible on the end of the mark near the bottom of the picture.   Photograph by W. H. Twenhofel of mark on the beach near the mouth of St. John River, north shore of the Gulf of St. Lawrence, Quebec Labrador.

and there its load is partly dropped, leaving a small wavy ridge consisting of fine sand, mica flakes, pieces of seaweed, and other vegetable matter. This is the swash mark.   The different swash marks form an irregular network of fine lines or ridges, each more or less convex toward the land, and in some instances a dendritic pattern is developed (fig. 90).   Markings which

[192] Johnson, D. W., Shore processes and shoreline development, 1919, p. 514.

appear to be of this origin have been described from the Portage of New York,[193] and wave lines are stated to be "frequent in great perfection on the smoother flags" of the Medina sandstone.[194]

Another type of mark made by waves is the miniature terrace and cliff effect eroded on a beach of sand or other fine material during low tide or any stationary position of the water level. These are occasionally well shown on the large ripples of tidal estuaries. They can form only above water and have a poor chance of preservation. They do not appear to have been observed in the geologic column.

FIG. 90. SWASH MARK

The sea is on the left. Photograph by W. H. Twenhofel. Between Long Point and mouth of St. John River, north coast of the Gulf of St. Lawrence, Quebec Labrador.

Rill Mark

Each high tide or each advance of a wave saturates the sands and muds covered. On the retreat of the wave or tide, water may drain from the sands and muds and aggregate itself into rills in a narrowly dendritic pattern,

[193] Clarke, J. M., Strand and undertow markings, etc., Bull. 196, New York State Museum, 1917, pp. 199–238.

[194] Fairchild, H. L., Beach structure in Medina sandstone, Am. Geol., vol. 28, 1901, p. 10.

the rills being 2 to 10 mm. wide. These erode small channels on the surface. The same feature may be developed on any inclined body of sand or mud after it has been uncovered by retreat of water. Dodge[195] has described occurrences of small dendritic rills on the seaward slopes of ripples of 18 inches amplitude, and their occurrence is common on most shores of suitable material. Patterns of similar character develop where small streams debouch on a flat sandy or clayey surface. The distributaries spread away from the main stream, and as they advance the water is absorbed and ultimately disappears.[196]

Each rill pattern or system is rarely more than a couple of feet long and from a fourth to a third as wide, the tendency being to narrowness. Fossilized, they resemble plants, and it is possible that some of them have been so considered, as pointed out by Nathorst[197] and Williamson.[198]

On beaches composed of fine sands, the returning waters of waves may be succeeded by a net-work of anastomosing rills or small currents whose minute erosion produces a sculpturing of the beach surface resembling the surface pattern of a *Lepidodendron* tree, the uneroded surface or polygons between the minute currents being diamond-shaped, with the long axes of the diamonds normal to the water's edge. The diamond-shaped polygons approximate 12 to 25 mm. wide and 25 to 50 mm. long; the minute channels are less than 1 mm. deep. These may be the "ripple marks" that resemble the "overlapping scales of a ganoid fish" (p. 655). Marks of this character have been seen on many miles of beaches about the Mingan Islands, the Atlantic Coast about Cape Henry, and on beaches of California south of San Francisco and they probably are present on most sand beaches.

As the various varieties of rill mark are made above water, they have the same chances of preservation and the same significance as other marks made under like conditions. Occurrences in the geologic column should be rare.

Beach Cusps

Beach cusps are large anticlinal shaped structures which project outward from the shore and are composed of materials ranging from sand to cobbles. According to Johnson,[199] the ideal beach cusp has a shape suggesting an

[195] Dodge, R. E., Continental phenomena illustrated by ripple marks, Science, vol. 23, 1894, pp. 38–39.

[196] Grabau, A. W., Principles of stratigraphy, 1913, p. 708.

[197] Nathorst, A. G., Om några förmodade växtfossilier, Öfv. Köngl. Vet. Akad., Förhandl., vol. 30, 1873, pp. 25–52.

[198] Williamson, W. C., On some undescribed tracks of invertebrate animals from the Yoredale rocks, and on some inorganic phenomena, produced on tidal shores, simulating plant-remains, Mems. Manchester Lit. and Philos. Soc., vol. 10, 1887, pp. 19–29.

[199] Johnson, D. W., op. cit., 1919, p. 463.

isosceles triangle with its base parallel to the shoreline and its apex extending into the water. The angle between the "equal" sides of the triangle may be large or small, making the cusp wide or narrow. Ordinarily the sides are curved, and the curving may be either convex or concave outward. They may gradually merge without distinction into the beach or be sharply set off therefrom. The heights may be such as not to vary appreciably from the beach slope, or they may rise several feet above the beach level, the highest point of the cusp being located at any point. Lengths range from a few feet up to about a hundred. Johnson records the occurrence of cusps on Long Island with distances from apex to base of 20 to 30 feet and with 75 to 90 feet between apices of adjacent cusps. Kemp[200] has described cusps from Florida which were 90 to 95 feet from base to apex and 3 to 4 feet high. Beach cusps usually extend straight out into the water, and the slopes, unless wave-eroded, are symmetrical. They are more or less equally spaced along beaches and somewhat resemble large ripple marks.

There does not appear to be agreement respecting the origin of beach cusps. Johnson's explanation is as follows:

Selective erosion by the swash develops from initial irregular depressions in the beach shallow troughs of approximate uniform breadth, whose ultimate size is proportional to the size of the waves, and determines the relatively uniform spacing of the cusps which develop on the inter-trough elevations.[201]

Whatever the origin, structures of this character seem to develop only on beaches, where they form ridges at right angles to the shoreline.

The fairly sharp-crested ridges of symmetrical profile described by Gilbert[202] and Fairchild[203] from the Medina sandstone of New York may be fossil beach cusps. Gilbert considered them giant ripples made by waves with a probable height of 60 feet, but in view of the type of sediments in which they occur, this explanation is an impossible one. Branner[204] suggested that the "giant ripples" might be fossil beach cusps. Fairchild assigned them to a beach origin.

STRUCTURES MADE BY FLOATING OBJECTS

Objects floating in the water—ice, logs, trees with limbs attached, seaweeds, grass, small shells, living animals, etc.—develop markings on the

[200] Kemp, J. F., cited by Johnson, D. W., op. cit., 1919, p. 466.

[201] Johnson, D. W., op. cit., 1919, p. 481.

[202] Gilbert, G. K., Ripple-marks and cross-bedding, Bull. Geol. Soc. Am., vol. 10, 1899, pp. 135–140.

[203] Fairchild, H. L., Beach structure in Medina sandstone, Am. Geol., vol. 28, 1901, pp. 9–14.

[204] Branner, J. C., Ripples of the Medina sandstone, Jour. Geol., vol. 9, 1901, pp. 535–536.

muddy bottoms with which they come in contact. These floating objects, dragging on the bottom, produce a great variety of markings.

Floating objects moving in one direction produce straight grooves on bottoms which they touch, the grooves ranging in dimension from those that are deep and wide to thread-like scratches. If a floating object pursues a curved path, curved markings result; if it rotates around a vertical axis while moving in a given direction, sinuous markings develop. Objects whirled in eddies produce circular and elliptical markings. A tree with many limbs dragging on the bottom may leave a well marked multiple trail in its wake.

In very shallow waters, small floating dead shells may become responsible for many trails. These may be developed in laboratory experiments by using the shells of *Limnæa* or *Planorbis*, two common lake shells, and placing them in water of a few millimeters depth. After a few days the bottom will be found covered with markings which cross and recross in the manner of worn trails.

Most marks developed in these ways are probably limited to shallow water; water of 8 to 10 feet depth would include most of them. From this generalization, however, markings made by icebergs and some floating seaweeds should be excepted. Ice may scratch the bottoms for depths of several hundred feet. Some of the seaweeds are very long, the giant kelps of the North Atlantic rivaling forest trees in this respect, and these, with rocks still grasped in their holdfasts, may scratch the bottom to depths of about 100 feet. Some have great floats which enable them to travel long distances.

Markings arising from floating matter may occasionally be seen in great development on lake and sea bottoms, and their occurrence in the geologic column should be not uncommon. As the markings usually are made in mud which ordinarily weathers before it reaches the surface, their best chance of preservation exists where muds become covered with sand or lime sediments. Counterparts of the markings on the mud are then made on the underside of the overlying beds.

Clarke[205] has described beautiful examples of straight ridges found on the undersides of hard flaggy sandstones in the Portage of New York. The photographs suggest glacial grooves and ridges, but it is not likely that they would be mistaken for such, as the surfaces are not polished. Clarke suggested an origin due to floating ice.

Powers[206] found similar markings preserved on the undersides of Penn-

[205] Clarke, J. M., Strand and undertow markings, etc., Bull. 196, New York State Museum, 1917, pls. 15–20.

[206] Powers, S., Strand markings in the Pennsylvanian sandstones of Osage County, Oklahoma, Jour. Geol., vol. 29, 1921, pp. 66–80.

sylvanian sandstones in Texas and Osage County, Oklahoma. The markings are extremely abundant on some slabs, a photograph of one $5\frac{1}{2}$ feet wide showing 48 ridges, representing as many grooves in the underlying rock. Many of the markings figured by Powers could have been made only by floating flexible objects, and they suggest that fronds of dendritic algæ or branches of land plants were being dragged by a sinuous current over a mud surface. In some cases the marks diverge, suggesting that currents separated drifting objects.

Objects floating in water and rising and falling with the waves might come in contact with the bottom while in the troughs and be above it on the crests. An object floating from shallow to deeper water might drag bottom for a space, but after getting over deeper water would touch the bottom only while in the troughs of the waves. Its path would thus be indicated on the bottom by a continuous trail for a space, then by a series of pits. Seaweeds floating with holdfasts weighed down with rocks might cover the surface of a mud bottom with pit-like markings. Dr. J. B. Woodworth[207] stated that the tentacles of a floating jellyfish also make pits in this fashion.

MARKINGS MADE BY BASALLY ATTACHED PLANTS

Areas covered with loose material and having a sparse growth of plants, either above or below water, may show an abundance of markings of concentric curves. A plant usually is found with its branches or leaves in contact with the markings, and it is to the waving of this plant that the markings are due. Each portion of a plant touching mud or sand develops an impression which is an arc of a circle. Extremely delicate plant structures make them, and as they occur abundantly on existing surfaces, they should occur over similar surfaces of the past. Structures more or less similar which have been described as *Taonurus* or *Spirophyton* have been considered plant structures by some and by others as mechanically or organically produced.[208] Whatever they may be, it is certain that very similar structures are of the origin given above.

TRACKS AND TRAILS

Throughout all zoologic history, animals have left tracks and trails on the muds and sands over which they moved. Some of these show the contests of animals with each other, and still others their struggles in the agonies of death. Some "tracks" are exceedingly difficult to differentiate from markings made by inorganic agencies.

[207] Personal communication.
[208] It does not seem possible that the *Taonurus* in the New Providence shale of Kentucky could have been produced as described in this topic.

A discussion in detail of the different kinds of tracks would mean pages of description to little end in this connection. They consist of worm trails from the rocks of all ages since the Proterozoic; tracks of crustaceans, as perhaps *Climatichnites* from the Cambrian of Wisconsin, which resembles the trail of a small automobile and may be an algal impression, and double rows of pits, as in the Richmond of Anticosti, where they have been followed over a 6-inch bed of limestone for 75 miles; tracks of amphibians from the Kansas Coal Measures; and the famed reptile tracks of the Newark sandstone.

The rocks of many horizons are marked by the holes in which worms or other organisms lived. These may be vertical, as *Scolithus* of the Cambrian; transverse, or U-shaped, as *Arenicolites*[209] and *Arenicola*.[210] Not uncommonly the openings of the holes have small elevations about their entrances.

ICE CRYSTAL IMPRESSIONS

When wet mud or fine sand or other fine-grained sediment freezes, the water in the mud may become more or less segregated as ice crystals or needles on and within its upper portion. Similar but much coarser and less defined crystals form in medium- and coarse-grained sands. Crystals are better developed in sediments completely saturated with water than in those only partially saturated.[211] These crystals or needles are extremely common in springtime when the ground is saturated with water, but seem to be less common in the autumn. They are best shown on mud surfaces that are even and smooth. The lengths of the crystals approximate one-half inch, but occasionally some occur with lengths of one or more inches. They trend in many directions on a very small surface, occur irregularly isolated, intersect irregularly, and in many instances are arranged in bundles or radiate from a point. Most commonly they are straight, but some are curved. The greatest width generally is 1 to 2 mm. and not uncommonly the width is not greater than a thread. When ice melts a small groove remains to

[209] Coysh, A. W., U-shaped burrows in the Lower Lias of Somerset and Dorset, Geol. Mag., vol. 68, 1931, pp. 13–15; Salter, J. W., On annelid-burrows and surface markings from the Cambrian rocks of the Longmynd, Quart. Jour. Geol. Soc., vol. 13, 1857, pp. 199–205.

[210] Soergel, W., Spuren mariner Würmer im mittleren Buntsandstein (Bausandstein) und im unteren Muschelkalk Thüringens. Neues Jahrb. f. Min., Beil.-Bd. 49, 1923, pp. 510–549; Richter, R., Flachseebeobachtungen zur Paläontologie und Geologie VII–XI, Senckenbergiana, Bd. 6, Heft 3/4, 1924, pp. 119–140; Stather, J. W., U-shaped markings in estuarine sandstone near Blea Wyke, Proc. Yorkshire Geol. Assoc., vol. 20, 1923–1926, pp. 182–184; and Bather, F. A., U-shaped burrows near Blea Wyke, Ibid., pp. 185–199. Bather gives excellent illustrations and diagrams and a review of the literature.

[211] Allen, J. A., Ice crystal markings, Am. Jour. Sci., vol. 11, 1926, pp. 494–500; see also Marbut, C. F., and Woodworth, J. B., 17th Ann. Rept. U. S. Geol. Surv., 1896, pt. i, p. 992; and Powers, S., Strand markings in the Pennsylvanian sandstones of Osage county, Oklahoma, Jour. Geol., vol. 29, 1921, pp. 75–76.

FIG. 91. COUNTERPART OF ICE CRYSTAL IMPRESSIONS

Photograph of a counterpart made by pouring plaster over a mud surface in which ice crystals had formed and had ... ly disappear into the atmosphere, leaving depressions in the mud. The small ridges on the

mark the place of the crystal, and the surface has somewhat the appearance of having been minutely mud-cracked (fig. 91). Clarke has pointed out that a similar effect may be produced by spicular or anchor ice.[212]

Ice-crystal impressions are best made in clay or mud, but as clay usually is broken down before exposure, original ice crystals are not likely to be found. Counterparts may be found on the undersides of overlying beds, particularly sandstones.

Udden[213] has described markings interpreted as ice-crystal impressions from the Dakota sandstone of South Dakota and the Upper Cretaceous Eagle Ford shales of Texas.

On the undersides of flaggy sandstone from the Portage of New York, small rod-like markings, usually single, but occasionally in radiating sheaths, and generally of irregular orientation, were early figured by Vanuxem and Hall as *Fucoides graphica*. The dimensions range up to about an inch long and 1 to 2 mm. wide. Clarke[212] suggested that these markings developed from ice crystals formed in the muds on the bottom of the Portage sea in connection with ground or anchor ice.

RAIN, DRIP, AND HAIL IMPRESSIONS

Rain falling on wet mud of not too high fluidity produces circular or elliptical pits margined by ragged rims slightly elevated above the surrounding mud. The surfaces of the depressions are visibly rough. The rims are slightly higher and the depressions slightly deeper on the sides toward which the falling drops are directed, and the depths of the depressions vary with the size of the drops which make them, the force with which the drops fall, and the softness of the mud. Pits form but do not persist in very fluid mud. The maximum depths appear to be about 3 mm., and the widths range from about 2 to 12 mm. Rain also makes impressions on sand, but the rims are not so sharp as those bordering impressions made in mud. After many impressions have been made on a sand surface, it becomes sculptured by coalescing pits (fig. 92),[214] and upon this surface there may also be rill markings produced by draining away of the rain water. Rain impressions in the geologic column have been many times recorded, but it is extremely doubtful if they really occur so abundantly as the literature indicates. So many agents form somewhat similar pits or impressions that

[212] Clarke, J. M., Strand and undertow markings, etc., Bull. 196, New York State Museum, 1917, pp. 205–210, pls. 20–23. Clarke is stated to have later abandoned the view that *Fucoides graphica* represents ice crystal impressions, see Schuchert, C., Am. Jour. Sci., vol. 13, 1927, p. 159.

[213] Udden, J. A., Fossil ice crystals, Bull. 1821, Univ. Texas, 1918, pp. 1–8, ten plates.

[214] Wasmund, E., Rieselfelder und Blattfäckerabdrücke auf rezentem und fossilem Süsswasser-flachstrand, Senckenbergiana, Bd. 12, 1930, pp. 139–151, figs. 1–2, p. 143.

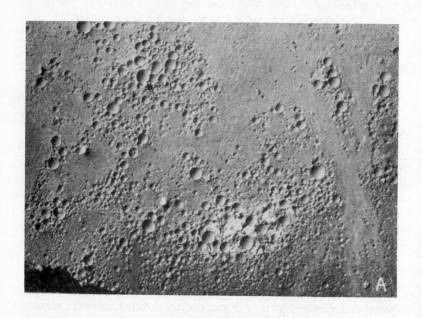

FIG. 92. *A*, BUBBLE IMPRESSIONS; *B*, RAINDROP IMPRESSIONS

The left illustration of *B* shows the coalescing pits produced by many drops.   Photograph by Diemer, University of Wisconsin.

it is extremely likely that some of the supposed rain impressions are due to other causes.[215]   The tendency has been to designate any circular impression a rain print.

Drip impressions (fig. 93) are like those made by rain, but the maximum and average widths appear to be greater.   As water dripping from objects usually falls without a horizontal component, the tendency is for the pits to be circular.

Spray and splash impressions develop on beaches and shores where the wind drives spray against the mud and sand of the beach.   The impressions are like those made by rain except that there is greater variation in dimen-

FIG. 93. DRIP IMPRESSIONS MADE IN THE LABORATORY
The scale is given by the small shells.   Photograph by Diemer, University of Wisconsin

sion, and, as the horizontal component invariably is large, the impressions tend to be elliptical.

Hail impressions (fig. 94) are larger and have deeper and higher margins for the same character of mud and sand than do those made by water. Hailstones descending perpendicularly produce circular impressions; those coming down at a slant make elliptical impressions with greater depths and higher margins on the sides toward which the hailstones are directed.   Impressions made by hail ought to occur in the deposits of the geologic column, but they do not appear to have been noted, except that Lyell pictures supposed hail prints from Triassic red shale of New Jersey.   Hailstones with

[215] Lyell, C., On fossil rain-marks of the Recent, Triassic, and Carboniferous periods, Quart. Jour. Geol. Soc., vol. 7, 1851, pp. 238–247; Ibid., vol. 13, 1857, pp. 199–206; Andrée, K., Geologie des Meeresbodens, Bd. 2, 1920, pp. 91–92; Twenhofel, W. H., Impressions made by bubbles, etc., Bull. Geol. Soc. Am., vol. 32, 1921, pp. 369–370.

diameters of 62.5 by 50 by 31 mm. have been measured,[216] and hailstones as large as grapefruit and weighing 1½ pounds are stated to have fallen at Potter, Nebraska, on July 6, 1928.[217] Particles of these dimensions are able to make very large impressions.

Each of these marks except that made by hail is formed only on surfaces exposed to the atmosphere; hail may make impressions in very shallow water. Their finest development occurs on flood plains, deltas, and tidal flats like those of the Bay of Fundy.

FIG. 94. HAIL IMPRESSIONS MADE IN THE LABORATORY
The ice spheres were dropped from a height of about ten feet. Photograph by Diemer, University of Wisconsin.

PIT AND MOUND STRUCTURES[218]

Kindle[219] seems to have been the first American author to describe the structures designated "pit and mound," these structures developing in his experimental work in muds precipitated in salt water, the settling of the mud being accompanied by small upward currents therein. These struc-

[216] Bevan, A., Peculiar hail, Science, vol. 58, 1923, pp. 443–444.

[217] Blair, T. A., Hailstones of great size at Potter, Nebr., Monthly Weather Review, vol. 58, 1928, p. 313.

[218] Designated convection current impressions in the first edition of this book.

[219] Kindle, E. M., Small pit and mound structures, etc., Geol. Mag., vol. 3, 1916, pp. 542–547.

tures had been previously described by Hughes.[220]   Later work by Twenhofel[221] proved that salt water is not essential and that exactly similar features develop in fresh water under conditions of rapid settling.   The mechanics of formation have been given by Schofield and Keen.[222]   When mud concentrations acquire a certain rigidity, small fissures develop which become filled with clear liquid whose density is less than that of the surrounding mud-laden liquid, thus setting up a circulation of upward currents in the fissures, while the surroundings sink.   The fissures tend to close at the bottom and enlarge toward the top into conical chimneys through which

FIG. 95. PIT AND MOUND STRUCTURES

The little mounds are about 1 mm. in height and about 1 cm. across, each mound having a well defined hole at the summit.   The mounds are determined by the development of slight rigidity of the upper part of materials settling from suspension.   It is thought that the introduction of new material in suspension shortly after the pit and mound structures begin to form would give the structure known as landscape marble.   After Schofield, R. K., and Keen, B. A., Rigidity in weak clay suspensions, Nature, vol. 123, 1929, pp. 492–493.

the upward motion of the liquid can be traced by small particles of mud held in suspension.   These particles are deposited in a ring around the top of each chimney.   Weaker suspensions settle until a layer is built upon the bottom which has the necessary concentration, following which the chim-

[220] Hughes, T. McK., Quart. Jour. Geol. Soc., vol. 40, 1884, p. 183, pl. 11, fig. 6.

[221] Twenhofel, W. H., Impressions made by bubbles, etc., Bull. Geol. Soc. Am., vol. 32, 1921, pp. 367–370.

[222] Schofield, R. K., and Keen, B. A., Rigidity in weak clay suspensions, Nature, vol. 123, 1929, pp. 492–493.

neys develop. The critical concentration necessary for formation of a chimney increases with the coarseness of the suspended particles. Schofield and Keen state "that the critical concentration, even in the coarser suspensions is only about 1.5 per cent by volume." The small mounds are about 1 mm. high, range from 3 to 10 mm. in diameter, and each has a small crater-like depression on its summit with diameter approximating $\frac{1}{2}$ to 1 mm. (fig. 95). Cross sections of sediments in which currents of this type have developed strikingly resemble landscape marble, and it is possible that this latter structure originates in this way. These cross sections are readily seen in glass vessels in which mud concentrations are permitted to settle. The formation of landscape marble seems generally to have been ascribed to emanations of gas through sediments or to shrinkage attending consolidation.[223] Whatever the origin of landscape marble, it seems very probable that pit and mound phenomena can give rise to an almost identical feature.

Pit and mound structures probably develop in any depth of water. They should be common in the deposits of delta environments or others where conditions permit rapid settling.

BUBBLE IMPRESSIONS

Impressions made by bubbles[224] are of two types, depending on whether or not the bubble remains stationary after coming in contact with the mud surface. If a bubble becomes attached to the bottom, either being brought there by the weight of sediment settling on its surface, by becoming stranded, or by being expelled from the mud itself, mud settles on its surface for a while; but ultimately the bubble may rise to the surface of the water, leaving an impression which is a section of the bubble less than half its volume. The impressions ordinarily are not margined by raised rims, and the surfaces are smooth. So far as observed, diameters range from microscopic to about 7 mm., but it appears probable that greater diameters may be attained (fig. 92). The bubbles develop in the first place from gas produced in the sediments through decay of organic matter, through the expulsion of air held in the sediments, or as a consequence of some agitation of the waters.

Buckland[225] seems to have been the first to call attention to bubble impressions, and they were later noted by Lyell,[226] who described small con-

---

[223] Woodward, H. B., Remarks on the formation of landscape marble, Geol. Mag., vol. 9, 1892, pp. 110–114; Thompson, B., Landscape marble, Quart. Jour. Geol. Soc., vol. 50, 1894, pp. 393–410.

[224] Twenhofel, W. H., Impressions made by bubbles, etc., Bull. Geol. Soc. Am., vol. 32, 1921, pp. 369–370.

[225] Buckland, W., Rept. Brit. Assoc., 1842, p. 57.

[226] Lyell, C., op. cit., 1851, pp. 241–242.

vexities on the surface of mud due to small cavities made by bubbles, the mud having acquired rigidity before the bursting of the bubbles. Lyell also described circular pits made by bubbles rising in mud to its surface and there bursting.

Such impressions seem to be formed most abundantly beneath waters carrying a heavy burden of sediments. They may be seen on any recently flooded mud flats, on the surface of ice, and on the bottoms of water bodies.

Bubbles forming in muds and rising to the surface may leave impressions consisting of tubes which are margined at their upper ends by elevated rims. These have been experimentally formed in muds, with yeast used to form gas. The tubes resemble those known as *Scolithus*.

It is known that structures of this origin may form in shallow water, and it is probable that most of them originate under such conditions. Impressions made by gas expelled from muds may be developed on bottoms of any depth.

Compared with raindrop, drip, and spray and splash impressions, most of those made by bubbles are not margined by raised rims and have smooth surfaces, but these differences probably would be extremely difficult to detect in fossil form.

Bubbles wandering over the surface of very shallow water make shallow impressions where they come in contact with soft mud. Often these are of intricate pattern. Bubbles floating on the wave-agitated surfaces of waters but little deeper than the diameters of the bubbles may touch bottom in the troughs and rise above it on the crests. Each contact with a bottom of suitable materials may produce a circular pit. These are so shallow that it is doubtful if they could be preserved.

SAND HOLES

Closely related to bubble impressions are the sand holes made on sand beaches on the advance of a wave over a beach. The mechanics of their formations are as follows. The retreat of a wave leaves the sand saturated with water. This escapes to the surface on the lower part of a beach in seepage which frequently becomes aggregated into small rills, air entering the sands as the water escapes. The advancing wave expels the air by replacing it with water, the air reaching the surface of the sands on the upper part of the beach almost at the moment of wave retreat. The air escapes rather violently and leaves a pit which has a depth ranging to 7 or 8 mm. and a width a little less than the depth. The pits have raised margins.

Sand holes seem to have been first described by Bryson[227] in 1865, who referred their origin to sand-hoppers, and noted their resemblance to rain-

[227] Bryson, A., Surface-markings on sandstone, Geol. Mag., vol. 2, 1865, pp. 189–190.

drop impressions.   Their first description in America was made by Palmer[228] in 1928, who gave the correct explanation of their origin.   They have also been described by Deecke,[229] Högborn,[230] Andrée,[231] and probably others, and it has been suggested that some *Scolithus* tubes were thus formed.

Sand holes are extremely common on sand beaches, and the present author has seen them forming on Lake Michigan, the Gulf of St. Lawrence, the California coast, and elsewhere, each wave forming hundreds, the succeeding wave destroying these and forming others.   Falling waters leave the beaches covered with thousands.   These pits soon are taken possession of by sand-hoppers and perhaps other organisms, whence has arisen the opinion held by some that these organisms form the pits.   It is possible that similar pits may so originate, but in all cases observed by the present writer, the sand-hoppers seem to have occupied holes formed as described above.

Occurrence of sand pits in the geologic column should be rare, but as they form in the same environment as swash mark, whose preservation is known, it seems probable that some "rain prints" may be sand pits.

SPRING PITS

Spring pits are made by springs reaching the surface through sands on beaches.   Similar pits are made elsewhere, but as their chances of preservation are nearly zero, such are not considered.   Only a single description seems to exist in the literature;[232] this is by Quirke, and the pits were studied on the shores of Maple Lake, Ontario.   However, occurrences probably are common.   The pits on Maple Lake shores are 1 to 3 feet or more apart, have funnel or bowl shapes, are usually less than 2 feet in diameter, and are about 6 inches deep of which 4 inches represents excavation and 2 inches fillings around the margins.   The pits have the coarsest sands in their bottoms and the finest around the margins at the top.   They form not only on the shore above water but also in the shallow waters adjacent to the shore.   Their formation ends when water ceases to flow into the sands on the upward or landward margin.

Spring pits seem possible of preservation in the geologic column, but it is not certain that such have been observed.   Logan[233] described features

---

[228] Palmer, R. H., Sand holes of the strand, Jour. Geol., vol. 36, 1928, pp. 176–180.

[229] Deecke, W., Einige Beobachtungen am Sandstrande, Centralbl. f. Min., etc., 1906, pp. 721–727.

[230] Högborn, A. G., Zur Deutung der Scolithus-Sandstein und "Pipe-Rocks," Bull. Geol. Inst. Upsala, vol. 13, 1915, pp. 45–60.

[231] Andrée, K., Geologie des Meeresbodens, Bd. 2, 1920, pp. 187–191.

[232] Quirke, T. T., Spring pits; sedimentation phenomena, Jour. Geol., vol. 38, 1930, pp. 88–91.

[233] Logan, W. E., Geology of Canada, 1863, pp. 121–122.

in the Romaine dolomites of the Mingan Islands which he thought might have been caused by submarine springs, but the present writer's studies of the same features have indicated the impossibility of such origin.

SAND DOMES

Sand domes have been described by Reade.[234] While the structures have little or no geological application, they are sedimentary structures, and completeness requires attention to them. As described by Reade, they are small hollow domes or blisters 12 to 75 mm. in diameter and about 12 mm. high. The composing materials are sands which hold the arched position over the hollow due to being held together by enclosed water. In the examples described by Reade the sands overlay a blue clay, and the hollow space is ascribed to air that collects between the clay and the sand and lifts the latter. Sand domes have little chance of making a record in the geologic column.

MUD CRACKS

Mud cracks, also known as sun cracks and shrinkage cracks, bound polygons of irregular outlines. The directions and spacings of the cracks vary, being functions of the character of the materials, the rate of drying, the thickness, the presence of foreign matter, the degree of stratification, and the quantity of water held by the underlying material. There is a widespread impression that mud cracks are commonly six-sided, but polygons with six sides appear to be less common than those with three to five.

Mud cracks are developed wherever muddy sediments are exposed to the atmosphere for a considerable period of time, and their presence is thought to indicate that such conditions existed, but it is also possible for sediments to crack beneath water, although this does not seem to be common in nature.[235] Ice-crystal impressions somewhat resemble mud cracks, but the pattern is smaller.

Mud cracks occur most commonly in sediments composed of clay and silt, but they are present in sands which contain sufficient cohesive matter, and also develop in calcareous muds. The bottom surface of a stratum overlying one that is mud-cracked carries a counterpart of the mud-cracked surface, and these counterparts may occur in any sedimentary rock. Such counterparts are readily distinguished from originals by the absence of filled

[234] Reade, T. M., Miniature domes in sand, Geol. Mag., vol. 21, 1884, pp. 20–22.

[235] Twenhofel, W. H., Development of shrinkage cracks in sediments without exposure to the atmosphere, Abstract, Bull. Geol. Soc. Am., vol. 34, 1923, p. 64; Rept. Comm. Sedimentation, Nat. Research Council, 1925. Moore, E. S., Mud cracks open under water, Am. Jour. Sci., vol. 38, 1914, pp. 101–102.

cracks extending into the rock, as is the case in the originals. These characteristics are valuable criteria for determining tops and bottoms of beds.

The cracking of mud appears to start at places of greatest weakness; a buried stick or other object, the presence of a hole, the occurrence of sandy spots, or any substance weakening the cohesion leads to the development of cracking at that place. A hole or any object not uncommonly may be the source from which several cracks radiate. While not known, it is possible that pit and mound action may be responsible for initiation of radiate cracks. The various cracks develop in different directions, and their cross-

Fig. 96. Mud-Crack Polygons of Which Many Have Six Sides

The possession of six sides is thought to be due to the homogeneity of the mud. The central parts of the polygons, according to Longwell, are slightly concave and there is some rounding at the edges due to falling off. The failure to turn up on the edges is thought to be due to the thickness of the mud layer. On a playa in the Las Vegas Quadrangle, Nevada. Photograph by Professor C. R. Longwell.

ing defines the polygons. The commonly assumed three cracks radiating from a point are probably exceptions in nature, though they may be seen to develop in very carefully prepared homogeneous muds. The general tendency appears to be for a crack to curve. A single crack may have a continuity of several feet, and the cracks first formed are usually longer than those which subsequently develop, and these latter ordinarily end abruptly at the older cracks. There is, however, wide variety.

The shapes of polygons vary within wide limits, those with three, four, five, and six sides being most commonly seen. There is no essential equal-

FIG. 97. DEVELOPMENT OF MUD CRACKS IN DIFFERENT PARTS OF THE SAME TANK

In the lower right-hand corner the polygons are arched upward in the middle. In the lower left-hand corner there is neither arching upward nor downward. Elsewhere there is turning upward on the edges. It will be noted that most cracks curve and that polygons are produced by intersection of cracks. The thicker the layer of mud, the wider the polygons, and where it is extremely thin, as in the upper right-hand corner, the cracks are close together. The pipe at the bottom of the photograph is one inch in diameter. Photograph by Diemer, University of Wisconsin.

ity to lengths of sides and to angles between sides. The commonly assumed six sides to mud-crack polygons with angles of 120° between the sides are fiction, but that such is true in some cases is shown by figure 96,[231] and perhaps is explainable as due to homogeneity of the muds. The variety in shape of mud-crack polygons may be seen in figure 97.[237] Cracks of a secondary or minor order may develop upon the polygons first formed. These are of less depth than the earlier cracks.

The spacing of mud cracks depends upon the character of the mud, the rate of drying, the thickness of the mud, the character of the water in which the mud was deposited, the nature of the material below, and the presence of foreign matter.

The width of the cracks probably is determined largely by the character of the muds and the spacing. Cracks are not uncommon with widths of 2 or more inches at the top. These are most common in thick-bedded muds. Studies made in the desert basin of northwestern Peru[238] showed an older system of cracks radial to the margin and a younger system parallel to the margin, the latter closely spaced at the margin and becoming further apart with approach to the center. The central area had great irregularity of crack trend. The crack polygons near the margin were four-sided, whereas in the middle most of them had five sides. It was thought that the controlling factors in spacing and trends of the cracks were shape of basin, thickness of mud, character of mud, and rate of drying.

Thick clay muds of homogeneous character give wider spacing than do muds that are in thin layers. Marly and limy muds give a narrow spacing. Sandy muds also tend to narrow spacing. "Rapid drying . . . seems to produce comparatively widely spaced mud cracks, while slow desiccation gives closely spaced mud cracks."[239] Muds which contain much foreign matter in the form of sticks, bits of straw, etc. give closer spacing than do the same muds in which such material is lacking. The mud cracks developed in water with a high degree of salinity are stated by Kindle to be very narrow, and highly saline muds show a slight lateral expansion which is accommodated "by the arching upwards of the median portions of the polygons,"[240] the arching in the cases observed on a marine beach in Florida being sufficient "to lift the centre of the polygon clear" of the underlying material.

[236] Longwell, C. R., Common types of desert mud cracks, Am. Jour. Sci., vol. 15, 1928, pp. 136–145.

[237] Kindle, E. M., Contrasted types of mud cracks, Trans. Roy. Soc. Canada, vol. 20. 1926, sect. iv, pp. 71–75.

[238] Suter, H., Beobachtungen über die Bildung von Trochnungsrissen in der Wüste von Nordwest-Peru, Centralbl. f. Min. etc., Abt. B. 1926, pp. 350–353.

[239] Kindle, E. M., Some factors affecting the development of mud cracks, Jour. Geol., vol. 25, 1917, p. 136.

[240] Kindle, E. M., op. cit., 1917, p. 142.

Mud-crack polygons may turn up or turn down at the edges, or do neither. This appears to depend upon the thickness of the mud layers and upon which portion of the cracked mud drys the more rapidly. Blocks composed of thin layers which dry more rapidly on top than elsewhere curve upward at the edges. If drying or extraction of water by underlying sands takes place more rapidly on the bottoms or the margins, the edges turn down, and in those cases where the rates of drying of the mud are the same on the top and bottom the top surfaces remain flat. All three types may be developed in the laboratory in the same tank with the same mud and water

FIG. 98. MUD-CRACK POLYGONS CURLING INTO ROLLS

The photograph shows that the rolls are most perfect where the mud is thinnest. (The cylinders, after being broken, roll on the edges of the fragments and ultimately a coin-shape is produced.) These cylinders rolling into deposits of sand form the Tongallen of the Germans. Meadow Valley Wash, Nevada. Photograph by Professor C. R. Longwell.

(fig. 97). It is probable that there are few conditions in nature which permit the bottom side to dry the faster. According to Kindle, "A high degree of salinity develops the formation of mud cracks in which the margins are inclined downward," and "the polygons formed in mud with the salinity of ordinary sea water warp neither upward nor downward at the margins, but retain a flat surface."[241] Kindle[242] further notes that mud cracks developed in air-slaked lime and fresh water are similar to mud cracks de-

[241] Kindle, E. M., op. cit., 1917, p. 139.
[242] Kindle, E. M., Separation of salt from saline water and mud, Bull. Geol. Soc. Am., vol. 29, 1918, pp. 479–488.

veloped in ordinary fresh-water mud. The same material with salt water gave surfaces with shallow V-shaped depressions of shallow depth, the surfaces between the depressions being flat. Mud-cracked clays from strongly saline solution show throughout the material "numerous very minute cavities and irregular pipe-like passages which are wanting in muds dried in fresh water." Mud-cracked polygons formed in fresh water ordinarily turn up at the edges if the surface mud can separate from the material below; if the latter is not possible, the edges remain flat and they may even turn down. Fine-grained muds in thin layers do the greatest turning up at the edges, this reaching extreme development in those instances where the mud curls into hollow cylinders to form the Tongallen of the Germans (fig. 98). Mud cracks in extremely saline muds may become filled with salts expelled by the drying polygons, thus giving a ridged rather than a cracked aspect to the surface.

Differential drying has been stated to be responsible for ribbon-shaped polygons, the cracks starting in the part first drying and thence extending into the other mud as it dries, the experiments having been carried out in small vessels.[243] Experiments conducted by the writer in large tanks have, however, only partly supported the generalization.

Temperature seems to be a factor in mud cracking. "Sediment deposited and kept under relatively high temperature conditions tends to crack freely in various directions while sediments kept under low temperature show no inclination to crack when desiccated."[244]

Mud-cracked polygons, on being wetted, begin slaking at the margins, which crack and slump away, leaving the middle of circular outline. The same results are produced by freezing and to some degree by the concentration of salts in the marginal portions. The slaking of muds on being wetted may be defined as wilting, and in some muds this requires considerable time, particularly when they carry a high content of lime carbonate and other salts and some colloids.

It has generally been assumed that when water covers mud-cracked surfaces the edges wilt so rapidly that no sediments are deposited beneath the upturned margins, but experiments have shown that where water-borne sediments are brought in large quantities to a mud-cracked surface, some may be deposited beneath the upturned edges of polygons of slow wilting. The deposition of sediments beneath the edges of mud-cracked polygons is best accomplished in arid regions by drifting sands, and an abundance of fossil mud cracks of this character is suggestive of an arid environment.

Mud cracks are far more abundant in non-marine than in marine sedi-

---

[243] Kindle, E. M., op. cit., 1917, p. 139.
[244] Kindle, E. M., Rept. Comm. Sedimentation, Nat. Research Council, 1924, p. 42.

ments.   In modern marine and near-marine sediments they have a limited development on the littoral mud flats, particularly the upper portions.   •An extremely broad littoral of very gentle slope would have extensive areas exposed for every small variation of tide level, and mud cracking of considerable extent might obtain on beaches of suitable material.   Such might have been the case during those times of the Paleozoic when the lands surrounding the interior seas were low and when swamp vegetation had not yet come into existence.   The best example of supposed comparable conditions prevailing at the present time is over the Rann of Cutch about the mouth of the Indus River, where 8,000 square miles of area are bared for months at a time and at other times covered with marine water.   Over this plain, mud cracking with marine associations occurs.

River flood plains and deltas, after subsiding of flood waters, become mud-cracked over areas which under some conditions may be coextensive with the areas flooded.   This to some degree occurs annually over parts of the flood plains of the Mississippi, Missouri, Ohio, and other rivers.   Conditions are particularly favorable if the climate is too dry to permit the development of much vegetation, as exemplified by the lower flood plain of the Euphrates-Tigris system, where the receding floods "leave a baked and burning wilderness of cracked mud behind."[245]

The finest development of mud cracks appears to obtain over the areas covered by the ephemeral lakes of arid regions.   Each lake during its brief existence deposits a thin layer of mud, which after the water is gone becomes thoroughly cracked with the margins of the polygons strongly warped; but if the waters contain a great deal of salt, the growth of salt crystals in the polygons may reduce them to dust and fill the cracks with salt ridges.   Longwell[246] has described three varieties of mud cracks found in the arid region of southern Nevada: (1) mud curls which are developed in fine muds in thin layers under conditions of rapid evaporation, (2) playa cracks with very symmetrical polygons, and (3) slope cracks of irregular trend with irregular outlines.   The polygons of the second variety average about 3 inches in diameter, are composed of homogeneous materials, and are bounded by shallow cracks.

During long dry weather the deposits of deltas, flood plains, etc., may crack to depths of many feet, cracks with depths of several feet being known. Each time of cracking may lead to the formation of a crack in a different place, but the tendency appears to be to follow established lines.   Every time of deposition fills all existing cracks, and the wetting causes wilting about the margins of the cracks.   The result is greater or less destruction

[245] Peters, J. P., Am. Rev. of Rev., 1918, p. 404.
[246] Longwell, C. R., op. cit., 1928.

of bedding, and after deposits have passed through this experience for several years they may have undergone a thorough kneading and mixing, leading to total loss of stratification.

Cracks which are stated to be very similar to those made in the drying of muds develop on hard freezing. They have been noted by Spethmann[247] after a night temperature of −10°C. Hawkes[248] found by experiment that no effect was produced at temperatures of −2° to −3°C., but that fissures formed at −15°C. According to Leffingwell, the polygons have a tendency toward hexagonal form and resemble mud-crack polygons, but have larger dimensions, averaging about 16 feet in diameter.[249]

CLAY GALLS, CLAY PEBBLES, AND CLAY BOULDERS

Clay galls (Tongallen) develop from the cracking and curling up of thin layers of fine mud of great cohesion. The hollow cylinders may be rolled for considerable distances by wind and become incorporated in eolian or aqueous sediments. The cylinders then flatten and a thin lenticle of mud results. Cylinders may also become filled with sediments without much flattening and thus give rise to stem-like structures which may seem to be of organic origin. Structures thus interpreted have been described from sandstones of Scotland.[250]

Grabau expressed the opinion[251] that the presence of clay galls denoted subaerial origin; Richter[252] has shown, however, that they may develop between tides and are possible under water without any drying having taken place, the mechanics of origin being as follows. A sand flat in quiet water becomes covered with a thin sheet of mud which on retirement of the water attains considerable rigidity. Returning waters tear this sheet of mud from the underlying sands and break it into small plates with irregular outlines. These plates are easily transported. During transportation the angles may be reduced and deposition may take place in sandy or other sediments either seaward or shoreward from the place of origin.

Another very interesting method of clay-gall origin in which drying is

[247] Spethmann, H., Über Bodenbewegungen auf Island, Zeits. d. Gesell. für Erdkunde, 1912, p. 246.

[248] Hawkes, L., Frost action in surficial deposits, Iceland, Geol. Mag., vol. 61, 1924, pp. 509–513.

[249] Leffingwell, E. de K., Prof. Paper 109, U. S. Geol. Surv., 1919, pp. 205–206.

[250] Harkness, R., On the sandstones and breccias of the south of Scotland of an age subsequent to the Carboniferous period, Quart. Jour. Geol. Soc., vol. 12, 1856, pp. 264–265.

[251] Grabau, A. W., Principles of stratigraphy, 1913, pp. 564, 711.

[252] Richter, R., Flachseebeobachtungen zur Paläontologie und Geologie, XVI, Senckenbergiana, Bd. 8, Heft 5/6, 1926, pp. 312–315; see also Natur und Museum, Bd. 59, Heft 1, 1929, pp. 77–79, figs. 8–10.

only a minor factor has been described by Trusheim.[253]   This was observed on the tidal flats of the North Sea, where thin muds covering the surface of the tidal plates contain more or less binding organic matter.   Activity of micro-organisms forms gas in these muds, and much of this remains therein, leading to a porous texture and low density.   Snails crawling about on this surface lead to the separation of the mud to some extent, so that with the incoming tide many flakes of mud float and may be carried far and wide over the tidal flat or out into open water, to be ultimately deposited with

FIG. 99. A CLAY BOULDER

This clay boulder, picked up on the shore of Lake Michigan, consists of clay in the inside and is studded with pebbles on the outside.   The actual boulder is 16 cm. in its longest diameter, about 8 cm. in the medium diameter, and a little more than 4 cm. in the shortest diameter.

other sediments in strange association.   The area of the flakes ranges from 1 to 10 square centimeters.

Thin lenticles of clay have been recorded from many sandstones into which entrance was obtained either as wind-transported cylinders or as wet plates. Criteria are lacking to distinguish the two methods of entrance.   Beautiful examples of "Tongallen" are the lenticles of green clay in the Dresbach sandstones of western Wisconsin.

Most mud boulders and pebbles are formed from chunks of wet compacted

[253] Trusheim, F., Eigenartige Entstehung von Tongallen, Natur und Museum, Bd. 59, Heft 1, 1929, pp. 70–72, figs. 1–3.

mud loosed from a bank or cliff and rolled by a current on the bottom of a stream or other body of water. Pebbles, sand grains, pieces of vegetation, shells, and other substances may adhere to the mud as it rolls along (fig. 99). Adhering shells ordinarily appear to have the convex sides outward, seemingly because the sharp edges of shells make it easier for the concave side to adhere to the mud. Shells should not be far within a mud boulder, thus differing from concretions. A mud pebble or boulder may increase in diameter by adhesions of additional mud, thus acquiring a concentric structure, each band of which may be characterized by pebbles, sand grains, or other adhering objects. Cartwright[254] designates those boulders which are studded with small pebbles "pudding balls." Some mud boulders and pebbles form from dry mud which through undercutting falls into a stream in large or small chunks. These become wet and thus impervious on the exterior while remaining dry within, and through abrasion they may become round. Examples described by Haas[255] thus formed had diameters ranging to a foot. Boulders formed in this way from bentonite ultimately crack on the surface.

The operation of a dredge on Lake Wingra near Madison, Wisconsin, forced lake clay, sand, and water through a pipe about a half mile long. A great deal of the clay came out as small spheres studded with sand and small shells. Merrill[256] cites a similar occurrence arising from the operation of a dredge in the Potomac at Washington, D. C.

Mud balls, 2 inches in diameter, were seen in Bridger Canyon, Montana. Gardner[257] has described mud balls from the Rio Chaco of the San Juan Basin of New Mexico, and Patton[258] from the Red River of Oklahoma. The balls described by Gardner averaged $1\frac{1}{4}$ inches in diameter and occurred in great abundance. Some of them had nuclei of pebbles and possessed concentric lamination. The balls from the Red River of Oklahoma ranged up to 6 inches in diameter, and with them were cylinders up to a foot long. Both Gardner and Patton suggest that some concretions may have developed in this way. Fraas[259] and Walther[260] have noted the occurrence of mud pebbles on the shores of the Red Sea, and the former has described

[254] Cartwright, L. D., Sedimentation of the Pico formation, etc., Bull. Am. Assoc. Pet. Geol., vol. 12, 1928, p. 254.

[255] Haas, W. H., Formation of clay balls, Jour. Geol., vol. 35, 1927, pp. 150–157.

[256] Merrill, G. P., Rocks, rock weathering and soils, 1906, p. 37.

[257] Gardner, J. H., Physical origin of certain concretions, Jour. Geol., vol. 16, 1908, pp. 452–458.

[258] Patton, L., In support of Gardner's theory of the origin of certain concretions, Jour. Geol., vol. 30, 1922, pp. 700–701.

[259] Fraas, O., Heuglin's geologische Untersuchungen in Ost Spitzbergen, Bd. 18, 1872, pp. 275–277.

[260] Walther, J., Einleitung in die Geologie, etc., pt. 3, 1894, p. 847.

them from the Jurassic of Spitzbergen. They have also been described from the North Sea by von Meyn (1876), from the Caspian by Tietze (1881), from Lake Constance by Schroeter and Kirchner (1902), and from the Baltic by Deecke. They have been discussed by Grabau,[261] and by Richter,[262] who has described them from the North Sea. Suter[263] has recorded them from the coast of Peru, where it is thought they are being deposited in sands.

The mud pebbles and boulders may become incorporated in sediments of any character, in which ordinarily they flatten as other sediments accumulate over them. They form under marine as well as continental conditions.

Closely related to mud boulders are those of peat, to which reference has already been made in connection with coarse clastics. These are not uncommon on some beaches, and they may possibly occur in the geologic column. Boulders of peat possess considerable coherence, have low specific gravity, and thus may be transported in waters of low competency.

COLUMNAR STRUCTURE

Columnar structure is given separate treatment, as it seems probable that the structure may arise in several different ways. Columnar structure in Silurian limestones of Quebec has been described by Kindle[264] and assigned to mud-cracking, the cracks extending to depths of 10 to 24 inches and later becoming filled with sediments more argillaceous than those in which the cracks developed.

Branson and Tarr[265] have described columnar structure normal to bedding planes in the Gallatin limestone of Wyoming, most of the columns ranging from 4 to 6 feet long, but with a few of less length. Diameters range from 3 to 12 inches. The columns are sub-angular in cross section and have three to eight striated and fluted sides, the striations, as a rule, being parallel to the axes of the columns. Some of the columns contain rude cones at ir-

[261] Grabau, A. W., Principles of stratigraphy, 1913, p. 711.

[262] Richter, R., Flachseebeobachtungen zur Paläontologie und Geologie, VI, Ton als Geröll im gleichzeitigen Sediment, Senckenbergiana, Bd. 4, Heft 5, 1922, pp. 137–141; XI, Schlickgerölle, auf dem Meeresgrund entstehend, Ibid., Bd. 6, Heft 3/4, 1924, pp. 163–165; XVI, Die Entstehung von Tongeröllen und Tongallen unter Wasser, Ibid., Bd. 8, Heft 5/6, 1926, pp. 305–312. Richter gives a considerable review of the literature, and the uncited references given above are on his authority.

[263] Suter, H., Eine Beobachtung über die Bildung von Geröllen aus Tonen, Mitth. Schweiz. Min. u. Petrogr. Bd. 6, 1926, pp. 202–203.

[264] Kindle, E. M., Columnar structure in limestone, Mus. Bull. No. 2, Geol. Ser. No. 14, Geol. Surv., Canada, 1914, pp. 35–39.

[265] Branson, E. B., and Tarr, W. A., New types of columnar and buttress structures, Bull. Geol. Soc. Am., vol. 39, 1928, pp. 1149–1156.

regular intervals, the cones being from 2 to 4 inches in diameter at the base and up to $1\frac{1}{2}$ inches high. Their axes are parallel to the sides of the containing column. These are not true cone-in-cone and are considered exceptional developments of stylolitic structure. The columns also contain stylolitic seams which are roughly parallel to bedding planes and normal to the side of a column. Branson and Tarr consider each column "an unusually large development of a stylolitic column which extends from the top to the bottom of the bed."

Columnar structures have been described in the Ordovician limestone forming Silliman's Fossil Mount, Frobisher Bay, Baffin Land, where they are considered to have developed from tensional forces developed in the uplift of the area.[266] If such is the origin, these are not sedimentary structures. Salisbury[267] has described columnar structure in clay and referred the origin to concretionary processes.

CONCRETIONS[268]

BY W. A. TARR AND W. H. TWENHOFEL

A concretion is defined as an aggregate, in sediments, of inorganic matter in nodular, discoidal, rhizoid, cylindrical, or other form. A nucleus of some sort is frequently present and the structure is very commonly concentric, although neither feature is essential. Oolites and pisolites are the most abundant concretionary bodies, but as these have a different significance from other concretions, they are separately considered. Concretions are common in most sedimentary rocks and may be found in those of any age from the oldest to those now forming.

Much diversity of opinion exists respecting the origin of concretions, and it is probable that they develop as a consequence of combinations of several different groups of variable factors. As an asset in geologic work, they are given little standing, generally being regarded as little more than curiosities.

Composition

A concretion is commonly composed of a single material, but one or more other substances are apt to be present as impurities. The most common composing materials are calcite, silica, hematite, limonite, siderite, pyrite and marcasite, gypsum, barite, aragonite, witherite, manganese oxide,

---

[266] Roy, S. K., Columnar structure in limestone, Science, vol. 70, 1929, pp. 140–141.

[267] Salisbury, R. D., Columnar structure in subaqueous clay, Science, vol. 5, 1885, p. 287.

[268] Kindle, E. M., Range and distribution of certain types of Canadian Pleistocene concretions, Bull. Geol. Soc. Am., vol. 34, 1923, pp. 609–646. This paper contains an extensive bibliography on concretions.

calcium phosphate, fluorite, and bauxite, the six first named being the most common.

Calcite is the chief material in claystones and in the calcareous concretions so common in shales and sandstones.   The loess concretions are very largely calcite.   Concretions composed of calcite have been dredged from the sea bottom of Auckland Harbor, New Zealand, and are also now forming in the soils of many arid regions.   Aragonite is not commonly known in concretions, but a recent paper[269] describes concretions composed of this mineral which occur in a single locality in the Tertiary of the Kettleman Hills region of California.   They are found in a zone of fine silt a few inches thick; this zone locally resting upon a bed of gypsum.   The concretions are less than 6 inches in diameter, have radial structure, and some have a small central cavity.   The surfaces are like those of marlyte balls.

Siliceous concretions usually are nearly pure silica, most commonly in the form of chert and flint, though some are chalcedony.   Some concretions in sandstone consist of quartz sands cemented by silica or carbonate; such are the sand concretions in the Cambrian sandstones of the upper Mississippi Valley, those known as "Acrespire" in the Millstone Grit of Yorkshire,[270] and those of many other horizons.   The cement in the concretions of the regions just named is carbonate.

Hematite and limonite concretions are the most common ones in sandstones, the concretions usually being composed of quartz sands cemented by hydrous or anhydrous iron oxide.   In limestones, the entire concretion may consist of hematite or other oxide of iron.   The "buck shot" concretions of soils, and the pseudomorphs after concretions of pyrite, marcasite, and siderite, are usually nearly pure iron oxide.   Iron-oxide concretions have been collected in modern Swedish and American lakes,[271] and are forming in some soils, particularly laterites.

Siderite is often an important constituent of clay ironstones, and many concretions in clay, the exteriors of which appear to be composed of iron oxide, have siderite on the interior, the carbonate having altered to the oxide on the exterior.

Pyrite and marcasite concretions are of widespread occurrence.   They are found in shale, limestone, coal, and sandstone, and are particularly common in dark shales of marine origin.

[269] Reed, R. D., Aragonite concretions from the Kettleman Hills, California, Jour. Geol., vol. 34, 1926, pp. 829–833.

[270] Stocks, H. B., On a concretion called Acrespire, Proc. Yorkshire Geol. and Polyt. Soc., vol. 9, 1887, pp. 149–150.

[271] Shaler, N. S., Tenth Ann. Rept. U. S. Geol. Surv., pt. i, 1890, p. 305; Harder, E. C., Prof. Paper 113, U. S. Geol. Surv., 1919, p. 53; Beck, R., The nature of ore deposits, 1909, pp. 98–101.

Gypsum concretions are very common in some of the shales and sand-stones of the Red Beds. Very commonly, however, the gypsum is in the form of selenite crystals or crystalline aggregates.

Barite occurs as concretions (known under such names as "petrified roses" and "barite dollars") in the Red Beds of Oklahoma and Texas, the Elgin Triassic of England, and elsewhere. Nodules composed largely of barium sulphate occur on the sea bottom, and small ones have been taken from an oil well in the Saratoga oil field of Texas. Concretions of witherite are rare, those known consisting of bodies of sand cemented with this material. Manganese oxide in the form of wad or psilomelane forms concretions in many sedimentary rocks, and cements other materials on the present sea bottom to form nodular bodies. Calcium phosphate also forms nodular bodies like those of manganese on the present sea bottom, and it is found in the form of small nodules in marine deposits. Bauxite is very commonly aggregated in pisolitic and concretionary form, as in the bauxite deposits of Arkansas. Fluorite concretions are rare, occurring as small aggregates and isolated individuals in the Triassic sandstones of England.

Shape

Shapes of concretions are so extremely variable that it is difficult to formulate a classification. For purposes of convenience, they may be grouped as (1) spherical, including discoidal and ellipsoidal; (2) cylindrical; and (3) nodular or irregular.

1. Calcite concretions of spherical or nearly spherical shapes occur at Kettle Point, Ontario. Nearly spherical concretions are present in the Virgelle sandstone member of the Eagle formation northwest of Lewistown, Montana, and such are extremely abundant in some of the Cambrian sandstones of the upper Mississippi Valley. Spherical concretions of pyrite or marcasite are locally common in the Morrison shales south of Billings, Montana, some being nearly 2 inches in diameter. The ellipsoidal and discoidal forms of concretions may be original, or both may have developed through flattening of spherical concretions. Excellent examples of discoidal concretions are those in the Champlain clays of the Connecticut River Valley, and many of these have shapes resembling real or fancied organisms. Chert and flint concretions frequently have ellipsoidal shapes.

2. Cylindrical shapes are not uncommon among pyrite, marcasite, and iron-oxide concretions; and calcite concretions, particularly those of loess, not infrequently have this shape. Common lengths do not exceed a foot, and diameters are an inch or more, but log-like concretions in the "Laramie" of South Dakota are said to attain lengths exceeding 100 feet.[272]

[272] Todd, J. E., Loglike concretions and fossil shores, Am. Geol., vol. 17, 1896, pp. 347–349.

3. Concretions of irregular shapes may develop through the lateral union of separate concretions, or they may assume these shapes as original growths. Extremely fanciful forms have developed, particularly among concretions composed of silica and iron oxide, some of which have been identified as roots,[273] animals, birds, household articles, or parts of the human body. An odd variety of concretion is that in the form of a ring found in glacial clays of Iceland, and one of this form has been collected in England. These are less than 4 inches in diameter, and are assumed to have formed around pebbles.[274]

Size

The largest concretions are thought to form in sandstone. The Wilcox formation of eastern Texas and western Louisiana is said to contain sandstone concretions 20 to 30 feet long, and some of the log-like concretions of the Laramie, as above noted, reach a length of 100 feet.[275] Concretions up to 12 feet in diameter occur in the Dakota sandstone of Kansas. Newberry described concretions 10 feet in diameter in the Devonian of Ohio, and many concretions as large as 8 feet in diameter occur in the Virgelle sandstone of central Montana. The Cretaceous Carlile shales in the northern Black Hills contain spherical concretions 5 to 7 feet in diameter, and discoidal concretions 12 feet wide and 1½ feet thick.

Chert and flint concretions rarely attain large size, about 5 feet being a fair maximum, although the large chert bodies may merely be unions of smaller ones. Claystones, as those found in the Champlain clays of the Connecticut Valley, rarely exceed a few inches in length, the largest one found by Sheldon being 22 inches long, and it may have been due to the coalescence of smaller concretions. Most concretions obtained from the sea bottom are only a fraction of an inch in diameter. A few are larger.

Theoretically, epigenetic concretions in sandstone might attain almost any dimensions, as the limiting factors are the quantity of cementing material available and the thickness and extent of the sandstone. The sizes of concretions in shale are more limited, as growth of syngenetic concretions ceases after burial, and epigenetic concretions in shale have their growths limited by the virtual impossibility of replacement or displacement of the enclosing shale. The size of concretions replacing limestone is limited chiefly by the amount of the replacing material available.

[273] Kindle, E. M., A note on rhizoconcretions, Jour. Geol., vol. 33, 1925, pp. 744–746.
[274] Hawkes, L., A note on calcareous "rings" formed in glacial clays, Proc. Geologists' Assoc., vol. 35, 1924, pp. 260–262.
[275] Todd, J. E., Concretions and their geological effects, Bull. Geol. Soc. Am., vol. 14, 1903, pp. 353–368.

Surface features

Some concretions are readily separable from the enclosing rock, and these usually have relatively smooth surfaces; most surfaces are more or less rough and irregular. The surfaces of some concretions are covered with fossils, and some have slickensided surfaces on the upper side. It is not known whether the latter are due to the surrounding beds slipping down around the concretions during consolidation or to the upward growth of concretions.

Internal structure

Concretions may have concentrically laminated or radial structure or may be amorphous. The calcite concretions in the Devonian at Kettle Point,[276] Ontario, and in Michigan[277] have both radial and concentric structure. Many pyrite and marcasite concretions are radial in structure, and this type may also be found in gypsum and iron-oxide concretions. Most concretions show concentric structure to some degree, the formation of which has been accomplished through addition of successive layers to the outside. Each layer may have a radiate structure.

Concretions may have uniform texture and color throughout, but usually there are variations in different parts, giving rise to color banding and mottling. Mottling is best seen in chert concretions, the differences in color being due to varying quantities of carbonaceous material, iron oxides, or other coloring agents. Siderite concretions show a mottling which is chiefly due to secondary changes of oxidation and hydration.

Lines of horizontal stratification extend through some concretions. These are thought to represent bedding planes: they may or may not correspond to those of the enclosing rock. Some sandstone concretions have this stratification in a marked degree. It is usually less obvious in claystones and calcareous and chert concretions, although it may appear sharply after weathering.

Septaria are a form of concretion that possesses filled or open cracks or veins, the cracks seemingly widening toward the interior.[278] Septaria are usually composed of calcite, and this is the most common substance found filling the cracks or veins. Veins are commonly less than 2 inches in width, and the composing minerals usually are oriented perpendicular to the walls. In veins not completely filled, the minerals may terminate in crystal faces.

[276] Daly, R. A., The calcareous concretions of Kettle Point, Lambton Co., Ont., Jour. Geol., vol. 8, 1900, pp. 135–150.

[277] Rominger, C. L., Black shales of Michigan, Geol. Surv., Mich., vol. 3, 1873–1876, pp. 63–67.

[278] Geikie, J., Structural and field geology, 1920, p. 122.

Beautiful crystals of barite and selenite have been obtained from septaria in the Pierre shale of Nebraska,[279] and crystals of marcasite, pyrite, arseno-pyrite, millerite, galena, sphalerite, and chalcopyrite from septaria of other localities.[280] Septaria resemble and are frequently mistaken for fossil turtles. Cone-in-cone not infrequently is associated with septaria as well as other concretions, and the septaria not uncommonly possess slickensided surfaces.

The cracks of septaria have been considered by many students as arising from the shrinking and cracking of the material of the interior;[281] Todd[282] suggested that the exterior expanded through the addition of material and thus pulled the interior apart; and Davies[283] advanced the view that the interior expanded to produce the cracks. The views of Richardson with slight modifications, or rather, additions, seem the best explanation proposed to date. To form a septarium, a concretion with a colloidal central area is postulated. This ultimately becomes a crystalline solid, the process resulting in shrinkage accompanied by cracking. Shrinkage may also be postulated to result from expulsion of water from the saturated central area. At some later date minerals are deposited in the cracks, the walls of which are pushed farther apart by such growth and the cracks are extended to the exterior, the process being like that by which geodes develop within fossils.[284] Under such conditions the cracks or veins become widest in the exterior part of the structure. The common occurrence of septaria in clays is explained on the basis that the clays are composed in large part of colloids and these are suited for forming the central parts of septaria.

Septaria are widely distributed throughout the world in Paleozoic and Mesozoic strata. They are particularly abundant in the Cretaceous formations in Nebraska, Wyoming, the Dakotas, and Montana; the Devonian in New York, Pennsylvania, and Ohio; and the Pennsylvanian of the Mississippi Valley region.

It may sometimes happen that a septarium is acted upon by a solution, resulting in removal of everything except the fillings of the cracks, thus giving a skeleton structure of peculiar form. In the early Quaternary alluvial deposits of Brazos County, Texas, are structures composed of quartz

[279] Barbour, C. A., Observations on the concretions of the Pierre shale, Publ. 7, Nebraska Acad. Sci., 1901, pp. 36–38.

[280] Lindgren, W., Mineral deposits, 1913, p. 237.

[281] Richardson, W. A., On the origin of septarian structure, Min. Mag., vol. 56, 1919, pp. 327–338.

[282] Todd, J. E., op. cit., 1903, p. 359; Geol. Mag., vol. 50, 1913, pp. 361–364.

[283] Davies, A. M., The origin of septarian structure, Geol. Mag., vol. 50, 1913, pp. 99–101.

[284] Bassler, R. S., The formation of geodes, etc., Proc. U. S. Nat. Mus., vol. 35, 1908, pp. 133–154, pls. 18–20.

which resemble such septarium skeletons and at first were believed to be such. These have been designated *melikaria*,[285] and they are stated to have formed in place through deposition of silica from rising waters in the bottoms of deep desiccation cracks. Dimensions are as large as 18 by 8 by 4.5 inches. Similar structures are present in some of the gypsum-bearing beds of the Permian of Oklahoma, but whether the origin is the same is not known.

A structure allied to the concretion is the geode, the term being applied to a partly filled hole in a rock which has weathered out from its surroundings and also to a cavity lined with crystals. A geode may form through the deposition of material from solution upon the walls of a hole, but a very common method of origin is by the deposition of material from solution, chiefly calcite and quartz, along structural and fracture lines of the shells of organisms, with the result that the volume enclosed within the shell progressively increases in diameter. The secondary enlargement is not essential, however, if the interior part of the shell is empty as deposition may occur within this cavity. This type of geode is common in the Mississippian strata of Missouri. Every stage in the growth of geodes through secondary enlargement from crinoids, brachiopods, gastropods, and other shells may be seen in Mississippian strata on the west side of the Cincinnati Arch in Indiana and Kentucky.[286]

Some concretions are composed of concentric laminæ differing in composition, and through solution the more soluble of these laminæ may be removed and thus a central part may become detached, forming a *rattlestone* or Klapperstein. In a similar manner, parts of the interior of septaria may be released. Sandstone concretions of iron oxide frequently have a central core of uncemented sand which rattles on shaking. This sand is frequently pure white, possibly the original color, or it may have been leached of an original iron content.

Nuclei

The majority of concretions do not contain nuclei, and it does not seem essential that there should be one. Any saturated or supersaturated solution by a change in physical or chemical conditions, or by reaction, may precipitate some of the substances in solution, and these first particles would serve as nuclei around which aggregation might take place. It would be impossible to locate this originating center. It is also possible, of course, that a nucleus originally present may have disappeared.

Nuclei that have been found consist of inorganic materials, chiefly detrital

[285] Burt, F. A., Melikaria: vein complexes resembling septaria veins in form, Jour. Geol., vol. 36, 1928, pp. 539–544.

[286] Bassler, R. S., op. cit.

grains; and of organic materials, such as shells and parts of shells, coprolites, complete organisms (as insects and fish), and leaves and other parts of plants.

Nuclei or organic matter not uncommonly are extremely well preserved, as exemplified by the leaves, insects, and other fossils in the famous Mazon Creek locality of Illinois and the fish skulls with perfect preservation of the cranial cavity in the Douglas stage of the Pennsylvanian near Lawrence, Kansas. The preservation of the organic matter is usually much better in the concretions than it is in the enclosing rocks, a fact having important bearing on the time of origin of such concretions.

Modes of Occurrence

The modes of occurrence of concretions are important and essential to an understanding of their origin. Occurrences need to be studied as to (1) the nature of the enclosing rock and the concretions, and (2) the relationships of concretions to the enclosing rocks, that is, whether the concretions are within beds or between beds, and what the orientations are to the bedding planes.

NATURE OF ENCLOSING ROCK. Concretions occur in all or nearly all varieties of sedimentary rock, evaporation products being the only possible exception and there seem to be no good reasons why they should not also be there.

Concretions in clay and shale, in their approximate order of abundance, are composed of calcite or calcite mixed with clay, pyrite or marcasite, siderite, calcium phosphate, gypsum, and barite. The concretions in black shales are most often composed of pyrite or marcasite, and those of gray shales containing considerable organic matter, as those of the Coal Measures, seem to be commonly of siderite or sideritic. Concretions in sandstone consist mostly of sand grains cemented by iron oxide, calcite, or silica, the three cements in their approximate order of abundance. Less commonly, the cement is barite or the manganese oxides. The most common concretions in limestones are composed of silica in the form of flint or chert, and concretions in coal are chiefly pyrite and marcasite.

RELATIONS TO ENCLOSING ROCK. Concretions in general are distributed along bedding planes or lie within beds.

Concretions along bedding planes usually lie in shallow depressions in the underlying bed. Stratification planes in the overlying bed may curve upward over the concretion, or terminate against it abruptly or with a slight upward curve. Some stratification planes pass through concretions without interruption. Rarely, stratification planes curve equally over and under a concretion.

Concretions within beds are common, with the exception of those of flint and chert, but are less so than along bedding planes. They may occur irregularly within a bed, but usually they are along a definite horizon. All variety of distribution may be seen in many quarries, as those in the Oneota dolomite near Madison, Wisconsin, the Mississippian limestone at Branden-

FIG. 100. CHERT NODULES IN THE ST. LOUIS LIMESTONE

The upper bedding plane is shown. The nodules in the St. Louis limestone, Mississippian, in the region where this slab was collected tend to be spherical or ellipsoidal. Specimen collected in the old lithographic stone quarry, Brandenburg, Meade County, Kentucky. About one half natural size. Photograph by Diemer, University of Wisconsin.

burg, Kentucky, the Foraker limestone of Cowley County, Kansas, the Burlington limestone in Missouri, and the chalk cliffs of the south coast of England. Some concretions cross stratification planes.

The most common orientation of concretions is with the longest axes parallel to stratification planes, though this is not always the case (fig. 100).

MODE OF OCCURRENCE AFFECTED BY KIND OF ROCK. Differences in

stratification in different rocks cause one or another of the modes of occurrence to be associated with certain rocks. The rather abundant occurrence of stratification planes in shales causes most concretions therein to be associated with such planes, though concretions also occur wholly within beds of shales and even extend across stratification planes whereupon they present the appearance of superimposed disks or lenses. Concretions within beds are more possible in the thicker bedded limestones, but even so, in some localities they seem more abundant along stratification planes. Concretions in sandstones usually represent bodies of sandstones locally cemented since deposition. The bedding planes of sandstones are generally no more important in permitting the passage of cement-carrying solutions than are other parts of the rock, and there is thus a lesser tendency for concretions to be confined to bedding planes. This condition makes it possible for concretions in sandstone to become very large, and for stratification planes in the sandstones to pass through them without interruption. Concretions in coal are commonly along stratification planes, where they are often associated with clay partings. Concretions of pyrite are not of uncommon occurrence with a coal bed.

Geologic Distribution

Concretions occur in the rocks of all systems. Chert concretions are common in Cambrian, Ordovician, and Mississippian rocks, and flint concretions in the chalks of the Cretaceous. Calcareous concretions are abundant in the eastern Devonian, the Cretaceous east of the Rocky Mountains, and some Pleistocene deposits. Siliceous concretions appear to be most abundant in Paleozoic rocks, and calcareous in the later systems. Whether this time distribution has any important significance is not known.

Classification

Classification of concretions may be based upon origin, form, composition, or time relation to the enclosing rock. Neither form nor composition offers a satisfactory basis, and a classification based on origin and time relations to enclosing rock must necessarily be tentative as existing knowledge on these scores is very incomplete. This work considers a classification based on time relations to the enclosing rock as most satisfactory.

Todd's[287] classification based on method of growth proposed four divisions:

A. Accretions, or growth outward.
B. Intercretions, concretions with cracks on the inside more or less filled with minerals.

---

[287] Todd, J. E., Concretions and their geological effects, Bull. Geol. Soc. Am., vol. 14, 1903, pp. 353–368.

   C. Excretions, or growth inward. (Todd rightly questions placing these among concretions.)

   D. Incretions, or growth inward, as around root cavities. (These are common in loess.)

Todd considers the last two terms questionable. As there is limited information relating to the method of growth of concretions, its use as a basis for classification is not satisfactory.

Merrill's[288] classification based on time relationships to the enclosing rock places concretions in two groups:

   A. Primary concretions, formed contemporaneously with the enclosing rock.

   B. Secondary concretions, due to segregating influences acting subsequently to the formation of the enclosing rock.

Except for differences of statement, this classification is also that of Sorby[289] and Grabau.[290]

Richardson's[291] classification, also based on time relationships, gives three groups:

   A. Contemporaneous; formed at the same time as the surrounding rock.

   B. Penecontemporaneous; segregated close to the surface of recently deposited sediments.

   C. Subsequent; formed after the rock was consolidated.

A two-fold grouping with respect to time relationships is favored, using *syngenetic* rather than primary or contemporaneous, and *epigenetic* rather than secondary or subsequent. The use of penecontemporaneous is not favored. Syngenetic is here used to include concretions formed at the same time the surrounding sediments were being deposited, and epigenetic to include those concretions formed after deposition of the enclosing rock. It naturally follows that there is no sharp division, and concretions no doubt exist of which the central portions are syngenetic and the exterior portions epigenetic because of additions after burial beneath sediments. Syngenetic growth would stop as a concretion becomes buried, but epigenetic growth might then begin.

Origin

Much has been written relating to the origin of concretions, and there is considerable difference of opinion. The chief difficulty seems to have been

---

[288] Merrill, G. P., Rocks, rock weathering and soils, 1906, pp. 35–37.

[289] Sorby, H. C., Concretions, Quart. Jour. Geol. Soc., London, vol. 64, 1908, pp. 215–220.

[290] Grabau, A. W., Principles of stratigraphy, 1913, pp. 718–726, 763.

[291] Richardson, W. A., The relative age of concretions, Geol. Mag., vol. 58, 1921, pp. 114–124.

the assumption that a single method of origin was necessary. It seems probable that the various structures known as "concretions" may originate in three ways, as follows:

1. Physical, as rounding and enlargement of mud balls.
2. Organic, as algal growths.
3. Chemical, aggregated through chemical action, either
     a. As precipitates while enclosing rock was being deposited, or
     b. As aggregates deposited within the enclosing rock after its deposition.

CONCRETIONS OF PHYSICAL ORIGIN.   The only structures developing in a purely physical way which might be identified as concretions are clay pebbles and boulders enlarged by mechanical accretion.   Bourne[292] believed that certain little pellets exposed by a slide on the Connecticut River had developed in this way; Merrill[293] gives this as a method of the origin of some concretions; and Gardner[294] has suggested that many claystones may be of this origin.   It is not thought best, however, that such structures as clay pebbles and boulders should be included among concretions, and, where it can be shown that their origin was mechanical, they should not be so classified.

CONCRETIONS OF ORGANIC ORIGIN.   Many structures of concretionary appearance are of organic origin.   Such are exemplified by those of some algæ, as *Cryptozoon*, and hydroid corals, as *Clathrodictyon*.   Roddy[295] has stated that calcareous "concretions" 8 to 10 inches in diameter may be formed by plant agencies in streams rich in dissolved calcium carbonate, and Clarke[296] has described similar structures in Canandaigua Lake, New York.   Mawson[297] shows their occurrence, by thousands, in depressions between dunes in southwestern Australia; Stow[298] has noted their presence in streams near Lexington, Virginia; and there are many other descriptions.   The writers do not believe in designating these algal structures concretions, though they are unable to give the criteria to differentiate algal bodies from concentric concretions if the organic structure of the algal body has been destroyed by crystallization.

[292] Bourne, C. E., History of Wells and Kennebunk, 1875.

[293] Merrill, G. P., Rocks, rock weathering and soils, 1906, p. 33.

[294] Gardner, J. H., The physical origin of certain concretions, Jour. Geol., vol. 16, 1908, pp. 452–458.

[295] Roddy, H. J., Concretions in streams formed by the agency of blue-green algæ and related plants, Proc. Am. Philos. Soc., vol. 54, 1915, pp. 246–258.

[296] Clarke, J. M., The water biscuits of Squaw Island, Canandaigua Lake, New York, Bull. 39, New York State Museum, vol. 8, 1900, pp. 195–198.

[297] Mawson, D., Some South Australian algal limestones in process of formation, Quart. Jour. Geol. Soc., vol. 85, 1929, pp. 613–623.

[298] Stow, M. H., Calcareous concretions in streams near Lexington, Virginia, Am. Jour. Sci., vol. 20, 1930, pp. 214–216.

CONCRETIONS OF CHEMICAL ORIGIN.   The majority of concretions probably owe the aggregation of their composing materials to chemical processes,
time relationships being either syngenetic or epigenetic.

Syngenetic concretions.   Syngenetic origin involves precipitation of
material from solution, or the coagulation of a colloidal suspension.

Prestwich was the first to advance the theory that chert concretions are
of syngenetic origin, considering the precipitating agents to be either siliceous
sponge spicules or decaying organic matter.   Tarr[299] advocated the syngenetic origin of the chert concretions in the Burlington limestone, and a
like origin for concretions in Pennsylvanian shales in Missouri and Cretaceous shales in South Dakota, Montana, and Saskatchewan, and he concludes that "Most concretions which occur in shales are probably of
syngenetic origin."   Rubey[300] is in accord with Tarr with respect to the calcareous concretions in the Cretaceous about the Black Hills.   Sargent[201] advocated a syngenetic origin for the Carboniferous cherts of Derbyshire,
England, considering the silica to have been precipitated along with the
associated sediments.   Brydone[302] holds that the hollow flints of the chalk
beds are most likely of contemporaneous or penecontemporaneous origin
and that "on the whole a penecontemporaneous origin for row and tabular
flints seems to present the minimum of conflict with facts."   Studies made
by Brinkmann of Jurassic ammonites collected in England from concretions
in dark shales show that fossils in the concretions are undeformed, whereas
any part of a shell projecting from a concretion into the surrounding shale
is mashed flat and distorted, seemingly proving the syngenetic origin of the
concretions.[303]

The idea that concretions of calcium carbonate might be of syngenetic
origin was advanced many years ago by Hall[304] in describing a concretionary
layer of the Tully limestone.   He stated that "the layer seems to be due
to the fact of there not being enough of the calcareous material to form a
stratum, when it was collecting on the bottom, and so it collected into
spheres."   Tarr independently reached the same conclusion, that calcareous

[299] Tarr, W. A., Origin of the chert in the Burlington limestone, Am. Jour. Sci., vol. 44,
1917, pp. 409–452; Syngenetic origin of concretions in shale, Bull. Geol. Soc. Am., vol. 32,
1921, pp. 373–384; Science, vol. 51, 1920, p. 520.

[300] Rubey, W. W., Prof. Paper 165A, U. S. Geol. Surv., 1930, p. 11.

[301] Sargent, H. C., The Lower Carboniferous cherts of Derbyshire, Geol. Mag., vol. 58,
1921, pp. 265–278.

[302] Brydone, R. M., The origin of flint, Geol. Mag., vol. 57, 1920, pp. 401–404.

[303] Brinkmann, R., Statistisch-biostratigraphische Untersuchungen an mittel-juras-
sischen Ammoniten über Artbegriff und Stammesentwicklung, Abh. d. Gesells. d. Wiss.
zu Göttingen, Bd. 13, 1929, pp. 249; Reviewed Neues Jahrb., 1929, p. 400.

[304] Hall, J., Geology of New York, pt. iv, 1843, p. 192.

concretions may represent insufficient material to make a bed, and Lucas[305] explained some nodular clay ironstones as having formed in depressions on the floors of lagoons.

Calcareous concretions (coal balls or "bullions") found in the coal beds of the Lower Coal Measures in England are regarded by Stopes and Watson[306] as due to material introduced into the coal from the sea water immediately above, after the coal had been laid down but before it had become consolidated, thus assigning a syngenetic origin to the coal balls. Stocks[307]seems to have held a similar view.

The calcareous concretions dredged from Auckland Harbor, New Zealand,[308] however, confirm the correctness of the syngenetic view, as they show that concretions may grow during the accumulation of the sediments. The concretions contain about 70 per cent calcium carbonate, and are less than 6 inches in diameter. Shells, small crabs, and other matter serve as nuclei. A few of the larger concretions have irregular drusy cavities as large as 0.5 inch in diameter. These are not due to solution. Shells lacking a horny epidermis do not serve as nuclei, whence it was assumed that decomposition of epidermal matter initiates the deposition of carbonate, resulting in the concretions. The concretions formed on the sea bottom at depths of 28 to 35 feet.

The concretions of the famous Pennsylvanian locality at Mazon Creek, Illinois, which have such wonderfully preserved enclosed fossils, seem to be syngenetic. The iron concretions of Swedish, Canadian, and other lakes are certainly syngenetic, and of like origin are the manganese and phosphatic nodules of the present sea bottom.

The pyrite concretions of the dark Pennsylvanian shales of north-central Missouri have been shown by Mathias[309] to be of syngenetic origin and all pyrite concretions (and marcasite as well) seem best interpreted as of this origin.

Epigenetic concretions. Epigenetic concretions are very abundant in sandstone and to a less degree in shale and limestone. They may be either displacive or replacive. To form an aggregate of any material in a rock, it

[305] Lucas, J., On the origin of clay-ironstone, Quart. Jour. Geol. Soc., vol. 29, 1873, pp. 363–369.

[306] Stopes, M. C., and Watson, D. M. S., On the present distribution and origin of the calcareous concretions in coal-seams, known as "coal-balls," Philos. Trans. Roy. Soc., ser. B., vol. 200, 1909, pp. 167–218.

[307] Stocks, H. B., On certain concretions from the lower Coal Measures and the fossil plants which they contain, Proc. Roy. Soc. Edinburgh, vol. 20, 1893, pp. 70–75.

[308] Bartrum, J. A., Concretions in the recent sediments of the Auckland Harbor, New Zealand, Trans. New Zealand Inst., vol. 49, 1916, pp. 425–428.

[309] Mathias, H. E., Syngenetic origin of pyrite concretions in the Pennsylvanian shales of north-central Missouri, Jour. Geol., vol. 36, 1928, pp. 440–450.

is essential that solutions should be able to move through the rock in order to obtain the material for the concretion. Most sandstones readily permit migration of solutions. This is shown by the usual spherical form of concretions in sandstones, the solutions being able to bring material from all sides. The porosity of shales and limestones is low, and free movement of solutions should be mainly confined to divisional openings, to which, therefore, epigenetic concretions should be largely limited. However, the two factors of time and materials initiating precipitation must be considered, and where these materials are within a bed it seems probable that diffusion, however slow, if given sufficient time may develop epigenetic concretions in any sedimentary rock. This is thought to be proved by the development of lime concretions in clay soils of dry regions. Sheldon[310] states that the Connecticut Valley concretions resulted from the aggregation of small quantities of calcium in the clays, and that circulating ground waters acted as the collecting and transporting agent. This calcium carbonate cemented into the concretions most of the materials of the clays at the places where the concretions formed. Nichols[311] pointed out the difficulty of explaining why the same solution should dissolve at one point and deposit in another, and suggested that much of the dissolved calcium carbonate was originally in the form of aragonite, a suggestion of doubtful value and certainly applicable with difficulty to such concretions as those in the post-glacial clays of the Connecticut River Valley. The difficulty of explanation is a real one, but differential solution is unquestionable and the highly variable character of the materials composing clays, as well as the extreme variability of circulation, permits the assumption that many factors might favor differential deposition. Studies of glacial clays of Wisconsin have shown that many of them contain calcium carbonate in quantity adequate to form an abundance of concretions. The Connecticut Valley clays seem to be actually siltstones or fine sandstones, a fact favoring the view that the concretions are epigenetic. This view is further supported by the distribution of the concretions, which occur mainly in the sandy layers in which the porosity is greatest. The flat disk-like shapes of the concretions are best explained as being due to the thinness of the sandy layers to which the concretions are largely restricted.

Concretions of chert and flint are largely confined to limestone and dolomite. They have usually been considered epigenetic in origin, the silica for their formation coming from the enclosing rock in which it had been deposited mainly as tests of organisms. This view has long been held by

[310] Sheldon, J. M. A., Concretions from the Champlain clays of the Connecticut Valley, 1900.

[311] Nichols, H. W., On the genesis of claystones, Am. Geol., vol. 19, 1897, pp. 324–329.

many British geologists, and it is supported by many of their American colleagues.[312]

Experimental work by Cox, Dean, and Gottschalk[313] suggested that solutions containing calcium carbonate in the presence of carbon dioxide would not be likely to acquire and transport colloidal silica, as these two substances are precipitants of silica. However, Lovering[314] has shown, and his conclusions have been checked by Moore and Maynard,[315] that it is only in solutions of relatively high silica concentration that calcium carbonate and carbon dioxide have any decided precipitating effect and that even then some silica remains unprecipitated. The presence of protective colloids may thoroughly nullify the effects of the carbonate and carbon dioxide. The studies of these three men indicate that solutions would have little difficulty in transporting silica into carbonate sediments.

Daly[316] states that the large calcareous concretions in the Devonian at Kettle Point, Ontario, were formed within the enclosing shale by displacing it, and that their formation antedated the development of the joints and the final consolidation of the shale. He states that the force of crystallization of calcite was the deforming agent that enabled the concretions to push the shale aside. Rominger, on the other hand, regarded the curvature of the beds around these concretions as evidence of the settling of the strata around an already solid structure.

The question arises as to the time of the epigenetic development of concretions. Is it antecedent to the solidification of the containing strata; contemporaneous therewith; or does it occur when, due to weathering or diastrophism, the strata have entered the zone of active ground-water circulation? It is probable that concretions are forming in all stages of a rock's history, but it is also probable that the maximum development is at the beginning and the end of that history, that is, that most epigenetic concretions develop before the containing strata are solidified and after these strata are subjected to the influence of active ground-water circulation. It is possible also that many flint and chert concretions develop during the

[312] Moore, E. S., Siliceous oolites and other concretionary structures in the vicinity of State College, Pennsylvania, Jour. Geol., vol. 20, 1912, pp. 259–269; Van Tuyl, F. M., The origin of chert, Am. Jour. Sci., vol. 45, 1918, pp. 449–456; Dean, R. S., The formation of Missouri cherts, Ibid., vol. 45, 1918, pp. 411–415.

[313] Cox, G. H., Dean, R. S., and Gottschalk, V. H., Studies on the origin of Missouri cherts and zinc ores, Bull. 2, Mining Experiment Station, Missouri School of Mines, vol. 3, 1916, pp. 9–15.

[314] Lovering, T. S., The leaching of iron protores, Econ. Geol., vol. 18, 1923, pp. 537–538.

[315] Moore, E. S., and Maynard, J. E., Solution, transportation and deposition of iron and silica, Econ. Geol., vol. 24, 1929, pp. 398–402.

[316] Daly, R. A., The calcareous concretions of Kettle Point, Lambton Co., Ontario, Jour. Geol., vol. 8, 1900, pp. 135–150.

process of weathering, just as the silicification of fossils[317] is related thereto, although the two processes of silicification are entirely different. (See discussion under chert and flint.) It is certain, moreover, that many iron-oxide and calcium-carbonate[318] concretions are formed in the zone of weathering above or near the water table.

Epigenetic formation of concretions requires that the composing material shall be brought from outside sources or be obtained from the enclosing formation. Rate of growth hinges upon availability of material, rate of movement of the transporting solution, its solvent ability, and the activity of the precipitating agent. The difficulties become apparent when these factors are studied in detail. When the type of rock is considered, it seems obvious that limestones and shales, because of general impermeability when far from the surface, are not promising hosts for the formation of epigenetic concretions under those conditions, and that sandstones are. However, when any rock enters the zone of weathering, its permeability, through the increase in size and number of divisional openings, is largely increased, and it becomes easier for epigenetic concretions to form therein. On the whole, however, field studies seem to furnish little evidence that concretions, other than iron oxide and calcite ones, are extensively developed in this zone.

CRITERIA FOR THE DETERMINATION OF SYNGENETIC OR EPIGENETIC ORIGIN. Criteria for the determination of time relationship to enclosing rock are few, and the same facts have been interpreted in opposite ways by different observers. Features bearing on the problem are: (1) curvature of beds around concretions, (2) lines of stratification passing through them, (3) fossils within or on concretions, (4) physical character of the enclosing rock, (5) volume of concretions, and (6) their distribution.

(1) Curvature of Beds around Concretions. Bedding planes may curve both over and under concretions, the former curvature usually being the more pronounced. Such curvature is most common in clays and shales, occurs rarely in thin-bedded limestones and dolomites; and usually is absent in sandstones and thick-bedded limestones. Curvature of bedding around concretions has been differently interpreted by different geologists. Daly[319] concluded that the Kettle Point concretions developed within or between the beds, forcing them apart and forming the curvature. Newberry[320] considered the curvature due to the shrinkage and settling of the shale beds around

[317] Bassler, R. S., The formation of geodes, etc., Proc. U. S. Nat. Museum, vol. 35, 1908, pp. 134–135; Bain, H. F., and Ulrich, E. O., Bull. 267, U. S. Geol. Surv., 1905, pp. 27, 30.

[318] Kindle, E. M., Range and distribution of certain types of Canadian Pleistocene concretions, Bull. Geol. Soc. Am. vol. 34, 1923, pp. 623–624.

[319] Daly, R. A., op. cit., 1900.

[320] Newberry, J. S., Geol. Surv. Ohio, vol. 1, 1873, p. 155.

the solid concretions. Tarr[321] reached a similar conclusion for the chert concretions in the Burlington limestones of Missouri, and to the same cause Sargent[322] assigned the curving about the concretions in the Carboniferous of Derbyshire. Salisbury[323] expressed the opinion that

certain calcareous concretions in shale about which laminæ bend appear to be syngenetic. These concretions appear to have grown in a shale and to have bent laminæ above themselves and down beneath. In these cases laminæ are greatly thinned above the highest part of the concretions and below the lowest, while at the sides of the concretion between the bent laminæ there is evidence of space filled in, the filling showing laminæ. Laminæ bent above a concretion hereby seem to prove a syngenetic origin.

This is in harmony with the generalization of Sorby[324] that curvature of laminations about a concretion is due to consolidation and settling of sediments deposited during its formation. Richardson[325] found that laminæ of sediments deposited in thin layers over pebbles thickened and bent upward toward the pebbles and terminated against their sides. The major curvature was above. Layers beneath pebbles showed little bending downward, but a shallow depression was formed. However, this last characteristic would depend upon the character of the underlying materials. Syngenetic concretions in thick beds produced no characteristic that would indicate their origin. It would thus seem that thickening and bending upward of laminæ toward concretions, with some laminæ terminating against them, strongly suggest a syngenetic origin.

Curvature of laminæ around a concretion may also be developed by displacive growth, but, unless the concretion was very shallowly buried, the displacement would be more or less uniform above and below, and if growth proceeded uniformly in all directions beds at the sides of concretions should show crumpling or thickening in conformity with the pressure. No record of such has been found. Cone-in-cone is a common feature of many concretions, and the presence of this feature has been adduced as evidence of pressure connected with growth. However, until the factors responsible for development of cone-in-cone are known, it is idle to offer this feature as evidence for the epigenetic origin of concretions. Major curvature of laminæ above a concretion suggests, but by no means proves, a syngenetic origin.

[321] Tarr, W. A., The origin of the chert in the Burlington limestone, Am. Jour. Sci., vol. 44, 1917, pp. 409–452.

[322] Sargent, H. C., The Lower Carboniferous cherts of Derbyshire, Geol. Mag., vol. 58, 1921, pp. 265–278.

[323] Salisbury, R. D., Bull. Geol. Soc. Am., vol. 32, 1921, pp. 26–27.

[324] Sorby, H. C., Application of quantitative methods to the study of rocks, chap. 9, Concretions, Quart. Jour. Geol. Soc., vol. 64, 1908, pp. 205–220.

[325] Richardson, W. A., The relative age of concretions, Geol. Mag., vol. 58, 1921, pp. 114–121.

The slickensided surfaces of some concretions have been interpreted as due to settling of the material over the concretion and also to the growth of the concretion upward into the shale. Either seems possible.

(2) *Lines of Stratification Passing through Concretions.* Lines of stratifications passing through concretions have been held by most students as proof of epigenetic origin, it being thought that the concretions arose through local cementation of the enclosing rock. This is particularly obvious in concretions found in sandstones. Concretions of replacement ought to be common in carbonate rocks, and should also show these stratification planes, but, as a general rule, the concretions in carbonate rocks rarely show stratification planes or other structural features of the enclosing rocks. This does not prove a syngenetic origin, however, as it is not essential in replacement that such structural lines should be preserved. Lines of stratification are common in calcareous and ferruginous concretions in clays and shales. As such rocks are relatively impervious and the usual forms of the concretions are elliptical or discoidal, the aggregating agent is supposed to have followed the bedding planes. As a rule, there is little replacement and the concretions originated largely through cementation.

It is possible that laminæ in concretions might also be formed during the growth of the concretion if the growth was simultaneous with that of the enclosing bed, and the absence of nuclei in so many claystones is favorable to this view.

Concretions having horizontal laminæ that are discontinuous with those of the enclosing beds which in turn curve over the concretions would seem conclusively to be of syngenetic origin. Tarr[326] has shown this to be true of concretions in the Cretaceous shales of South Dakota and in the Lias of the Dorset coast of England.

(3) *Fossils within or on Concretions.* Observers have noted that the fossils in the centers of many concretions are wonderfully well preserved, even to the minutest detail. Such remains are the leaves and insects in the Mazon Creek concretions of Grundy County, Illinois; the fish brains in concretions from Pennsylvanian strata near Lawrence, Kansas; medusæ in the Middle Cambrian of Alabama; and the "Capelin" fish in concretions of glacial clays in Greenland.[327] It is probable that the organic matter in the concretion played an important part in causing the precipitation to which the concretion is due. This precipitation must have been initiated shortly after the organisms came to rest upon the sea bottom, and it is probable

---

[326] Tarr, W. A., Syngenetic origin of concretions in shale, Bull. Geol. Soc. Am., vol. 32, 1921, pp. 373–384. Article relating to the Lias in press.

[327] Guide to fossil reptiles, amphibians, and fishes, British Museum (Nat. Hist.) 1922, p. 98.

that all concretions containing excellent fossils are of syngenetic origin or, at least, that they were only very shallowly buried at the time of formation.

Fossils are also present within the other portions of concretions and upon their surfaces, and it is not uncommon that these fossils are almost the only ones occurring in a given formation, as are those in the Oneota dolomite of the upper Mississippi Valley. Such conditions suggest a syngenetic origin or, at least, only very shallow burial.

(4) *Physical Nature of the Enclosing Rock.* The physical character of the enclosing rock in which concretions occur has some bearing on their origin. The foremost factors are porosity and permeability, the latter being of greater significance, for unless the pores are connected there is little or no immediate passage of water.

Shales are decidedly impervious both to liquids and gases, but dissolved material may diffuse through them, and in the course of a long time perhaps some movement may take place. There is little chance for the development of replacive concretions in shales, but displacive and cementation concretions are possible. The carbonate rocks may be very permeable along certain lines; they are very soluble and hence they may be readily replaced. Sandstones are very permeable, but little soluble. Therefore, there can be little replacement in sandstones, and the concretions in them are largely the result of cementation.

(5) *Volume of Concretions.* A vital consideration with respect to supposed displacive concretions is the volume. The following table gives the approximate cubical contents of spheres of various diameters.

	cubic feet
2 feet in diameter	4
5 feet in diameter	66.5
10 feet in diameter	523

The introduction of an epigenetic displacive concretion of 2 feet diameter means that the surrounding rock must be sufficiently compressed to account for 4 cubic feet of volume. This may occur, but when the diameters greatly exceed 2 feet it does not seem possible to account for the concretions by any theory of displacement.

Concretions of syngenetic origin might attain any dimension, and upon burial the beds would curve over them in the manner described. Compression of the enclosing sediments would increase the curvature. In syngenetic concretions, volume has no significance. Volume considerations also have no significance in concretions of replacement or cementation.

(6) *Distribution of Concretions.* The common distribution of concretions along bedding planes may mean deposition in the interval between the formation of two strata. On the other hand, it may mean deposition of

material carried in solution by ground water which found easy passage along the bedding planes. The fact that concretions are not common along joint planes, however, suggests that the syngenetic origin is the more probable.

Summary

It is impossible to harmonize all occurrences of concretions with one theory of origin, and the composition, sources of material, aggregation, cause of deposition, form, internal structure, nucleus, external features, and character of the enclosing rock must be considered and evaluated in each case. In other words, each concretion presents an individual problem. Some concretions are certainly specialized cases of original deposition: others may equally well be the result of permeating water action.

CONE-IN-CONE

BY W. A. TARR

Cone-in-cone is a structural feature of sedimentary rocks that has attracted wide attention. It has been described by many authors whose descriptions are all very similar but whose ideas of its origin differ considerably. The first reference made to cone-in-cone is that by David Ure in his "History of Rutherglen and East Kilbride, Scotland," published in 1793. The cone-in-cone was found near Kilbride and was known to the miners as "maggy band." A fine specimen of cone-in-cone from the Carboniferous of Derbyshire in the British Natural History Museum is labeled "Petrificato Derbiensia" and is dated 1809. William Martin in describing it states that although it has been regarded as a fossil by some it is not, any more than fibrous gypsum is, but he offers no further explanation of it. Hausmann mentions tutenmergel (cone-in-cone) in 1812, and von Leonhard describes it in his "Charakteristik der Felsarten," 1823. S. P. Hildreth described cone-in-cone in the American Journal of Science in 1836 (vol. 29, p. 99) as a fossil, but James Hall in 1843 recognized it as inorganic material. Murchison illustrates cone-in-cone in "The Silurian System," 1839 (pl. 26, fig. 12), under the name "Cophinus dubius," supposing it to be a fossil zoophyte. His account of the structure and the evidence he advanced to prove its organic origin make interesting reading.

Description

Cone-in-cone structure usually consists of a nest of concentric cones, though some cones occur singly. Heights of cones range from 1 to 200 millimeters; those from 10 to 100 millimeters are most common. Basal diameters depend upon the heights and angles of slope of the cones. In some cones, height and basal diameter approximate equality; ordinarily the diameter is less than the height. Apical angles range from 15 to 100°, with seemingly no dominant development for any angle in the range although angles of 30 to 60° are thought to be most common. Specimens of each occurrence seem to have more or less uniformity of angle. The apical angle is not always continuous, as some cones have flaring bases.

A   B

FIG. 101. CONE-IN-CONE STRUCTURE

The cones in the larger specimen are about 5 inches long. The smaller specimen shows what seems to be a cone in process of being lifted out. The annular ridges and depressions are shown in B. Collected at Langley in southeastern Ellsworth County, Kansas, Lower Cretaceous. Photograph by Diemer, University of Wisconsin.

Sides of cones are usually gently ribbed or fluted, and some have the fine striations typical of slickensided surfaces. The ribs of a cone have counterparts on the enclosing cone. Most cones possess the "conic scales" of Gresley,[328] that is, conical laminæ which extend over only a part of the cone. The sides of the depression in which a cone rests are characterized by more or less discontinuous annular depressions and ridges which are parallel

[328] Gresley, W. S., Cone-in-cone, Quart. Jour. Geol. Soc., vol. 50, 1894, pp. 731–739.

to the surface of the cone-in-cone layer. These range in width from mere lines to five or six millimeters, and usually are a millimeter or less. Much smaller, but similar depressions occur rarely on the cones and are parallel to the bases. The annular depressions and ridges are largest in the upper part of the cone cup (and on the basal parts of cones) and become finer and finer nearer the apices. They are found in greatest widths and abundance on impure (that is, having a high clay content) cone-in-cone. Each depression is filled with clay, which may continue as films of various thicknesses between cones or between conic scales and cones. These various features are shown in figures 101–102.

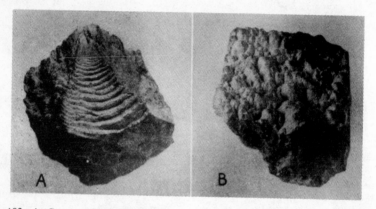

Fig. 102. *A*, Cone-in-Cone Showing the Annular Depressions and Ridges; *B*, Bottom of Cone-in-Cone Shown in *A*

A. The circular areas on the surface shown at the bottom of the figure are bases of other cones.

B. This shows the bottom of the cone-in-cone of figure *A* and illustrates the development of the cone. The development of shear planes gives this specimen its cone structure.

Both figures natural size. Photographs by W. A. Tarr.

The internal structure of cone-in-cone material is usually fibrous. The fibers are never terminated by crystal faces. In cross section, they are rudely circular. The fibers are parallel or inclined to the axis of the cone, and may or may not be parallel to its surface. Richardson[329] has described some simple types of cones having parallel fibers that are parallel to the cone axis and that terminate at the surface of the cone. The writer, also, studied these simple cones in the "beef" (which is a fibrous layer of calcite) on the southern coast of England and found that the *ends* of the fibers are actually parallel to the sides of the cone. Some cones an inch long, in which the fibers of the outer part of the cone are parallel to the sides, are part of a

[329] Richardson, W. A., Petrology of the shales with "beef," Quart. Jour. Geol. Soc., vol. 79, 1923, pp. 91–92.

layer of parallel fibrous calcite five inches long.   Richardson states that the elongation of the calcite fibers in the "beef" is in the direction of the vertical (c) axis, and the mean value of the apical angle of the terminations of the fibers is nearly equal to that between the rhombohedral cleavages of calcite. The writer has measured the angles of the conical surfaces with the cone axis in a section of cone-in-cone made by Prof. T. G. Bonney from a specimen of the "beef" from the Isle of Wight and found them to range from 22 to 33°, averaging 30°.   This is considerably less than the values noted by Richardson, and indicates that the angles may depart widely from the rhombohedral cleavage angle of calcite.   Parting planes occur in some cone-in-cone layers and in the materials studied by Richardson, Twenhofel, and the writer the fibers and the cones end abruptly at such planes.

Cone-in-cone structure occurs also, however, in massive material, though the following description of it is the first that has been given anywhere. Cone-in-cone in massive material was first studied by the writer in Sedgwick Museum at Cambridge University, the material coming from the Coal Measures of Tipton near Dudley in Staffordshire.   These cone-in-cones are splendidly developed, showing all the usual external features of those occurring in fibrous materials.   The annular depressions are minutely developed on some cones, no less than 43 having been counted in the space of one-half inch.   The bases of the cones show a remarkable system of concentric lines that mark the development of the cone-in-cone structure. These lines are similar to those formed by pressure in testing materials. Many of the cones have sharp apices and flaring bases.   (The cone-in-cone Murchison described is in a similar massive material.)

Other cone-in-cone structures in massive material that have since been studied by the writer occur in Perry County, Kentucky, and in western Kansas.   The Kentucky material has a marvelous series of cones (fig. 103). The material from Kansas is an impure chalk or marl and likewise has well developed cones but not such completely nested series.   The annular depressions are very small in these specimens.

Undoubtedly, the most remarkable conical structures known are those that occur in the coal of Monmouthshire, England, and in southern Wales (see fig. 104).   These cones never occur singly but are united to form curved parallel ridges.   The cones average 38 to 40 millimeters in height, and their apical angle is 36°.   Their sides are brilliantly slickensided, and bear occasional tiny chatter marks.   Conic scales occur on the cones, also.   There are two sets of cones, with their apices pointing in opposite directions and their bases separated by a thin layer of shale or coal.[330]

[330] Garwood, E. J., Geol. Mag., vol. 29, 1892, pp. 334–335; Gresley, W. S., Geol. Mag., vol. 29, 1892, p. 432 (does not consider this cone-in-cone).

FIG. 103. CONE-IN-CONE DEVELOPED IN A FINE-GRAINED MASSIVE LIMESTONE

There should be noted the repeated series of cones and the uniformity of the shape, features characteristic of cones in such materials. From the Pennsylvanian of Perry County, Kentucky. Specimen given by Professor A. C. McFarlan. Natural size. Photograph by W. A. Tarr.

Another type of cone structure should be mentioned for the sake of completeness, although it is probably rare. This type is a percussion cone occurring in pebbles of a fine-grained quartzite. The specimen in the writer's possession was found by Sidney Powers on Bear Creak, south of Bozeman,

Fig. 104. Conical Structures in Coal from Merthyr Tydvil, Wales
Specimen in Brighton Museum, England. Photograph by W. A. Tarr.

Montana. The apices of the cones are at the surface of the pebble, which is covered with concentric fractures that intersect and cross each other at various angles. The angle between the smooth sides of the cones is 53°.

A percussion cone in quartzite occurring near Birmingham, England,

is in the British Museum.   This cone has approximately a 90° apical angle.
Another mechanical cone formed in chert from Antrim, Ireland, is in the
same museum and has a very similar shape.   French[331] in studying the
fractures developed in homogeneous media found that percussion cracks on
the surface were concentric, and that the resulting cone with its internal
apical angle of 90° had its apex at the surface.   Light blows produced the
best circular fractures and cones.   In some media, radial fractures were
developed from the point of contact.   These cones show that percussion
can produce cones, but it should be noted that the apices and not the bases
are at the surface.   In the calcite, it is the cleavage that causes the base of
the cone to develop at the surface.

Composition

Most cone-in-cone is largely composed of calcium carbonate in the form
of calcite; the amount of $CaCO_3$ ranges from 60 to 98 per cent and the
remainder is mostly clay.   Cone-in-cone composed of gypsum is present
in the Comanchean of south-central Kansas; this is probably best regarded
as a replacement of calcite or aragonite.   It has been suggested that some
cone-in-cone is composed of aragonite, but the writer has found none, and
Twenhofel reports a similar fact.   Cone-in-cone might very well be composed of siderite, as the structure has been reported in association with
ferruginous concretions, but no cones of siderite have been described.

Mode of Occurrence

Cone-in-cone structure is most common in shales and marls.   It occurs
also very commonly in association with concretions.   It may form a layer
both above and below a concretion and usually does not extend beyond it.
Cone-in-cone layers may be persistent or they may be lenticular in character.
Small lenses and plates are common in some formations.   The layers of
cone-in-cone may be single with the apices of the cones all pointing downward, or they may be double in which case the apices of the cones in each
layer point toward each other.   In cone-in-cone occurring at the ends of
concretions or in disturbed material, the apices of the cones may point in
any direction.   In one remarkable aggregate of cones studied by the writer,
the long axes of the cones were horizontal and the apices pointed in every
direction in the horizontal plane.

Cone-in-cone is also associated with beds of limestone and may be coextensive with the limestone or only in connection with a part of the bed.
The Comanchean of central Kansas has a single cone-in-cone layer extending
for 40 miles in a northeast-southwest direction and for 25 miles at right

[331] French, J. W., Trans. Geol. Soc. Glasgow, vol. 17, pt. 1 (1919-1922), pp. 50–68.

angles to that direction.   In places, the bed assumes a nodular aspect.
Well developed cone-in-cone occurs in about 70 feet of marine shales (known

FIG. 105. CONE-IN-CONE FROM THE "SHALES WITH 'BEEF'"

Collected by W. A. Tarr from the Lias below Black Ven Cliff east of Lyme Regis,
Dorset, England.   Natural size.   Photograph by W. A. Tarr.

as the "shales with beef") in the Lias on the Dorsetshire coast of England.[332]
The cone-in-cone is well developed in more than twenty-five persistent layers
of the fibrous calcite ("beef") and in many more that are more or less im-
persistent. In some of these layers, concretions are enclosed between a
double band of cone-in-cone. Some of the horizons are marked by lenticular
cone-in-cone units, and others carry concretions surrounded by cone-in-cone
layers. The overlying shale beds also contain fibrous layers of calcite and
concretions with cone-in-cone (figs. 105–106).

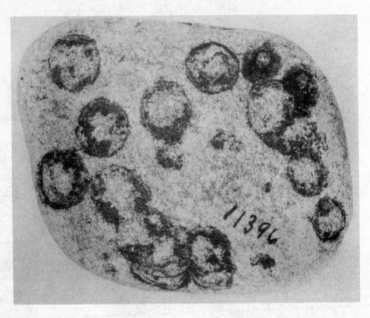

FIG. 106. TOP OF A SPECIMEN FROM THE "SHALES WITH 'BEEF'"
Collected by W. A. Tarr at a locality east of Lyme Regis, Dorset, England. The distribution of the cones in the "beef" should be noted. The cones extend to the shale parting of the "beef," a distance approximately the same as the diameter of the base of the
cones. Photograph by W. A. Tarr.

Geographical and Geological Distribution

It is probable that cone-in-cone has a rather general distribution over all
continents. In the United States, it was early reported from western New
York, Pennsylvania, and Ohio. It occurs also in the Pacific Coast region.
It is known to have a considerable distribution in England, France, Germany,
and other parts of Europe.

[332] Lang, W. D., Shales with "beef," a sequence in the Lower Lias of the Dorset coast,
Quart. Jour. Geol. Soc., vol. 79, 1923, pp. 47–66 (52–53, and fig. 2).

The oldest geological occurrence of cone-in-cone that has been reported is in the Middle Cambrian of Utah. It is present (in the Arisaig section) in the Silurian of the St. Lawrence region; the Devonian of New York, Pennsylvania, Ohio, and Michigan; the Carboniferous of the Appalachian and mid-continent regions, and many parts of Europe; the Permian of Kansas, Montana, and elsewhere; the Jurassic of Europe; the Cretaceous of the Great Plains region; and the Tertiary of many parts of the world.

Origin

Great difference of opinion has been expressed with respect to the origin of cone-in-cone, and there is also difference of opinion concerning the time of its development. Views relating to origin may be placed in three categories: (1) those representing the structure as a consequence of gas rising through unconsolidated sediments; (2) those holding that it is a form of crystallization; and (3) those holding that the cones were caused by pressure due to the weight of the overlying sediments, or to pressure connected with the growth of the associated concretions.

(1) The gaseous theory has little support. Its chief advocate was Young,[333] and it is not known that it has any adherents at the present time. It was Young's view that gas generated in unconsolidated sediments produced the cones in a surface or near-surface layer through which the bubbles passed as they rose to the surface. Thus, the structures were, under this theory, essentially contemporaneous with the sediments in which they occurred.

(2) There have been a number of supporters of the crystallization theory. Many minerals are known to crystallize in fibrous form; such is a common occurrence of calcite in pisolites, oolites, and veins. Spheres having radially directed fibers are well known, and veins and layers with fibrous minerals are not uncommon, but it has been difficult to understand how crystallization could develop such a complex structure as cone-in-cone. Sorby[334] seems to have been the first to advocate this origin, explaining the cones as the result of radial crystallization around an axis. This hypothesis was also advocated by Cole,[235] who maintained that the clay between the cones was the residue forced aside during the crystallization of the calcite.

The latest advocate of the crystallization theory is Richardson,[336] who states that there are three essential facts bearing on the origin of the cone-in-cone structure in the shales with "beef:" (1) limitation of cone-in-cone

[333] Young, J., Geol. Mag., vol. 29, 1892, pp. 138, 278, 480.

[334] Sorby, H. C., On the origin of cone-in-cone, British Assoc. Adv. Sci., vol. 29, 1859, p. 124; The Geologist, vol. 2, 1859, p. 485.

[335] Cole, G. A. J., On some examples of cone-in-cone structure, Mineralogical Mag., vol. 10, 1893, pp. 136–141.

[336] Richardson, W. A., op. cit., 1923, pp. 92–95.

to the fibrous or acicular calcite (this limitation is now known to be incorrect, as the descriptions above show); (2) direct increase in complexity of cones with the increase in thickness of cone-in-cone layers; and (3) penetration of a cone-layer ("beef"-veins) as a whole, by the cones without regard to internal structure. The writer does not agree with this last statement as his studies of the shales with "beef" showed that the cones were on both sides of the parting but did not cross it. Richardson thinks that the cone-in-cone is due to internal stresses set up during the crystallization of calcite in fibrous form. During this crystallization, the load was that of the overlying strata with some minor deductions which need not be considered. This load produced a vertical stress. In the horizontal planes, lateral stresses were generated by resistance to the lateral growth of the fibers. These two sets of stresses produced conical surfaces of maximum shear, the apical angles of the cones being determined by the relative magnitude of the stresses. The inclination of the perfect rhombohedral cleavage to the vertical axis of the fibers would probably render them extremely sensitive to the conical surfaces of shear. Richardson thinks that "Where master shear-planes were established, fibers already formed might be fractured; but, more probably, the action would be to inhibit growth in such a way that the fibre could not cross the plane." Spacing of shear cones, he thinks, would be due to many factors difficult to evaluate.

The writer believes that the "beef" layers are the result of the redeposition of the calcium carbonate of the associated marls (most of the so-called shales are marls). The deposition of the fibrous calcite started along a bedding plane, and as the solutions carried more calcium carbonate to this plane growth continued in both directions from the plane. This method of growth could not produce pressures in the growing fibers, however, as their growth was entirely vertical, proceeding only from the exposed ends of the fibers. The crystalline fibrous calcite undoubtedly occupied less space than did the original marl. In this transference of the $CaCO_3$ of the marl to the "beef" layer, the associated clay was left behind and formed the "paper shales" described by Lang.[332] Lang states that "the upper division (of the shales with 'beef'), some 30 feet thick, consists of paper-shales, is of a brown rather than blue colour, and has more numerous beef-seams than the lower division." This association is in keeping with the writer's theory of the origin of the "beef." There is no support for Richardson's assumption that lateral growth of the fibers produced horizontal stresses, because after growth was once started they *grew upward* and not laterally. Richardson's sketches (ibid. pp. 91 and 92) show this, for he represents the fibers as being parallel sided.

Furthermore, the time of development of the cone-in-cone is a fundamental factor in its origin. Richardson says nothing about the time, but does furnish time proof against his own theory. He postulates stresses, induced by supposed lateral growth, which are thought to act with vertical stresses (load) to produce a shear plane. As the mass of fibers grew, this shear plane was supposed to continue *upward*, separating the *new growth* from the old, a physical impossibility, as Richardson actually admits (ibid. p. 94). Furthermore, his own sketches (ibid. fig. 4, p. 89 and fig. 5, p. 91) prove that the *cones* must have formed after the layer had completed its growth as he shows the cones crossing from one side to the other (an assumption, however, with which the writer does not agree) and such a development is impossible during growth. Further evidence against Richardson's theory is that cone-in-cone occurs in very thin layers of "beef." Stresses that would aid in forming cones could not develop in layers $\frac{1}{16}$ inch thick.

The evidence, not only in the cone-in-cone in the "beef" but in that of many other localities where the writer has studied it, shows that the *cones are always later than the fibrous layer in which they occur*. This is proved by the following facts: (1) cone-in-cone is irregularly distributed (uniformity should be the rule if cone-in-cone was due to crystallization) within a layer; (2) the cones develop universally in the *outer part of the fibrous layer and with their bases at the surface*; and (3) the evidence is positive that the cones have moved downward (or upward) and that solvent action has accompanied the movement.

The writer believes, however, that Richardson's point about the relationship between the cleavage of calcite and the angular forms of cones is of value in explaining the true origin of cone-in-cone. Likewise, pressure is essential in explaining the origin, but the writer does not agree that the force developed by crystallization was a factor.

(3) The pressure theory was developed in considerable detail by the writer[337] in 1922. It was shown that nearly all cone-in-cone bears evidence of movement of the cones with respect to each other; (1) in the displacement of horizontal bands, and (2) in the penetration of an inner cone into an outer without breaking the surface of the latter (the place of the inner cone is thus indicated on the base by a depression). It should be added that the faintly developed slickensided surfaces seen on some cones, and the general occurrence of striations are further evidence of movement of cones within cones. Solvent action accompanied the movement of the cones, for otherwise the outer cones would have been destroyed. Further evidence that solution must have occurred is the clay in the depressions on the inner surfaces of cones (actually in the cone cups), and the films of clay over the surface between the depressions. This clay is the insoluble residue of the cal-

[337] Tarr, W. A., op. cit., 1922, pp. 205–213.

cite that was removed in solution. This residue is analogous to that on the ends and sides of stylolitic columns. It can scarcely be doubted that the movement was due to pressure, which may also have been an aid in the solvent work.

The two facts of movement and solution in connection with cone-in-cone are fundamental and must be accounted for in explaining the origin. The cones in coal and in quartzite involve only movement in their formation, but they are the only exceptions to the rule that movement and solution have both been involved in the formation of cone-in-cone. In the writer's previous paper (ibid. p. 332), he stressed the fibrous character of the material, regarding it as essential. It is true that the greater part of all cone-in-cone occurs in fibrous material, but the discovery that cone-in-cone has developed in massive material has shown that the fibrous character is not essential. It is undoubtedly an important factor, however, when present. The position of the fibers in a layer is also a factor, for the cone axis is usually parallel to the elongation of the fibers. Another important factor to be considered is the closeness of the cleavage angle of calcite to the angle of the fracture produced by any outside stress, as discussed by Richardson.[336] In the writer's opinion, this factor has more value in the pressure theory of the development of cone-in-cone than it does in Richardson's application of it to crystallization.

The source of the pressure is the most difficult factor to explain. Possible sources of pressure previously suggested were the change of aragonite to calcite (assuming the original fibrous mineral was aragonite), a change that involves a volume increase of 8.35 per cent; the growth of concretions associated with cone-in-cone; the pressure of overlying beds; and diastrophic movements. As was stated in the writer's original article, the conception of the importance of one or all of these factors might be revised or discarded altogether after further study, and this has proved to be true.

If it could be shown that the original form of the calcium carbonate was aragonite, as was assumed by some men in earlier studies, a source of considerable pressure would be available. Neither the writer nor Twenhofel, who has also examined many cones, has ever found any that consisted of aragonite. In his original paper, the writer cited what appeared to be corroboratory reasons for thinking that the original form might have been aragonite but he does not now believe they have much weight for the following reasons: cone-in-cone is not confined to fibrous material, and the fibers in both the original layer and the cones are usually parallel and but rarely radiating. Furthermore, it is just as easy to explain the initiation of conical forms by pressure as to explain how and why the change to calcite from aragonite should result in conical forms.

The possible growth of associated concretions as a source of pressure was discarded before, as vast numbers of cone-in-cone structures are unassociated with concretions, and because the concretions associated with cone-in-cone in the Dakotas and Wyoming, as well as those with the "beef" of the Lias in England, have been shown (by the writer) to be syngenetic, whereas the cone-in-cone is unquestionably later.

Diastrophic disturbances might induce various strains and stresses in fibrous calcite that would favor fracture and the formation of cones; but, as the majority of cone-in-cone structures occur in undisturbed formations, such a source of pressure is not of wide application.

The remaining sources of pressure are those due to the weight of overlying beds and to crystallization. As was pointed out above, the development of the cones must have followed the cessation of crystallization, for the bases of the cones are at the surface of the layer. Moreover, *the cones cut across the fibers near the surface*, a condition that could take place only after the fibers had formed. Thus, crystallization is eliminated as a source of pressure, though it will be shown later that some secondary (post-cone in time) deposition has taken place, producing certain features.

The weight of overlying beds is thus the remaining source of pressure, although previously it was not regarded as important. Reasons for believing in a differential vertical pressure due to overlying materials as a cause of cone-in-cone are as follows: (1) the great majority of cone-in-cone structures occur in horizontal, or what were originally nearly horizontal, beds; (2) the cones are dominantly on the upper side of a layer with their bases upward, though smaller ones occur also on the lower side, with their bases downward; (3) the most perfect cones have apical angles that approach those of the ideal cones developed in testing the crushing strength of materials, that is, angles of 70 to 110°; (4) the apical angles in cone-in-cone are nearly that of the rhombohedral cleavage of calcite (the cleavage of calcite would give an apical angle of 106°); (5) solution and rearrangement of the fibers occur along the minor fault planes that cut the fibers, parallel depressions developing on the lower side of the fault plane just as in the cone-cups; (6) layers with parallel fibers show stylolites, which are recognized as being due to differential pressure and solution; (7) sharp blows of a hammer on fibrous calcite produce percussion cones with angles that approximate many of those in cone-in-cone; (8) the surface of a layer of fibrous calcite containing cone-in-cone commonly shows concentrically curved fracture lines that are the result of pressure (these lines can be seen on a polished basal surface and in polished sections of the cones); and (9) the increasing pressure of overlying beds during their accumulation (1000 feet of average rock exerts a pressure of 1,100 pounds per square inch) and its *constant* application induced stresses within the fibers that eventually resulted in fracturing which made possible the solvent work. There is far more reason for believing that the pressure that developed cone-in-cone was due to the weight of overlying beds than there is that it was due to the force of crystallization, as the latter force was exerted only *during the growth* of the calcite and the *cone-in-cone was developed after calcite fibers had ceased growing*. If crystallization had been a factor, cone-in-cone should occur on the upper and lower surfaces of *all fibrous calcite layers*, for the very elements of the theory demand that the effects of crystallization must be active everywhere during growth. The enormous number of fibrous calcite layers that are free from cone-in-cone is ample proof -that crystallization is not the cause of its formation. Furthermore, as was pointed out before, the growth of the fibers takes place at their *outer ends* and hence the crystallization could not be the cause of the development of stresses, either vertically or laterally.

Localization or uneven distribution of the vertical pressure along the top of a layer was probably due to (1) varying density of the material immediately overlying it (dense material would transmit the vertical pressure most effectively), and (2) irregularities on the surface of the fibrous layer. Purely as a contributing factor, an earthquake vibration passing rapidly through the rocks might possibly have caused the release of the stresses induced by the slowly accumulating pressure. This may seem fanciful, but we need to correlate more factors of this type.

Minor elements that influence the development of cone-in-cone are the position, size, and shape of the calcite fibers. Perfectly parallel fibers are rare. They vary, likewise, in size and shape, becoming thicker as they grow outward, but conforming to the influence of the rate of growth of surrounding fibers. Some fibers are long slender columns; others taper on one end or both ends; and others are spindle shaped, although rudely circular in cross section. In layers two inches thick (a very common thickness), few of the fibers are continuous through the entire layer, as some pinch out and others are initiated alongside of them. Rapid growth would favor a tendency toward radiating structure, but as no specimen of fibrous calcite in the writer's collection shows a radial arrangement, he concludes that growth was largely a uniform process. In some specimens, closely spaced joints have broken a fibrous calcite layer into numerous polygonal columns along which solution work has produced thin rods with cones at the ends. Some long slender cones starting with a base one-half to three-fourths inch across have been reduced to columns one-quarter inch in width. This change from the typical pressure cone at the base to the slender column is due to the downward deflection of the shear plane by the vertical joint planes between the fibers, the process continuing until the sides of the column are nearly (in some specimens actually) parallel to the fibers.   The spindle shape of some fibers also aids in the downward deflection of the sides of cones. It is in this way that the long slender columnar cones are developed.   The larger the fibers the greater is the ease of downward deflection.   In very fine fibrous material and in massive material, the cones formed have a uniform slope from the apex to the base as there is less downward deflection.   Cones in massive material would have to be entirely due to pressure, as were those conical structures formed in coal and quartzite.   In one specimen of cone-in-cone in a massive marl, the cone-cup has splendidly developed rings and other features, showing that these features develop in massive materials. The angles are similar to those of cones formed in crushing tests.

The other factor aiding pressure in the formation of cone-in-cone is the work of solutions.   Acting along the shear planes, they remove material, leaving behind an insoluble clay residue.   In some specimens, this residue is minutely micaceous, which favors slipping along the shear plane.   The annular depressions of the cone cups are the result of solution of the *ends* of the fibers surrounding the cone.   Solution takes place there because the upper ends of the fibers are under pressure.   Once started, growth of the annular depressions continues downward, just as solvent action at the end of stylolitic columns causes their further development.   The circular character of the depressions is due to the fact that each successive group of fibers down the sides of the cone cups forms continuous rings around the cup (fig. 107).   Solutions moving along this shear plane attack the upper thin edges of the fibers first and continue the solvent action downward. Variations in the position, size, and composition of the fibers, along with variation in the character of the solvent, account for the discontinuity of the annular depressions.   The carbon dioxide content of the solution, as well as the rate of downward movement, probably has something to do with the effectiveness of the solvent action.   Another factor in the localization of the annular depressions would be the formation of the tiny chatter marks.   The distribution of pressure along the sides of the cones would also be a factor, solution occurring where the grains or fibers are under the greatest pressure.   In the massive material, chatter marks and the rate of penetration of solutions are the probable localizing factors.

The $CaCO_3$ removed may be carried downward and deposited in cracks as veins or even in septaria.   Some interesting lenses of cone-in-cone on the surface of large concretions in the Lias on the south coast of England are connected by cracks (now veins of calcite), with septaria below, making it evident where the dissolved material has gone.   Other results of solution work are shown in the convergence at the apices of the cones of what were originally parallel fibers.   This convergence is due to the removal of part of the fibers, thus permitting their deflection. Further proof of the solvent action is the higher percentage of insoluble residue between the fibers at the apical end of the cones. The shift of originally parallel fibers to a position paralleling the surface of the cone must be due to pressure, coupled with deflection due to removal of *some* of the CaCO₃ of the fibers. Cones within cones would produce the same effect, and we have already pointed out that pressure can induce one inside the other. The rounded, blunt apices are the result of solution work.

Cones not uncommonly extend above the surface of the layer. This is caused by the redeposition of CaCO₃ along the shear plane, resulting in the actual lifting upward of the cone (fig. 101). In some cones, secondary layers of calcite one-eighth inch thick occur. This deposition took place

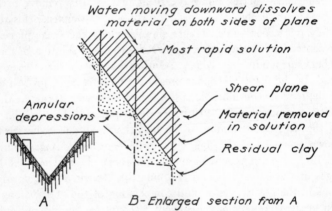

FIG. 107. DIAGRAM TO SHOW HOW SOLUTION ACTS ALONG A SHEAR PLANE, REMOVES SOME MATERIAL, AND DEVELOPS THE ANNULAR DEPRESSIONS IN THE CONE CUP

in the spaces between the cone and the cup, as the entrance of the saturated solutions was possible there.

Summary

Cone-in-cone is an epigenetic structural feature, characteristic of fibrous calcite layers (it is found rarely in massive material), in which it was induced by pressure that created conical shear surfaces. The angle of the shear surfaces to the elongation of the fibers varies widely, but in most cones it is closely similar to the rhombohedral cleavage angle of the calcite fibers, or to the typical angle in cones produced in crushing structural materials. Solvent work by ground water along these shear surfaces removes some CaCO₃, permits further movement of the cone (as is shown by displaced original features) and leaves the insoluble material in annular depressions around the sides of the cone cup. A combination of pressure and solution induces movement and causes the formation of one cone within another. Without the accompanying solvent action, the movement would have caused a disruption of surrounding materials. It is the fibrous character of the calcite together with its rhombohedral cleavage that permits the development of cone-in-cone instead of stylolites, which develop in limestone in which the calcite grains are irregularly arranged. Pressure and solution, causing movement, are responsible for the formation of both cone-in-cone and stylolites, and in both of the structures the insoluble residues are present as evidence of the solvent action.[338]

STYLOLITES

Description

Stylolites[339] consist of vertically striated columns, pyramids, or cones on bedding planes, composed of the same material as the rock of which they are a part. Each column usually has a thin cap of dark clay, and the sides may be covered with similar clay, but in much less thickness. The stylolites on any given bedding plane have counterparts on the bedding plane above or below (fig. 108). A stylolitic bedding plane or seam may pass laterally into one without this structure, but on which there may be a layer of clay similar in composition to that associated with the stylolites.

Columns range in length from 1 mm. to over 30 cm.; average lengths are

[338] Other articles describing cone-in-cone are: Barbour, C. A., Publ. 7, Nebraska Acad. Sci., 1897, pp. 36–38; Bonney, T. G., Mineralogical Magazine, vol. 11, 1895, pp. 24–27; Broadhead, G. C., Science, vol. 26, 1919, p. 15; Chadwick, G. H., Bull. Geol. Soc Am., vol. 32, 1921, p. 26; Daintree, R. Quart. Jour. Geol. Soc., vol. 28, 1872, p. 283; Dawson, J. W., Acadian geology, 1868, pp. 676–677; Geikie, A., Textbook of geology, 4th ed., 1892, p. 421; Grabau, A. W., Principles of stratigraphy, 1913, pp. 788–789; Gresley, W. S., Geol. Mag., vol. 24, 1887, pp. 17–22; vol. 29, 1892, p. 432; Grimsley, G. P., Michigan Geol. Surv., vol. 9, 1903–04, pp. 100, 109; Hall, J., Nat. Hist. New York, Geol. 4th Dist., 1843, pp. 131, 192, 220, 230, 232; Harnley, B. J., Proc. Kansas Acad. Sci., vol. 15, 1895, p. 22; Harker, A., Geol. Mag., vol. 29, 1892, p. 240; Hildreth, S. P., Am. Jour. Sci., vol. 29, 1836 pp. 99–100; Jukes, J. B., Manual of geology, 1872; Keyes, C. R., Proc. Iowa Acad. Sci., vol. 3, 1898, pp. 75–76; Leonhard, K. C. von, Characteristik der Felsarten, 1923, p. 418; Marsh, O. C., Proc. Am. Assoc. Adv. Sci., vol. 16, 1867, p. 142; Murchison, R. G., The Silurian System, 1839, pp. 199, 206, 697; Newberry, J. S., Geol. Surv. Ohio, vol. 1, 1873, p. 211; Geol. Mag., vol. 22, 1885, pp. 559–560; Reis, O. M., Ueber Stylolithen, Dutenmergel und Landschaftenkalk, Geognost. Jahresh. d. k. bayer. Oberbergamt in München, Bd. 15, 1903, pp. 157–279 (250); Abstracts in Geol. Zentralb. Bd. 4, 1903–04, pp. 369–371; Zeits. f. Pract. Geol., Bd. 12, 1904, pp. 419–422; N. Jahrb. f. Min. etc., Bd. 2, 1906, p. 201; Sach, A. J., Geol. Mag., vol. 29, 1892, p. 505; White, C. A., Am. Jour. Sci., vol. 45, 1868, pp. 401–402; Young, J., Trans. Geol. Soc., Glasgow, vol. 18, pt. IV, 1886, pp. 1–27.

[339] The name is derived from the Greek *stylos*, a column, and *lithos*, a stone. In the preparation of this topic extensive use has been made of the studies of Doctor P. B. Stockdale, Stylolites: their nature and origin, Indiana Univ. Studies, vol. 9, 1922, pp. 1–97.

about 20–100 mm.   The extent of a stylolitic seam is in proportion to the height of the stylolites, a seam with large stylolites having, as a rule, greater extent than one with small.   Small and large stylolites occur in association.   Associated with a layer of stylolites are numerous small, sharply intertoothed seams or sutures, the "Drucksuturen" of the Germans.   Except in the matter of dimension, "Drucksuturen" are like the stylolites, into which they pass by gradual transition.   The tops of stylolites have variable dimensions.   Some are broad and flat; others are rounded; and still others are pointed or consist of a number of points.   There seems little relation between the shape of a stylolite and its height, some being very broad and

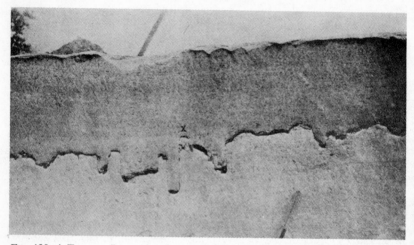

Fig. 108. A Typical, Large Stylolite-seam in the Salem Limestone of the Dark Hollow District, Lawrence County, Ind.

Note the irregularity in length and width of the interpenetrating parts.   The darker, upper stratum is blue stone; and the lower buff.   Note the small, minor stylolite-seam running across the column below X.   The clay parting is plainly visible.   The upper and lower strata are distinctly lithologically different.   The longest column is about 9 inches. After Stockdale.

also very short, others broad and long.   Diameters range from 1 to about 60 mm., 3 to 20 mm. being common.

Stylolites are usually straight, but occasionally curved examples occur. Instances are known in which one column cuts across another,[340] and small stylolite seams penetrated by large stylolites of an adjacent seam are not uncommon.   The surface of a stylolite seam, that is, the surface produced by separating a seam into its two parts, is extremely irregular, with pinnacles, ridges, domes, etc. of highly variable orientation, height, and shape.

[340] Wagner, G., Stylolithen und Drucksuturen, Geol. und Pal. Abh., Bd. 11, Heft 2, 1913, pp. 101–128.

The clay cap on the end of a stylolite column, cone, or dome is always present, and it may attain a thickness of 10 to 15 mm. It has the composition of the insoluble residue in the rocks of which the stylolites are a part. The cap thins out down the side to thicken again beneath the adjacent downward-projecting stylolite. It seems probable that this clay represents insoluble residue of material dissolved in stylolite formation.

Sides of stylolites are always striated, with the ridges and grooves parallel to the direction of penetration of the structure. In some cases the sides have the appearance of being slickensided. The striations range from mere lines to deep grooves, the sides often appearing fluted.

Stylolite seams range from a few millimeters apart to many feet. In some examples two or more seams unite to form one, occasionally cutting across laminæ to unite in this fashion, and Gordon[341] describes stylolite seams as forming "a network intersecting the stone in all directions." Where stylolites cut across bedding and lamination planes, these end at the stylolites without upward or other deflection.

Stylolite seams tend to be horizontal, but inclinations as great as 45° or more are known. Most of them follow stratification planes. Stockdale[342] notes a stylolite seam following what seems to be a fault plane cutting the bedding at an angle of about 60°. Stylolites usually are perpendicular to bedding and fracture planes, but in inclined bedding the stylolites tend to have vertical or other directions instead of perpendicularity to bedding planes. Examples of such arrangement are found in the steeply inclined strata of some of the coral limestones of northern Indiana.[343] Such orientation has also been described by Fuchs,[344] Reis,[345] Wagner,[346] Gordon,[347] and probably others.

It has commonly been stated that stylolite columns have a fossil shell on the summit of each, this shell being a responsible factor in the formation of the column. It is, however, difficult to see the basis for this statement, as the columns on which shells are present are few. In other words, the presence of the shell is incidental and not causal. Shells partially or wholly penetrated by a stylolite are not uncommon; Stockdale[348] has described large

[341] Gordon, C. H., On the nature and structure of the stylolitic structure in Tennessee marble, Jour. Geol., vol. 26, 1918, pp. 561–568.

[342] Stockdale, P. B., op. cit., 1922, p. 44.

[343] Stockdale, P. B., op. cit., 1922, p. 54.

[344] Fuchs, T., Über die Natur und Entstehung der Stylolithen, Sitz. d. k. Akad. d. Wiss., Wien, Math.-Natur. Kl., Bd. 103, 1894, pp. 673–688.

[345] Reis, O. M., Über Stylolithen, Dutenmergel und Landschaftenkalk, Geognost. Jahresh. d. k. bayer. Oberbergamt in München, Bd. 15, 1903, pp. 157–279.

[346] Wagner, G., op. cit., 1913.

[347] Gordon, C. H., op. cit., 1918, pp. 564–565.

[348] Stockdale, P. B., op. cit., 1922, pp. 62–63.

shells so penetrated and a stromatoporoid into which five stylolites have extended.

Stylolites are best developed in limestones and dolomites, but they have been found in quartzite and shale.[349] They occur in limestones and dolomite of all ages and are particularly well developed in the Niagaran limestones of New York, the Paleozoic limestones of the Cincinnati Arch region and the Michigan basin, the Mississippian limestones of Indiana and Missouri, and the Tennessee marble of Knoxville, and a rock long famous for its stylolites is the Muschelkalk of Germany.

Stylolites were first noticed in 1751 by Mylius, who described them as "Schwielen" and stated that they resembled petrified wood. They were later described in 1807 by Freiesleben[350] as "Zapfenförmige Struktur der Flözkalksteine." The name originated with Klödin,[351] who considered that he had a fossil, which he described as *Stylolites sulcatus*. They were first noted in America by Eaton,[352] who described them under the name of lignilites and considered them organic in origin. They were designated epsomites by Vanuxem[353] and crystallites by Hunt.[354] Other names that have been used are "crow-feet," "toe-nails," suture joints, etc.

Origin

Early explanations of the origin of stylolites are more or less fanciful and of little value.[355] They were referred to an organic origin by some; considered as resulting from crystallization by others; still others assumed that a soft limestone ooze was exposed and developed shrinkage cracks, and columns resulted when this ooze was eroded by rain, pebbles and shells among other factors determining the location of columns; a few have ascribed the structure to escaping gas; and one student as late as 1858[356] thought that rising drops of petroleum might be the cause of origin, the clay at the tops of the stylolites being mistaken for petroleum. Of more reasonable character are the theories of later date, which refer the origin to pressure or solution. There has also been much difference of opinion as to the time of origin of

[349] Tarr, W. A., Stylolites in quartzite, Science, vol. 43, 1916, pp. 819–820.

[350] Freiesleben, J. C., Geognostische Arbeiten, Bd. 1, 1807.

[351] Klödin, F., Beiträge zur Mineral. u. Geol. Kenntniss der Mark Brandenburg, Bd. 1, 1828, p. 28.

[352] Eaton, A., Geol. Agric. Surv., Dist. adjoining Erie Canal, 1824, p. 134.

[353] Vanuxem, L., Geol. Surv. New York, 2d. Ann. Rept., 1838, p. 271.

[354] Hunt, T. S., Geol. Surv. Canada, Rept. Prog. from Commencement to 1863, 1863, p. 632.

[355] For the different advocates of the various theories see Stockdale, P. B., op. cit., 1922, pp. 21–24.

[356] Alberti, F. von., Über die Entstehung der Stylolithen, Jahresb. d. Verein f. Väterl.. Naturk. in Württemberg, 1858, p. 292.

stylolites, the advocates of the pressure theory considering them syngenetic and formed when the associated sediments were soft and unconsolidated, whereas the supporters of the solution theory hold that stylolites developed after consolidation and that the origin is epigenetic. Prominent advocates of the pressure theory are Marsh,[357] Gümbel and Dames,[358] and Rothpletz.[359]

Summaries of the important features of the various pressure theories are given by Stockdale (pp. 25–29). In general, these hold that the stylolites developed while the containing sediments were soft. In places on the surface of sediments destined to contain stylolites there were deposited shells and pebbles, or parts of the surface became locally cemented. As this surface became covered with overlying sediments, the shells, pebbles, etc. protected the muds immediately below, but there was settling around them and thus the stylolites developed. The rarity of any capping to the column other than clay, the undisturbed condition of laminæ surrounding columns, the penetration of one stylolite seam by another, the occurrence of stylolite seams along faults, the vertical positions of stylolites on inclined bedding planes, and the complete penetration of fossils by columns make it certain that the structures are not due to pressure alone. Theories referring stylolites to pressure alone are therefore obsolete, although it is still believed that pressure is a factor in stylolite formation.

The prevailing view with respect to stylolite formation is that they are directly due to solution, but that pressure differentially applied is an aiding factor. The solution theory is comparatively young, having been first suggested in 1895 by Fuchs.[360] Wagner[361] in his great work on stylolites appealed to this explanation, Gordon[362] was also of this opinion, and Stockdale[363] has marshalled a great deal of evidence for its support.

The solution theory explains stylolites as due to the removal of a part of the material on opposite sides of a parting plane, whether this plane is due to bedding, fracture, or some other cause. The pressure of the overburden is thought to be a factor, this pressure having differential application

[357] Marsh, O. C., On the origin of the so-called lignilites or epsomites, Proc. Am. Assoc. Adv. Sci., vol. 16, 1867, pp. 135–143.

[358] Gümbel, C. W. von, and Dames, W., Über die Bildung der Stylolithen etc., Zeits. d. deut. geol. Gesell., vol. 34, 1882; pp. 642–648; Über die Natur und Entstehungsweise der Stylolithen, ibid., vol. 40, 1888, pp. 187–188.

[359] Rothpletz, A., Über eigentümliche Deformation jurassischer Ammoniten durch Drucksuturen und deren Beziehung zu den Stylolithen, Sitz. d. k. bayr. Akad. d. Wiss., Math.–Phys. Kl., Bd. 30, Heft 2, 1900, pp. 3–32.

[360] Fuchs, T., op. cit., 1894.

[361] Wagner, G., op. cit., 1913.

[362] Gordon, C. H., op. cit., 1918.

[363] Stockdale, P. B., op. cit., 1922.

along the parting plane. The stylolite seams develop along these parting planes where there are differences in solubility and where there are also differences of pressure. The parts which are more soluble are removed. This shifts the points of contact along the parting planes and concentrates pressure at the places of previous solution. This in turn increases solution. The result is that the stylolites grow by removal of the material ahead of each column, the insoluble residue of the rock removed remaining as a cap and as a film over the column's sides.

The solution theory is supported by many facts, among which are: the distribution of stylolite seams, the dark clay cappings with composition like that of the insoluble residue of the adjacent rock, the penetration of an older stylolite seam by a younger, the penetration of fossils by stylolite columns and the total disappearance of the parts removed, and the sharp and undeflected ending of lamination planes and other structural features at stylolite columns. Stockdale[364] has shown that the thickness of the clay cap is in direct proportion to the height of the column and in inverse proportion to the purity of the limestone, thus essentially proving that the clay originated through solution of the limestone. That solution is extremely active along some parting planes has also been shown by Stockdale's[365] studies relating to this problem. He finds that many clay partings in the Salem limestone of Indiana have nearly the same composition in insoluble materials as does the adjacent limestone, and he considers that this clay in many instances resulted from solution of the overlying or underlying limestones, or both, no stylolites being formed when solution is not differential. It is probable that the various stages of stylolite formation are possible of demonstration in the laboratory.

The solution theory thus rests upon differential solution, which in turn is determined by differences in solubility of the rocks enclosing the parting plane and differential pressures applied to these rocks along this parting plane. Time is a factor in determining heights of columns, but it does not follow that the highest columns were the longest in forming.

The occurrence of stylolites in quartzite and shale is difficult to explain under the solution theory, and possibly other as yet unknown factors may form structures similar to the stylolites of limestones and dolomites. It is possible, however, that solution is the explanation for stylolites in quartzites, but it seems improbable that stylolites in shale could have been so formed.[366]

---

[364] Stockdale, P. B., op. cit., pp. 83–85.
[365] Stockdale, P. B., The stratigraphic significance of solution in rocks, Jour. Geol., vol. 34, 1926, pp. 399–414.
[366] Other important papers treating stylolites are: Hopkins, T. C., Stylolites, Am. Jour.

CONTEMPORANEOUS DEFORMATION OF UNCONSOLIDATED SEDIMENTS

Deformation as here considered relates to surface movement of materials and not to movement of the crust. Named in the order of their probable importance, the different ways in which such deformation occurs are as follows:

Sliding (gliding)
Compacting
Lateral movement through pressure of overlying sediments
Thrust of surface agencies
Recrystallization
Removal of material by mining, solution, etc.

Deformation Resulting from Sliding

Sliding takes place in sediments for which support is inadequate and is defined as a downward movement of material with some degree of mobility over a plane built on material of much less mobility, the mobility being due to the nature of the composing material and its position, or to the presence of water. Inadequacy of support may be due to steepness of slope on which sediments are deposited, excessive local deposition, and removal of support through erosion of adjacent deposits, withdrawal of water, or melting of ice. It may take place either above or under water.[367]

Sediments settling on slopes with inclinations steeper than their angles of repose are certain to slide. There is much sliding on slopes the inclinations of which exceed 10° to 15°, and it is known to have taken place at inclinations as low as 2°31'.[368] Extensive areas of the sites of deposition have slopes of sufficient steepness to permit sliding. About volcanic islands and coral islands and reefs inclinations of 20° or more are common, and submarine fault slopes give far greater inclinations. On the eastern slope of the Bahamas the 2000-fathom depth is about 14 miles from land, giving an average inclination of nearly 16°, and Brownson[369] found depths exceeding 1900 fathoms 2½ miles from land, the inclination thus being 56.5°. The average value of the submarine slope for the 238 miles of the California coast between Point Conception and Point Descanso is 13.7°.[370]

Sci., vol. 4, 1897, pp. 142–144; Sorby, H. C., On the application of quantitative methods to the study of the structure and history of rocks, Quart. Jour. Geol. Soc., vol. 64, 1908, pp. 224–226.

[367] Heim, A., Über rezente und fossile subaquatische Rutschungen und deren lithologische Bedeutung, Neues Jahrb. f. Min., Bd. 2, 1908, pp. 136–157.

[368] Grabau, A. W., Principles of stratigraphy, 1913, p. 780.

[369] Agassiz, A., Three cruises of the "Blake," vol. 1, 1888, p. 97.

[370] Lawson, A. C., The continental shelf off the coast of California, Bull. Nat. Research Council, vol. 8, no. 44, 1924, p. 12.

Sliding brings sediments of shallow waters into deeper waters, where they become interstratified with the sediments of the latter. Such may have been the origin of the sands dredged in the South Atlantic from depths of 4000 to 4200 fathoms, a possibility suggested by the place of occurrence, although it has also been suggested that they arrived there through sinking of the bottom.[371]

The rapid deposition which locally obtains on the fronts of deltas creates slopes of high inclination, particularly in the smaller and less agitated bodies of water, and not uncommonly these slopes are of sufficient steepness to permit sliding. During the flood season of streams, sediments are deposited above normal water level. As the waters fall, support is removed and sliding may occur.

Subaqueous erosion of sediments is very common, particularly in streams. In the Missouri River in the vicinity of Nebraska City there are places where the bottom is thought to be scoured out to depths of 70 to 90 feet,[372] and at Omaha the sediments are removed at each flood season to bed rock, there about 40 feet below the bottom of the channel.[373] Similar scour probably occurs on sea bottoms, with sliding of marginal deposits into the depressions.

Glacial deposits not uncommonly are held up by ice against or over which they have been deposited. As the ice melts away, slumping takes place, with possible deformation of stratification.

Examples of recent subaqueous sliding of sediments are not uncommon, and data relating to many have been brought together by Heim.[374]

A slide in Lake Zuger, Switzerland, began March, 1435, and continued from time to time until July, 1887. The sliding material consisted of the sandy muds of a delta deposit which had been built in the lake when the latter stood at a higher level. The movement was initiated beneath the water and migrated landward through the removing of support on the lakeward side, ultimately forming a slide which was 1 to 12 meters thick, 250 meters wide, and extended lakeward for 1200 meters and 45 meters below lake level. The most pronounced movement took place over a slope with inclination of 2°31′, the average inclination of the surface on which the sliding occurred being 3°26′. The materials of the slide were brecciated, overfolded, and thrustfaulted, giving excessive thickness and overturning of beds.

A slide on the southern shore of Lake Zurich, Switzerland, involved sand,

[371] Philippi, E., Über das Problem der Schichtung, Zeits. d. deut. geol. Gesell., Bd. 60, Aufsätze, 1908, p. 366; Hahn, F. F., Neues Jahrb. f. Min., Beil.-Bd. 36, 1913, p. 13.
[372] Cooley, L. E., Rept. U. S. Engineers for 1879, pt. 2, pp. 1067–1073 (1071).
[373] Todd, J. E., Bull. 158, U. S. Geol. Surv., 1889, p. 15.
[374] Heim, A., op. cit., 1908, p. 136.

gravel, and clay underlain by soft clays, these in turn underlain by sands and marls of the Tertiary Molasse. Movement began in February, 1875, and continued to October, 1877. It appears to have been initiated through the squeezing out of the soft clays and continued until the rocks of the Molasse were bared for a distance of 300 meters. It began beneath water and was transferred landward, the slope on which the slide took place ranging in inclination from 15° to 17°. The material was carried lakeward to a depth of 125 meters.[375] Slides of similar magnitude and character have occurred in other Swiss lakes. Heim has described a very extensive slide which took place in 1895 near Odessa on the Black Sea. Others have been described from Sweden, and it is probable that many have escaped scientific record. Their occurrence in the geologic past was probably as common as it is today,

From the data collected it appears probable that the greater the volume undergoing movement, the smaller the slope on which movement can occur. The friction of the surface on which movement takes place tends to cause the materials behind to move over those in front, leading, in the lower portion of the sliding mass, to the development of asymmetrical or overturned folds, the steeper limb usually being down-slope. The upper portion of a slide is apt to have more open and symmetrical folds. In the lower portion of sliding sediments axial planes of folds incline into the slope at certain angles; they tend to be steeper in the upper portion, thus giving to the axial planes a radiate arrangement; but if the sliding material should encounter resistance above its base or pass to a reverse slope, the folds may have axial planes dipping down-slope, and more or less up-slope over-thrust may take place. Many folds are stretched on the axes, and some are apt to be faulted there. There usually is a considerable degree of mixing of materials along the bedding planes. Great complexity of structure may develop, depending upon the distribution of load, the character of the materials, the quantity of contained water, and the nature of the bordering conditions[376] (fig. 109).

Other features of importance resulting from sliding of sediments are as follows: (1) increase in number and thickness of the strata deposited in the deeper water, (2) decrease in number and thickness of the strata on that portion of the bottom from which the sediments slide, (3) superposition of older on younger beds, (4) displacement of facies, bringing sediment and fauna of shallow depth of water into the environment of greater depth, and (5) development of local unconformities. The diagram (fig. 109) illustrates these phenomena.

[375] Heim, A., op. cit., 1908, p. 136.
[376] de Terra, H., Structural features in gliding strata, Am. Jour. Sci., vol. 21, 1931, pp. 204–213.

The displacement of facies may lead to the assumption that the place of occurrence was in shallow water, and the close proximity to deposits of deeper water may seem to indicate oscillations of sea level. The local unconformity may suggest extremely erroneous views relating to the stratigraphy, paleogeography, and geologic history of the region and suggest the presence of this unconformity even in those exposures where it has not been seen.

Examples which have been interpreted as subaqueous slides are not uncommon in the geologic column. Ordovician strata exposed at Trenton Falls, New York, contain three zones of deformed strata lying between others which are not deformed. The deformed zones range in thickness up to 12

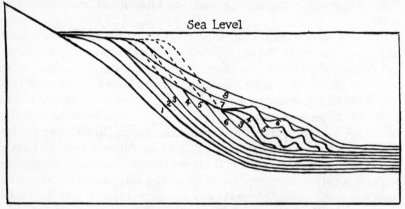

Fig. 109. Diagram Illustrating Effects of Sliding or Gliding of Sediments

Parts of beds 3, 4, 5, and 6 have slid from their original position shown by the dashed lines. After the sliding, beds 7 and 8 were deposited. If the tops of the sliding sediments were within reach of wave and current action they would be eroded to some level conforming to the conditions. On the upper part of the slope an unconformity exists between 7 and all beds below. At the place of the sliding mass there is a structural break between 6 and the beds above, and apparently an unconformity between 7 and 6.

feet. The crumpled portions are not continuous and the same beds are not always involved, the crumpled strata in some places consisting of granular limestones and in others of calcareous shales.[377] Hahn suggested that the crumpling was related to tectonic movement; Miller[378] referred it to hard-rock faulting.

The Miocene lake marls of Oenigen, Germany, have a greatly crumpled

[377] Hahn, F. F., Untermeerische Gleitung bei Trenton Falls, etc., Neues Jahr. f. Min., Beil.-Bd. 36, 1913, pp. 1–41.

[378] Miller, W. J., Highly folded between non-folded strata at Trenton Falls, New York, Jour. Geol., vol. 16, 1908, pp. 428–433; Intraformational corrugated rocks, Ibid., vol. 30, 1922, pp. 587–610 (589).

layer lying between others which are not deformed.   The limbs of some of the crumplings are notably thickened, and there is thinning on the axes. A splendid example of supposed sliding is the "krumme Lage" of the Solenhofen lithographic limestone.   The Muschelkalk of the Main region contains strata showing structure which is thought to have arisen from sliding.[379] In the Devonian Cape Bon Ami limestone of the Gaspé Peninsula there is a

FIG. 110. CONTEMPORANEOUS DEFORMATION OF DOLOMITE

The specimen illustrated was collected by Doctor R. R. Shrock from the Kokomo limestones (Silurian) at Kokomo, Indiana.   Traced laterally in the quarry wall the deformed strata pass into regularly bedded limestones.   The deformed bodies have lenticular outlines with range in the vertical dimension up to 10 feet and in the horizontal up to 25 or 30 feet.   According to Doctor Shrock the deformation took place while the materials were in soft condition.   About one-half natural size.

strongly crumpled 7-foot zone composed of thin layers of limestone interstratified with calcareous shale.   Many of the thin beds are broken into fragments.[380]   Rothpletz[381] has described folded layers between unfolded

---

[379] Reis, O. M., Beobachtung über Schichtenfolge, Geogn. Jahresh., München, Bd. 22, 1909 (1910), pp. 1–285, pls. 1–11.   This paper describes many occurrences of sliding.

[380] Logan, W. E., Geology of Canada, 1863, p. 392, fig. 425.

[381] Rothpletz, A., Meine Beobactungen über den Sparagmit und Birikalk am Mjösen in Norwegen. Sitz., K.-bayr. Akad. der Wiss., Math.-Natur. Kl., Bd. 15, 1910.

ones in the Biri limestone of Mjösen which may have originated through sliding. Similarly folded beds occur in three zones in the Anticosti Becscie formation in its exposures to the west of Fox Bay on the north side of the island. The involved beds are thin fine-grained limestones. The Casper sandstones of Wyoming (Pennsylvanian) "are locally crumpled into folds the axes of which are oriented in various directions and have various inclinations," the folds ranging from minute wrinkles to others with amplitude of 25 feet. Erosion planes cutting across the folded beds prove contemporaneous deformation, and the position of the folds in troughs due to scouring leads to the view that gliding was responsible.[382] Beautifully crumpled and brecciated strata are present in the Kokomo limestones of northern Indiana under such conditions that subaqueous sliding apparently must be responsible for their development (fig. 110).[383] Other examples are given by Miller[384] and Brown.[385]

If sliding sediments contain pebbles, these tilt in various directions, resulting in an edgewise conglomerate. Such conglomerates are common in one formation of the Cambrian sandstones of western Wisconsin and in Cambrian and Ordovician limestones of the Appalachian region. A conglomerate of this character in the lower part of the Pico formation of California has beds ranging in thickness from less than a foot to more than 20 feet. The pebbles show no assortment and have extremely random disposition. Cartwright states that gravity flows such as occur at present on the cliffed coast of California account for this type of conglomerate.[386] Conglomerates of this character may also develop in other ways, and it is not safe to assume a slide from their occurrence.

Deformation Arising from Compaction

Deformation caused by compaction of sediments may be grouped into two types, as follows: (1) settling of a coral reef through compaction and flow of underlying sediments, and (2) settling of sediments around a coral reef, a buried hill, or other rigid body. Compacting is important in clays, but probably not of great significance in sandstones and limestones. It is produced by closer spacing of particles and expulsion of water, and the

[382] Knight, S. H., The Fountain and the Casper formations of the Laramie Basin, Univ. Wyoming Publ., Geol. vol. 1, 1929, pp. 74–78; de Terra, H., Structural features in gliding strata, Am. Jour. Sci., vol. 21, 1931, pp. 204–213.

[383] Cumings, E. R., and Shrock, R. R., The geology of the Silurian rocks of northern Indiana, Publ. no. 75, Div. Geol., Dept. Conservation Indiana, 1928, p. 119.

[384] Miller, W. J., op. cit., 1922, pp. 596–605.

[385] Brown, T. C., Notes on the origin of certain Paleozoic sediments, etc., Jour. Geol., vol. 21, 1913, pp. 232–250.

[386] Cartwright, L. D., jr., Sedimentation of the Pico formation in the Ventura Quadrangle, California, Bull. Am. Assoc. Pet. Geol., vol. 12, 1928, pp. 253–254.

decrease in volume may rarely exceed 75 per cent and commonly exceeds 40 to 50 per cent.[387]

A coral reef may rest on muds or marls. The reef mass increases in weight and compacts the sediments beneath it, or causes flow toward its margins, with the result that the marginal basal strata incline toward the reef. Illustrations are stated by Bather[388] to be not uncommon about some of the reefs of Gotland, and the condition may obtain about other coral reefs.

A coral reef, an elevation on a pre-existing surface, or a lens of sands undergoes little or no compaction (a little in the case of the sands), whereas the sediments over and around such features may be so affected, particularly if they are muds, of which the compaction may equal 50 per cent or more.[389] Moreover, sediments about such features usually have an initial inclination therefrom. This is increased by the compaction, so that the strata which pass over the reef or other object become strongly arched and dip away at angles which locally rise to 30° or more. Deposits about high places tend to thicken away therefrom, particularly if there is much agitation of the water, or if the surface of deposition is sufficiently steep to cause sliding. This gradually builds up the marginal areas, and ultimately the surface becomes level. However, further settling of the underlying materials warps this level surface, and this continues until the effect of the original elevation is lost through compaction and deposition. A structure of this origin has been termed a compaction fold by Nevin and Sherrill.[390] Compaction folds cover progressively greater areas upward from the physiographic or depositional irregularities to which they are due; the sedimentary units which

[387] See on water content of uncompacted muds, Shaw, E. W., The rôle and fate of connate water in oil and gas sands, Bull. 103, Am. Inst. Min. Met. Eng., 1915, p. 1451; Meinzer, O. E., The occurrence of ground water in the United States, Water Supply Paper 489, U. S. Geol. Surv., 1923, p. 8; Lee, C. H. and Ellis, A. J., Water Supply Paper 446, U. S. Geol. Surv., 1919, pp. 121–123; Hedberg, H. D., Bull. Am. Assoc. Pet. Geol., vol. 10, 1926, p. 1042; Trask, P. D., Compaction of sediments, Bull. Am. Assoc. Pet. Geol., vol. 15, 1931, pp. 271–276.

[388] Bather, F. A., Proc. Geologists' Assoc., vol. 25, pt. iii, 1914, pp. 225–228.

[389] Mehl, M. G., The influence of the differential compression on the attitude of bedded rock, Science, vol. 1, 1920, p. 520; Blackwelder, E., The origin of the central Kansas oil domes, Bull. Am. Assoc. Pet. Geol., vol. 4, 1920, pp. 89–94; Monnett, V. E., Possible origin of some structures of the Mid-Continent oil field, Econ. Geol., vol. 17, 1922, pp. 194–200; Powers, S., Reflected buried hills and their importance in petroleum geology, Ibid., vol. 17, 1922, pp. 233–259; Teas, L. P., Differential compacting the cause of certain Claiborne dips, Bull. Am. Assoc. Pet. Geol., vol. 7, 1923, pp. 370–378; Lewis, J. V., Fissility of shale and its relation to petroleum, Bull. Geol. Soc. Am., vol. 35, 1924, pp. 562–566; Rubey, W. W., and Bass, N. W., Bull. 10, pt. i, Geol. Surv. Kansas, 1925, pp. 72–86; Bauer, C. M., Oil and gas fields of the Texas Panhandle, Bull. Am. Assoc. Pet. Geol., vol. 10, 1926, p. 734; Nevin, C. M. and Sherrill, R. E., Studies in differential compaction, Ibid., vol. 13, 1929, pp. 1–22, 1396–1397; Hedberg, H. D., The effect of gravitational compaction on the structure of sedimentary rocks, Ibid., vol. 10, 1926, pp. 1035–1072; Athy, L. F., Density, porosity, and compaction of sedimentary rocks, Ibid., vol. 14, 1930, pp. 1–25.

[390] Op. cit., p. 15.

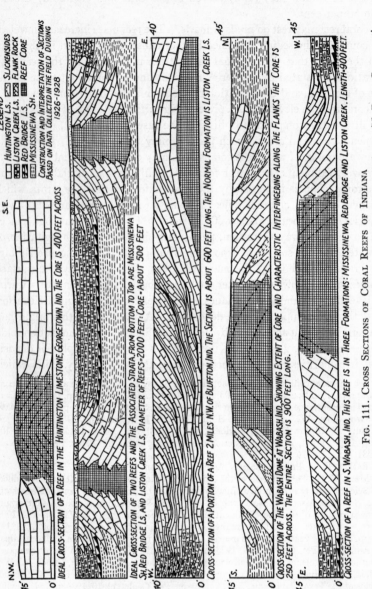

FIG. 111. Cross Sections of Coral Reefs of Indiana

After Cumings, E. R., and Shrock, R. R., The geology of the Silurian rocks of Indiana, Pub. no. 75, Dept. Conservation Indiana, Div. Geology, 1928, p. 146.

surround and cover these initial irregularities thicken outward therefrom, and dips increase with depth. Compaction folds should also show a general absence of system in distribution. It is to be noted, however, that not all of the "folding" is a result of compaction, but that the initial irregularity may give a warped bedding that is largely the result of deposition.

Steep dips about coral reefs are characteristic and are excellently shown about the Silurian reefs of Gotland, Anticosti, eastern Wisconsin, northern Indiana, and elsewhere. In the Shoonmaker quary, near Wauwatosa, Wisconsin, dips range to 54°, and dips around 30° are common.[391] In the reefs of Indiana dips range to 65°[392] (fig. 111). Dips in Gotland and Anticosti reefs are usually not more than 10°, but the "folding" is conspicuous because of excellent exposure in the seacoast cliffs. Coral reefs are likely to be characterized by steep slopes, and thus steep dips should be common. Langenbeck[393] notes slopes ranging to 90° or more, and Mayor states that the slopes of Tutuila range to 70° or more.[394]

Some of the domes and anticlines of Kansas and Oklahoma seem to be due to compaction of sediments around buried hills or sand lenses in the strata involved,[395] and Monnett found that in the Garber pool of Oklahoma a correspondence exists between the high parts of the structure and the thickness of a sandstone in the section.

Average surfaces of deposition are undulating,[396] and the undulations of successive sites of deposition are not necessarily parallel, and differential compacting modifies original positions. The results are that doming is almost certain to develop over little compactible materials, and the domes of one horizon are not necessarily in the same places in overlying and underlying horizons.

Lateral Movement from Pressure of Overlying Sediments

As sediments accumulate, the burden on those previously deposited increases, and if the overburden is differential, the muds in the section tend to move toward the places of least pressure. Experiments have shown that the flowing sediments thicken beneath the places of least pressure and thin

[391] Grabau, A. W., Principles of stratigraphy, 1913, p. 419.

[392] Cumings, E. R., and Shrock, R. R., The geology of the Silurian rocks of northern Indiana, Publ. No. 75, Dept. Conservation Indiana, 1928, pp. 138–156.

[393] Langenbeck, R., Die Theorien über die Entstehung der Koralleninseln und Korallenriffe und ihre Bedeutung für geophysische Fragen, Leipzig, 1890; Die neueren Forschungen über Korallenriffe, Hettsners Geogr. Zeits., 3. Jahrg., 1897, pp. 514–581.

[394] Mayor, A. G., Structure and ecology of Samoan reefs, Carnegie Inst. of Washington, vol. 19, 1924, pp. 1–25.

[395] See Blackwelder, Mehl, Powers, Bauer, op. cit.

[396] Shaw, E. W., Bull. Geol. Soc. Am., vol. 31, 1920, pp. 124–125.

beneath the greatest overburden, and that much crumpling results.[397] If the mud breaks through to the surface, collapse of the surface materials may take place. It has been suggested that the mud lumps at the mouth of the Mississippi owe their origin to the pressure of the sediments accumulating over the subaerial parts of the delta,[398] and that soft muds beneath the delta are being squeezed gulfward to break through at places of little resistance of the overburden. What actually takes place is not known, but figure 111 suggests the possibilities. It seems probable that similar phenomena are likely near the delta front where the fine-textured bottomset materials become overlain by the coarser sediments of the foreset beds.

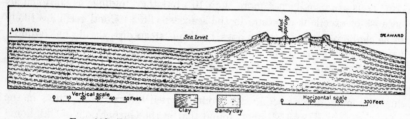

FIG. 112. PARTLY HYPOTHETICAL SECTION OF A MUDLUMP
This diagram of the eighth mudlump southeast of Pass a loutre Lighthouse, Mississippi Delta, shows the great clay body in the interior of the lump, the deformed clay and sandy clay strata above and on the sides, and the undeformed similar strata marginal to the lump. The arrows indicate the direction of supposed flowage of the clay from the landward side and the corresponding thinning of the clay beds on that side. The central part of this lump seems to have settled, but the central part of other lumps is known to have been raised. After E. W. Shaw, U. S. Geol. Surv.

Thrust of Surface Agencies

The thrusts may arise from glacial ice, grounding of floe ice and icebergs, lake ice, and sliding masses of earth or rock.

About the margins of glaciers the deposits are commonly unstratified, but in advance of these, and to some extent incorporated with them, are deposits which are stratified. Any advance of a glacier disturbs this material, leading to its brecciation, faulting, and folding. To the extent that the material is unstratified, no structural effect is produced, but in stratified material deformation results. It is thought that brecciation will be nearest the ice, succeeded outward by a zone of thrust faulting and overturned folds, and beyond this by a zone of low and gentle folding.[399]

[397] Kindle, E. M., Deformation of unconsolidated beds in Nova Scotia and southern Ontario, Bull. Geol. Soc. Am., vol. 28, 1917, pp. 323–334.

[398] Shaw, E. W., The mud lumps at the mouths of the Mississippi, Prof. Paper 85–B, U. S. Geol. Surv., 1913, pp. 11–27.

[399] Case, E. C., Experiments in ice motion, Jour. Geol., vol. 3, 1895, pp. 918–934; Sollas, W. J., An experiment to illustrate the mode of flow of a viscous fluid, Quart. Jour. Geol.

Glaciers may also deform strata over which they move or against which they may collide.   Soft strata at Gay Head on Martha's Vineyard and Clay Head on Block Island which have been overthrust and folded have been referred to the push of glacial ice.[400]   Intense local deformation of Cretaceous strata in the Mud Buttes and Tit Hills of Alberta (fig. 113) has been referred to the pressure of the Pleistocene ice sheet by Hopkins[401] and Slater.[402]   Similar deformation has been described from England and Denmark,[403] and many undescribed occurrences probably exist.

The grounding of floating ice disturbs the bottom materials, removes some of them, may produce deformation in the sediments beneath those removed, and folds and faults the surface materials around the front of the moving ice.   Some of the folds are likely to be overturned, and most of the

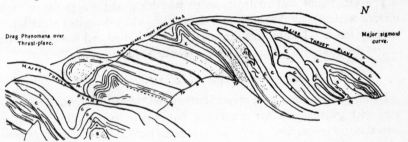

FIG. 113. A PARTIAL SECTION ACROSS THE MUD BUTTES OF ALBERTA

The dotted areas indicate sand, the white clay.   The thrust planes are the heavy black lines.   The thrust, caused by the advance of the Pleistocene glacier, came from the north. This is a part of the section given by Slater, G., in Bull. Geol. Soc. Am., vol. 38, 1927, opposite p. 724.   Covers between 350 and 400 feet.

faults are thrusts.   The clays of glacial lakes not uncommonly show these effects, and such have beautiful development in some of the glacial clays of the Connecticut River Valley and the Permian Squantum tillite.[404]   De-

Soc., vol. 51, 1895, pp. 361–368; Slater, G., Glacial tectonics as reflected in disturbed drift deposits, Proc. Geologists' Assoc., vol. 37, 1926, pp. 392–400; The disturbed glacial deposits in the neighborhood of Lønstrup, near Hjøvring, North Denmark, Proc. Roy. Soc. Edinburgh, vol. 55, 1927, pp. 303–315.

[400] Woodworth, J. B., Unconformities of Marthas Vineyard and Block Island, Bull. Geol. Soc. Am., vol. 8, 1897, pp. 197–212.

[401] Hopkins, O. B., Some structural features of the Plains area of Alberta caused by Pleistocene glaciation, Bull. Geol. Soc. Am., vol. 34, 1923, pp. 419–430.

[402] Slater, G., Structure of the Mud Buttes and Tit Hills in Alberta, Bull. Geol. Soc. Am., vol. 38, 1927, pp. 721–730.

[403] Slater, G., Studies of the drift deposits of the southwestern part of Suffolk, Proc. Geologists' Assoc., vol. 38, 1927, pp. 157–216; The structure of the disturbed deposits of Möens Klint, Denmark, Proc. Roy. Soc. Edinburgh, vol. 55, 1927, pp. 289–302.

[404] Sayles, R. W., Seasonal deposition of aqueo-glacial sediments, Mem. Mus. Comp. Zool., vol. 47, 1919, pp. 37–38; Lahee, F. H., Contemporaneous deformation, a criterion

formation from this cause should be present in considerable abundance in the shallow-water sediments of polar seas,[405] and they should be found in sediments deposited in marine and lake waters adjacent to the continental and other glaciers of past geologic periods.

Sliding masses of earth and rock transmit a thrust to the materials in front of them and produce a drag on the materials over which they move. Some deformation probably arises from this cause. The great slide at Turtle Mountain, British Columbia, could not have failed to deform any unconsolidated materials over which the sliding masses moved; the landslide on the Lièvre River, Quebec,[406] must have deformed the river sediments involved therein, and it is probable that the great landslides occurring in China in 1920 led to considerable deformation of the involved materials.[407]

The expansions and contractions of lake ice produce a thrust of the materials composing the shores and the shallow-water deposits to which the ice may freeze. Locally this expresses itself in folding and faulting. The effects decrease with distance from the shore.[408]

Deformation Due to Recrystallization

Deformation arising from crystallization and hydration is usually associated with gypsum or other evaporites, but it may be connected with the formation of concretions. The latter process is considered in another connection. Some of the deformative structures associated with salt deposits have been termed enterolithic.[409] They appear to have their best development among the mother-liquor salts and are very abundant in the Stassfurt salt deposits where kieserite layers have been changed to carnalite.[410]

Calcium sulphate deposited from solutions high in chloride and under arid conditions is thought to be generally in the anhydrous form. After

for aqueo-glacial deformation, Jour. Geol., vol. 22, 1914, pp. 786–790; Salisbury, R. D., and Atwood, W. W., Bull. no. 5, Wisconsin Geol. and Nat. Hist. Surv., 1900, p. 120, pl. 38.

[405] Stockton, C. H., Arctic cruise of the U. S. S. "Thetis," Nat. Geog. Mag., vol. 2, 1890, p. 182.

[406] Ells, R. W., The recent landslide on the Lièvre River, Quebec, Ann. Rept. Geol. Surv. Canada, vol. 15, pt. AA, 1906, pp. 136A–139A.

[407] Close, U., and McCormick, E., Where the mountains walked, Nat. Geog. Mag., vol. 61, 1922, pp. 462–464.

[408] Buckley, E. R., Ice ramparts, Trans. Wisconsin Acad. Sci., vol. 13, 1901, pp. 141–162.

[409] Grabau, A. W., Geology of the non-metallic mineral deposits, vol. 1, Principles of salt deposition, 1920, p. 372; Principles of stratigraphy, 1913, pp. 757–759, 788. It is quite certain that not all enterolithic structures are due to recrystallization. It seems to be established that many of the evaporites flow under conditions of pressures of moderate magnitude, the salt domes probably being formed in this way, and enterolithic structure develops as a consequence.

[410] Everding, H., Deutschlands Kalibergbau, Festsch. zum 10ten. Allgemeinen d. Bergmannstage zu Eisenach, vol. 1, 1907, pp. 25–133.

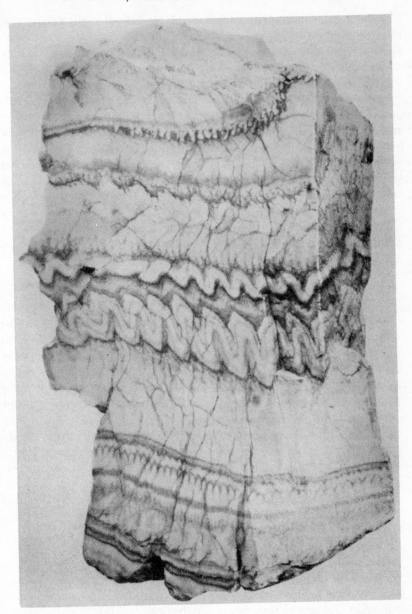

FIG. 114. DEFORMED GYPSUM AND ANHYDRITE, HILLSBOROUGH, NOVA SCOTIA
This deformation is believed to have resulted from the change of anhydrite to gypsum.
Photograph by Diemer, University of Wisconsin.

deposition and entrance into the zone of ground-water circulation, this changes to gypsum with an increase in volume of 30 to 50 per cent. Expansion of the beds involved is a necessary result, with folding and faulting as probable effects. Features which are believed to be the result of this process are beautifully shown in the gypsum quarries near Hillsborough, New Brunswick. The deformation commonly is in the nature of miniature geanticlines and geosynclines in which there may be layers independently folded and faulted throughout the larger structures. A geanticline or geosyncline may have a height or depth of 6 to 8 inches (fig. 114).

The gypsum-containing Permian strata of central Kansas are more or less greatly deformed. The larger structures seem best explained as due to solution, but the smaller ones are thought to owe their origin to the change of anhydrite to gypsum.

Some deformation probably develops from the change of gypsum to anhydrite and aragonite to calcite, but no occurrences of such deformation are known to the writer.

Deformation Due to Removal of Material by Mining, Solution, or Other Agencies

Some deformation of stratification arises from mining, but most of this takes place in consolidated rocks and thus is not the concern of sedimentation. Similar deformation may be consequent to the formation of limestone caves; little of this also relates to sedimentation. Solution, however, acting on such soluble substances as rock salt and gypsum may produce more or less deformation of soft sediments. The Permian strata of Harvey and some portions of adjacent counties of Kansas are greatly deformed, with anticlines and synclines ranging up to 150 feet wide and 20 feet vertical dimension. The deformation seems to be best developed where gypsum constitutes a considerable percentage of the thickness, but it is also present where no gypsum is visible. Much minor deformation is associated. The latter is referred to alteration of anhydrite to gypsum, and it may be that the larger deformation was so caused.

DIMENSIONS OF SEDIMENTARY UNITS

The areal distribution of sedimentary units varies with the type of sediment and the environment of deposition. In general, the coarsest sediments have the most limited distribution and the greatest variations in thickness. All strata and aggregates of strata are lenticular, either thinning to disappearance or grading laterally into other varieties of sediments through decrease of the major constituent and increase of a minor constituent. Large loads and rapid decreases in the competency and capacity of the transporting agents lead to limited areal distribution. On the other hand, the longer the transportation, the smaller the load, the slower the deposition, and the finer the materials: the more extensive the units.

Strata of very rapid deposition are apt to thin rapidly in a sourceward direction; those of slow deposition thin more or less equally in all directions. So many variables, however, influence the result that it is difficult to generalize.

The deposits of alluvial fans and cones and of river flood plains, channels, and deltas usually exhibit great variation in colors, materials, and thickness within short distances. Thus, one may find mud, sand, and gravel distributed in lenses of a few feet and even a few inches in diameter, and from these dimensions they pass upward into lenses of more extensive distribution on alluvial fans of wide extent and low slope, the flood plains of large rivers, and the surfaces of great deltas. Excellent illustrations are present in the Fort Union formation of Montana and Wyoming, the Tertiary of Nebraska and Kansas, and the subaerial delta deposits of the Pennsylvanian of Oklahoma, Kansas, Indiana, and elsewhere. In these deposits one may observe coal lenses ranging from those too thin and of too limited areal distribution for mining, to others miles in extent, and from sand and clay lenses a few feet in diameter to others which may be followed for several miles.

Extremely variable dimensions of sedimentary units exist in the deposits of the littoral environment and over those shallow marine bottoms subjected to strong wave and current action. The latter requires that the shallow bottoms be not too extensive or too shallow; otherwise strong waves and currents are not likely to develop. Along the littoral there are places where the same variety of sediment prevails for miles; other parts of the same coast have changes in sediments every few feet. On the permanently submerged shallow bottoms the conditions are not greatly different. This is particularly conspicuous about coral reefs where the lagoon, the channels between the reefs, and the sea outside the reefs possess different varieties of sediments on their bottoms. With increasing distance from land there is greater stability, and sedimentary units have wider extent, but even here more or less lateral variation may be expected for many miles from the shore and to depths of a couple of hundred feet. The submarine physiography is a factor of great importance. A sea bottom like that in the Channel Islands region of California, with deep basins separated by ridges, has different varieties of sediments in the basins and on the ridges, sedimentary units of one variety in a basin passing laterally into a coarser variety on an adjacent ridge.[411] Even bottoms deeper than the profile of equilibrium also have

[411] Trask, P. D., Sedimentation in the Channel Islands region, Econ. Geol., vol. 26, 1931, pp. 24–43.

variation, as some portions are receiving sands and muds derived from higher parts of the bottom, and other parts are the sites of organic colonies whose deposits vary with the responsible organisms.   The units may be small or large, but are more likely to be of considerable dimension.   In the still deeper waters beyond the sites of large deposition of terrigenous materials the areal limits are determined by the organisms which inhabit these depths. In the very deep waters up to 15,000 feet there are variations arising from the type of calcareous ooze, and below that depth they depend upon whether the deposits are radiolarian or diatom ooze or red clay.   Deep sea units probably have the most extensive areal distribution.

Thus, the general rule obtains that the deposits of most existing environments of sedimentation are variable in extent and character, and each stratum and each formation is a lens of larger or smaller dimension.   Past deposits, as Shaw[412] has noted, are more or less interpreted as not showing this variation, and the question is raised as to whether this is a matter of error in correlation or an actual occurrence.   Ulrich has argued that the existing variations are abnormal in the same respect that he considers the existing climatic and topographic conditions out of the ordinary, and that during other geologic periods the seas were so shallow and the shores so low that the variations as they now are shown would have been impossible of materialization. He hence argues for a wide extension of the sedimentary units of the Paleozoic epicontinental seas.[413]   Kindle[414] has presented evidence against such interpretation, and it seems rather improbable that sedimentary units could often have had the distribution postulated by Ulrich.   That the waters had successive competencies to carry muds and sands is good evidence that these sediments grade laterally into each other and into limestones.   That some of the Paleozoic seas give rise to deposits of limited distribution is certain.   Thus, in the Silurian of Gotland coral limestone grades into other limestones, shale, or limestone conglomerate; in the Upper Ordovician of the Island of Anticosti limestones on the south side of the island are represented by quartz sandstones on the north side, less than 35 miles distant; and in the Pennsylvanian of Kansas and Oklahoma the variations are locally so abundant that the strata of two oil wells less than a half mile apart may show altogether different sequences.   Splendid illustrations of lateral variations of sediments are found in the Tertiary of Trinidad where in the Naparima region "the lateral variation in some directions is so rapid that the rock-types of one area differ completely from their equivalent types a few miles

---

[412] Shaw, E. W., Discussion, Bull. Geol. Soc. Am., vol. 31, 1920, p. 123.

[413] Ulrich, E. O., Revision of the Paleozoic systems, Bull. Geol. Soc. Am., vol. 22, 1911, pp. 318–320.

[414] Kindle, E. M., The stratigraphic relations of the Devonian shales of northern Ohio, Am. Jour. Sci., vol. 34, 1912, pp. 187–196.

away," and in one locality in a distance of 3 miles a "marl formation disappears and is replaced by clays." A formation known as the Williamsville clays changes in thickness from 40 to 200 feet in a distance of 5 miles; a marl formation increases in a distance of 2.5 miles from 50 to 1500 feet; and a green clay from 50 to 650 feet.[415] Remarkable variations in thickness are present in the Tertiary of the Pacific Coast.

The fact of variations in thickness may determine other increase and variation. Lime accumulations due to planktonic and pelagic agencies are made only on those bottoms not so deep and not so abundantly provided with carbon dioxide that the lime passes into solution and does not attain permanent deposition. Bottoms permitting lime deposition would be built up, whereas surrounding bottoms of greater depth or with waters of higher solvent properties for lime would receive no or limited lime deposits. With rising sea level there might result a large accumulation of calcareous sediments surrounded by insolubles deposited from suspension. Adams[416] has suggested that the margins of such calcareous irregularities would rise faster than the central area, and thus there would develop a basin on top of the high place. This is his explanation of the "high" forming the Yates pool of west Texas. The suggestion is interesting and no doubt has some application.

However, it is known that some sedimentary units have very great areal distribution. The Pennsylvanian sequence of the Mid-Continent region has units of essentially constant thickness and composed of limestone, shale, or coal that may be followed for hundreds of miles.[417] The Iatan limestone of Kansas has one bed in its upper part which with essentially uniform thickness and composition extends from the vicinity of Leavenworth, Kansas, southwestwardly beyond the Oklahoma line, a distance around 200 miles, and this distribution is equalled and even exceeded by other units in the sequence. Condra, Dunbar, and Moore state that some coal units only an inch or two thick are "traceable for more than 300 miles." In the Pennsylvanian of southwestern Indiana is a fine-grained dark limestone, locally known as the "Steel Band." This has been seen with approximately uniform characteristics over an area of fully 1500 square miles, and it certainly has greater extent. In the Richmond of the Anticosti section is a 3 to 6 inch bed of compact, fine-grained limestone which is known as the "Track

[415] Illing, V. C., Geology of the Naparima region of Trinidad, British West Indies, Quart. Jour. Geol. Soc., vol. 84, 1928, pp. 7, 37–40.

[416] Adams, J. E., Origin of oil and its reservoir in Yates Pool, Pecos County, Texas, Bull. Am. Assoc. Pet. Geol., vol. 14, 1930, pp. 705–717.

[417] Condra, G. E., Dunbar, C. O., and Moore, R. C., Persistence of thin beds in the Pennsylvanian of the northern Mid Continent region, Abstract, Bull. Geol. Soc. Am., vol. 41, 1930, p. 104.

Bed" because of the occurrence on its upper surface of double rows of pits which have been interpreted as tracks. This bed is known to have an east-west distribution of 75 miles, with the certainty that it extends farther east than it has been seen and that it once had far greater westward extent. The Silurian of Gotland has a thin bed filled with the brachiopod, *Dayia navicula*, which has been traced across the width of the island. Many of these examples of extensive areal distribution are remarkable because of association with units of considerable lenticularity.

As already noted, many sedimentary units have great range in thickness from place to place. These variations are partly due to variations in the rate of deposition, but some variations must be referred to local and temporal failure of deposition and in some instances to erosion. Hunter[418] has shown that over an area of the bottom in Chesapeake Bay in the fifty-two year interval from 1848 to 1900 about 66 per cent received no deposits, 26 per cent received deposits, and 8 per cent underwent deepening and erosion. This means variations in thickness from place to place and hence lenticularity of beds.

TEXTURES OF SEDIMENTS

The textures of sedimentary rocks have a wide range and are intimately related to the characteristics of the materials deposited. To attempt their individual consideration would lead to such length that it is not considered justified. They may be grouped, with a few exceptions, in three classes: fragmental, crystalline, and oolitic. This does not include the textures of such sediments as coal.

FRAGMENTAL TEXTURES

Fragmental textures of sediments range from those found in clays and shales to those of sandstones and conglomerates. Limestones also very commonly have fragmental textures. The particles have a considerable range in dimension in the same specimen and a very wide one if all detritals are considered.

CRYSTALLINE TEXTURES

Crystalline textures are found in limestone, dolomite, gypsum, rock salt, and similar substances. Many sandstones have enlarged particles so that a crystalline texture is produced, and, although it is not visible to the eye, many shales in greater or less degree are finely crystalline. More or less crystalline material, however, may be expected in every sedimentary rock

---

[418] Hunter, J. F., Erosion and sedimentation in Chesapeake Bay around the mouth of Choptank River, Prof. Paper 90–B, U. S. Geol. Sur., 1914, p. 14.

except the coarse clastics.   There is a wide range in the dimensions of the crystalline particles from those so small as to be invisible with an ordinary lens to others 6 to 12 mm. in diameter.   The crystallization considered is that developed as a consequence of surface processes.   Studies made of dolomites derived from a deep well at Spur, Texas,[419] showed an increase in the dimensions of crystals with depth, suggesting that in the crystallizing of the original materials of the sediments to form dolomite, complete growth was not acquired at the time of burial, and that enlargement continued after burial.   Adverse to any view that depth of burial and time involved are functions controlling dimension is the occurrence at several levels in the Spur well of crystals of smaller dimension than those in overlying strata. That time is a factor of importance in growth seems certain, but it does not seem probable that depth has much influence.   The occurrence is considered a coincidence.

OOLITES AND PISOLITES, AND OOLITIC AND PISOLITIC TEXTURES

Oolites are small rock particles of elliptical or spherical shapes with concentrically laminated structure.   Rocks in which oolites occur in comparative abundance are said to have an oolitic texture.   The maximum dimension of an oolite may be placed at about 2 mm.   If the dimensions are greater, the particles are called pisolites and the containing rocks have pisolitic texture.   Particles of dimensions similar to oolites and pisolites but with radiate and not concentric structure are designated spherulites.   It is to be noted, however, that this latter term has also been applied to spherical aggregates without either radiate or concentric structure.   Many oolites and pisolites have radiate structure in some or all of the laminations.   This is notably the case in the Great Salt Lake oolites and in artificial oolites later to be described.   Most oolites and pisolites have nuclei.   These commonly are particles of quartz, feldspar, or other minerals, fragments of shells, or gas bubbles,[420] and oolites in some Mexican lakes are said to have insect eggs as nuclei.[421]

There are many particles formed or deposited in sedimentary environments which have spheroidal shapes but are without concentric or radiate structure.   Among these are greenalite, common in the Pre-Cambrian of the Lake Superior region; glauconite, abundant in the marine sediments of many systems; and the coprolites, now abundant over many parts of the

[419] Udden, J. A., The deep boring at Spur, Bull. 28, Univ. Texas, Sci. Ser., 1914, p. 55.

[420] Vaughan, T. Wayland, Florida Studies, Carnegie Inst. of Washington, Year Book No. 11, 1913, pp. 157–158; also earlier suggested by Linck, op. cit.

[421] Virlet d Aoust, Théodore, Sur des œufs d'insectes servant à l'alimentation de l'homme et donnant lieu à la formation d'oolithes dans des calcaires lacustres, au Mexique, Paris, Compt. Rend., vol. 45, 1857, pp. 865–868.

sea floor and also identified in some ancient sediments. These are not oolites, pisolites, or spherulites.

Oolites and pisolites may be composed of hematite, limonite, pyrite, bauxite, dolomite, calcite, aragonite, flint or chert, clay, barite, phosphate, and siderite. Limestones, dolomites, hematite, limonite, phosphate, bauxite, and flint or chert are the rocks most commonly possessing oolitic texture. In many of the occurrences it has been suggested that the oolites were originally calcite or aragonite and were replaced by other substances. This suggestion cannot be generally sustained, and it seems certain that oolites of substances other than calcite or aragonite may develop directly.

Oolites and pisolites are generally spheroidal or ellipsoidal, although depressions may be present on their surfaces due to contact of one against another. Lacroix,[422] Shrock,[423] and Rodolico[424] have described polyhedral pisolites. The pisolites described by Shrock were found in a glacial cobble, and the terrane of origin is not known. Lacroix' examples were collected in Madagascar and in Algeria. Rodolico's specimens were collected in Italy. Shrock's pisolites have concentric and radiate structure with bands of iron oxide forming some of the concentric laminæ. The interior laminations are spherical. The polyhedral shapes are probably to be assigned to interference with each other as the pisolites grew.

The problems of oolites and pisolites are considered from the two points of view of the substances of which these structures are composed and something with respect to their distribution, and the facts, experiments, and theories relating to their origin.

Materials of Which Oolites and Pisolites Are Composed

OOLITES AND PISOLITES OF SILICA. The basal part of the Oneota dolomite of the upper Mississippi Valley contains nodules of oolitic chert distributed through a thickness of about 30 feet. The surrounding dolomite is also oolitic, and it is obvious that the silica oolites developed through replacement of other materials. Silica oolites in Center County, Pennsylvania, were assigned by Wieland to hot-spring origin,[425] but Brown[426] and

---

[422] Lacroix, A., Sur la ctypéite, etc., Compt. Rend. vol. 126, 1898, p. 601; Minéralogie de la France, vol. 3, 1901, p. 733; Minéralogie de Madagascar, vol. 1, 1922, p. 288.

[423] Shrock, R. R., Polyhedral pisolites, Am. Jour. Sci., vol. 19, 1930, pp. 368–372.

[424] Rodolico, F., Pisoliti poliedrici di magnisite e di dolomite, Rendiconte della R. Accademia Nazionale dei Lincei, vol. 12, ser. 6, 1930, pp. 457–460.

[425] Wieland, G. R., Eopaleozoic hot springs and the origin of the Pennsylvania siliceous oölite, Am. Jour. Sci., vol. 4, 1897, pp. 262–264; Further notes on Ozarkian sea-weeds and oölites, Bull. Am. Mus. Nat. Hist., vol. 33, 1914, pp. 248–255; Ziegler, V., The siliceous oölites of central Pennsylvania, Am. Jour. Sci., vol. 34, 1912, pp. 113–127.

[426] Brown, T. C., Origin of oolites and the oolitic texture in rocks, Bull. Geol. Soc. Am., vol. 25, 1914, pp. 745–780, pls. 26–28.

Moore[427] considered these same oolites to have been originally composed of calcium carbonate which was later replaced by silica. Silica oolites occur in the Pre-Cambrian of the Lake Superior region, and some of these have some laminæ composed of iron carbonate. Takimoto has described spherulitic hyalite from hot springs of Ugo Province of Japan,[428] and Jimbo[429] from another province. These Japanese occurrences, however, do not appear to be replacements. Tarr[430] found siliceous oolites of laminated structure in red, yellow, and green shales of the Red Beds of the Wind River Mountains near Lander, Wyoming. They are of two dimensions, the larger with diameters around 0.6 mm. and the smaller with diameters of 0.1 to 0.2 mm. Some of the oolites contain sand grains which were enclosed as the particles were growing. The oolites are not confined to definite laminations in the shale, but are scattered throughout and in no way disturb the shale laminæ. The shales also contain particles of calcite. If two oolites interfered while growing, a regular contact was preserved, and in some instances large oolites grew around smaller ones. Tarr considers that the relations prove the oolites were always siliceous, formed in muddy waters and were deposited contemporaneously with the surrounding materials. He thinks that the silica was precipitated as a colloidal gel and that the union of the gel particles formed the oolites.

It is not unlikely that oolites of silica occur in every geologic system, but they appear to be more abundant in the earlier ones. Many are certainly replacements, but it seems probable that some may have been precipitated directly.

OOLITES AND PISOLITES OF HEMATITE AND LIMONITE. Particles with oolitic structure form to some extent in the iron oxides which are being deposited on the bottoms of some Swedish and Finnish lakes and certain lakes of other regions.[431] These are certainly not replacements. Oolitic hematite and limonite are present in the Lower Cambrian on the Strait of Belle Isle, the Ordovician of Bell Island, Newfoundland, the Upper Ordovician of Wisconsin, the Clinton of the Appalachian region, the Jurassic Minette ores of Luxemburg and Lorraine, etc. The oolites have been variously considered to have been iron oxides from the beginning, replacements of calcite

[427] Moore, E. S., Siliceous oolites and other concretionary structures in the vicinity of State College, Pennsylvania, Jour. Geol., vol. 20, 1912, p. 266.

[428] Takimoto, T., The siliceous oolite of Sankyo, Ugo Province, Beiträge zur Min. von Japan, no. 2, 1906, pp. 60–61, quoted from Neues Jahrb. für Min., etc., vol. 1, 1907, p. 197.

[429] Jimbo, K., The siliceous oolite of Toteyama, Etchu Province, Beiträge zur Min., Japan, 1905, pp. 11–75. Abstract in Zeits. f. Chemie und Industrie der Kolloide, vol. 4, 1909, p. 287.

[430] Tarr, W. A., Oolites in shale and their origin, Bull. Geol. Soc. Am., vol. 29, 1918, pp. 587–600.

[431] Beck, R., The nature of ore deposits, Transl. by Weed, W. H., 1909, p. 101.

oolites, alterations of other iron-bearing minerals, and in the case of the Clinton ores Wieland[432] suggested that these were due to the alternate precipitation of silica and hematite about nuclei, suggested by the fact that when the iron oxide is dissolved concentric tests of silica remain. Some of the Clinton oolites are green and are composed of alternate laminæ of differently colored chloritic and siliceous matter surrounding grains of quartz. The cherts of the Lake Superior region contain oolites or concretions which are composed of concentric bands of chert, chert and iron oxide,[433] or of red jaspery and black graphitic material.[434] According to Aldrich,[435] some of the chert oolites have carbonate cleavage planes, strongly suggesting that they are replacements of carbonate by silica.

Van Werveke[436] expressed the opinion that the Minette oolites were deposited as carbonate, silicate, sulphide, and possibly as ferric hydrate. Pisolitic or "shot" particles are present in the lateritic iron ores of Cuba[437] and in the laterites of many regions. They are produced in the formation of the laterite. Some of them contain magnetite, also a product of decomposition.

OOLITES AND PISOLITES OF PHOSPHATE. Oolites and pisolites of phosphate are present in Montana, Idaho, Utah, and Wyoming in strata of late Carboniferous age. Mansfield[438] considered that they have been deposited as aragonite which was later phosphoritized by impregnation with ammonium phosphate produced from bacterial decay of marine organisms. He considers this to have been done in shoal waters under conditions of warm and moderate temperature. Pardee[439] was of the opinion "that conditions especially favorable to the solution and retention of calcium carbonate by the sea water, but not hindering the ordinary precipitation of phosphate, existed for a considerable time," so that the oolites were composed of phosphate from the beginning. He considered that the waters were too cold to favor the abundant development of lime-secreting organisms, and this coldness favored a high retention of carbon dioxide which would lead to the solution of much of the lime that might be precipitated, so that the calcium

[432] Wieland, G. R., op. cit., 1914, pp. 253–254.

[433] Van Hise, C. R., and Leith, C. K., Geology of the Lake Superior region, Mon. 52, U. S. Geol. Surv., 1911, p. 536, pls. 42 and 45.

[434] Gruner, J. W., The origin of sedimentary iron formations: The Biwabik formation of the Mesabi Range, Econ. Geol., vol. 17, 1922, p. 414.

[435] Aldrich, H. A., Personal communication.

[436] Van Werveke, L., Ueber die Zusammensetzung und Entstehung der Minetten, Reviewed Zeits. für Pract. Geol., 1901, pp. 496–503.

[437] Leith, C. K., and Mead, W. J., Metamorphic geology, 1915, p. 37.

[438] Mansfield, G. R., Origin of the western phosphates of the United States, Am. Jour. Sci., vol. 46, 1918, p. 591.

[439] Pardee, J. T., The Garrison and Philipsburg phosphate fields, Montana, Bull. 640, U. S. Geol. Surv., 1917, pp. 226–227.

phosphate would acumulate in essentially pure form.   The fact that many of the spherical particles have neither concentric nor laminated structures prevents these from being considered oolites, and hence their origin may not be related to the origin of the oolites.   These particles are probably best interpreted as excremental or coprolitic in origin, and many of them seem to have functioned as nuclei around which were deposited concentric laminæ. Dimensions range from very small to pisolites 6 mm. in diameter.

OOLITES AND PISOLITES OF BAUXITE.   Oolites and pisolites of bauxite have been described by Mead[440] from Arkansas, and they appear to be common in bauxite deposits elsewhere.   They range in dimension from microscopic to a maximum of about 25 mm.   The Arkansas oolites and pisolites are residual products resulting from the surface weathering of "syenite by normal processes of rock decomposition."

OOLITES AND PISOLITES OF BARITE.   Oolites and pisolites of barite were obtained from wells in the Saratoga oil field, Texas.   They were formed in the wells after the latter had been equipped, and it is quite certain that the oolites and pisolites had developed in the fluid—oil and water—in the wells, as their dimensions are such as to preclude passage into the wells through screens connecting with the penetrated sands.   The fluid in the wells had a temperature of 125°F., and it contained some sulphuric acid, which may have been concerned in the formation.   Diameters range from 1.25 to 5 mm.   The color is a dirty white, and the shapes range from spherical to ovoid and disk shaped.   The disk-shaped individuals have nuclei which seem to be pieces of pipe scale.[441]   The structure is concentric, with the center of barite in more porous form than that surrounding.   There is no evidence of replacement.[442]

OOLITES OF SIDERITE.   Oolites of siderite appear to be rather rare.   An example has been described by DeWalque[443] from the Belgian coal measures, the siderite having calcite and pyrite in association.

OOLITES OF SILICATE.   Grains of light green silicate are present in Devonian limestones of Bath County, Kentucky, the particles having maximum diameters of 0.07 mm.[444]   The greenalite particles of the Lake Superior

---

[440] Mead, W. J., Occurrence and origin of the bauxite deposits of Arkansas, Econ. Geol., vol. 10, 1915, pp. 39 40.

[441] Barton, D. C., and Mason, S. L., Further notes on barite pisolites from the Batson and Saratoga oil fields, Bull. Am. Assoc. Pet. Geol., vol. 9, 1925, pp. 1294–1295.

[442] Wuestner, H., Pisolitic barite, Jour. Cincinnati Soc. Nat. Hist., vol. 20, 1906, pp. 245–250; Moore, E. S., Oolitic and pisolitic barite from the Saratoga oil field, Texas, Bull. Geol. Soc. Am., vol. 25, 1914, pp. 77–79; Moore, E. S., Additional note on the oolitic and pisolitic barite from the Saratoga oil field, Texas, Science, vol. 46, 1917, p. 342; Suman, J., The Saratoga oil field, Bull. Am. Assoc. Pet. Geol., vol. 9, 1925, p. 275.

[443] DeWalque, G., Ann. Soc. Géol. Belg., vol. 15, 1888, pp. lxxviii–lxxx.

[444] Bucher, W. H., On oolites and spherulites, Jour. Geol., vol. 26, 1918, pp. 598, 600.

country are spherical, but they do not have concentric or radial structure. The chamosite of the Minette ores of Europe is stated to be commonly in oolitic form. Bucher also has described oolitic texture present in a fire clay from the base of the Pottsville of eastern Kentucky, and he states that Tarr has noted a similar occurrence. Cady[445] gives a section of the St. Peter sandstone of Illinois in which he records the presence of a few inches of oolitic clay.

OOLITES OF PYRITE. Oolitic pyrite in lenticular but persistent beds is present in the Wabana iron ores of Bell Island, Newfoundland.[446] The oolites seem to be of syngenetic origin. Beds of a similar character are in the Devonian of Westphalia, where they average about 10 feet thick and are composed of pyrite and barite, the pyrite being oolitic only in part.[447] Bucher[448] tells of the occurrence of pyrite oolites in a black limestone of the upper Lias of northwest Germany, the oolites consisting of alternating layers of yellow pyrite and black calcium carbonate.

OOLITES AND PISOLITES OF CALCITE AND DOLOMITE. Most oolites and pisolites are composed of either calcite or dolomite, the latter thought to be secondary. The range in dimension is from microscopic to about 25 mm. Most ancient calcite and dolomite oolites are associated with marine strata, but Mansfield has described limestone pisolites from the non-marine Tertiary of southwestern Idaho. Whether these were formed in fresh- or salt-water bodies is not known. Oolites are now forming in Great Salt Lake, the Carlsbad Springs of Bohemia, the waters about Florida, the Red Sea, etc., and they are probably present in the rocks of every geologic system.

SUMMARY. The foregoing shows that oolites may be of residual origin, may develop in oil wells, may form in both fresh and salt water, but appear most commonly to have developed in a salt-water environment.

In studying oolites and pisolites it should be remembered that the particles after formation are of sand, granule, or pebble dimensions, and that they may be transported and deposited as and with those substances. Thus, oolites may be differentiated into those which were developed where they are found and those which underwent considerable transportation before final deposition. In the latter case they are the result of mechanical deposition and exhibit the structures of such in the presence of ripple mark and cross-lamination, and either feature may have been developed by wind or water. Deposition by wind is now occurring on the shores of Florida, Great

[445] Cady, G. H., Bull. 37, Geol. Surv. Illinois, 1919, p. 39.

[446] Hayes, A. O., Wabana iron ore of Newfoundland, Mem. 78, Geol. Surv. Canada, 1915, pp. 10, 15.

[447] Stelzner, A. W., and Bergeat, A., Die Erzlagerstätten, Bd. 1, 1904, pp. 339–342.

[448] Bucher, W. H., op. cit., p. 600.

Salt Lake, Red Sea, etc.   Cross-laminated oolites are present in the Silurian of Gotland, the Pennsylvanian of Kansas, the Mississippian of Kentucky (fig. 115), etc.   Some of these have the wedge-shaped cross-laminated units characteristic of wind deposition.   A feature of such mechanically deposited oolites is the presence of small fossils which are usually the young of species normally larger.   They are associated with the oolites for the same reason that the latter are there,—they are within the range of competency of the agents which transported the oolites.   An occasional large shell may drift into a

FIG. 115. CROSS-LAMINATED OOLITIC LIMESTONE

The foresets, or inclined beds, are fully 20 feet long.   Exposure in Mississippian lime-stone in the Poplar Quarry, Carter County, Kentucky.   Photograph by W. H. Twenhofel.

deposit of transported oolites, or it may have been grown at the place preceding or during their deposition.   Mechanically transported oolites derived from preexisting formations seem to be rare, and it is not known that any exist, although such an origin has been postulated[449] for oolites in the Sylamore sandstone (Lower Mississippian) of Arkansas.   It is more probable that these oolites were formed on the bottom or shores of Sylamore waters.

[449] Swartzlow, C. R., Pan-Am. Geologist, vol. 53, 1930, pp. 197–200.

Oolites which underwent no transportation after origin should not be found in cross-laminated sediments unless it is possible for them to develop therein, and they should be more or less uniformly embedded in the layers in which they occur.

Facts, Experiments, and Hypotheses Relating to the Origin of Oolites

There is little general agreement with respect to the ways in which oolites develop, probably due to the fact that their origins may be various and may result from several different combinations of conditions.

The pisolites of the Carlsbad Springs of Bohemia are said to develop through the deposition of calcium carbonate about various nuclei as the latter are suspended and rotated in the rising waters. The nuclei commonly consist of small particles of quartz and feldspar, and in some instances bubbles appear to have functioned.[450] Similar deposition around nuclei seems possible in any water saturated with lime carbonate, particularly at times of agitation when there is much release of carbon dioxide. Some of the oolites in the Gotland section may have originated in this way, as associated shells are often thickly coated with lime carbonate, although it is possible that algæ may have been the agents responsible for the deposition around the shells. Oolites of concentric structure with small particles of iron or iron oxide as nuclei developed in the hot-water coil of the writer's furnace. In this case the water was at high temperatures and in circulation, which at some times was rapid. The nuclei are supposed to have come from particles of rust detached from the pipes or from particles of iron left in the pipes at the time of their installation. The water entering the coil came from the Potsdam sandstone and was conspicuously hard. When first studied, the concentric laminæ of these oolites did not seem to have had radiate structure, although such was sought for. They have such structure at the present time.

An extremely interesting occurrence of oolites and pisolites is that described by Hess[451] from the Carlsbad Cave of New Mexico. These range in diameter from 1.5 to 25 or 30 mm. and are composed of calcite. Most are spherical; some are oval or of irregular shapes. Most are white, but impurities give some a yellowish color. Nuclei are calcite. The structure is concentric, and some laminæ have radial structure. These oolites form in little pools on the cave floor in which the water is agitated by drops falling from the roof. The agitation facilitates escape of carbon dioxide, leading

---

[450] Hochstetter, H. V., Karlsbad, seine geognostische Verhältnisse und seine Quellen, 1856.

[451] Hess, F. L., Oölites or cave pearls in the Carlsbad caverns, Proc. U. S. Nat. Mus., no. 2813, vol. 76, 1929, pp. 1–5, pls. 1–8.

to precipitation and deposition of calcium carbonate upon and around anything in the pools.   It is postulated that the agitation also rotates the nuclei and the forming oolites and it is assumed that such rotation is necessary for oolite formation.   The oolites seem to be built by deposition of calcium carbonate directly from solution.   As pointed out by Hess, hail seems to form somewhat in the same way, except that in hail deposition may be directly from water vapor, and he states that nickel oolites form in the Mond process for obtaining nickel from its ores through direct precipitation from the gaseous state.   Oolites which seem to have been formed under conditions somewhat similar to those described by Hess have also been found at four localities in Mexican mines except that rotation of the oolites during their formation seems precluded.[452]

Rothpletz[453] came to the conclusion that the oolites of Great Salt Lake developed through the agency of algæ belonging to the genera *Glæocapsa* and *Glæotheca*, the oolites forming in the slimy masses of the assembled organisms, and he asserted a similar origin for the oolites which have extensive development in some portions of the Red Sea.

The streams flowing into Great Salt Lake carry notable quantities of calcium carbonate in solution.   The waters of the lake contain no calcium carbonate and only small quantities of calcium chloride and calcium sulphate.   The lime on entering the lake probably is precipitated because of the inability of the strong brine to hold it in solution, and it may be that the precipitated material is in such state as to favor the formation of oolites. Wethered's[454] studies of the Jurassic oolites of England led him to the view that oolites are largely the result of the activities of filiform algæ, and he distinguished several species of *Girvanella* which he considered of importance in this respect.   Kalkovski[455] has described oolites from the salt lakes of the Kalihari desert which he assigned to an algal origin, and Rothpletz[456] formulated the generalization that the "majority of the marine calcareous oolites with regular and radial zonal structure are of plant origin; the product of microscopically small algæ of low rank, capable of secreting lime carbonate."   Some of the oolites studied by Rothpletz had vermiform and

[452] Davidson, S. C., and McKinstry, H. E., "Cave pearls," oolites, and isolated inclusions in veins, Econ. Geol., vol. 26, 1931, pp. 289–294.

[453] Rothpletz, A., On the formation of oölite, Bot. Centralb., Nr. 35, 1892, Transl. by Cragin, F. W., Am. Geol., vol. 10, 1892, pp. 279–282.

[454] Wethered, E., On the occurrence of Girvanella in oolitic rocks and remarks on oolitic structure, Quart. Jour. Geol. Soc., vol. 46, 1890, pp. 270–283; The formation of oolite, Ibid., vol. 51, 1895, pp. 196–209.

[455] Kalkovski, E., Die Verkieselung der Gesteine in der nördlichen Kalahari, Sitz. u. Abh. Gesell. 'Isis', Abh. pp. 55–107, 1901, 1902.

[456] Rothpletz, A., op. cit., 1892, pp. 265–268.

branching canals, for whose origin filiform algæ living in symbiosis with the lime-secreting types have been suggested. Van Tuyl[457] described oolites from the Ordovician of Iowa which contained "minute sinuous fibers" like those characteristic of "the *Girvanella* type of calcareous algæ." Bradley[458] in his earlier studies of the oolites in the Green River formation advanced the view that microscopic plants were concerned in their origin, but later abandoned this view.[459] The minute canals and "sinuous fibers" found in some oolites do not prove that algæ were concerned in their formation, as they may be due to algæ enclosed within a growing oolite, or they may have been later produced by minute boring organisms.

According to Linck,[460] whenever the quantity of calcium carbonate in sea water exceeds the limit of maximum solubility[461] for the conditions, it is precipitated as calcium carbonate in temperate, and as aragonite in tropical latitudes,[462] in either case without the formation of spherulites. If the precipitation of calcium carbonate arises from the reaction of sodium or ammonium carbonate on calcium sulphate, the product is always aragonite, which may have radiate or concentric structure, and in the latter case with or without the nucleus. Linck's approach was experimental, and he concluded that all oolites and pisolites are of inorganic chemical origin and that any organic matter included is merely incidental, and instead of the oolites being secreted by algæ they served as places of attachment for the latter. He considered the algous rods of Rothpletz as minute crystals of aragonite having no connection with algæ.

Following his investigations of the bottom muds of the waters about the Bahamas and Florida, Vaughan expressed the opinion that the deposition of much of the lime mud of these bottoms was due to bacteria, and he stated that some of the precipitated lime was in the form of aggregates of aragonite needles which by growth might become oolites.[463] The aggregates observed

[457] Van Tuyl, F. M., Science, vol. 43, 1916, p. 171; A contribution to the oolite problem, Jour. Geol., vol. 24, 1916, pp. 792–797.

[458] Bradley, W. H., Shore phases of the Green River formation in northern Sweetwater County, Wyoming, Prof. Paper 140–D, U. S. Geol. Surv., 1926, p. 126.

[459] Bradley, W. H., Algæ reefs and oolites of the Green River formation, Prof. Paper, 154-G, U. S. Geol. Surv., 1929, pp. 221–222.

[460] Linck, G., Die Bildung der Oolithe und Rogensteine, Neues Jahr. f. Min., Beil. Bd. 16, 1903, pp. 495–513. Über die Bildung der Oolithe und Rogensteine, Jenaische Zeits. f. Wiss., vol. 45, pp. 267–278.

[461] The maximum solubility of calcium carbonate in sea water at 17° to 18°C. is about 0.0191 per cent.

[462] The experiments of Murray, J., and Irvine, R., in Proc. Roy. Soc. Edinburgh, vol. 17, 1890, pp. 79–109, show that at a temperature of 34°F., calcium carbonate is precipitated as calcite, at 47°F. as a mixture of calcite and aragonite, and at 80°F. and above as aragonite.

[463] Vaughan, T. Wayland, Papers from the Tortugas Laboratory, Carnegie Inst. of Washington, vol. 5, 1914, pp. 49–54.

ranged in diameter from 0.004 to 0.006 mm. and did not have concentric structure. As the shapes of the cores of some of the oolites forming in the same waters are similar to the aggregates in the muds, he considered that it may yet be shown that the formation of the latter is initial to that of the former.[464]

Wieland[465] has suggested that siliceous oolites may have developed originally in the same manner as calcareous oolites. He states that many siliceous oolites have the silica arranged radially, with the particles projecting inward from an outer rind of concentric layers, suggesting a tiny geode and possible development from a bubble coated with silica. He further suggested that lime and silica may be deposited alternately on a single nucleus by chemical reactions reversible for these two substances, or silica and hematite, as is suggested by the observations of Smyth on the oolites of the Clinton hematites where siliceous shells are left after the hematite is dissolved.[466]

An interesting contribution to the oolite problem is that of Schade.[467] This arose from experimental work relating to gallstones, the experiments demonstrating that when a substance passes from the state of an emulsion colloid to solid form the resulting particles have radiate crystalline arrangement if the substance is pure, but if other substances are present, the particles have concentric structure. Bucher[468] has examined oolites from the point of view of the occurrences of the constituents in the colloidal state, and he comes to the conclusion that the assumption is justified:

that most if not all, oolitic and spherulitic grains were formed by at least one constituent substance changing from the emulsoid state to that of a solid; that the spherical shape of the grains is due to the tendency of the droplets formed during this process of separation to coalesce; and that the difference between radial and concentric structure depends on the amount of other substance thrown out simultaneously with, and mechanically enmeshed in the growing structure.

Oolites in the Green River formation[469] do not have radial structure. The concentric laminæ are conspicuous and the oolites have a darker color

[464] Vaughan, T. W., Oceanography and its relations to other earth sciences, Jour. Washington Acad. Sci., vol. 14, 1924, p. 327.

[465] Wieland, G. R., Further notes on Ozarkian seaweeds and oölites, Bull. Am. Mus. Nat. Hist., vol. 33, 1914, pp. 248–255.

[466] Smyth, C. H., On the Clinton iron ore, Am. Jour. Sci., vol. 43, 1892, pp. 487–496.

[467] Schade, Heinrich, Zur Entstehung der Harnsteine und ähnlicher konzentrisch geschichteter Steine organischen und anorganischen Ursprungs: Zeits. f. Chemie u. Industrie der Kolloide, vol. 4, 1909, pp. 175–180, Über Konkrementbildungen beim Vorgang der tropfigen Entmischung von Emulsionskolloiden, Kolloidchemische Beihefte, vol. 1, 1910, pp. 375–390.

[468] Bucher, W. H., On oolites and spherulites, Jour. Geol., vol. 26, 1918, pp. 593, 609.

[469] Bradley, W. H., Algæ reefs and oolites of the Green River formation, Prof. Paper, 154–G, U. S. Geol. Surv., 1929, pp. 221–222.

than their matrix, the coloring being due to iron which is concentrated in them with respect to the matrix.   It is postulated that the oolites in a dense matrix formed in an ooze or gel consisting of "colloidal ferric hydroxide with a large admixture of extremely finely divided calcium carbonate," and "it is possible that the calcium carbonate may also have been in a colloidal state."   Bradley suggests that the absence of radial structure to the calcite may have been due to the

protective action of the colloidal ferric hydroxide. . . . The ferric hydroxide must have been coagulated by negative ions as carbonate or chloride in the solution, and then because the minute coagulated particles are unstable in the presence of larger ones, and apparently also in the presence of any larger foreign particle such as a quartz or feldspar grain, they coalesced into spheres, mechanically enmeshing a considerable quantity of the suspended calcium carbonate. By that process the oolite grains grew.   Apparently their growth was limited by the supply of ferric hydroxide, as they seem to have extracted the greater part of it from the matrix.

Bradley further suggests that the oolites not in a dense matrix may have been formed in the same way, but that the matrix was later washed away; also, that an ooze or a gel may not have been essential and that the oolites may have developed in fluids no more viscous than natural waters, these waters containing colloidal components as ferric hydroxide, silica, algal gelatin, or some other colloid.   It is further suggested that the simultaneous precipitation of the colloid and calcium carbonate, the latter through action of plants or other agent, might lead to the formation of oolites in waters over almost any bottom and that the particles might grow while lying on the bottom.

The writer is of the opinion that many oolites have formed without suspension in an ooze or gel.   The specimens derived from the hot-water coil and from pools on the floor of Carlsbad Cavern were certainly not in an ooze, and it does not seem that a colloid need be assumed for their formation any more than for the formation of the scale lining the wall of the same coil. The polyhedral pisolites described by Shrock do not seem to have formed in an ooze or gel unless the matrix was entirely utilized to form the pisolites. Oolites forming in an ooze or gel should appear as if floating in the matrix and more or less separated from each other.

The latest explanation of the origin of oolites is that of Mathews.[470] According to him, the Great Salt Lake oolites originate at the water's edge whence they are washed upon the mud flats and grow as driven inland by the wind.   The laminæ correspond to seasons and result from the direct precipitation of amorphous aragonite from evaporation of capillary water.

[470] Mathews, A. A. L., Origin and growth of the Salt Lake oolites, Jour. Geol., vol. 38, 1930, pp. 633–642.

Growth takes place during early summer months when the rise of temperature is greatest. Little if any growth occurs in the water. The oolites on the bottom of the lake are small, with only one or two laminæ. The accumulation of soot on the exteriors of the crystalline laminæ of the oolites is considered proof that formation took place on land and that each band of soot was collected after the rainy season. Most oolites formed around some solid nucleus, and of 574 examined only 4 were found that might have formed around a gas bubble or an alga.

The depths at which oolites form have not been determined. Neither has it been shown what are the limits wherein oolites may be deposited. The preceding paragraphs show there is great difference of opinion relating to the environment of formation. At the present time oolites are being transported in sand dunes about the shores of some lakes and over sea bottoms wherever currents exist that can obtain them and are competent to transport them. If oolites are formed in the manner suggested by the observations of Vaughan, Linck, or Rothpletz, there do not appear to be any reasons precluding their occurrence to great depths unless pressure and light are factors in their formation. Perhaps high temperature is a factor. If so, they should at the present time develop in greatest abundance in the upper waters which are warm in contrast to the deeper waters which are cold, and in tropical waters rather than those of high latitudes. Modern oolites are most abundant in the warmer latitudes, but they also occur in temperate. Some hot weather seems to be a favoring factor. The writer does not consider that the facts warrant the sweeping assumption that oolite and pisolite formation require materials to be in the form of a colloid before they can participate in such formation. It seems probable that all of the material can be in true solution. The "shot" in laterites and pisolites in bauxite shows that a water cover is not required. The writer considers it reasonable to assume that no generalization relating to oolite and pisolite formation has universal application.

Colors of Sediments[471]

Colors of sediments may be either primary (original) or secondary, the latter a consequence of weathering and important in various residual ma-

---

[471] The manuscript for the topic on the colors of sediments given in the first edition of the Treatise on Sedimentation was prepared by Doctor Eliot Blackwelder and it was planned that such should be true of the manuscript for the second edition. The state of Doctor Blackwelder's health has precluded his assisting in the preparation. He has, however, read the manuscript and made suggestions for its improvement. Gratitude is due Doctor Blackwelder for this assistance. The material of the first edition has been freely used in preparing the manuscript of the second.

terials such as laterite and bauxite. The distinction between primary and secondary is more or less arbitrary, and in many cases there may be considerable difference of opinion as to whether a given color was syngenetic with deposition or developed subsequently thereto. Generally speaking, a color may be considered primary if it existed in the sediment at the time the latter was buried, but it is extremely difficult to prove such was the case except in those cases where colors are due to the original colors of composing detrital minerals.

Many sediments would be white if it were not for the admixture of other materials. This is exemplified by such rocks as limestone, gypsum, anhydrite, rock salt, bauxite, kaolin, and most quartz sandstones. Others are black or dark for the same reason, as coal and some graywacke and volcanic ash. The most common condition is for sediments to be composed of several ingredients, with corresponding variations in color. Color in some cases arises from the colors of the detrital minerals, but in many and probably most cases the colors result from organic matter or iron, the abundance or concentration of the former giving gray, blue, or black, and the degree of oxidation and combinations of the latter yielding yellows, browns, pinks, reds, blacks, and greens. Low states of oxidation give colors ranging from gray to blue, and higher from yellow to red. Organic matter plays a double rôle in that it not only imparts color to the materials of which it is a part, but through its reducing properties it may and is likely to take color from these associated materials.

The significance of the colors of sedimentary materials is an important but tantalizing problem. There is first the wide range of colors and the matter of referring them to some generally accepted color scale or chart. The generally used method of referring colors to one of the seven primary colors has little to recommend it and is extremely indefinite. The red of one geologist may be the brown of another. The color chart of Goldman and Merwin was designed to replace the inaccurate and generally meaningless methods of color designation in use prior to its preparation and still in use by many geologists.[472] Another problem connected with color is that of the condition of the rocks when observed. The colors of rocks are not the same when wet as when dry, and when in bright sunlight as when in shadow. Thus, many shales are blue when wet and gray when dry. Still another important problem connected with color is the latter's significance in terms of the environment of formation. This is a field wherein there has been

[472] National Research Council, 1928. Until something better is devised this chart should be used by every sedimentationist. It has been suggested that a photometer be used in determining colors of powders. Grawe, O. R., Quantitative determination of rock color, Science, vol. 66, 1927, pp. 61–62.

much speculation, as witness the oft repeated statement that red is indicative of aridity.

The various colors of sediments are divided into four groups: white to light gray, dark gray to black, green, and yellow to red. It is not to be understood, however, that there are sharp divisions among these groups, as such is by no means the case. Black, gray, yellow, brown, and red colors are common. Green is a not uncommon color, and blue is common in wet sediments, but less so in dry. However, many shales and some limestones and sandstones are blue.

WHITE TO LIGHT GRAY

The light colors indicate that the materials of the sediments are either finely divided or pure. Many limestones are white to light gray because composed of pure or nearly pure calcite or dolomite. The same is true for most gypsum and rock salt. Many clays are white, and such is the case for much bauxite. Most quartz sands are white to gray, and the resulting rocks may have the same color. Many feldspars are light colored; sands derived from these are white to gray, and they may yield rocks similarly colored. The presence of muscovite gives a more or less silvery white color.

DARK GRAY TO BLACK

Colors ranging from dark gray through blue to black are due in most cases to one or more of four varieties of constituents. These are: matter of organic origin, minerals intrinsically dark, certain sulphur compounds, and the black oxides of manganese. The most important of these four coloring agents is probably that of organic origin.

Organic matter is divisible into the carbonaceous and hydro-carbonaceous, the former including graphite and carbonized organic matter of all kinds, the latter asphalt, tar, and any of the dark colored hydrocarbon compounds. Carbonaceous materials may be sufficiently concentrated to give the black of coals and thence by gradual decrease to yield the less dark colors and the grays of many shales, sandstones, and limestones. The hydrocarbons have somewhat similar degrees of concentration and give different degrees of darkness to shale, limestone, flint, and sandstone.

Dark-colored minerals and rock fragments are probably second in importance in imparting dark colors to sediments. The minerals are chiefly the unaltered silicates of igneous and anamorphic rocks, among which are hornblende, biotite, augite, magnetite, and ilmenite. Dark rock fragments are derived from black slates, black flints, basalt, diabase, scoria, and obsidian, and these fragments in places are so abundant as to give dark colors to the clastic sediments derived from them. Conditions favoring accumulation of such clastics are those of rapid rock breaking with limited decomposition, and thus they are most common in the conglomerates, graywackes, and tills of the colder climates. Pyroclastics very commonly have dark colors. Sediments which are dark colored because of the presence of dark minerals seem to be most common on beaches whereon magnetite, ilmenite, and other minerals produce dark-colored to black sands. Beach sands of such color are by no means rare and have been worked for gold and platinum on the coast of Oregon and for iron on the coast of Quebec and elsewhere. A black sand from Idaho contained ilmenite, garnet, magnetite, zircon, monazite, samarskite, titanite, columbite, polycrase, small percentages of thirteen other minerals, and also some obsidian.[473]

Some of the oceanic muds and certain other sediments deposited under water in the presence of a limited quantity of oxygen range in color from blue or gray to black, the blue seemingly largely due to the presence of water, as many blue shales become gray on drying. The colors of these sediments are largely or partly due to the presence of the black amorphous ferrous monosulphide, hydrotroilite, or the black ferrous disulphide, melnikovite. These same sediments also usually contain some organic matter to which they partly owe their color. As the two black sulphides are relatively unstable, they tend to crystallize on induration of the sediments into the more stable forms of marcasite and pyrite; this change takes darkness of color from the sediments, but the products rarely give color to the rock because the pyrite and marcasite usually are not present in sufficient quantity, particularly as they are associated with sediments which are already dark because of their content of organic matter. If the sulphides develop in sediments relatively free from organic matter, colors become light as the former change to marcasite and pyrite, and after exposure to the atmosphere a buff or tan color develops in consequence of oxidation of the sulphides, exposed surfaces having such colors, whereas fresh fractures may be blue, gray, or white. Thus, the white or gray Salem limestones of Indiana become buff after exposure to the agents of the atmosphere.

The black oxides of manganese form nodules and black coatings on rock fragments and detritals over many parts of the sea bottom, and color the fine sediments of some bottoms. Similar coatings are made over rocks in fresh waters. Black coatings also are made over rock fragments and rock outcrops in both dry and wet regions on land. Manganese oxides also impart dark colors to the deposits of some swamps and the residual soils of warmer latitudes. In comparison with the other materials imparting dark colors, manganese oxides are relatively unimportant.

[473] Shannon, E. V., Mineralogy of some black sands from Idaho with a description of the methods used for their study, Proc. U. S. Nat. Mus., vol. 60, 1921, pp. 1–33.

Black sediments are common in the geologic column and are known to be forming over many parts of the world.   Among the black sediments are the peats, coals, black shales, the black muds of the limans of the Baltic and elsewhere, the black muds of fresh-water lakes, the black muds of the Black Sea (the Black Sea muds become lighter colored when dry), etc.   Sediments within the range dark gray to blue and black are still more common.   Blues are common in wet sediments, but some shales, sandstones, and limestones remain blue after drying.   MacCarthy[474] ascribed this color to the presence of hydrated ferrous-ferric iron, but it seems likely that in some cases it is due to carbonaceous matter or mineral structure.

GREEN

The green colors of sediments are due to a considerable variety of minerals, but of these only two groups have more than local significance.   They are such hydrous silicates as the serpentines, chlorites, and epidote; and glauconite.   Green is not an uncommon color, being found in muds, shales, sands, sandstones, and some limestones.   In many cases the coloring materials are iron-bearing, but such is not always the case.   In the hydrous silicate coloring materials it seems that the iron is generally in the ferrous-ferric condition.[475]   To the layman in geology the presence of green colors in rocks connotes the presence of copper, and in rare instances such is the case.

The hydrous silicates are common coloring minerals in shales, tuffs, and agglomerates.   Many muds and shales are decidedly green, but not enough work has been done to be certain that a hydrous silicate is responsible, though chemical analyses showing a preponderance of ferrous iron would exclude glauconite as the coloring material.

In marine sediments, modern and ancient, a mineral frequently responsible for the green color is the hydrous potassium iron silicate, glauconite, in which ferric iron dominates over ferrous.   Glauconite gives color to green sands and green muds which are peculiar to slightly reducing areas of slow deposition on the continental shelves and slopes.   As previously noted, its distribution ranges from very shallow to very deep bottoms, and as a coloring material it is a constituent of many ancient sands.   Whether many of the green shales of the geologic column owe their color to glauconite cannot be stated positively, but it has been more or less generally assumed that such is the case and that the glauconite is in a fine state of division.   A somewhat similar mineral, greenalite, gives color to some of the Pre-Cambrian forma-

[474] MacCarthy, G. R., Colors produced by iron in minerals and the sediments, Am. Jour. Sci., vol. 12, 1926, pp. 17–36.

[475] Hager, D. S., Factors affecting the color of green sedimentary rocks, Bull. Am. Assoc. Pet. Geol., vol. 12, 1928, pp. 911–913.

tions of the Lake Superior region. This mineral contains no potash and has not been discovered in modern sediments, or sediments subsequent to the Proterozoic.

A greenish color in some cases is due to original colors of detrital minerals, as green hornblende, actinolite, uralite, bastite, and olivine. Such rocks are not of common occurrence, but in rare instances there is a local abundance. Thus, along some beaches of the Hawaiian Islands the beach sands are olive green because olivine particles are the most abundant constituent.[476]

In rare and local instances the green copper carbonate, malachite, serves as a color for shales and sandstones, but as a coloring material this mineral has little quantitative significance.

YELLOW TO RED

The colors ranging from yellow to red through buff, purple, brown, etc., are among the most common in sediments, particularly after the latter have become indurated and exposed to atmospheric action. Most residual materials of temperate and tropical regions have a color within this range. In most cases this color is lost in transportation, so that the color on deposition falls within the range of gray to black, this being due to reduction of the ferric oxides, usually more or less hydrated, to which yellow, red, etc., colors are due. As shown by Rogers,[477] these hydrated ferric oxides are almost entirely amorphous. He groups them into two divisions, using the name "hematite" for those giving a red streak and "limonite" for those which give a yellow-brown streak. Most sediments with colors of the range yellow to red probably contain mixtures of these oxides. Hematite gives color to some of the Red Beds and red soils. Laterite is red for the same reason, but the magnetic properties of some of the particles show that some reduction has taken place and that a part of the iron is in the form of magnetite. Hematite also colors limestones, cherts, and other rocks in varying degrees of intensity, and red limestones are not particularly rare. Yellow, buff, and brown soils and sediments probably have the iron in the form of limonite. This color is common in mid-temperate latitudes in subsoils under conditions of good drainage.

Some beach sands have various degrees of red due to the abundance of garnet particles. Such are not particularly common, but they may be seen on shores where igneous and anamorphic rocks are undergoing erosion, as along the shores of Lake Champlain, the east coast of Quebec, the Labrador

---

[476] Wentworth, C. K., and Ladd, H. S., Pacific Island sediments, Univ. Iowa Studies, vol. 13, 1931, p. 30.

[477] Rogers, A. F., A review of the amorphous minerals, Jour. Geol., vol. 25, 1917, pp. 515–541.

coast, and elsewhere.   Many sands are colored pink to red because of the presence of pink to red feldspars.   The Newark series of the eastern part of North America owes the red colors of some of its sandstones partly to the abundant presence of feldspar.

Detritals of red rocks in places compose the major parts of beach and other sands and gravels and are responsible for the color of the aggregate. The Keweenawan conglomerates near Calumet, Michigan, locally are made up in large part of detritals of jasper, red quartzite, red slate, and red felsitic lavas and are red as a consequence.

ENVIRONMENTAL SIGNIFICANCE OF COLOR

The environmental conditions determining the colors of sediments are not fully understood, but are of great importance.   These conditions need to be appreciated and studied if past environments are to be visualized in any degree of accuracy.   The environmental problems of color are clouded with traditional ideas and obscured by assumptions with little or no factual basis, as for instance the oft-repeated and erroneous statement that redness of sediments denotes aridity.   The problems are here considered from the point of view of continental and marine sediment.

Continental Conditions Controlling Color

The most influential land factors influencing colors are: (a) the nature of the parent rocks, (b) the conditions under which they disintegrate or decompose, (c) the conditions at the place and time of deposition, and (d) diagenesis subsequent to deposition.   The conditions under which transportation takes place are also important.   The colors of the sediments deposited on land are resultants of the various factors, the particular color being determined by which factor or factors dominated.

In hot, rigorously arid regions the original colors of the country rocks largely govern the colors of the resulting sediments, and as rock powders and fine detritals tend to be lighter colored than their source rocks, the result is that desert sediments tend to be light.   Acidic igneous and anamorphic rocks, themselves usually gray to pink in color, generally give rise to pale gray to flesh-colored products of weathering; the derivatives of basic igneous rocks are gray to dull brown, and red rocks yield red sediments.   Pure quartz sandstones break down into white quartz sands, and limestones and gypsum produce white sands of these materials.   If decomposition is small and subordinate to disintegration, the particles released for transportation may contain little thoroughly decomposed matter, and as decomposition likewise has little affected the particles resulting from disintegration, the original colors of the rock particles may be little changed.   The rock particles tend to be moved largely by wind and to be heaped into dunes of light-colored sands.   The deposits of the playas and ephemeral streams are light- to buff-colored silts and salts of various composition.   Prevailing colors of desert sediments produced within a desert are therefore light rather than dark, and white, buff, pale gray, lavender, and pink are characteristic, buff probably being commonest.   However, it may be that sediments are produced outside of, but carried into a desert.   Under these conditions the colors of the region of derivation are likely to be retained.   There is a prevailing view that sediments of deserts are red; this is a tradition that is not supported by many examples.

The other extreme of temperature conditions gives such cold arctic and subarctic regions as Alaska, Labrador, etc., and the cold highland regions of the world.   The sediments produced in these regions have undergone little decomposition and thus pattern their colors after those of the parent rock, with the difference that the low evaporation, high humidity, and generally higher precipitation favor the growth of vegetation, whose slow decay leaves a copious residue of black carbonaceous matter to be mingled with the region's sediments.   This carbonaceous matter is generally present to some degree in all varieties of the sediments of such regions, even in sands and gravels, in the form of stems, bark, etc.   Its immediate effect is to modify the colors of the original rock particles directly and primarily through its presence, and secondarily by reason of its reducing action upon any ferric compounds which the sediments may contain.   The clays, silts, sands, arkoses, and gravels in which carbonaceous matter is present in not too great abundance are thus bleached to grays, and the color of the aggregate is prevailingly gray.   As the organic matter increases, and such is likely to be the case over the lower areas, the colors become darker, and coal is at this extreme.   The most common variety of sediments over the flood plains, deltas, and other lowland sites of deposition is blackish gray carbonaceous shale, and according to Blackwelder[478] such shales "are more abundant than all other subarctic deposits combined."   The generalization is thus made that the sediments of the arctic and subarctic regions, where not modified by enclosed carbonaceous matter, have their colors, as in the deserts, largely determined by the colors of the parent rocks and minerals.

The tropical and warm temperate regions of plentiful rainfall have their rocks destroyed chiefly by decomposition.   These regions have little or no frost action and have the surface permanently or perennially covered with vegetation, and nearly all rocks tend to decompose and have their soluble constitu-

[478] Blackwelder, E., Treatise on Sedimentation, 1st ed., 1925, p. 546; The climatic history of Alaska from a new viewpoint, Trans. Illinois Acad. Sci., vol. 10, 1917, pp. 275–281.

ents removed, leaving a residue largely composed of aluminum hydroxide, hydrous aluminous silicates, hydrous iron oxides, quartz, and a few other rather insoluble materials. Colors tend to be brown to red, but they may be gray if the vegetable matter is adequate to reduce the ferric oxides. These residual materials are quite certain to be transported and deposited in association with organic matter, and this association and the conditions at the times and places of deposition will largely determine colors. If a region is continuously moist and the places of deposition are subaqueous or on damp, poorly drained, flat surfaces, the ferric oxides are quite certain to be reduced to the ferrous form and appear as colorless carbonate or sulphate, either possible of removal, or of precipitation as carbonate or as black iron sulphides. Under such conditions much of the organic matter may not completely decay and may remain as blackish coloring matter in quantity sufficient to color the associated inorganic materials gray to black.

In most tropical and warmer temperate regions with sufficient relief to produce effective downward drainage through the surface and subsurface materials, oxidation of all iron compounds is probable, and the colors of the residual materials become brown to red. In tropical regions there is also likelihood of considerable removal of the silica and decomposition of the clay to produce aluminum hydroxide and silica, the latter probably in turn removed, leaving the regolith composed of aluminum hydroxide and hydrous iron oxides. The transportation of these sediments to and on lower and poorly drained levels is likely to incorporate considerable organic matter, with reduction of the iron and loss of the brown to red colors as sequels. The general results are that red sediments are not to be expected in the steadily moist and warm tropical and warm temperate regions and gray colors tend to prevail.

However, in tropical and warm temperate regions with a wet season alternating each year with one that is hot and dry, similar conditions of decomposition may prevail, and residual soils with the same colors of red to brown are produced; but the vegetation is eliminated or greatly reduced during the hot dry season, so that the quantity available for deposition with the sediments is small, and the latter retain their vivid colors after deposition. The same results are obtained if the red sediments are carried from a moist and warm region into a bordering one. Again, the red residual material may be produced in a region during a moist epoch and deposited during a succeeding dryer epoch. Good illustrations of these principles may be found in the Hawaiian Islands. The windward sides of the islands where they are exposed to the trade winds are continuously wet, and the hillside soils are brown to purplish red. After deposition on the river flood plains these soils, now sediments, become gray to black. On the leeward side of the islands, where there is a short wet and a long dry season, the soils are brick-red and the sediments deposited on the river flood plains have the same color.

It is inferred that most of the red sandstones and shales of the geologic column were formed as thus outlined, that is, in a warm region with good underground water circulation and with seasons of warmth and dryness alternating with those of great rainfall and floods, and that deposition took place in a region of the same climatic character or in a semi-arid to arid marginal region or in a succeeding epoch of dryness. To these conditions are referred the Red Beds of the Rocky Mountain region and similar sediments elsewhere. These are not necessarily the deposits of deserts.[479] They may have been deposited under desert conditions, but they could not have originated there.

Marine Conditions Controlling Color

In the ocean and other large bodies of water not so salty as to prohibit the growth of many organisms, the prime factors responsible for color seem not to be climatic, but rather the sufficiency or insufficiency of oxygen in the bottom waters and especially in the interstices of the accumulating sediments, and the greater or less abundance of aquatic life.

Under aërobic or oxygenated conditions and slow accumulation of sediments all organic matter is apparently devoured by the many scavenger animals of the sea bottom or destroyed through bacterial decomposition, and none is left to accumulate with the sediments. Under some conditions glauconite forms and introduces a green component. Prevailing colors are therefore gray, cream color, or pale green, appropriate to the colors of the calcareous or siliceous shells, plant material, or associated muds. In deeper waters below the densely populated neritic bottoms the quantity of oxygen probably is smaller than in neritic waters, but so also is the organic matter, the result being that colors are not unlike those over the neritic bottoms with apparently a tendency toward darker hues, which arises from organic matter escaping oxidation or from the development of the black mono- and disulphides of iron. Glauconite may also form under these conditions. Accumulations of globigerina and other calcareous oozes have gray to cream colors consistent with the colors of the composing calcareous shells. In the deep abysses, lime carbonate passes into solution before reaching bottom, and the deposits are either composed of siliceous shells and insoluble residues, or of the latter alone. The former constitutes the diatom and radiolarian

---

[479] Barrell, Joseph, Dominantly fluviatile origin under seasonal rainfall of the Old Red Sandstone, Bull. Geol. Soc. Am., vol. 27, 1916, pp. 345–386; Relations between climate and terrestrial deposits, Jour. Geol. vol. 16, 1908, pp. 285–294.

oozes with gray, cream, and other colors, and the latter, because of the insoluble ferric oxides, is red, constituting the red clay.   This red has been produced because of the sediments sinking through the thousands of feet of water and becoming oxidized while so doing, and it persists because of the rarity of organic matter on the very deep ocean bottom.

Under anaërobic conditions the action of scavengers and the oxidation of materials are largely decreased or even prevented.   Organic matter is not completely destroyed, and the undestroyed portion becomes incorporated in the sediments, where it exercises a reducing action and takes ferric iron colors from the sediments and darkens them by its presence.   These anaëro-bic reducing areas also become populated with sulphur bacteria forming the black mono- and disulphides of iron, which likewise give blackness to the sediments.   Under slightly reducing conditions glauconite forms to impart a green component.   The results are that the sediments have colors ranging from gray to green and black, and these are characteristic colors of the deep holes and places of poor circulation over the ocean bottom, as the deep fjords of the Norway coast, the deep Bay of Kiel, the holes in Chesapeake Bay, the deeper waters of the Black Sea, Lake Baikal, and many if not most deep fresh-water lakes.   Here are formed the gray (often called "blue") muds of the continental slopes and the black oily shales of cul-de-sacs. However, all reducing areas are not in deep water.   Marginal parts of a sea may be so shallow for some distance from the shore that there is no wave activity reaching the shore or seriously affecting the waters for some dis-tance therefrom.   This condition is favored by weak tides and is found in such existing seas as the Baltic and probably obtained in many epiconti-nental seas of past geologic periods.   Under these conditions of poor circu-lation the fresh waters of the land mingle indifferently and slowly with those of the sea, and at a given place one frequently replaces the other.   Plant life thrives more or less indifferently; scavengers have difficulty in existing; and the deposits are black like those in the limans on the east Baltic coast, the coast of the Black Sea, and a few places elsewhere.   It is the writer's opinion that many black shales, as those of the New Albany, Chattanooga, etc., formed in shallow waters as outlined, thus representing the deposits made by a retiring sea or the initial deposits made by a sea advancing over a plain rising gently from sea level so that slight rises flooded great areas.

Some tropical rivers, as the Amazon and Orinoco, more or less continu-ously deposit red muds about their mouths.   Varying amounts of organic matter become incorporated with these muds so that beneath the surface the ferric oxides responsible for the redness may become reduced and be converted into sulphides and carbonates, with loss of redness in the parts so affected and change of color to gray or black.   How extensive such changes are in these tropical muds cannot be stated, but it is considered unlikely that the redness persists far beneath the surface.

The red marine limestones not uncommon in the geologic column are usually inferred to have had that color from the beginning, and such may have been the case in some instances.   Examples are the Devonian limestone of Percé Rock of Gaspé, part of the Hoburgen limestones of Gotland, and the Cambrian Smith Point limestones of Newfoundland.   According to Galloway,[480] red calcareous deposits are not known to be forming today under marine conditions, and it is his conclusion that all red limestones are due to atmospheric weathering, a view in which White and others concur. The generalization seems to be too sweeping, however, and it may be that red calcareous sediments are deposited under certain marine conditions.[481]

The shore deposits of seas and lakes are affected by local influences, and particularly by the nature of the country rock, much more than are the off-shore deposits.   Thus, along certain parts of the Alaska coast the sands and gravels are dark gray owing chiefly to the copious admixture of particles of black flint and black slate worn from the adjacent cliffs.   Likewise, on some of the shores of the Hawaiian Islands the sands are brownish green, or even black, because of the comminuted basalt rich in olivine.   Some of the sands of the Quebec coast are red, pink, or black due to garnet, feldspar, or magnetite.   Examples of this character are numerous and in all cases are due solely to the comminution of unaltered rocks.

SUMMARY

1. Sediments whose colors are due to the composing detritals indicate one of several origins.   They may have been formed under conditions of rigorous aridity, rigorously cold climates adjacent to steep slopes, or upon the beaches of lakes and seas.   On land these colors denote either topography of considerable relief, or a climate either too dry or too cold to permit rapid decay of minerals.   Colors of this origin in marine deposits have little or no climatic significance; they are due to a coastal terrane breaking down through wave attack, but frost action favors wave erosion.

2. Black is due largely to incomplete decay of organic matter under more or less anaërobic conditions in marshes, wet (and cold) plains, lakes, particularly those with no annual overturn, very shallow waters of tideless or almost tideless seas, and in deep holes of the seas and the ocean.

3. Grays, if dark, have something of the significance of black, but the

---

[480] Galloway, J. J., Red limestones and their geologic significance, Abstract, Bull. Geol. Soc. Am., vol. 33, 1922, pp. 105–106; White, D., etc.   Discussion, pp. 106–107.
[481] Clarke, J. M., 60th Ann. Rept. New York State Museum, 1908, pp. 63–64.   Clarke cites other authorities on the significance of red limestones.

lighter shades have a much wider range of origin. If the deposits are continental, several environmental conditions are possible. If the gray sediments contain evaporites, a desert playa or lake may be postulated. Similar grays without evaporites may develop in the flood-plain deposits of a river of a region with not too permanently wet climate. The gray sediments may be those of a delta, of parts of the neritic bottom or of the continental slopes, or they may have been deposited in very deep water.

4. Variegated colors, that is, those altering from one bedding unit to another, are considered characteristic[482] of continental deposits—river flood plains, alluvial fans, deltas, etc.—but it is known that such combinations also are found in the deposits of the neritic environment. The non-marine Morrison shales of Montana and Wyoming show this variation in decided development.

5. Green, when not due to green detritals, indicates chiefly the more or less altered pyroclastics or the glauconitic muds and sands of slightly reducing and slowly accumulating areas of the sea.

6. Red colors generally imply an origin of the composing materials under conditions of a water table sufficiently low to give good underground drainage, plenty of rainfall to support a good but not abundant growth of vegetation, and a warm climate comparable to that of the tropics all over the globe, though hot and dry seasons may have alternated with moist, as is the case in southern Oklahoma at the present time. Deposition took place under climatic conditions of hot and dry seasons alternating with rainy seasons, or under conditions of general dryness, deposition in the latter case occurring in a region and climate marginal to the region of origin of the sediments or in the same region, but in a geologic epoch subsequent to that in which the materials became red. Deposition may take place on river flood plains, deltas, or in shallow seas or lakes, but if much organic matter is buried with the red sediments, the red colors disappear. It may happen that a red terrane, as the Red Beds, under extremely arid conditions may yield red sediments, and this must be kept in mind in interpreting the significance of red in continental deposits. Red sediments also characterize over 50,000,000 square miles of the abyssal parts of the ocean basin. Pinks, lavenders, yellows, and other pale shades may be due to several unlike environments.

There is danger that the reader of the preceding paragraphs may form too simple a concept of the significance of colors in the sedimentary formations. In actual practice the geologist will often be confronted with cases which have had complex histories. For example, the Nile River carries out the products of chemical decay from the tropical rain forest into the

[482] Barrell, J., op. cit., 1916, p. 376.

arid climate of northern Egypt for deposition. Again, the products of glacial wear and frost disintegration around alpine mountains may be carried down by streams and deposited under conditions favoring rapid chemical decay *in situ*, as in northeastern India and Burma. Surface-deposited beds of ash and cinders in the Eocene formations of the San Juan Mountains of Colorado have become highly colored by the action of the thermal waters after the deposits had been buried in the course of subsequent eruptions. Such action produces colors entirely foreign to the original deposit. Likewise, one must be on his guard against mistaking for true colors those which have been induced by weathering. Surface exposures of a gray limestone may appear red from the products of residual decay. A black shale containing abundant pyrite grains may appear yellowish or gray on account of limonite stains or the efflorescence of soluble sulphates.

"In short, the color of each sedimentary bed must be regarded as a problem in itself to which simple rules cannot be applied blindly without danger of serious error."[483]

[483] Blackwelder, E., Treatise on sedimentation, 1st ed., 1925, p. 550.

CHAPTER VII

ENVIRONMENTS OR REALMS OF SEDIMENTATION

General Considerations

It has been repeatedly emphasized in preceding chapters that sediments are adaptations to environments and that their various characteristics are resultants of the rocks of derivation, the environments in which detachment from parent rocks took place, the environments through which transportation was effected, and the environments of deposition. Much has been said relating to environments of deposition. These are many and they differ more or less greatly. Furthermore, each environment passes laterally into others, the change being gradual in some cases, as that between the waters of the deep and shallow sea, and abrupt in others, as between a lake and its bordering swamp deposits. Also, environments are sequential, and the sediments of one pass vertically into others, the change being of various degrees of abruptness.

It is known that some environments are identifiable by the sediments deposited therein, and it is thought that there is a sedimentary reaction to every environmental difference. Many of these reactions are known, and their identifications permit the environments of origin to be determined. Certain sediments are known to be extremely sensitive to environmental factors, and when all the facts are known it is thought that most if not all sediments will be found to have a high degree of environmental sensitivity. Too little attention has been paid to the influence of the environment from the points of view of both the sediments forming therein and the organisms living upon and in these sediments. It is a field inviting research.

Environments are possible of classification upon a variety of bases. That which seems best to the writer has the two major divisions of continental and marine. As these two environments have contact along the shoreline, the result is that an area adjacent to this shoreline partakes of the character of both, giving a third division of mixed continental and marine. The continental environments in turn are subdivided on the basis of whether the deposits are made by aqueous or non-aqueous agencies. The factor of depth of water is the basis for classification of the marine environments, and the mixed continental and marine environments are subdivided very largely on a physiographic basis. The various environments are as follows:

> Continental environments
>> Terrestrial
>>> Desert
>>> Glacial
>> Fluvial
>>> Piedmont
>>> Valley-flat
>> Paludal (swamp)
>> Lacustrine
>> Cave (spelean)
> Mixed continental and marine environments
>> Littoral
>> Marginal lagoon
>> Estuarine
>> Delta
> Marine environments
>> Neritic or shallow water
>> Bathyal or intermediate depths
>> Abyssal or deep sea

It should be fully realized that these divisions and subdivisions are purely arbitrary and that by some variety of gradation each may pass into one or several others. Thus, the valley-flat environment of streams passes into that of the delta, and the latter into the shallow-water marine. The valley flat contains lakes, and the deposits of one may pass laterally and vertically into the deposits of the other. The sediments should, however, show the transitions.

CONTINENTAL ENVIRONMENTS

Continental environments may be divided into terrestrial, or those in which water plays a subordinate part in the deposition; fluvial, in which flowing water is the chief agent of deposition; paludal, in which the deposits accumulate in swamps through merely falling from the animals and plants which form them; lacustrine, in which the deposition is in lake waters; and caves. The terrestrial environments may be placed in the two groups of desert and glacial. In the desert environment the deposits are largely of wind and temporary water deposition; in the glacial environment ice and water derived from its melting are the chief depositing agents. The fluvial environment may be divided into that of the upper portions of streams, here designated the piedmont environment, and that of the other portions of streams exclusive of the deltas, designated the valley-flat environment.

The Desert Environment and Its Sediments[1]

It is estimated that one-fifth of the present earth's surface is without drainage to the oceans and that the approximate area of the arid regions of the earth is 11,500,000 square miles.[2] Thus, regions of existing desert environment are of great extent, and such must have been the case to some extent during every period of geologic time. However, only small parts of a desert are places of deposition. The Sahara contains 3,500,000 square miles; 700,000 square miles are dune- or sand-covered; the remainder has a rock floor.[3] In other words, four-fifths of the desert is being eroded, and it is thought that this figure is below the average. Contrary to popular conception, only small parts of deserts are covered with drifting sands.

The sediments of deserts accumulate by wash from upland slopes, by streams whose channels at times are filled with torrents of muddy water and at other times are dry coulees, by deposition from waters of ephemeral and salt lakes, and by deposition from the atmosphere.

The essential condition necessary for a desert environment is that vegetation does not grow or grows with difficulty. This may be due to lack of rainfall, low temperature, infertility of soil, and continued covering of a surface by sediments. The desert environment due to lack of sufficient rainfall is the most important at the present time, but before the advent of land-plant life large areas of low rainfall must have received many sediments having the characteristics developed in the desert environment. It is not certain that these have ever been identified. The existing large deserts are on the leeward sides of mountains, in the trade-wind belts, and on warm lands leeward to cold waters. Low temperature at the present time is not an important factor in creating desert environment, but during the Pleistocene, regions marginal to the retreating ice sheet may have been of desert character, and they certainly received deposits which appear to be of wind deposition, the loess anterior to the front and perhaps dunes nearer the ice. Infertility of soil and repeated covering of a surface with sediments give rise to small desert areas in other environments. Cold climate and infertility of soil deserts are not considered in this connection.

A typical mountain desert basin—and most deserts to some degree will exhibit the same characteristics—has three distinct parts:[4] the rock moun-

[1] Walther, J., Das Gesetz der Wüstenbildung, 4th ed., 1924. This should be read by every one interested in desert geology.

[2] Murray, J., Origin and character of the Sahara, Science, Vol. 16, 1890, p. 106.

[3] Cana, F. B., The Sahara in 1915, Geog. Jour., vol. 46, 1915, pp. 333–357.

[4] Tolman, C. F., Erosion and deposition in the southern Arizona 'bolson' region, Jour. Geol., vol. 17, 1909, pp. 136–163.

tain slope on parts of which there may be considerable moisture and therefore vegetation, the graded piedmont slope and pediment[5] more or less covered with débris from higher lands, and the central lake, playa, or dry lake bed. The mountain slopes are covered with loose boulders ranging to 5 or 6 or more feet in diameter; on the pediment the range is to about 6 inches in diameter.[5] The mountain slopes are sites of active erosion. Such is also the case upon the mountainward portions of the pediments. The graded piedmont slopes and the central basin are sites of deposition, and the depositional area may be extended by filling of the basin and upward advance of the deposits upon the pediment, each advancing mountainward. However, the central basin may not entirely be given over to deposition, as deflation may be active and removal thus keep pace with, or even exceed, deposition. Such may also be the case on the higher areas of the desert where the only deposits may be in the temporary streams.

CHARACTERISTICS OF THE DESERT ENVIRONMENT. The most important characteristics of the desert environment are the scarcity of vegetation and special adaptations in the vegetation that is present, physiography, nature of the rainfall, salt and ephemeral lakes, occasional wholesale destruction of animals, methods of rock destruction, methods of transportation and deposition, and character and association of deposits.

Desert Vegetation. The vegetation of the desert is especially adapted to the conditions. Four types may be distinguished. One is perennial, with long tap roots, the length of the roots being altogether out of proportion to the heights of the plants above ground. Such flourish over those desert areas where ground water is not too far from the surface to be reached by roots. A second type has structures for storing the water which falls during rainy seasons, and these also have structures which minimize transpiration. The third type is found in semi-arid rather than arid regions, the plants being either annuals or biennials. The annuals spring up rapidly during the rainy season, develop quickly, seed, and die. The biennials start growth during the cool weather of autumn and seed during the moist weather of spring. The roots of this third group are characteristically close to the surface and wide spreading. The same type of root develops in swamps. A fourth type is adapted to a small use of water and has leaves minimizing transpiration: These plants are perennials and are represented by the sage, creosote bush (*Larrea mexicana*), grease wood (*Sarcobatus*, *Atriplex*, or *Grayia*), etc. A characteristic of most desert perennials is the possession of spines, and such are also borne by many annuals.

[5] Bryan, K., Erosion and sedimentation in the Papago country, Arizona, Bull. 730-B, U. S. Geol. Surv., 1922, pp. 52–66; McGee, W. J., Sheet-flood erosion, Bull. Geol. Soc. Am., vol. 8, 1897, pp. 92, 110; Lawson, A. C., The epigene profiles of the desert, Univ. California Publ., Geol. Bull., vol. 9, 1915, p. 34.

Desert Physiography. Desert physiography is somewhat different from that of more humid regions. It is due either to destruction or construction. In the region of destruction sand may be so abundantly carried by the shifting air currents as to seek out every weak spot in the exposed rocks. Hollows may be developed in loose or easily eroded materials. In the desert of Gobi these hollows "range from about 300 yards to 30 miles or more in length and from 50 to 400 feet in depth."[6] The depths are limited by ground-water level. Erosion cavities in rock walls range from shallow excavations to deep caves, and the wall rocks which bound the cavities are little decayed. As drifting sands stay close to the ground, much erosion may take place about the bases of cliffs, and these become very steep to overhanging. Rocking stones, mesas, buttes, mushroom rocks, caves, and etched surfaces are characteristic features of those portions of a desert where deflation dominates. The central region of construction may be a salt-encrusted mud flat or salt lake with marginal mud-flat and dune areas, or it may be entirely covered with dunes. The surfaces of the mud flats or playas are gently sloping toward the lowest parts; the dune areas have the irregular topography characteristic of such. The higher areas are mostly bare and etched rock surfaces covered with those rock particles not yet moved or too large to be moved by the existing agents of transportation. The final stage of the desert cycle is a flat plain covered to a greater or less extent by rock fragments resulting from wind blasting, insolation, and some chemical action.[7] The lowest areas may be salt or mud flats, and intermediate areas alone may correspond to popular conceptions of deserts.

Desert Rainfall. Although generally without rainfall, deserts occasionally have water falling in torrents and flowing to the low parts more or less in the form of sheets. McGee[8] states that within half an hour after a local rain in the Santa Rita Range of Arizona a sheet of water "thick with mud, slimy with foam loaded with twigs, dead leaflets, and other flotsam" appeared on the lowlands, "advancing at race-horse speed at first, but, slowing rapidly, died out in irregular lobes." The water "was nowhere more than 18 inches deep, and generally only 8 to 12 inches." In half an hour the water had almost disappeared, leaving over the surface a deposit of the débris it had carried. The débris of the higher lands is thus washed into the depressions where it is deposited with structures ranging from extreme

[6] Berkey, C. P., and Morris, F. K., Origin of desert depressions, Abstract, Bull. Geol. Soc. Am., vol. 36, 1925.

[7] Passarge, S., Über Rumpfflächen und Inselberge, Zeits. d. deut. geol. Gesell., vol. 16, Protokol, 1905, pp. 193–215; Davis, W. M., The geographical cycle in an arid climate, Jour. Geol, vol. 13, 1905, p. 393; Free, E. E., Bull. 68, Bur. Soils, U. S. Dept. Agric., 1911, p. 37.

[8] McGee, W. J., Sheet-flood erosion, Bull. Geol. Soc. Am., vol. 8, 1897, pp. 101–10.

irregularity to the finest of laminæ.   Seasonal rains and glaciers of bordering highlands may bring some water into a desert.   The volumes of water falling during some of the torrential rains may change the lower parts of a desert region into a vast shallow lake, Russell stating that the Black Rock Desert of northwestern Nevada has been changed in a few hours from dry burning sands to a lake with an area of 400 to 500 square miles which was not more than a few inches deep.   This lake was impassable because of the softness of the mud of its bottom, but in a few weeks this became so dry that it was broken into polygons by mud cracks and so hard that a horse's hoof hardly made an impression.[9]   Lake Goongarrie of western Australia presents a similar change of appearance.   This lake is one of the so-called "dry lakes" and usually it is a "vast, smooth, bare surface, frequently white owing to a film of salt," but during times of moderate rainfall it becomes a wide sheet of water.[10]

Salt and Ephemeral Lakes of Deserts.   The central depressions of deserts may be the sites of permanent salt lakes or playas, the latter covered only occasionally with water.   In the salt lakes are deposited salts commensurate with those brought from the surrounding regions.   The playas contain salty waters following rains, but during the intervals between rains they are either salt-encrusted or sand-, silt-, or clay-covered surfaces, the silt and clay (generally known as adobe in the southwest) containing crystalline particles of salts whose development crumbles and comminutes the silt and clay, thus rendering these easily susceptible to the attack of deflation.   Mud cracking develops on an extensive scale, many cracks extending downward for several feet and being several inches wide at the top.

Destruction of Animals about Desert Lakes.   Most desert regions are permanently inhabited by some animals, and others wander in during the seasonal development of vegetation.   The indigenous animals are adapted to the dry condition and are little affected by the moisture conditions. With the decrease and final disappearance of the vegetation the migrant animals may not leave the region but may congregate about the water holes and ephemeral lakes, where they leave their tracks in the mud and ultimately die in large numbers.   The flesh of herbivores is eaten and their bones gnawed by carnivores and carrion feeders, and many of the eaters ultimately add their bones to those already about the holes.   These bones

[9] Russell, I. C., Present and extinct lakes of Nevada, Physiography of the United States, Mon. 4, 1895, pp. 105–110.

[10] Jutson, J. T., The sand ridges, rock floor and other associated features at Goongarrie in sub-arid western Australia, and their relation to the growth of Lake Goongarrie, a "dry lake" or playa, Proc. Roy. Soc. Victoria, vol. 31, n. ser., pt. i, 1918, pp. 113–128; The process of wind erosion in the Salt Lake District, Bull. 61, Geol. Surv. Western Australia, 1914, pp. 142–158.

lie on the surface until the next rain, when they may be buried, but in sediments whose porosity is high or whose mud cracking produces repeated exposure to the action of the atmosphere, there is little chance of permanent preservation.   The great abundance of tracks in the Newark sandstone of the Connecticut Valley perhaps tells a sequence of this character—tracks are extremely abundant, but bones are exceedingly rare.

Methods of Rock Destruction. Bryan[11] states that mechanical methods of rock destruction consist of ruption and spalling, exfoliation, and granular disintegration, changes of temperature being held to be responsible.   Mechanical methods of destruction are generally considered to dominate over the chemical, but Blackwelder[12] has emphasized the importance of chemical decay and minimized the effect of changes of temperature in desert regions, and Bryan states that "loose boulders are marked by concentric bands of color showing solution and deposition."   The rather common presence of desert varnish shows some chemical activity on the surface materials, and it seems obvious that more exists beneath the surface.   Blackwelder's[13] summary of the processes producing rock fragments in deserts states that insolation is not important, stream corrosion is minor, wind abrasion is rarely conspicuous, frost action is locally important, and chemical weathering and diastrophism are very important.   The chemical processes are either neutral or oxidizing except in the desert lakes wherein reducing processes may exist.

Methods of Transportation and Deposition. It has been previously noted that transportation in arid regions is effected by sheet floods, ephemeral streams, and mud flows.   After the materials become dry, all loose materials within the competency of the winds pay tribute to that form of transportation, the sands being swept into dunes and the fine materials lifted from the surface and carried from the desert.   Blackwelder[14] has shown that deflation is of importance in thus removing dust, the Danby playa of southeastern California having thus been lowered 12 to 14 feet, remnants in the form of small mesas and buttes showing the former elevation.   Walther, Richthofen, Udden, Keyes, and others have urged the importance of deflation in lowering the surface of desert regions.[15].   Black-

[11] Bryan, K., op. cit., pp. 39–42.

[12] Blackwelder, E., Exfoliation as a phase of rock weathering, Jour. Geol., vol. 33, 1925, pp. 793–806; Barton, D. C., Notes on the disintegration of granite in Egypt, Ibid., vol. 24, 1916, pp. 382–393.

[13] Blackwelder, E., Desert weathering, Bull. Geol. Soc. Am., Abstract, vol. 38, 1927, pp. 127–128.

[14] Blackwelder, E., The lowering of playas by deflation, Am. Jour. Sci., vol. 21, 1931, pp. 140–144.

[15] For papers by Udden and Keyes see Geologic Literature of North America, Bulls. 740, 741, U. S. Geol. Surv., 1924.

welder's paper gives a factual quantitative basis to former opinions and permits the view that removal of materials may be quite rapid.

Characters and Associations of the Deposits of the Desert Environment. The deposits of the desert environment are more or less etched, varnished, and polished lag gravels over the pediments and other areas not sites of deposition of fine materials; quartz and other sands and pebbles and gravels in the dune areas around and within some of the depressions and in the stream channels crossing the pediments; clays, silts, and evaporation products within the depressions; and coarse piedmont deposits about highland areas within or marginal to the desert. Thus, there may be torrential stream, sheet-flood, and mud-flow deposits about the highland areas; eolian and fluvial deposits in an intermediate belt; and a depression deposit of more or less mud-cracked clays and silts or these with evaporation products. Sands of deserts, as elsewhere, should be mainly quartz, but some may be feldspar, calcite, dolomite, gypsum, etc. The sphericity may be high and many of the particles have mat surfaces. Minerals of low stability are likely to be present to some degree in most sands.[16] It seems likely that the minerals of the clays should be those of the early stages of decomposition and that much of the fine materials should be powdered rock and not composed of clay minerals.

Although much of a pediment may be bare rock surface veneered with lag gravels, the deposits upon it often attain great extent and not only mantle the feet of the highland areas, but extend up the valleys of streams into the highlands so that the mountains appear to rise out of the gravel accumulations. According to Blanford,[17] the gravel slopes in Persia range from 1° to 3°, and the accumulations attain their greatest dimensions over the drier areas. These deposits are fan-shaped, have their surfaces covered with gravel, cobbles, and boulders, and are evidently alluvial fans. The Shinarump conglomerate of the arid southwestern regions seems to be of desert piedmont origin. It "is everywhere lenticular; lenses of conglomerate overlap lenses of coarse and fine sand, and plasters of pebbles many feet in area or long, narrow cobble pavements appear and disappear within the formation in a capricious manner. Cross-bedding is characteristic; short laminae meet each other at large angles, and longer beds form smaller angles with the horizon."[18] The Overton fanglomerate[19] of Nevada is

[16] Reed, R. D., Bull. Am. Assoc. Pet. Geol., vol. 12, 1928, pp. 1023–1024.

[17] Blanford, W. T., On the nature and probable origin of the superficial deposits in the valleys and deserts of central Persia, Quart. Jour. Geol. Soc., vol. 29, 1873, pp. 493–503.

[18] Gregory, H. E., Geology of the Navajo Country, Prof. Paper 93, U. S. Geol. Surv., 1917, p. 39; Longwell, C. R., Geology of the Muddy Mountains of Nevada, Bull. 798, U. S. Geol. Surv., 1928, pp. 52–54.

[19] Fanglomerate. A term proposed by Lawson, A. C., for the materials of alluvial fans. The petrographic designation of alluvial-fan formation, Univ. California Publ., Dept. Geol., vol. 7, 1913, pp. 325–334.

considered to be a deposit of an arid country of high relief and is stated to be like the alluvial fan formations now forming in the same region. The materials are unsorted,

the fragments in each thick layer or lens averaging coarser at the base than at the top, but in all beds pebbles and boulders of various sizes are jumbled together, their long axes trending in all directions. . . . In places many large boulders are banked together, with little finer material between them, but as a rule the matrix of pebbles, sand and cement envelops each boulder. Some boulders of the largest size occur isolated in a matrix of small pebbles and sand. In a large way the bedding planes are regular and parallel, but in detail irregularity is extreme, lenses everywhere interfingering. Thick narrow lenses of sand essentially free from pebbles occur, but they are exceptional in this phase of the formation.[20]

In the region about Goongarrie, western Australia, the sediments of the desert, here not extreme, are gully deposits of coarse detritus which are 2 to 6 feet thick and situated in longitudinal valleys of bordering highlands on the west; piedmont slope deposits lying upon gently sloping plains, composed of coarse detritus 6 to 8 feet thick, and formed by the coalescence of alluvial fans on the sides of the valleys; deposits on gentler slopes composed of a thin veneer over the underlying rock; samphire (salt-loving plants) flat deposits consisting of sands and clays in which locally there is considerable crystalline and powdery gypsum, sand ridges almost entirely restricted to the lake area and consisting of small, low, irregularly shaped ridges 3 to 8 feet high which eastward gradually pass into long, regularly shaped ridges 8 to 30 feet high, and westward into ridges smaller than those in the middle; and the deposits of the lake floor which consist of silt in which some fine sand is present. The silt usually has a dark red color and is commonly impregnated with sodium chloride and contains many crystals of gypsum. It has a determined thickness of 12 feet. The dunes are composed of small, rounded grains which are chiefly quartz and, subordinately, ironstone.[21]

Calcareous concretions may develop in the fine sediments containing considerable calcium carbonate. Not infrequently these are hollow and have cracked or bread-crust exteriors. The colors of the muds and silts range from gray through red and brown to black. The black is due either to carbonaceous matter or iron sulphide. On exposure the sediments with black colors due to iron sulphide become reddish. The silts and fine sands deposited in the lakes and playas may be beautifully ripple marked with symmetrical ripples; current ripples may also be present. These structures may be almost obliterated in the deposits of the playas, however, by reason of the action of salts in the clays and silts by which the mud on drying is

[20] Longwell, C. R., op. cit., 1928, pp. 68–74.
[21] Jutson, J. T., op. cit., 1918, pp. 113–128.

reduced to powder. Mud cracks are likely to be abundant in all sediments which permit their formation; the cracks may be deep and wide. There is likely to be much cross lamination of eolian origin in sand deposits. The central portions of the depressions may have evaporation deposits, and these may also have deposits of iron carbonate and silica. Some of the lakes may be margined by swamps, and small swamps may lie among the dunes. There is thus an intermingling or interlensing of deposits made by water, ranging from those of extremely torrential streams to those of small bodies with weak wave and current action, and those made by wind. The deposits made by water range from very fine to very coarse. Those made by wind are mostly sands. Marginal and leeward to the desert environment should be deposits of loess, and some dust may be deposited with coarse sediments to fill the interstices among them.

The sediments of the desert environment usually may be little oxidized. Some reduction may occur in the lakes and over the salt-encrusted flats. On the whole, neither oxidation nor reduction is particularly obvious. The colors of sediments under the conditions of a rigorous desert environment are light unless the country rock has other colors. Under less rigorous conditions oxidation may occur and the colors change to browns and reds. After deposition there may be introduction of iron, or oxidation of iron compounds, with consequent reddening of the sediments. Such seems to have occurred in the case of the sands of the Arabian desert described by Phillips.[22] This desert, known as the Nefud, has a width of 150 miles and an extreme length of 400 miles. It contains such ridges and depressions as characterize deserts, but the sands are not in motion, and except on the highest summits of the sand hills, the surface is thickly sprinkled with vegetation. The redness of the sands is due to a mere film over the rounded grains, the iron oxide being only 0.21 per cent of the weight. It seems obvious that the iron oxide could not have been present when the sands were in motion. Sands from the Sahara Desert, near the village of Aoulef Cheurfa, about a thousand miles south of the Mediterranean Coast, are a maroon red, but the iron oxide is only a small per cent of the whole. The time of formation of this color is not known.[23]

A summary of the characteristics of the deposits of desert environments is as follows: The stratification ranges from that of the laminated or bedded clays of the lakes and playas through the wedge-shaped cross-laminated units of the wind-deposited sands to the almost unstratified gravels of the

[22] Phillips, J. A., The red sands of the Arabian desert, Quart. Jour. Geol. Soc., vol. 38, 1882, pp. 110–113.

[23] These sands were obtained through the kindness of Mr. Alonzo Pond of the Logan Museum of Beloit College, Wisconsin.

piedmont slopes. The material is mostly light colored when deposited and, except for the evaporation and chemical deposits of the depressions, of mechanical deposition. The finer sediments may contain much calcareous matter and other products of evaporation. The fine sands and silts may be wave and water-current ripple marked, and the fine to coarse sands may have eolian ripple mark, the latter difficult of preservation. Tracks of organisms may occur locally in great abundance; skeletal matter is not common. The thickness of deposits which may accumulate in the desert environment has not been carefully investigated, but it would seem that 1000 feet would be a fair maximum, although conditions are conceivable which might make a greater thickness possible. There is a dovetailing of salt lake, playa, dune, and piedmont deposits and the occasional occurrence of black shales of lake and swamp origin. It needs to be emphasized that the entire set-up of the environment must be present in order to establish that a given sedimentary deposit was made in the desert environment. It seems probable that a deposit similar to any formed in the desert environment may form under other conditions. Thus, deposits of evaporites, wind-blown sands, or ventifacts do not prove a desert. The tendency to assume an ancient desert every time eolian cross-lamination, sand grains of high sphericity with frosted surfaces, ventifacts, or evaporites are found needs discouragement.

DEPOSITS OF PAST DESERT ENVIRONMENTS. The oldest deposits which have been ascribed to deposition in desert environments are the Torridonian sandstones of Scotland and the Eophyton sandstones of Sweden. Ventifacts have been described from each. If these were deposited in desert environments, there are few reasons for believing that the conditions were arid, and the desert areas may have been due more to the absence of a land vegetation than to dryness. It would appear that deposits of the desert environment should be extremely abundant in the geologic column until the time of development of vegetable protection, and if general conceptions of the absence of a vegetable cover over the lands of Pre-Cambrian times approximate correctness, there should be extensive deposits with desert characteristics in the systems of those times.

Desert conditions possibly obtained in the deposition of parts of the Old Red Sandstone of Britain. Grabau and Sherzer have assigned the deposition of the Sylvania sandstone to a desert environment.[24] The particles of this sandstone are clean, well rounded, and well sorted grains of quartz of nearly uniform size. The rock is white and ordinarily very poorly cemented. The stratification and cross-lamination are said to have the characteristics

[24] Grabau, A. W, and Sherzer, W. H., The Sylvania sandstone; its distribution, nature and origin, Michigan Geol. and Biol. Surv., Publ. no. 2, 1909, pp. 61–86.

of those of eolian deposition. Grabau and Sherzer state that these sands are superior in sphericity and uniformity of dimension to the sands of most desert areas, or they "*out-Sahara* the Sahara sands" in rounding, purity, and assorting. If the Sylvania sandstone originated in a desert environment, and the evidence for this seems to be only the cross lamination of the sands and their shapes and surfaces, the conditions must have been extremely rigorous.[24]

The Triassic of England bears the features suggestive of desert origin in the cross-laminated sands of uniform grain, wedge-shaped units, dovetailing of stream-deposited gravels, piedmont deposits marginal to highland areas, thickening and thinning of the deposits, clay lenses of lake deposits with beds of salt and gypsum, etc.[25] The Triassic deposits of eastern United States have been inferred to have originated in the desert environment, but they are best interpreted as the deposits of an environment bordering on aridity. They will be further considered in connection with the piedmont phase of the fluvial environment.

Because of the occurrence of well worn quartz grains in the Chalk of both England and France it has been suggested that the lands surrounding the waters in which the Chalk was deposited were hot deserts of the Sahara type. Although the suggestion may approximate correctness, it is certain that the evidence on which it is founded is possible of other interpretation.[26]

The close of the Pennsylvanian saw the raising in Europe of the Hercynian mountains extending from southern Ireland to central Europe. Northern Europe was separated by these mountains from the seas of the time and became arid during the Permian and parts of the Mesozoic. During the early Permian the deposition of red beds appears to indicate oxidizing conditions at the sources of the sediments and dry conditions over the sites of deposition. During the deposition of the salt deposits rigorously arid conditions probably obtained. The Permian red beds of the western parts of the United States were probably deposited under semi-arid to arid conditions. The Lyons formation of the red beds of Colorado has been interpreted[27] as the deposit of the desert environment, but the films of ferric oxide which cover the quartz grains, if primary, preclude the possibility of rigorously arid conditions.

[25] Lomas, J., Desert conditions and the origin of the British Triassic, Proc. Liverpool Geol. Soc., vol. 10, pt. iii, 1907, pp. 172–197; Geol. Mag., vol. 44, 1907, pp. 511–514, 554–563. Beasley, H. C., Some difficulties with regard to the formation of the upper Keuper marls, Proc. Liverpool Geol. Soc., vol. 10, pt. ii, 1906, pp. 79–97.

[26] Bailey, E. B., The desert shores of the Chalk seas, Geol. Mag., vol. 61, 1924, pp. 102–116.

[27] Tieje, A. J., The Red Beds of the Front Range in Colorado, a study in sedimentation, Jour. Geol., vol. 31, 1923, pp. 198–202.

The deposition of the Jurassic sandstones (La Plata, Wingate, Todilto, Navajo) of southern Utah and parts of adjacent states seems to have taken place in the desert environment.[28]   These sandstones range in thickness from 2000 feet in their southern distribution to 500 feet in southwestern Colorado, and the assumed desert over which the sandstones accumulated is estimated[29] to have had an area nearly equal to the sandy portion of the Libyan desert of northeast Africa.   This desert is thought to have bordered the Jurassic sea on the south.   The sandstones in the White Cliff formation are generally white; the grains are uniform in size, well rounded, have frosted surfaces, and are mostly of clean quartz.   An iron oxide coating is generally wanting.   Some bands of sandstones, 75 or more feet thick, show essentially no bedding.[30]   Other beds are highly cross laminated with both eolian and aqueous types present, the latter indicating the existence of streams and other bodies of water, for whose presence additional evidence is given in the conglomerates and aqueous ripple marks.   Some of the sandstones are red.   Sandstones which may be of desert or semi-desert origin occur in the Comanchean of Kansas, and the white sandstones beneath the Magnesian limestone of England may have developed in an arid environment.   Possibly parts of the St. Peter and Cambrian sandstones of the upper Mississippi Valley may be of eolian deposition, but neither can be held to have developed in typical desert environments.   It is probable that deposits of the desert environment will ultimately be discovered in every geologic system.

The Glacial Environment and Its Sediments[31]

The glacial environment is characterized by low temperature, excess of snowfall over dissipation, abundance of water during the melting season, and erosion and deposition.   At the present time this environment has great extent and its deposits great importance, but during those times of the geologic past when the environment possessed continental proportions its deposits covered areas as extensive as those of most other environments.   At the present time there are over 60,000 square miles in Alaska which are receiving glacial or fluvio-glacial sediments.[32]

The conditions about the margin of a glacier have been so often described

[28] Longwell, op. cit., 1928, pp. 62–68; Gilluly, J., and Reeside, J. B., jr., Sedimentary rocks of the San Rafael Swell and some adjacent areas in Utah, Prof. Paper 150–D, U. S. Geol. Surv., 1928, pp. 70, 72; see also Gregory, H. E., Prof. Paper 93, 1917.

[29] Grabau, A. W., Comprehensive geology, pt. ii, 1921, p. 648.

[30] Cross, W., and Ransome, F. L., Rico Folio, no. 130, U. S. Geol. Surv., 1905, p. 5.

[31] Summaries of North American studies of glacial sediments have been prepared for a number of years by Doctor M. M. Leighton and published in the annual reports of the Committee on Sedimentation.

[32] Tarr, R. S., and Martin, L., Glacial deposits of the continental type in Alaska, Jour. Geol., vol. 21, 1913, pp. 289–300.

that only the barest outline is here given.   At the immediate margin is a
frontal moraine bordered on the stoss side by kame deposits and those made
in small ponds.   On the lee side of a moraine is outwash, beyond which are
valley deposits of streams which form from the melt waters flowing over the
outwash.   As a glacier retreats, the successive moraines constitute dams
between which lakes form, and in these are deposited lake or varve clays.
Beneath a glacier is the ground moraine consisting of drumlins, eskers, and
unorganized drift.   As a glacier retreats, the ground moraine receives deposits of outwash and lake clays, the latter in many instances later becoming
overlain by marl and peat.   The evaporating ice and the outwash plains
supply dust which is carried by wind to areas beyond the ice front and deposited as loess.   These outwash plains may also be the sites of dunes.[33]
Successive advances and retreats of an ice sheet may superimpose a succession of these deposits.

PROCESSES OF THE GLACIAL ENVIRONMENT.   These have already been
considered in detail.   It may be repeated that chemical action is extremely
limited in the glacial environment and in many instances deposits are made
which are supported by ice either in the form of buried blocks or by a glacier
itself and that the melting of this ice leads to slumping and contemporaneous
deformation.   Further, ice floating in the lakes, which are created by the
irregular deposition, may at times drag the bottom, leading to crumpling
and deformation of any sediments already deposited.[34]

CHARACTERISTICS AND ASSOCIATIONS OF THE DEPOSITS OF THE GLACIAL
ENVIRONMENT.   Typically glacier-deposited materials are unstratified, unsorted, and highly variable in kinds and dimensions of material.   The
water-deposited sediments on the stoss side of a moraine range from rapidly
deposited coarse and fine material at those places where streams flowing
from the ice debouch against a moraine or hill, to thin laminated clays in
the various ponds and lakes formed by irregular deposition.   On the leeward
side of a moraine the sediments are better sorted, but range from rapidly
deposited stream sands and larger particles to the finest of lake clays in the
depressions without outlet.   Over these lie the wind-deposited loess and the
peats and marls of the succeeding swamps and lakes.   The sequence may
be several times repeated in greater or less perfection, usually less, due to
the fact that each advance is apt to obliterate the previous deposits.   All of
these materials dovetail in an intimate manner.

The clays and silts of the glacial lakes may be varved.   The lower part
of the varve of each year is usually characterized by coarser grain and lighter
color; the upper part has finer grain and darker color.   The lower part is
also thicker.   This part represents summer deposition.   A varve may con-

[33] Walther, J., Das Gesetz der Wüstenbildung, 4th ed., 1924, pp. 393 ff.
[34] Sayles, R. W., Seasonal deposition in aqueo-glacial sediments, Mem. Mus. Comp.
Zool., vol. 47, no. 1, 1919, pp. 19–20.

sist of clay and silt in various proportions, almost exclusively of silt, or almost exclusively of clay. If the materials are coarse, the summer part will be relatively thick as compared to the winter part. The winter parts remain almost equally thick from year to year, so that variations in thickness of varves are largely due to variations in thickness of the summer parts. Each varve tends to be sharply distinguished from the preceding and succeeding, but in some cases varves are distinguishable with difficulty. Summer parts pass gradually into those of winter. Varved clays are without macroscopic fossils, this probably being due to the low temperatures of the waters in the glacial lakes. If the waters of glacial lakes or other places of melt-water discharge are such as to flocculate the sediments rapidly, varves do not form. Hence, they are not likely to be found in marine waters into which melt waters discharge.[35]

Deposits of the glacial environment ordinarily range from white to gray to gray-blue, but original colors of the rock particles tend to be controlling factors, and thus any color is possible, as exemplified by the red glacial clays of northern Wisconsin and Michigan. The sandy and silty parts of varved clays range from white to gray. As the fineness of the clays increases the colors tend to become darker and range from dark gray and blue-gray to red and black. However, in some instances fine clays are light colored.

The thickness of the deposits of the glacial environment perhaps may reach 1000 to 2000 feet; ordinarily the thickness is of an order of magnitude of a few hundred feet. There is great variation, and locally the deposits may be entirely wanting.

Glacial deposits contain decomposed materials only to the extent that the sources from which they were derived had undergone weathering. The consequence is that there is little leaching of fine-grained sediments.

Proof of the glacial origin of a deposit requires that the entire set-up be present, that is, the unstratified heterogeneous mixtures of coarse and fine particles bordered laterally by and dovetailing into the stratified deposits of kames, lakes, and outwash.

The surface on which glacial deposits rest is locally striated, and some of the larger particles may show striations and have one or more sides flattened or soled.[36] It must not be assumed, however, that striated particles are proof of the glacial environment or that they are particularly common in glacial sediments. Striated rock floors are more common and at the same time are better evidence of the one time existence of the glacial environment.

[35] Antevs, E., Retreat of the last ice sheet in eastern Canada, Mem. 146, Geol. Surv. Canada, 1925. This work contains an excellent bibliography. For work on varved sediments since 1925 the summaries by Antevs in the Reports of the Committee on Sedimentation should be consulted.

[36] Tarr, R. S., and Martin, L., Alaska glacial studies, 1914.

GLACIAL DEPOSITS IN THE GEOLOGIC COLUMN. The most ancient known glacial deposits are those of the Pre-Cambrian. The lower Huronian of the Cobalt region of Canada contains the Gowganda formation which was assigned by Coleman to deposition in the glacial environment.[37] Miller recognized the same possibility.[38] A succinct summary of the facts relating to this conglomerate was given by Collins.[39] It is described as essentially similar to conglomerates which are of known glacial deposition. Striated and soled rock particles are present, and they seem clearly not to be due to deformational processes; boulders of large size occur miles from the nearest source; the underlying surface is striated in places; and the laminated graywackes associated with the conglomerate are like, and hold relations similar to, those existing among the lake clays, outwash clays, and morainal materials in the Pleistocene glacial deposits. The only known environment in which a concurrence of all of these characters obtains is the glacial, and the Cobalt series (of which the Gowganda formation is the basal unit) compared to the Pleistocene glacial and genetically associated deposits has members which are equivalent.[40]

An ancient tillite with striated boulders and a thickness of 150 to 500 feet was found by Willis and Blackwelder in the Yang-tse Canyon of China beneath marine strata of probably Middle Cambrian age,[41] and Pre-Cambrian tillites with striated boulders extend in south Australia over an area of 460 miles from north to south and 250 miles from east to west and with a thickness of 1500 feet.[42] Pre-Cambrian tillites have been described by Blackwelder in the Rocky Mountains region.[43]

[37] Coleman, A. P., Rept. Ontario Bureau Mines, vol. 14, pt. iii, 1905, p. 127; A lower Huronian ice age, Am. Jour. Sci., vol. 23, 1907, pp. 187–192; Glacial periods and their bearing on geological theories, Bull. Geol. Soc. Am., vol. 19, 1908; The lower Huronian ice age, Jour. Geol., vol. 16, 1908, pp. 149–158; The lower Huronian ice age, Compt. Rendu, Internat. Geol. Cong., 1912, pp. 1069–1072; Ice ages, recent and ancient, 1926, pp. 220–240. This book should be consulted for data relating to deposits of the glacial environment.

[38] Miller, W. G., Rept. Ontario Bureau Mines, vol. 14, pt. ii, 1905, p. 41.

[39] Collins, W. H., Onaping map-area, Mem. 95, Geol. Ser. no. 77, Geol. Surv. Canada, 1917, pp. 82–84.

[40] Wilson, M. E., Kewagama Lake map-area, Quebec, Mem. 39, Geol. Ser. no. 55, Geol. Surv. Canada, 1913, pp. 88–98.

[41] Willis, B., and Blackwelder, E., Research in China, Publ. 54, pt. i, Carnegie Inst. of Washington, 1907, pp. 264–269; Schuchert, C., Climates of geologic time, Publ. 192, Carnegie Inst. of Washington, 1916, pp. 293–295.

[42] David, T. W. E., Rept. Ninth Meeting, Australasian Assoc. Adv. Sci., 1903, pp. 199–200; Glaciation in Lower Cambrian, possibly in pre-Cambrian time, Compt. Rend., Internat. Geol. Cong., Mexico, 1906, pp. 271–275, 275–298. Howchin, W., Rept. South Australian Glacial Investigation Committee, Rept. Ninth Meeting Australasian Assoc. Adv. Sci., vol. 30, 1906, pp. 227–262 (228–234); Glacial beds of Cambrian age in South Australia, Quart. Jour. Geol. Soc. London, vol. 64, 1908, pp. 234–263; Australian glaciations, Jour. Geol., vol. 20, 1912, pp. 193–227.

[43] Blackwelder, E., Bull. Geol. Soc. Am., vol. 37, 1926, pp. 627–631.

With the exception of the Pleistocene glacial deposits, those of the geologic past best known are of Permian age. These have been observed in South Africa,[44] Australia,[45] India,[46] South America,[47] and North America.[48]

In South Africa the glacial deposits constitute the Dwyka conglomerate with a thickness up to 1000 feet and great areal extent. The Dwyka ice sheet appears to have had an east-west extent of 600 miles and to have advanced poleward about 500 miles from an apparent source on the southern border of the Tropics. The associated deposits are of continental origin. In Australia Permian glacial formations are interstratified with marine beds. The Permian glacial deposits of India form the Talchir tillite. Associated sediments are non-marine.

Extensive glacial deposits of Cretaceous age have recently been described from central Australia. The area covers about 40,000 square miles. Rocks foreign to the region are present in the Winton series of Cretaceous age, and the supposed tillite is overlain by plant-bearing Tertiary strata. The rock particles range from a few inches to 5 feet in diameter. Most are rounded; a few are angular; water distribution is said not to be possible.[49] Eocene tillites have been described from Colorado[50] and from British Columbia.[51]

Sediments referred to a glacial origin have been described from other portions of the geologic column,[52] and it is not improbable that they may have local occurrence in the rocks of every system.

[44] Davis, W. M., Observations in South Africa, Bull. Geol. Soc. Am., vol. 17, 1906, pp. 401–415; Schwarz, E. H. L., The three Paleozoic ice ages of South Africa, Jour. Geol., vol. 14, 1906, pp. 683–691.

[45] David, T. W. E., op. cit.; Howchin, W., op. cit.

[46] Koken, E., Indisches Perm und die Permische Eiszeit, Neues Jahrb. f. Min., Festband, 1907, pp. 446–546.

[47] White, D., Permo-Carboniferous climatic changes in South America, Jour. Geol., vol. 15, 1907, pp. 615–633; Woodworth, J. B., Geological Expedition to Brazil and Chili, 1908–09, Bull. Mus. Comp. Zool., vol. 56, 1912, pp. 46–82.

[48] Sayles, R. W., and La Forge, L., The glacial origin of the Roxbury conglomerate, Science, vol. 32, 1910, pp. 723–724.

[49] Woolnough, W. G., and David, T. W. E., Cretaceous glaciation in Central Australia, Quart. Jour. Geol. Soc., vol. 82, 1926, pp. 332–350.

[50] Atwood, W. W., and Atwood, W. R., Gunnison tillite of Eocene age, Jour. Geol., vol. 34, 1926, pp. 612–622; Atwood, W. W., Eocene glacial deposits in southwestern Colorado, Prof. Paper, 95–B, U. S. Geol. Surv., 1915.

[51] Drysdale, C. W., Mem. 56, Geol. Surv. Canada, 1911, pp. 65, 95.

[52] Schuchert, C., Climates of geologic time, Publ. 192, Carnegie Inst. of Washington, 1916, pp. 263–298; Keith, A., Cambrian succession of northwestern Vermont, Am. Jour. Sci., vol. 5, 1923, pp. 118–122, 134–135; Kirk, E., Paleozoic glaciation in southeastern Alaska, Ibid., vol. 46, 1918, pp. 511–515; Shepard, F. P., Possible Silurian tillite in southeastern British Columbia, Jour. Geol., vol. 30, 1922, pp. 77–81 (glacial origin abandoned, Ibid., vol. 34, 1927). For complete consideration of the occurrence in the geologic column of deposits of the glacial environment, Coleman's "Ice Ages," 1926, should be consulted.

Fluvial environments are those in which flowing water is the most important agent of deposition. The environment is possible of division into three phases: the piedmont, the valley-flat, and a part of some deltas. The last is considered in connection with the delta environment. The valley-flat environment consists of the channel and the flood plain, the former shifting through the latter. Under conditions of extensive aggradation, such as those in Tertiary times over extensive areas east of the Rocky Mountains and at present in some of the more or less arid basins of western United States, valleys may disappear, and a part of the area of a stream's course may assume the aspect of a huge fan. This also is included in the valley-flat environment although it has many of the characters of the piedmont. There is no sharp division between the piedmont and the valley-flat, one passing gradually into the other. The processes on the subaerial parts of a delta are fluvial, but there is the occasional entrance of marine or lacustrine agents. Here again, there is no sharp separation.

The Environment and Sediments of the Piedmont

The piedmont environment is about the bases of highlands[53] and in intermontane valleys where accumulate creep, talus, rain-wash, rock-stream, alluvial fan and cone, and mud-flow deposits, all of these going to form the piedmont. Landslides may also make contributions; usually these are confined to mountain valleys. Great development of deposits of this environment is favored by steep slopes, marked relief, freezing weather in the highlands, and aridity and subsidence about the bases. The areas of deposition may extend for many miles from the highlands.

The surface of a piedmont deposit slopes more or less gently from the highlands. Over the higher areas the slopes may approximate the angles of repose for the materials. With distance from the highlands the slopes flatten, but on a typical piedmont they range from 4° or 5° to 15° or more. Depressions and ridges may occur, the former the channels of streams. On piedmonts in process of dissection the depressions may be wide and deep. On aggrading piedmonts the places of stream flow may be higher than interstream areas (fig. 116).

CHARACTERISTICS AND ASSOCIATIONS OF THE DEPOSITS OF THE PIEDMONT ENVIRONMENT. Adjacent to the bases of highlands the deposits have poor stratification and sorting, the materials having been more or less indis-

---

[53] The term highland is relative, as deposits of piedmont characteristics accumulate about the foot of any steep slope. It is only about the feet of highlands of considerable magnitude that the deposits are large enough to merit separate consideration.

Fig. 116. An Alluvial Fan Showing New and Old Mud-flow Welts
The angle of the fan is 19°. Upper Twin Lakes, Bridgeport Quadrangle, California. Photograph by Eliot Blackwelder.

criminately piled together by torrential streams, sheet floods, mud flows, rock slides, and creep. Some of the blocks are of large dimensions. A cloudburst in the San Gabriel Mountains of southern California carried blocks up to about 17 tons weight for a distance of a quarter of a mile.[54] Organic matter is relatively scarce and, as transportation is short, the rock fragments are little rounded. With distance from the highlands the poorly stratified deposits grade into others of more regular stratification. Still farther distant the deposits pass insensibly into those of the valley-flat environment.[55]

Small basins may form on a piedmont surface through the colaescence of two fans along their lower outer margins. Small lakes and swamps may develop in these depressions and form deposits dovetailing with typical deposits of the piedmont environment. Some eolian deposition may also occur upon the fans. The stream deposits are deposited at relatively high inclinations, and they are likely to be considerably cross-laminated, with inclinations in the same general direction. Mud cracks may develop in suitable sediments. Highlands with glaciers contribute a volume of gravels to the fans and cones which is much greater than where such are not present; the deposits may then have some characteristics of those formed fluvio-glacially.

The colors of piedmont deposits vary somewhat with the climate, but the colors of the composing rocks exert a large influence. Most of the sediments are gray or yellow, but there may be red and brown colors. Local accumulation of sufficient organic matter may give dark colors.

The rocks which result from deposition in this environment are conglomerates, sandstones, arkoses, graywackes, and shales. The aggregate is best designated as a fanglomerate.[56] There are no original limestones, ferruginous deposits, salt, or gypsum, and little carbonaceous material. However, some of the deposits may be entirely composed of limestone, flint, etc., depending upon the character of the rocks from which the sediments come.

The thickness of deposits which accumulate in the piedmont environment may be very great. With stationary crust one or two thousand feet appears possible, but as many piedmont accumulations seem to be in regions subject to periodic downfaulting or synclinal warping, and the sources of the sedi-

[54] Wolff, J. E., Cloudburst of San Gabriel Peak, Los Angeles County, California, Bull. Geol. Soc. Am., vol. 38, 1927, pp. 443–450.

[55] An historical summary and bibliography of studies relating to fluvial deposits is that of Professor A. C. Trowbridge, Rept. Comm. on Sedimentation, 1928–29, 1930, Nat. Research Council.

[56] Lawson, A. C., The petrographic designation of alluvial-fan formations, Bull. 7, Univ. California Publ., Dept. Geol., 1913, pp. 325–334.

ments appear to be in regions of uplift, it is possible for many thousands of feet to accumulate.

Piedmont deposits usually do not contain much organic matter because of the torrential nature of deposition and the high porosity of the composing materials. However, floods due to cloudbursts may overwhelm the entire surface of a piedmont and produce great destruction of such life as is present. A large quantity of organic matter may thus be entombed and preserved.

In general, deposits of the piedmont environment are rudely stratified or without stratification; stratified beds have high initial inclinations and are considerably cross-laminated; fine sediments may be mud cracked; channeling is locally common; occasional beds of shale are present; particles should range from very small to blocks of large dimension; fossils should be generally absent; and colors tend to be largely determined by the character of the composing rocks. There is a dovetailing of gravels, sands, silts, and clays, or the indurated equivalents.

The following criteria suggested by ,Trowbridge and amended after him may serve to distinguish piedmont deposits from those of other environments:[57]

1. The range in dimension of particles is from very small to boulders 30 feet in diameter. Particles are more or less slightly shaped by water.

2. The coarse material has wide but irregular distribution.

3. The materials tend to be homogeneous lithologically because of local derivation.

4. The deposits are not well stratified or sorted and grade in one direction into essentially unstratified deposits and in the other into the better stratified deposits of the valley-flat environment. Stratified, partly stratified, and thoroughly unsorted materials are present in more or less equal proportions.

5. Stratification planes have inclinations up to 16° to 18° and have fan-like arrangement.

6. The stratification is of the lens and pocket type and never in uniform continuous layers. Stratified units extend but short distances.

7. Fossils are not common. Those present are of types related to the environment.

8. Particles may have experienced some decomposition but they are largely the result of some form of rock breaking.

9. Colors tend to be yellow and gray, colors of the composing rocks being the determining factors.

10. Materials become finer with distances from the uplands.

THE PIEDMONT CYCLE. The piedmont cycle is as follows: The sediments begin to accumulate near the base of the upland where the change to a more gentle slope decreases competency and capacity to the extent that deposition results. Subsequent deposition takes place upon and inward and outward from the initial deposits, the sediments thus rising on the upland slopes and

[57] Trowbridge, A. C., The terrestrial deposits of Owens Valley, California, Jour. Geol., vol. 19, 1911, pp. 706–747.

extending outward over the bordering plains or lowlands. In course of time deposition over a piedmont comes to an end and is succeeded by erosion. The deposits are then removed in somewhat reverse order to their development, that is, the deposit is lowered and its margins retreat toward the place or places of initial deposition.

EXISTING DEPOSITS OF THE PIEDMONT ENVIRONMENT. The present extent of piedmont deposits is very great on the flanks of the great highland regions of the world, particularly those bordering great arid regions. According to Barrell,[58] the extent of these deposits in western United States, Argentina, and Italy may be considered roughly equal in area to those portions of the lofty mountains from which they come, but some deposits belonging to the valley-flat environment may be included in this estimate. The piedmont or bajada[59] deposits along the east foot of the Sierra Nevada are fairly typical. The streams enter the fans on the apices and may or may not follow the axes. The stream depressions range to about 40 feet deep and less than 100 feet wide; average maximum depths are 20 to 25 feet. The composing sediments consist of material derived from the granitic rocks of the Sierras and are products of immature weathering. The components are pieces of rocks rather than individual minerals. The dimensions of particles range from very small to large, one 10 by 20 by 30 feet above ground with an unknown extent beneath the ground being known. This boulder is at least $1\frac{1}{2}$ miles from its source and probably reached its present position as a part of a mud flow. The deposits are stratified into a series of radiating lenses of which no one has great extent; sorting is extremely poor and lenses of coarse material lie laterally and vertically with others of fine material.[60]

Piedmont deposits of the Cucamonga district of California are more than a thousand feet thick and still growing, the materials consisting of boulders, cobbles, gravels, sand, and silts, all poorly sorted and indistinctly bedded.[61] Sizes of particles decrease rapidly away from the apices of the fans. The process of the building of a fan was illustrated by a flood on February 16, 1927. The flood waters flowed in shallow channels cut below the general surface. As these waters spread, a part of their load was dropped, thus lessening the grade above and steepening it below. This increased the deposition of sediments with the result that a low dam was built across the channel. This dam divided or diverted the waters, and the process was

[58] Barrell, J., Relative geologic importance of continental, littoral, and marine sedimentation, Jour. Geol., vol. 14, 1906, p. 332.

[59] Tolman, C. F., Erosion and deposition in the southern Arizona bolson region, Jour. Geol., vol. 17, 1909, p. 141.

[60] Trowbridge, A. C., op. cit.

[61] Eckers, R., Alluvial fans of the Cucamonga district, southern California, Jour. Geol., vol. 36, 1928, pp. 224–247.

repeated at some other place in the current.- Orange groves cover parts of the upper or mountain portions of the fans of the Cucamonga district and thousands of tons of boulders have been removed in order to concentrate sufficient fine materials for cultivation. In some places the boulders are so numerous as to make cultivation essentially impossible.

Parts of the Sespe formation (Tertiary) of California have been interpreted as of alluvial fan origin.[62] The Overton (Tertiary) fanglomerate of Nevada varies in thickness from 20 to more than 3,000 feet.

Average and maximum sizes of fragments range between wide limits. . . . Heavy beds are made of fragments 4 to 24 inches in diameter, small pieces occurring only in the interstices. Boulders 3 feet through are common, and one remarkable layer has numerous masses of Kaibab limestone 10 to 30 feet in greatest dimension. . . . Among the smaller boulders and pebbles sharp angularity is not uncommon, but as a rule the fragments are subangular, and a small percentage of the pebbles are well rounded. : . . Nowhere is there more than the slightest approach to sorting. Evidence of pulsation in deposition is general, the fragments in each thick layer averaging coarser at the base than at the top, but in all beds pebbles and boulders of various sizes are jumbled together, their long axes trending in all directions, though they show a tendency to parallel the bedding. In places many large boulders are banked together, with little finer material between them, but as a rule the matrix of pebbles, sand, and cement envelops each boulder. Some boulders of the largest size occur isolated in a matrix of small pebbles and sand. In a large way bedding planes are regular and parallel, but in detail irregularity is extreme, lenses everywhere interfingering. Thick narrow lenses of sand essentially free from pebbles occur, but they are exceptional in this phase of the formation.[63]

Tertiary piedmont deposits occur in other parts of the Pacific Coast states and about other mountain areas of the west, and much of the Tertiary along the east front of the Rocky Mountains was deposited in this environment. Parts of the Molasse and Flysch of the Alps and the mountainward portion of the Siwalik[64] formation of India originated under piedmont conditions. The Triassic Newark series throughout its distribution from Nova Scotia to North Carolina has piedmont deposits over extensive areas along the margins of the basins of accumulation,[65] and such seem to have development in the various Old Red Sandstone areas of the British Isles.

[62] Kew, W. S. W., Bull. 753, U. S. Geol. Surv., 1924, p. 30; Reinhart, P. W., Origin of the Sespe formation of South Mountain, California, Bull. Am. Assoc. Pet. Geol., vol. 12, 1928, pp. 743–746.

[63] Longwell, C. R., Geology of the Muddy Mountains, Nevada, Bull. 778, U. S. Geol. Surv., 1928, pp. 68–74.

[64] Oldham, R. D., Geology of India, 1893, pp. 315, 356, 465; Pilgrim, G. R., Correlation of the Siwaliks, Rec. Geol. Surv. India, vol. 43, pt. i, 1913, pp. 264–326; Weller, J. M., The Cenozoic of northwest Punjab, Jour. Geol., vol. 36, 1928, pp. 368–369.

[65] Davis, W. M., The Triassic formation of Connecticut, 18th Ann. Rept., pt. ii, U. S. Geol. Surv., 1898, pp. 9–192; Kummel, H. B., The Newark rocks of New Jersey and New York, Jour. Geol., vol. 7, 1899, pp. 23–52; Reynolds, D. D., and Leavitt, D. H., A scree of Triassic age, Am. Jour. Sci., vol. 13, 1927, pp. 167–171.

In older systems piedmont deposits are: parts of the Keweenawan conglomerates of the Lake Superior region, the Doré series of western Ontario,[66]
parts of the Great Smoky and Cochran conglomerates of the Ocoee and Chilhowee groups of the southern Appalachians,[67] some of the Pennsylvanian
sediments of the Appalachians, and considerable parts of the New Glasgow
conglomerate of northern Nova Scotia.[68] It can hardly be doubted that
many systems have the deposits of the piedmont environment in as extensive
development as is the case at the present time.

Environment and Sediments of the Valley-flat

The valley-flat environment is that of the channels and flood plains. The
two are very unlike in conditions and in sediments, but there are such intimate relationships between them that separation is not possible. In this
environment there is considerable stability of stream position as opposed
to the rather general instability over a piedmont. Under conditions of
extensive aggradation, however, a valley may become completely filled
and disappear. Valley-flats are likely to have many lakes and swamps,
features which ordinarily are not present on a piedmont.

The deposits of the valley-flat differ from those of the piedmont in greater
lithologic diversity, lesser range of dimension and more extensive transportation of particles, greater degree of modification of sediments, somewhat
different methods of deposition, different sedimentary structures, much
better sorting and stratification, absence or scarcity of large fragments, and
greater abundance of organic matter.

An environment may be considered valley-flat and not piedmont if the
stream is situated in a valley, possesses a channel of fairly fixed position as
opposed to one that is constantly changing, and has the channel bordered by
a flood plain. As previously noted, however, the distinction does not always
hold. The environment may be considered deltaic if the flat land near the
mouth of a stream developed through building outward by stream deposition
into the body of water into which the stream empties, and which is still
more or less subject to invasions by that body of water. The distinctions
of the valley-flat environment from those of the piedmont and delta are in
position, relations to other deposits, and character and structure of the
deposits.

[66] Collins, W. H., Quirke, T. T., and Thomson, E., Michipicoten iron ranges, Mem. 147,
Geol. Surv. Canada, 1926, pp. 22–23.
[67] Barrell, J., Nature of the Lower Cambrian sediments of the southern Appalachians,
Am. Jour. Sci., vol. 9, 1925, pp. 1–20.
[68] Young, G. A., Guide Book, no. 1, pt. ii, 12th Internat. Geol. Cong., 1913, pp. 229–239.
Coleman assigns the New Glasgow conglomerate to a glacial origin, Late Paleozoic climates,
Am. Jour. Sci., vol. 9, 1925, p. 200.

Deposition upon any part of the valley-flat and in any part of a channel is determined by the rate of supply from a stream's headwaters and by what is occurring downstream from the particular place. The deposition of sediments over a delta will compel deposition upstream. Rise of sea level will submerge mouths of streams, compelling deposition upstream. Any increase in volume of sediments from the regions of supply is likely to increase deposition in stream channels and ultimately over the flood plains. Decrease in supply may replace deposition by erosion. Fall of sea level may do the same thing.

CHARACTERISTICS AND ASSOCIATIONS OF THE DEPOSITS OF THE VALLEY-FLAT ENVIRONMENT. The deposits of the valley-flat environment, as has been said, are formed in the channels and on the flood plains. The latter deposits are made during floods over many parts of the flood plain, in flood-plain lakes and swamps, and under certain climatic conditions there may be dune and other wind deposits such as obtain at the present time over parts of the flood plains of the Platte River of Nebraska, the Arkansas River of Kansas and Oklahoma, and elsewhere.[69] Deposits of the valley-flat environment appear to have their greatest development during the mature and later stages (not extreme old age) of the erosion cycle.

The nature and color of flood-plain deposits depend largely on the sources of the sediments, the climatic and topographic conditions at the sources, the climatic conditions over the flood plain, the duration and distance of transportation, and the extent and depth of water on the flood plain during each year. On flood plains having an abundance of vegetation it makes little difference what were the colors of the sediments at the times they were deposited, as any contained iron oxide is certain to be reduced and the sediments given gray and perhaps dark colors. On dry river plains, like the Great Plain of China, the sediments may be further oxidized, leading to greater intensity of the colors of oxidation. This may occur over parts of the flood plain of any stream, and an oxidized layer, or portion of a layer, may be found in any flood-plain deposit.

Flood-plain sediments are mainly silts and clays, but sands are common and gravels are occasional. Considerable organic matter usually is present. The deposits also contain a considerable content of soluble matter precipitated from solution following the evaporation of water contained in the sediments, or resulting from chemical or organic action. In semi-arid regions calcium carbonate, calcium sulphate, and other salts precipitated from evaporating water may be large in amount. Calcareous deposits due to evaporation, algal growths, etc., may be made in flood-plain lakes in suffi-

[69] Hill, R. T., Sand rivers of Texas and California and some of their accompanying phenomena, Abstract, Bull. Geol. Soc. Am., vol. 34, 1923, p. 95.

cient quantities to form beds of limestone. This is the case in Tertiary strata of South Dakota and elsewhere.[70]

Channel sediments consist of gravels, sands, silts, and clays.[71] They are made during all stages of a stream's history: in the deeps during slack water, when the shallows are being eroded, and on the shallows during flood water; but unless a stream is generally aggrading or migrating laterally, channel deposits are entirely ephemeral. If the conditions permit some degree of permanence to the deposits, an extremely erratic distribution of gravel, sand, silt, and clay results. The gravels show wear commensurate with the transportation and imbricate upstream.[72] All deposits are lenticularly bedded, more or less extensively cross-laminated, usually with a component of inclination downstream but with possibilities of minor cross-lamination in an upstream direction, and contain current ripple marks consistent with the directions and velocities of the currents. Wave ripple marks are rare. Sections through channel deposits show lenticular and cut and fill bedding and are replete with local unconformities of considerable relief.

The channel sediments of a stream migrating over its flood plain are deposited unconformably over an eroded surface cut on flood-plain, channel, lake, and swamp sediments. The channel sediments in turn may become unconformably overlain by others similar to those on which they rest.

The deposits made in the valley-flat environment are mainly the result of mechanical processes. Some are of organic origin, and some may arise from chemical reactions caused by the mingling of waters of different tributaries. There is much flocculation of colloids for the same reason. This seems to be obvious in the Mississippi River system below the mouth of the Missouri, due to the latter's high content of dissolved sulphates.[73]

The dense populations of plants and animals over many flood plains suggest that remains of such should occur in abundance in flood-plain sediments. The rate of accumulation, however, is ordinarily not rapid, and the major portions of the organic remains are destroyed before burial. Only in cases of floods destroying and locally burying organisms beneath thick cover is there much chance of remains being preserved. The chances are much better in flood-plain lakes, in the deposits of which shells and tests of invertebrates, skeletons and impressions of fishes, impressions of leaves, etc., may be excellently preserved.

[70] Wanless, H. R., The stratigraphy of the White River beds of South Dakota, Proc. Am. Philos. Soc., vol. 52, no. 4, 1923, pp. 191, et al.

[71] Lugn, A. L., Sedimentation in the Mississippi River between Davenport, Iowa and Cairo, Illinois, Augustana Library, Publ. no. 11, 1927, pp. 1–104. This paper gives the results of an extensive study of channel sediments.

[72] Johnston, W. A., Imbricated structure in river-gravel, Am. Jour. Sci., vol. 4, 1922, pp. 387–390.

[73] Knight, J. H., Unpublished thesis, University of Wisconsin, 1925.

Each flood season is succeeded by one of low water during which the materials of a flood plain may become thoroughly dry and crack, the extent of the cracking being determined by the character of the sediments and the duration of the drying. Subsequent wetting, either by rains or floods, produces more or less closing of cracks. The next drying leads to a reopening of old cracks or the development of new, and partial or complete obliteration of lamination and bedding may result. Organisms burrowing in the materials of the flood plain assist in this obliteration.

As flood plains contain lakes and swamps and as both change position because of deposition and migrations of streams and their tributaries, there develops a dovetailing of marls and gray and black muds of the lake environment; black muds and peats of the swamp environment; gravels, sands, silts, and clays of the channel environment; and varicolored clays and silts of the flood plain. There is a wide range in variety of sediments in different sections. As streams wander in their flood plains, particularly under conditions of aggradation, local unconformities of considerable relief are developed.

The Tertiary sediments of western Nebraska, North and South Dakota, eastern Montana and Wyoming,[74] and western Kansas excellently illustrate the characteristics of the valley-flat environment. The sediments are clays, silts, sands and sandstones, and gravels and conglomerates. The clays and silts have greenish, pink, maroon, and yellow colors; the colors of the sands and sandstones are yellow, gray, and reddish. All varieties of sediments may contain considerable lime, and this may be so abundant in the sands and gravels as to cement them into a firm rock, as is the case in the Tertiary "Mortar Beds" of Kansas and Nebraska.

THICKNESS OF DEPOSITS IN THE VALLEY-FLAT ENVIRONMENT. Under average conditions the deposits of the valley-flat environment are thin and ephemeral. Most streams alternately aggrade and degrade, and the sediments have but temporary lodgement. It is said that the "construction of about a square mile of new deposits, 60 feet deep, in about two months time, is an almost annual occurrence locally on the Indus."[75] The materials of these deposits have been derived from upstream where parts of previous deposits have been eroded. Most degrading streams have local base levels, and some have narrow flood plains, usually developed either through erosion or erosion followed by deposition. As channels deepen, the flood plains cease to be covered with water at any time and the composing materials there begin to be removed. Streams flowing through semi-arid regions may make deposits of great thickness therein, and a greater thickness may accu-

[74] Darton, N. H., Folios 85, 87, 88, 108, U. S. Geol. Surv.
[75] Hill, A., Erosion and deposition by the Indus, Geol. Mag., vol. 47, 1910, pp. 289–290.

mulate over a valley-flat environment where it passes over or enters a subsiding region. Where all conditions—climatic, physiographic, and diastrophic—are favorable, tremendous thicknesses may be attained, as, for
instance, the present and past deposits of the Indo-Gangetic plain and the
Tertiary of the states east of the Rocky Mountains.

VALLEY-FLAT DEPOSITS OF THE PAST. The Tertiary sediments of the
states east of the Rocky Mountains are largely of stream deposition, and
large parts were certainly deposited in the valley-flat environment.[76] Formerly these were considered to have been deposited in lakes, a view shown
to be incorrect first by Haworth[77] and subsequently by Davis.[78] There is
a great extent of similar deposits in the Rocky Mountain region, of which
large parts, however, developed in the piedmont environment, and on the
coastal plain of Texas the Reynosa formation possibly thus developed.[79]
The Cretaceous formation of Kansas and southern Nebraska generally
known as the Dakota was deposited in considerable part in the valley-flat
environment of streams, some of which are thought to have flowed[80] from
the east. The Morrison formation of Montana, Wyoming, and Colorado,
with its lenticular conglomerates and sandstones and marginal clays and
shales, seems best interpreted as a flood-plain and channel deposit. Associated limy beds may have been made in lakes on the flood plain. The
Todilto (?) formation of Gilluly and Reeside has characters indicating deposition on flood plains and in channels.[81] Channel deposits are present in
the Pennsylvanian strata of Missouri,[82] Kansas, Kentucky, and Illinois, the
channels having been cut in marine and delta sediments. The materials
are mainly sandstones, but there is considerable shale, some conglomerate,
and a little coal. The sandstones have brown, red, and gray colors and are
more or less cross-laminated. Some are firm and massively bedded; others
are thin-bedded and poorly cemented. The particles of the conglomerates
are mainly composed of limestone in Missouri and of vein quartz in Kentucky,
and range up to several inches in diameter. Some are rounded; others are

[76] Ward, F., The geology of a portion of the badlands, Bull. 11, South Dakota Geol. Nat.
Hist. Surv., 1922; Wanless, H. R., op. cit.

[77] Haworth, E., Physical properties of the Tertiary, vol. 2, Kansas Geol. Surv., 1897.

[78] Davis, W. M., Continental deposits of the Rocky Mountain region, Bull. Geol. Soc.
Am., vol. 11, 1900, pp. 590–604.

[79] Trowbridge, A. C., Reynosa formation in lower Rio Grande region, Bull. Geol. Soc.
Am., vol. 37, 1926, pp. 445–462.

[80] Rubey, W. W., and Bass, N. W., The geology of Russell County, Kansas, Bull. 10,
pt. i, Kansas Geol. Surv., 1925, pp. 54–62.

[81] Gilluly, J., and Reeside, J. B., jr., Sedimentary rocks of the San Rafael Swell and
some adjacent areas in eastern Utah, Prof. Paper 150, U. S. Geol. Surv., 1928, pp. 70–72.

[82] Hinds, H., and Greene, F. C., The stratigraphy of the Pennsylvanian series of Missouri, Missouri Bur. Geol. Mines, 1915, pp. 91–106.

angular. The Pleistocene and Recent deposits of the Indo-Gangetic plain consist of gravels, sands, silts, and clays of unknown, but great thickness. At Lucknow a well was drilled in these deposits to a depth of 1336 feet without finding a rock floor or marine deposits.[83] The sediments contain many concretionary masses of lime carbonate, known as kankar,[84] and in some places the carbonate serves as a cement for other sediments. Nodules of pisolitic limonite are not uncommon. To the north of the plain deposits are those of the Siwalik formations consisting of clays, sandstones, and conglomerates with a thickness of 16,000 to 20,000 feet. As previously noted, great parts of these were deposited in the piedmont environment.

The Great Plain of China is underlain by fluvial deposits of unknown, but probably great thickness. These sediments contain an occasional marine layer on the coastal side, they are strongly oxidized, and when consolidated will probably give rise to a series of red beds. Grabau has recently presented the view that the "normal graptolite shales," consisting of thin layers of black mud intercalated between thicker beds of coarser sediments, were deposited on a river plain similar in relief to the Great Plain of China, the beds bearing the graptolites representing occasional inundations of the sea.[85]

It is the view of Kiaer[86] that the Downtonian sandstones of Norway were deposited over flood plains, and their lithological characters and the spotted distribution of the organic remains are in harmony with this interpretation. It seems probable that parts of the Ocoee and Chilhowee series of the southern Appalachians[87] originated in the valley-flat environment, and parts of the Keweenawan of the Lake Superior region had a like origin.

THE PALUDAL (SWAMP) ENVIRONMENT AND ITS SEDIMENTS

Swamps develop in regions of immature topography, on the deltas and flood plains of rivers, along the coasts of lakes and the ocean; and under the climatic conditions of high relative humidity and regular and abundant rainfall they may form on almost any surface. Vegetation usually covers the entire surface of swamps, although some of it may be beneath water. In most swamps the plants are not of large size, but some, as the cypress swamps of southern United States, support large trees. Except in the shallow

[83] Oldham, R. D., Geol. of India, Geol. Surv. India, 1893, p. 432.

[84] Oldham, R. D., op. cit., pp. 436–437; called kunkar by Reed, F. R. C., Geology of the British Empire, pp. 61, 144.

[85] Grabau, A. W., Origin, distribution, and mode of preservation of the graptolites, Mem. Inst. Geol., Nat. Res. Inst. China, no. 7, 1929, pp. 1–52.

[86] Kiaer, J., The Downtonian fauna of Norway, Vidensk. Skrifter, Mat. naturv. Klasse, no. 6, 1924, pp. 1–15.

[87] Barrell, J., Nature and environment of the Lower Cambrian sediments of the southern Appalachians, Am. Jour. Sci., vol. 9, 1925, pp. 1–20.

pools and sluggish stream channels, the sediments undergo little reworking after their first deposition other than that due to organisms.

Distribution and Classification of Swamps

Existing swamps have their greatest development in polar temperate latitudes. Two factors are responsible: one climatic, due to small evaporation in relation to rainfall, the other topographic, due to the immature topography resulting from Pleistocene glaciation. There are extensive swamps in tropical and subtropical latitudes. Examples are those of Florida,[88] Virginia and the Carolinas,[89] the Amazon Valley, Sumatra, Brahmaputra delta, Central America, etc.

In North America swamps abound over the glaciated areas, where both topographic and climatic conditions are favorable, and on the Atlantic-Gulf-Mississippi coastal and delta plain. It has been estimated that the area of swamp land in the United States approximates 100,000 square miles.[90]

Swamps may be classified as follows:

> Marine (paralic) swamps or marshes
> > Grass and reed swamps (salt marshes)
> > Mangrove swamps
> Fresh-water swamps
> > Swamps connected with basins
> > > Lake swamps
> > > River swamps
> > Swamps on flat or gently sloping surfaces, terrestrial bogs.

MARINE SWAMPS OR MARSHES. Marine swamps or marshes represent a mixed continental and marine environment and usually begin their development in a protected part of the shallow-water zone, which may have been produced by the development of an off-shore barrier beach, by spits and bar between two headlands, by emergence of a sea bottom, or by submergence of a land area. In tideless seas, or those in which the tides are small, the development of barrier beaches and bars is not so essential as in the open ocean, and many shallow bays become marine marshes without the intervention of a protecting barrier.

The history of a marine swamp formed behind a barrier has been stated

[88] Harper, R. M., Preliminary report on the peat deposits of Florida, Geol. Surv. Florida, Third Ann. Rept., 1910, pp. 197–366.

[89] Davis, C. A., Preliminary report of peat deposits in North Carolina, Economic Paper 15, North Carolina Geol. Surv., 1908, p. 151.

[90] Shaler, N. S., General account of the fresh-water morasses of the United States with a description of the Dismal Swamp district, 10th Ann. Rept. U. S. Geol. Surv., 1890, pp. 261–339 (264).

to be as follows:[91]   Prior to the building of the barrier the environment is marine (in some cases lacustrine), and the sediments are of that origin. After the building of the barrier, quiet water prevails behind it, and the deposition of sediments continues as before except that they may be finer and may be deposited in brackish and at times fresh water.   When the water becomes sufficiently shallow, eel grass takes possession and develops submerged meadow-like areas.   These shelter numerous animals and filter sediments from the water, and ultimately the bottom is built to above mean tide.   Grass and reed plants adapted to the conditions take possession. These plants have xerophytic structures and are typified by such species as *Spartina glabra* and *S. patens*.   The former grows nearer the water, attains a maximum height of 6 feet, and has thick underground stems with long, much branching roots.   *S. patens* is a more grass-like plant.

The different plants capture sediments brought into the swamps from the land and from the sea, storm waves bringing in gravel, shells, sands, and muds.   Gravel is not common; the others are, and the shells usually are small.   If dunes are in the vicinity, considerable wind-deposited material may be carried into the swamps.   The quantity of inorganic matter brought to a swamp during this portion of its history is large and ordinarily exceeds that of organic origin.[92]

Tidal waters (if tides are present) flow inward and outward through marine swamps in tortuous channels.   As the outward flow generally is rapid and the materials of a swamp are easily eroded, considerable quantities of vegetable matter may be carried to deeper waters.   Such sediments in the eastern Baltic near Hapsal are carried 6 to 8 miles from the swamp.   Ultimately, however, the accumulations of materials build the swamp above salt-water level; fresh waters invade the accumulations; and fresh-water plants take possession.   Since the accumulations may settle, there is a possibility of a return of salt water conditions.

A history as outlined could obtain only in a region of stationary strandline.   If slow submergence occurred, any phase of the building might be long continued; if emergence, any stage would be much abbreviated.   Rapid, but intermittent submergence might repeatedly bring the swamp below the eel-grass level, and thus marine and swamp sediments might be many times repeated.

In the marshes of the east Baltic reed-like plants grow to the seaward edge of the swamps on surfaces consisting of soft mud.   They reach a maximum height of 7 to 8 feet.   On the land margin the plants are more grass-like,

[91] Davis, C. A., Salt marsh formation near Boston and its geological significance, Econ. Geol., vol. 5, 1910, pp. 623–639.
[92] Davis, C. A., op. cit., p. 631.

and the ground is firm.   Shallow pools of brownish colored water occur locally, and the muds are highly impregnated with hydrogen sulphide.

The salt marshes of Norfolk, England, have

the lowest and always submerged parts of the inlets . . . either practically bare or show a luxuriant growth of marine algæ, especially *Fucus*.   At the next higher level different plant assemblages are found which are not necessarily constant along the same level. Frequently the first stage above the Fucus zone is typified by species of *Salicornia* (Marsh Samphire or Glasswort) and of *Suæda maritima* (Seablite).   In some places, notably on soft mud and at a somewhat lower level, *Zostera marina* and *Z. nana* (Grasswrack or Wigeon-grass) are met with, and are often associated with various algæ.   All these lower marshes are covered by every high tide.   There is a transition to higher levels, and *Salicornia* gradually gives place to other plants such as *Glyceria maritima* (Salt-marsh Grass) and *Trilochin* sp. (Sea-arrow Grass), or *Aster tripolium* (Sea-aster).   These are succeeded upward by *Limonium* spp. (Sea-lavender), *Plantago maritima* and *P. coronopus* (Sea-plantains), *Spartina* spp. (Rice-grass, etc.), *Spergularia media* (Sea-spurry), and *Armeria maritima* (Sea-thrift), though the associations are not always distinct.   It cannot be emphasized too strongly that a *gradual transition* is apparent between all these various phases.   The highest levels are characterized by *Juncus maritimus* (Sea-rush), *Agropyron junceum* (Jointed couch-grass), and *Artemesia maritima*, but here again the association is mixed.   One other plant, *Atriplex (Obione) portulacoides*, is particularly characteristic of the Norfolk marshes.   It occurs at various levels, from the *Salicornia* horizon upwards, and often spreads over large areas, becoming dominant in those places.   Perhaps, the most striking thing about it is its tendency to grow along the banks of creeks, which it overhangs.   As it is a thick shrubby plant, it traps a great deal of material and may raise the levels of the creek banks above the levels of the marshes as a whole.[93]

Certain plants, as *Suæda fructicosa*, are important in fixing shingle bars, and others, as *Agropyron junceum*, *Elymus arenarius*, *Arenaria peploides*, and *Ammophila arenaria* play a like function in holding dune sands bordering the marshes.   In the above discussion it has been more or less assumed that bars are present, but these are not essential.   On the Gulf of St. Lawrence in the broad bay between Eskimo Point and the mouth of Mingan River a salt marsh borders the sea for several miles and probably gradually passes into a fresh-water marsh inland.   On Hudson Bay over long stretches between Port Churchill and Chesterfield Inlet there are areas up to 8 miles wide which are laid bare at low tide,[94] the tidal range averaging around 12 feet. Were it only a couple of feet and the climate congenial, these flats would be covered with a dense growth of salt-marsh vegetation on the outer or seaward margin and an equally dense growth of fresh-water marsh vegetation on the landward margin.   Also, during times of extremely low lying lands

[93] Steers, J. A., and Thomas, H. D., Vegetation and sedimentation as illustrated in the region of the Norfolk salt marshes, Proc. Geologists' Assoc., vol. 40, 1930, pp. 341–352.
[94] Lund, R. J., Personal communication.

such as existed over the American interior during some parts of the Paleozoic, there seem to be no good reasons why marshes of tens and even hundreds of miles width may not have bordered some of the epicontinental seas. Certain conditions of depth of water, range of tides, and slope of bottom would form such extensive swamps, in which, it is suggested, were formed some of the black shale formations found in the Paleozoic sections of the American interior.

Thickness of Marine Swamp Deposits.   Eel grass and most marsh plants do not begin to grow more than 10 to 12 feet below low-water level, and the deposits may not rise more than a few feet above high-tide level, so that the total thickness with stationary water level cannot be very great—the tidal range plus perhaps 20 feet as a maximum.   Under conditions of submergence so slow that water level keeps pace with accumulation of organic and other débris, any reasonable thickness of deposits is possible.   Such nicely balanced ratio between rise of water level and accumulation of sediment must have been not uncommon, and there must be several deposits in the geologic section which are indicative of the marine swamp environment. Such are some of the coals, and it is the writer's view that some of the dark shales poor in marine fossils formed under conditions allied to marine marshes.   Some of these are measured in tens and even in hundreds of feet.

Deposits of Marine Swamps.   Before the eel-grass stage the sediments of the bottom are gravels, shells, sands, muds, and organic matter of the average shallow-water environment.   When the eel-grass stage is reached, the remains of these plants mingle with the sediments, and the latter may accumulate more rapidly than before due to the straining action of the vegetation.   Under some conditions the sediments may be largely calcareous, and perhaps it was in this environment that developed some of the limestones and dolomites containing supposed seaweeds.[95]   Grabau has suggested that the "Bird's Eye" limestone of New York is of this origin.[96] At this stage the sediments are largely inorganic, ordinarily are well stratified, and contain marine shells.   When *Spartina glabra* makes its appearance, the organic matter forms a greater part of the sediments, and in the *S. patens* stage it may compose the major portion.   In both *Spartina* stages the formation of hydrogen sulphide may be large, and it is probable that sulphates are reduced and sulphuric acid formed.   Iron sulphide should develop at this time.   Calcium carbonate should be rare because of the high solvent ability of the waters due to abundance of carbon dioxide and the

[95] Wallace, R. C., Pseudobrecciation in Ordovician limestones in Manitoba, Jour. Geol., vol. 21, 1913, pp. 402–421.
[96] Grabau, A. W., Principles of stratigraphy, 1913, p. 488.

presence of sulphuric acid. The quantity of toxic products may, indeed, be so large as to make the waters unfit for animal life.[97]

The sequence of deposits of a swamp whose history is as outlined should be "sand, silt or mud at the bottom, up to about 12 feet below low water mark; between these two levels the easily recognizable remains of the eel grass mixed with the silt and the shells of mollusks and other marine organisms." Above this "should be found another layer of silty mud, up to the level above which the salt water grasses grow," where the "remains of these plants should be found in constantly increasing numbers, until they form the bulk."[98] In case of submergence or emergence there would be departures from this sequence.

Mangrove swamps are confined to warm regions, where they extend the mainland seaward and initiate the formation of islands. They build new land as follows:[99]

Behind the keys, in the regions of slack water, deposition of sediment is taking place, forming banks of calcareous ooze. After these shoals have been built to within a foot of water level (at low tide), young mangroves begin to catch and grow. . . . The plants become still more numerous, further increase in size, and ultimately form a mat of interlocking roots and branches resulting in keys. When the plants become thick they catch and retain sediment and ocean drift. . . . After a time, whether it be a newly formed key or the margin of a land area, the mangroves . . . form land, and thus cut off their roots from the necessary supply of sea water, causing their own death. The land surface then acquires another vegetation. But the marginal fringe of mangroves persists to protect the young island from the erosive action of the ocean waves, and young mangroves spread seaward to add new land to that already formed.

FRESH-WATER SWAMPS. Fresh-water swamps develop on flat and gently sloping areas and in connection with basins. The former require climatic conditions which keep the surface generally moist. The basins usually contain water, but they may be dry for parts of each year. Fresh-water swamps are also sequential to marine swamps and there probably attain their greatest extent.

Some flat-area swamps have large trees, and others are covered with low bushes. The alder is representative of the latter; the black spruce, tamarack and cypress are examples of the former. Most of these plants have widely spreading roots which are just beneath the surface.

The development of peat in swamps checks the drainage of an already poorly drained surface and also hinders evaporation. The level of the

[97] MacDonald, D. F., Some factors of Central American geology that may have a bearing on the origin of petroleum, Bull. Am. Assoc. Pet. Geol., vol. 4, 1920, pp. 263–268.
[98] Davis, C. A., op. cit., pp. 626–627.
[99] Vaughan, T. W., The geologic work of mangroves in southern Florida, Smithsonian Misc. Coll., no. 1877, vol. 52, 1909, pp. 461–466.

water rises, and the swamp expands laterally. This lateral expansion may result in the entire surface becoming swampy. Ultimately a "high moor" results, with the water surface of low domal shape. After a prolonged rainy period, this condition of instability may result in a "bog burst" and parts of the adjacent regions may become deluged with foul-smelling black mud. A bog burst inland from the town of Stanley on the Shetland Islands produced a stream of black mud over 100 yards wide and 4 to 5 feet deep which flowed through the town into the harbor, blocking the streets, wrecking one or two houses, completely surrounding others, and smothering a child and perhaps an old man.[100]

Extensive swamps not uncommonly have pools of water over the central portions which are so toxic that life cannot exist in them. Streams flowing into swamps may have the swamp vegetation "climbing" the stream channel to its source. Swamps on deltas and flood plains usually have considerable inorganic matter incorporated with the organic, and this may constitute the major portion of the deposits. In swamps not connected with streams the inorganic matter is limited to that derived from plants, carried in solution or in the colloidal state into the swamp waters, and that contributed by the atmosphere.

Most swamp accumulations of the present time exist under physiographic conditions which preclude preservation, as no possibility of burial exists. Such is the case for the vast accumulations of organic matter in many swamps over the Laurentian shield. It is very probable that accumulations under similar conditions obtained on some parts of the earth's surface during every period of earth history since the appearance of land vegetation. Extensive plains undergoing slow submergence, and large delta plains being built into shallow seas with rising sea level, present the conditions making possible the burial of organic accumulations. Tremendous thicknesses then become possible.

Hydrogen sulphide commonly is not apparent in fresh-water swamps. This is thought to be due to the scarcity of sulphates in solution in the fresh waters.

Swamps Connected with Basins. Basin swamps exist about the margins of small or shallow lakes having little wave activity, and marginal to protected bays of larger lakes. The lakes may be of any origin. The swamp accumulations may fill the bays and lakes so as to bring them to extinction.

Such plants as *Chara* grow in relatively deep water, and other plants in zonal arrangement fill up the entire space to dry ground. Each zone is characterized by some dominant group of plants whose arrangement in northern United States from deepest water shoreward is as follows:

[100] Barkley, A., Abstract, in Proc. Geol. Soc. London, 1887, p. 9.

(1) the pond weeds, Potamogeton; (2) the white and yellow pond lilies, Castalia and Nymphæa; (3) the lake bulrushes, Scirpus; (4) the amphibious sedges, Carex, Eleocharis, etc., especially the turf-forming slender sedge, *Carex filiformis L.*, or species of similar habit.[101]

In other latitudes there may be plants of different relationships, but similar habitat. Thus, on the Texas coastal plain area the arrow leaf is a common shallow-water plant.

The various plants form floating mats which catch sediments and afford support for grasses and other plants, and ultimately a mat may cover an entire lake. At first this mat rises and falls with the lake. It is then a quaking bog. New plants invade the mat, and finally it may support large trees. The result is the complete filling of the basin with a sponge-like mass of semi-decayed organic matter.

The swamp deposits of flood plain and delta basins are likely to differ in several important respects from the characteristics given. These swamps usually receive their waters from flooded streams, and at the same time they receive mud. They usually contain much black mud of which the inorganic constituents may compose the greater portion. Deposits of pure peat are exceptional, particularly in the swamps of rivers with narrow flood plains. The basins on wide flood plains densely covered with vegetation may become filled with good peat if the basins are sufficiently far from the streams for the vegetation to filter the water before the basins are reached. River swamps acquire fish from each flood, and their remains may become buried in the deposits. The swamps may dry out for parts of each year, and the deposits thus become more or less mud cracked and oxidized.

Swamps on Flat or Gently Sloping Surfaces. Swamps of this type are determined by the climatic conditions of high relative humidity, regular and relatively high precipitation, and low evaporation. They are most common in middle latitudes on both sides of the equator.

The plants inhabiting swamps of this class are of varied types and of different kinds in different stages of swamp development. In the latitude of the United States, mosses, ferns, canes, sedges, grasses, rushes, alders, cedars, spruces, tamaracks, etc. are common flat-area swamp plants. In Canada, mosses, ferns, and scouring rushes are important plants in this type of swamp. The tundra is the subpolar expression of the flat-area swamp.

Swamp Deposits

Swamp deposits consist of peat, iron oxides and carbonates, muds, sands, and occasional marls. The peat is usually entirely autochthonic. The iron

---

[101] Davis, C. A., Origin and formation of peat, Bull. 38, U. S. Bur. Mines, 1913, p. 172.

oxides are almost always porous and cavernous, but in some cases they are slag-like and hard and in others loose and earthy. The Fe_2O_3 content ranges from about 20 to 60 per cent. Silica is always present to a maximum of about 15 per cent. The phosphoric acid content is generally high, some deposits containing as much as 10 per cent.[102] The iron carbonate of swamps is usually in small quantity. Bog iron "ores" rarely attain a thickness of more than 3 to 4 feet and generally are without stratification. They are relatively resistant to erosion, and patches not uncommonly occur on the tops of residuals, and beneath flat lands they constitute one type of "hard pan." The shales of swamps may or may not be laminated. They are usually highly carbonaceous, and very commonly in paralic swamps they carry pyrite and marcasite as nodules, thin films, and replacements of shells. Sands are not common in swamps. The marls of swamps usually lie beneath the plant accumulations.

THE LACUSTRINE ENVIRONMENT AND ITS SEDIMENTS

From the point of view of the sediments, lakes may be classified as glacial river, seashore, and lakes formed by crustal movement. Each of these may not materially differ from the others in the general character of its deposits, but the manner of genesis determines relationships to other deposits. Lakes may also be considered from the points of view of freshness or salinity of waters. There are also differences dependent upon climate.

Fresh-water Lakes

Distilled water has its greatest density at 4°C., and this figure may be considered applicable to the waters of non-saline lakes. Cooling of non-saline water, hence, increases density to the maximum at about 4°C., following which the water expands to the freezing point. Deep lakes of temperate regions whose surface waters during some part of each year are chilled to the condition of greatest density have the surface waters sinking to the bottom, thereby displacing warmer waters which are brought to the top to become chilled in turn, thus producing a complete overturn of the lake waters. Further cooling at the top decreases the density until the water changes to ice. The ice protects the waters beneath, and these gradually rise in temperature. The spring melting of the ice finds the bottom waters warmer and lighter than the condition of maximum density, and thus the surface waters sink to the bottom and a second overturn takes place. The two overturns bring to the bottom waters plentifully supplied with oxygen, and this is utilized by bottom organisms and assists in de-

---

[102] Beck, R., The nature of ore deposits, Transl. by Weed, W. H., 1909, p. 99.

composition of organic matter on the bottom or in the bottom waters. In course of time the oxygen is removed and its place taken by carbon dioxide. During the times of overturn the lake waters have approximate density throughout, and circulation of course extends to the bottom. At other times circulation is largely confined to the upper waters.

The waters of tropical lakes do not overturn, with the consequence that the bottom waters remain low in oxygen and high in carbon dioxide. The heavier and colder waters are always on the bottom.

The lakes of polar regions likewise tend to have the heavier waters on the bottom, but these waters are warmer than those of the surface, as the latter are nearer the freezing point. Here, likewise, there is no overturn. It must not be assumed that there are sharp boundaries between the lakes of the different parts of the earth, as a lake may be of tropical character one year and temperate character the next.

Thus, fresh-water lakes fall into three general classes: (1) Tropical, colder waters at the bottom, warmer at the top, no overturn, direct stratification; (2) polar, colder waters at the top, warmer at the bottom, range 0 to 4°C., no overturn, indirect stratification; (3) temperate, warmer waters on top and colder waters on bottom in summer, and colder waters at top and warmer waters at bottom in winter, summer stratification direct, winter stratification indirect, two overturns annually.

The waters of lakes are thus more or less thermally stratified. There is an upper stratum, known as the *epilimnion*, whose temperature is much the same throughout, as it is stirred by convection and wind currents. The epilimnion contains an abundance of oxygen due to its broad contact with the air and to production by plants through release of oxygen from carbon dioxide. At the bottom is a stratum known as the *hypolimnion*, whose waters are relatively stagnant, generally low in oxygen and high in carbon dioxide, generally colder, and have a more uniform temperature and a higher hydrogen ion concentration (low pH) than the epilimnion. The intermediate stratum is known as the *thermocline*, or stratum of rapid decrease of temperature with depth, whose limits are somewhat arbitrarily fixed as those of the region in which decrease of temperature with depth equals or exceeds one degree per meter.[103] The thermocline is fairly sharply defined from the epilimnion, and it grades off into the hypolimnion.

The fact of thermal stratification has important bearings on the sedimentation and biology of lakes. Each stratum of a lake has its individual biological characteristics, with the total environment of that stratum giving

[103] Birge, E. A., and Juday, C., Bull. Bureau Fisheries, vol. 32, 1912, p. 547; Kindle, E. M., The rôle of thermal stratification in lacustrine sedimentation, Trans. Roy. Soc. Canada, vol. 21, 1927, pp. 1–35.

rise to its own peculiar sedimentary products. The epilimnion with its favorable summer temperature, abundance of oxygen, sufficiency of carbon dioxide, and favorable light relations will be the place of the greatest abundance of life. The conditions are those of oxidation. The heavy waters in the hypolimnion and the higher viscosity as a consequence of coldness favor wide distribution and excellent sorting of those fine sediments which remain for a considerable time in the upper waters of a lake. The high carbon dioxide content of the lower waters and the low pH content favor solution of settling and bottom carbonate matter, thus not favoring the formation of lime carbonate deposits in the hypolimnion and essentially limiting these to the epilimnion and the thermocline. The conditions in the hypolimnion favor reduction of inorganic matter.[104]

The hypolimnion of polar lakes is apt to have less organic matter passing through it, and there is generally less growth on the bottom with less use of oxygen; hence, these waters may not have a scarcity of oxygen and an abundance of carbon dioxide.

Transportation of mechanical sediments in fresh-water lakes varies with the type of lake, the size, the circulation, and the character of the water. In the lakes of temperate and warmer regions muddy waters, because of density, may settle beneath the surface to mingle with the cold and heavy waters beneath the thermocline, and the muddy waters may go to the bottom.[104] In Lake Geneva the water from the Rhone River flows as a strong current directly to the deep part of the basin, and the same is true of the Rhine where it flows into the Bodensee (Lake Constance). The mingling of the river and lake waters on the sides of the current of the former lowers the density of the cold waters, and sediments are likely to be precipitated, and structures of the nature of subaqueous dikes may be built. Warm stream waters relatively free from sediments are lighter than those beneath the thermocline and thus mingle with the waters of the epilimnion, and there is a tendency for any sediments in such stream waters to be deposited over wide areas of a lake. However, the lesser density and lesser viscosity somewhat lessen such distribution. Stream waters sinking beneath the thermocline tend to deposit their sediments in the deeper parts of the lake basin, and consequently there is a lessened areal distribution.

Glacial lakes or the lakes receiving the cold melt waters of glaciers differ

[104] Heim, A., Der Schlammabsatz am Grunde des Vierwaldstättersees, Vierteljahrschrift d. Naturf. Gesell. in Zurich, vol. 45, 1900, pp. 164–182; Forel, F. A., Handbuch der Seekunde, Bibliothek geogr. Handbücher, 1901, p. 34; Halbfass, W., Grundzüge einer vergleichenden Seekunde, Berlin, 1923, pp. 80–81. The work by Halbfass is a monograph on lakes in which their distribution, origin, morphology, hydraulics, the optical properties of their waters, etc. are considered in detail, but little is said about the life of lakes or their sediments.

in their inflow from lakes receiving their waters from streams, springs, and rains. In the first place, the melt waters may be just about the freezing point and hence on the low-temperature side of the conditions of greatest density, so that as the temperature rises they tend to sink, and thus these lakes may have indirect stratification; and secondly, many glacial lakes may have much of the inflow entering near the bottom, whence it rises toward the top, as shown in figure 117, thus giving to these lakes a circulation differing somewhat from that of those lakes into which the inflow enters in large part near the top. If the melt waters are lighter than the bottom waters and do not contain too great a burden of sediments, the transportation may largely be confined to the upper waters of the lake no matter where the melt waters enter. The high density and viscosity of the cold waters retard settling, and the various currents spread the melt waters; and thus fine

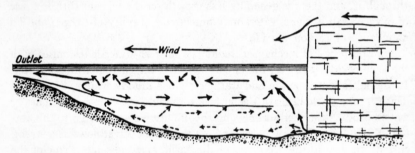

FIG. 117. CIRCULATION OF WATER IN A GLACIAL LAKE

The water is shown entering from beneath the bottom of the glacier and the wind blowing from the glacier over the lake. The assumed direction and strength of the water currents are indicated by the arrows. After Antevs, E., Mem. 146, Geol. Surv. Canada, 1925, p. 41.

material in suspension may become diffused throughout the lake waters and attain deposition over the entire basin. According to Antevs, "This is evident from the spreading of fine glacial mud over the entire area of large lakes and its deposition far away from the ice edge where the water was shallow as well as where it was deep."[105] Transportation seems to be brought about in the upper waters of glacial lakes by winds of an anticyclonic type which set the water in motion away from the ice, and through currents developed by the great volume of melt water during times of warmth. The transportation and deposition in a glacial lake would be governed by the agitation of the surface water, the temperature of the bottom, the temperature of the melt waters, the shape of the lake basin and thus the currents

[105] Antevs. E., Retreat of the last ice sheet in eastern Canada, Mem. 146, Geol. Surv. Canada, 1925, p. 25.

to the outlet, the physical and chemical properties of the lake and melt waters, and the characters of the transported sediments.

Lakes of tropical regions have their warmest and lightest waters always at the top and the heaviest and coldest adjacent to the bottom. There is no overturn and hence little circulation in the deeper waters, which are likely to become foul with partially decayed organic matter. Stream waters with a heavy burden of sediments may sink beneath the surface waters and thus carry sediments and oxygen to the bottom. The deeper waters of tropical lakes are likely to be copiously supplied with carbon dioxide, thus rendering unlikely the deposition of calcium carbonate in waters of any depth.

The sediments deposited in glacial lakes may or may not be varved, depending on the continuity and character of deposition. The sediments of temperate, tropical, and polar lakes not connected with glaciers may not even be stratified except in a large way, as deposition may be essentially continuous, and in the temperate lakes and the shallow waters of tropical lakes the sediments tend to be rather thoroughly worked over by organisms.

Salt Lakes

Waters flowing into salt lakes are usually lighter than the waters into which they flow, and thus the fresh waters tend to flow on top. Rapid deposition of suspended sediments and colloids takes place on the mingling of the two waters. If the salinity of the waters of the lake is high, the bottoms will have limited life, and thus working over of bottom materials will be negligible. Good stratification is likely.

Lake Processes

These are mechanical, chemical, and organic. The mechanical processes differ from those of the sea in the absence of tides and the possibility, in the fresh-water lakes, of small particles remaining indefinitely in suspension.

The inorganic chemical processes of lakes do not appear to be of great moment except in lakes of arid regions, where evaporation and processes initiated by concentration play an important rôle in the precipitation of saline residues and the flocculation of colloids.

Organic processes, on the other hand, play a considerable rôle. Lakes are inhabited both by animals and by plants. Gastropods and pelecypods are the most abundant animals and crustaceans are common. The shells usually are fragile and break up soon after the deaths of the builders. The plant life of lakes is of great importance. The margins of many small lakes are inhabited by many species, and much of the water coming to such lakes must filter through a sponge of living and dead vegetation, with the result that very little detrital matter may reach the bottoms, nearly the whole of the deposits being organic. The algæ and green plants of lakes precipitate large quantities of calcium carbonate.

Lakes have no true littoral deposits, but fluctuations of level may produce a shore zone which in some respects partakes of the characteristics of the ocean littoral. This fact may be expressed in the sediments in the mixing of the characteristics of two realms of deposition,—mud cracks, rain prints, and the tracks of land animals associated with shore bedding and the fossils of lacustrine animals. About shallow lakes with small wave activity the shore is not eroded, and it and the adjacent shallow bottom become overgrown with vegetation. The deposits of lakes with strong wave action grade outward from the sands and gravels of the shore to extremely fine muds in the center, and a typical deposit of a lake with strong wave action should consist of an encircling belt of shore gravels, an inner concentric belt of sands within which is a belt of sandy marly mud, and in the center fine muds or marls essentially free from grit, each belt grading gradually into those adjacént. As fresh water permits slow settling of the fine sediments, these remain in suspension a long time. Some are ultimately carried to the middle of the lake and deposited in thin laminations, each beginning with the coarsest material carried and grading upward into the finest in contrast to the deposits of marine deltas, where, because of flocculation, the coarsest materials may be found in the upper portion of a lamination.[106] As deposition of the central portion of a large lake may be essentially continuous, lamination may not develop, and there may be absence of sharp boundaries between beds. Such sharp boundaries are believed originally to form in most marine sediments because of the rapid precipitation which occurs in salt water.[107] Organisms may subsequently work over the fine deposits of lakes, with consequent destruction of any features of deposition.

The absence of significant tides in lakes decreases development of shore or littoral currents. This hinders the formation of asymmetrical ripple mark. Since there is nothing limiting the development of wave ripples, these may assume relatively greater importance in lakes than in the sea.

Since lakes generally are of limited area, their deposits are similarly so. These commonly have rudely spherical or elliptical outlines in horizontal plan, but they may be greatly elongated or horseshoe-shaped, as is commonly the case for river lakes.

The animals of fresh-water lakes are characteristic. Brachiopods, echinoderms, corals, and cephalopods never appear to have lived in fresh-water

[106] Kindle, E. M., Diagnostic characteristics of marine clastics, Bull. Geol. Soc. Am., vol. 28, 1917, pp. 907–909.
[107] Kindle, E. M., op. cit.

lakes, but strangely enough, medusæ occur in Lake Tanganyika and a few other places. Gastropods and pelecypods seem to have been inhabitants of lakes since the earliest geologic records of lake deposits; in fact, their shells are so abundant in some lakes as to give rise to considerable thicknesses of shell marl. Microscopic organisms, both animal and plant, are abundant in lakes and contribute to marl deposits, but they have rarely been identified in the deposits of ancient lakes. Fish are common in most lakes, but they have little value as criteria of environment, as many, like the salmon, periodically go from salt to fresh water, and others, as the eel, from fresh to salt water. Fish also appear to become easily adapted, as exemplified by the sharks of lakes Titicaca and Nicaragua. Seals also show the same adaptations. Kindle's studies of Lake Ontario indicate that in this lake "the great bulk of the species live within 25 feet of the surface" and that the "maximum depths appear to be tenanted chiefly if not exclusively by small hair or flesh colored worms."[108] It is not known whether or not this applies to other large lakes.

Most small lakes have an abundant growth of plants about their borders, and the shallow waters are aggressively invaded by a large number of species. Conspicuous in this respect are such plants as the water lily, arrow leaf, cattail, pickerel weed, and sphagnum. Small shallow lakes ultimately are brought to extinction through plant growth, and in this way their deposits pass vertically and laterally into those of swamps. The higher green plants in Lake Ontario extend down to depths of 15 feet. An algal and diatom flora extends to depths of 150 feet or more, and below 200 feet there seems to be no plant life.[109] Remains of terrestrial animals and plants may occur in the deposits of any lake.

In addition to the general characteristics given, there are others which are connected with, or arise from, the method of origin.

Glacial lakes receive glacial or glacio-lacustrine deposits in the early stages of their history, and the deposits rest upon, grade laterally into, and more or less dovetail with deposits of glacial origin and not uncommonly of glacial deposition. Lakes of this origin usually are small, contain fresh water, and exist under climatic conditions favoring the growth of such plants as sphagnum. Their deposits ultimately pass upward into some phase of peat material.

River lakes are shallow, usually elongated, and surrounded and underlain and overlain by deposits of the piedmont, valley-flat, or delta environment. They usually contain fresh water. The faunas of river lakes are as a rule

---

[108] Kindle, E. M., The bottom deposits of Lake Ontario, Trans. Roy. Soc. Canada, vol. 19, 1925, pp. 17–72.

[109] Kindle, E. M., op. cit.

derived from the waters which produced the lakes, and they may receive a new supply at each flood. River lakes may be much reduced during dry seasons, and wide areas about their margins may become extensively mud cracked and marked with rain prints and the tracks of animals. At each flood time they may receive a deposit of river mud. These deposits, with additions from animals and plants, bring them to extinction. The deposits are essentially mud, commonly well laminated, although this feature may be destroyed by mud cracking. The deposits of river lakes may contain an abundance of fish remains.

Seashore lakes develop where portions of the sea are cut off through the formation of a bar or barrier. They may contain either fresh or salt water. Lakes of this origin usually are shallow and generally have streams emptying into them on their landward sides. The deposits of these streams, together with material brought over the barrier by winds and occasional high waves, may bring the lakes to extinction or change them into marine swamps. The deposits of seashore lakes usually rest on shallow-water marine sediments, which by gradual transitions through brackish-water deposits may grade into those of fresh water. The fresh-water deposits may contain marine shells because of the occasional entrance of salt waters in storms and the occasional shells carried in by birds and other flying animals. The gradual change from salt water to fresh may lead to some animals becoming adapted to the fresh-water habitat. Difficulty of interpretation is obvious.

Lakes formed by crustal movement include the largest now in existence, and doubtless such has always been the case. They may be either fresh or salt. Lakes Nicaragua and Titicaca, the Great Lakes, and the Caspian are examples. Not uncommonly these lakes contain animals of marine ancestry, as exemplified by the seals of the Caspian Sea, the sharks of Lake Nicaragua, and the medusæ of Lake Tanganyika. The physical character of the shore deposits of large lakes differs little from those of the sea. As the centers are far from shore, there is plenty of opportunity for the elimination of the coarser materials before the centers are reached, with the consequence that the deposits there are of an extreme degree of fineness. The deposits of Lake Ontario probably are fairly illustrative of those of large lakes. The sediments of the deep-water area of depths ranging from 200 to 700 feet consist of very fine mud of jelly-like consistency. This contains no molluscan life, and shrimps, minute worms, and diatoms represent its fauna and flora (the bacterial flora is not considered). The deep-water sediments are surrounded by a belt of coarser sediments consisting of sandy mud, sand, and gravel. This belt has a molluscan fauna. Parts of this bottom consist of bed rock on which there are no sediments.[110]

[110] Kindle, E. M., op. cit.

Salt-water lakes seem to be characterized by a greater production of hydrogen sulphide than those of fresh water, and this may become so abundant in salt-water bodies as to render their bottoms and lower waters unfit for habitation by organisms.

The Lake Cycle

From the time of origin most lakes begin to disappear. They are filled up by deposition of sediments and cutting down of outlets (seashore lakes excepted). The latter event causes the waters to recede, and the shore deposits migrate downward and centralward, ultimately covering those of the deeper waters. The top deposits may thus be coarser than those immediately below,[111] but if a lake passes into a swamp the final deposits are composed of peat.

Lake Deposits

Lake deposits consist of marl, tufa, sands, gravels, peat, iron oxides, iron carbonate, silicon dioxide, salt, gypsum, and other evaporation products.

Lake marl is composed of calcium carbonate mixed with a variable proportion of impurities. The colors range from white to gray and red, depending on accessory substances and the degree of oxidation of iron which may be present. It is composed of a mixture of coarser and very much finer matter, the proportion of the former ranging from 50 to 95 per cent and both the finer and the coarser parts consisting very largely of incrustations formed on green plants. Many varieties of plants may participate in its formation. Davis[112] assigned the chief rôle to *Chara*, but there appear to be few good reasons for this assignment, and shells in some cases are important in forming marl deposits. All marls contain more or less carbonaceous matter. According to Kindle, marl accumulation takes place largely in the epilimnion under conditions where the "thermal stratification is protected from the mixing effect of high wind and waves."[113]

Deposits of marl are extensive in some lakes, particularly those smaller ones whose shores are protected by vegetation against the entrance of mud and sand or by barriers against wave and current action. A lake near English Bay, Anticosti Island, has an area of about 100 acres over which marl is known to have a maximum thickness of at least 12 feet. These marls appear to be largely composed of the shells of three species of gastropods. There are several other lakes on Anticosti more or less filled with marl.

[111] Mansfield, G. R., The origin and structure of the Roxbury conglomerate, Bull. Mus. Comp. Zool., vol. 49, 1906, p. 120.

[112] Davis, C. A., The natural history of marl, Jour. Geol., vol. 9, 1901, pp. 490–506.

[113] Kindle, E. M., op. cit., 1927, pp. 1–35.

Tufa has been stated to result largely from the evaporation of highly concentrated waters, but it seems certain that algæ may be of major importance in its deposition.   Its most significant occurrences are largely in regions which at the times of deposition seem to have been arid or semi-arid, as in former Lake Lahontan of the Great Basin region.[114]

Lake clays and silts are very similar to those of marine origin.   However, they of course contain fresh-water shells, and the great length of time that matter remains in suspension tends to make deposition fairly continuous, to eliminate sharp contacts, and to bring extremely fine grained muds to the centers of lakes.   Considerable carbonaceous matter is present in lake clays, on the basis of which it has been suggested that lake deposits might be differentiated from marine.[115]   The dry weight of vegetable matter annually formed in Lake Mendota at Madison, Wisconsin, totals 2,203,000 kgm., an average of about 800 kgm. per acre,[116] of which 1,112,000 kgm. are derived from *Potamogeton* and 736,000 kgm. from *Vallisneria*.   Considerable parts of this vegetable material are deposited with the clays; some of it is preserved, but much is dissipated by bacteria and other organisms after deposition.

The sands and gravels of lakes are not particularly different from those of marine origin.   The thicknesses are small.

Concentration or evaporation products are extensive in the lakes of some dry regions.   These have been considered in connection with the products of sedimentation.

Peat has been considered in connection with carbonaceous sediments.

Iron oxides and carbonates are deposited in some lakes and reach considerable extents.   Some lakes of Sweden,[117] Finland, European Russia, Canada, Maine, and probably elsewhere have deposits of limonite forming in them at the present time.   In the Swedish lakes the limonite is deposited about 10 meters from the shore and reaches a maximum thickness of about one-half meter.   The deposits occur in the form of elliptical and irregular patches which are in the quiet places where there is an abundant growth of vegetable matter.   The iron oxide settles to the bottom as mud of blackish, brownish, and greenish colors.   It is filled with plant débris, both of algal and higher plants, and is rich in gelatinous silica.   In hardening, the mud forms "either compact lumps (rusor), small disks or balls," or concre-

[114] Russell, I. C., Geologic history of Lake Lahontan, Mon. 11, U. S. Geol. Surv., 1885.

[115] Matthew, G. F., On a method of distinguishing lacustrine from marine deposits, Proc. Roy. Soc. Canada, vol. 4, 1883, pp. 147–149.

[116] Rickett, H. W., A quantitative study of the larger aquatic plants of Lake Mendota, Trans. Wisconsin Acad. Sci., vol. 20, 1921, pp. 501–527, particularly table 7, p. 521.   The smaller aquatic plants are not included in these figures.

[117] Beck, R., The nature of ore deposits, Transl. by Weed, W. H., 1909, p. 100.

tionary masses about animal and plant remains.   The deposits commonly contain phosphorus as earthy vivianite; and a considerable quantity of manganese, probably in the form of wad, is also very generally present.

Iron carbonate occurs in the deposits of lakes which are rich in organic matter.   Due to the readiness of oxidation, the quantity is usually limited. Sulphide of iron is present in the same relation.

The silicon dioxide brought to fresh-water lakes probably remains indefinitely in the water.   In salt-water lakes it is flocculated and precipitated as in marine waters.   Chert and flint thus result in the deposits of some lakes.

THE CAVE (SPELEAN) ENVIRONMENT AND ITS SEDIMENTS

Although caves in some regions have extensive ramifications, the deposits made in them are small.   The important cave regions of the United States are the Mississippian limestone areas of southwestern Indiana, southern Illinois, and west-central Kentucky and the continuation around the southern end of the Cincinnati arch into eastern Kentucky and Tennessee; the limestone areas of the Ozarks; and the Cambro-Ordovician areas of the southern Appalachians.   A great cave region of Europe is that of Karst on the eastern shores of the Adriatic.   From the quantitative point of view, the cave environment is the least important for deposition of sediments.

The darkness of caves limits their abundance and variety of life.   Many forms which make caves their permanent homes are eyeless, or have nonfunctional eyes.   Other animals make caves places of refuge, but spend the major portion of their lives in the open.   Some nocturnal forms, as bats, live in caves during the daytime.   There is thus the possibility of a considerable range in variety of organic remains in caves.

Water-worn caves are wet, and as they largely develop through solution of rock, insoluble parts remain for shorter or longer periods of time attached to the roofs and walls.   During times of heavy rainfall the smaller caves may be full of water, and the water may contain considerable quantities of suspended sediments.   Some of these may be deposited, but the tendency is to remove rather than to deposit.   Wind-worn caves ordinarily are without deposits so long as the conditions of formation obtain.

Sediments Deposited in Caves

The sediments in caves are deposited by the streams flowing therein, by the ocean or other waters in cases of submerged caves, by material falling from the roofs, by evaporation and chemical reactions of the waters which enter caves, by bacterial precipitation, by the ground waters which fill caves when they are brought below ground-water level, and by organisms.

The mechanical sediments deposited by streams are small in quantity and local in distribution. The material falling from the roof may be sufficiently great to cover the floor locally to depths of several feet. Caves of lands undergoing submergence become filled with deposits of the submerging waters. These may be either of mechanical or chemical origin and may be in layers parallel to the cave floors and approximating the horizontal.

Materials deposited in caves by evaporation or chemical action form the stalactites, stalagmites, and kindred substances. Calcium carbonate is the common composing material of stalagmites and stalactites, but some are composed of silica, iron oxide, and rarer substances as sphalerite, galena, etc. It is not recorded that bacterial precipitation takes place in caves, but as it has been reported in mines, there are no reasons why it should not also occur in caves.[118] The rates of growth of stalactites have been determined in a few instances.[119] Stalactites formed in the inspection tunnel of the Wilson Dam, Muscle Shoals, Alabama, the dam having been put in operation early in 1925, were measured early in 1930. They ranged in length between 12.7 and 22.8 cm., and the longest observed was 38.7 cm. The average diameter was 0.5 cm. near the top, and at the bases the diameters ranged between 1.2 and 3.8 cm. This gives an annual rate of growth ranging from 2.5 to 5 cm. A tubular stalactite 8.9 cm. long, 1.3 cm. in diameter at the base, and 0.6 cm. in diameter at the tip grew in the arch of a concrete culvert in Washington, D. C., in two years. A copper sulphate stalactite 67.5 cm. long and 2.5 cm. in average diameter formed in the 1400-foot level of the Briggs Copper Mine at Bisbee, Arizona, in seventeen months, a rate of growth averaging 3.95 cm. per month.[120] Allison[121] described stalactites forming in a coal mine and increasing in length at a rate of 0.1 to 1.44 cm. a month, and Curtis[122] states that aragonite aggregates grew in drops of water at the rate of about 0.9 cm. in three months. As the rates are dependent upon a considerable number of variable factors, it is doubtful if any generalization as to rates of growth can be made and be of much value, although Allison has presented methods by which the age of stalagmites and stalactites may be determined.

Caves which pass beneath the level of the ground-water table may be-

[118] Parry, J., Minerals deposited by bacteria in mine water, Chem. News, vol. 125, 1922, pp. 225–228, 241–243, 257–259.

[119] Johnson, W. D., Jr., The rate of growth of stalactites, Science, vol. 72, 1930, pp. 298–299.

[120] Mitchell, G. J., Rate of formation of copper sulfate stalactites, Trans. Am. Inst. Min. Eng., vol. 66, 1921, p. 64.

[121] Allison, V. C., The growth of stalagmites and stalactites, Jour. Geol., vol. 31, 1923, pp. 106–125.

[122] Curtis, J. S., Silver-lead deposits of Eureka, Nevada, Mon. 7, U. S. Geol. Surv., 1884, pp. 56–58.

come completely filled with minerals deposited from solution, and some of the onyx deposits are thought to have originated in this way.[123] The solution cavities which are said to occur in the Tamasopa limestone of Mexico are now beneath ground-water level, and it is not unlikely that some of them are receiving deposits from solution.

The organic deposits in caves consist of bones and excrements of cave-dwelling animals and the bones of the animals upon which they preyed. The Pleistocene caves of Europe, and southern France in particular, were inhabited by man, whose bones, implements, and the bones of the animals upon which he fed now occur in the deposits covering the floors. The guano of caves is usually referred to the excrements of bats. The distribution is irregular and the quantity is small.

Cave Deposits in the Geologic Column

Not many are known. The Mississippian and older limestones of Missouri and adjacent states contained caves prior to the deposition of the Pennsylvanian and younger sediments, and some of the caves became filled by these subsequent deposits. Some of the ore bodies of the lead and zinc district of Missouri, Kansas, and Oklahoma appear to have been deposited in caves.[124] Many of the Pleistocene caves are noted for their deposits of organic material.

MIXED CONTINENTAL AND MARINE ENVIRONMENTS

Mixed continental and marine environments are made where the ocean and the continents and smaller land masses meet. This contact may be placed in the four classes of littoral, delta, estuary, and marginal lagoon. Marine processes are dominant in the littoral; in the delta there is a strong contest between the sea and the land, the delta attesting the dominancy of the land processes; the estuary in some parts of its area changes to fresh or brackish water at each low tide and to brackish or salt water at each high tide; and the marginal lagoon ranges from fresh to salt water, and in some regions to highly saline waters. The sediments of the littoral are derived from both the land and the sea, but for the most part they are deposited by oceanic waters; those of the delta are mostly derived from the land and deposited by fresh waters; and both the land and the sea may make more or less equal contributions to the deposits of the estuary and the marginal lagoon.

[123] Merrill, G. P., The onyx marbles, Rept. U. S. Nat. Mus., 1895, pp. 541–585.
[124] Siebenthal, C. E., Origin of the zinc and lead deposits of the Joplin region, Bull. 606, U. S. Geol. Surv., 1915, pp. 159–161.

THE LITTORAL ENVIRONMENT AND ITS SEDIMENTS

The littoral environment is defined as that portion of the sea bottom which is exposed at low tide. During ordinary tides this has somewhat constant lower and upper limits; during the neap and spring tides the limits are both higher and lower than at other times. Exposure and submergence may also arise from storms and earthquake waves. These are irregular and may be of greater extent than are those due to tides.

Extent of the Littoral Environment

At the present time the ordinary width of the littoral zone is small. There are places, as in the Bay of Fundy, where the great rise of the tides gives to the zone a width of a mile or more. Such places, however, are few. It seems probable that during those times of earth history when the lands were near base level, high tide may have submerged many square miles which were exposed at low tide, and it is possible that the width of the littoral may have been a dozen or more miles. The west shores of Hudson Bay perhaps more nearly illustrate such conditions at the present time. Throughout long stretches of the coast between Port Churchill and Chesterfield Inlet there are extensive areas which are covered by water at high tide and exposed at low tide, the difference in water level being about 12 feet, and the widths of the tidal flats range from a few hundred feet to 6 or 8 miles, a couple of thousand or more square miles thus being alternately exposed and covered each day. The flats are particularly well developed for some 50 miles northwest of latitude 60° N., where at low tide the waters of Hudson Bay may not be visible from the shore of high tide level.[125] The Wattenmeer of the North Sea similarly is an extensive tidal flat.[126] It seems probable that some of the epicontinental seas of the Paleozoic, as for instance those covering the upper Mississippi Valley during the Cambrian and Ordovician, may have had conditions somewhat like those of Hudson Bay.

The present area of the littoral environment has been estimated at 62,500 square miles.[127]

Conditions in the Littoral Environment

The most important facts connected with the littoral environment are the exposure twice each day and the more or less constant wave activity.

[125] Lund, R. J., Personal communication.
[126] See papers by Richter, R., Senckenbergiana, 1920, and Krümmel, O., Über Erosion durch Gezeitenströme, Petermann's Mitth., vol. 35, 1889, pp. 129–138; Über Umformung der Küsten durch die Meeresströmungen, Mitth. Geogr. Gesell. Hamburg, 1889–90, p. 221.
[127] Murray, J., and Renard, A. F., Challenger Rept., Deep sea deposits, 1891, p. 248.

Each condition makes it difficult for organisms to establish permanent homes, with the result that few species have become adapted.   Some are attached forms, as certain algæ and such invertebrates as *Mytilus* and *Balanus*. *Mya* burrows in the mud and there are others which tide over the periods of exposure by crawling under rocks or have means for closing their shells. There are, however, many individuals of such species as have become adapted.

The strong wave action which frequently prevails in this environment produces great wear on everything that enters.   Rock particles are rounded; shells are ground to powder; logs are polished smooth; etc.

The shore environment is not the same everywhere.   Some portions consist of gently sloping bare rock surfaces; other portions are more or less vertical wave-cut cliffs; some shores are composed of gravels, others of boulders, and still others of sand, mud, and shell matter.   Some shores are none of these things, but from low to high tide level the entire sea bottom and the land surface inland are covered with a dense growth of vegetation consisting of algæ, grasses, sedges, reeds, etc.; the algæ live in the salt and brackish waters and the other plants in the fresh waters inland from the sea, a part of this inland surface being below high tide level, but bathed by fresh waters because of large contributions of such from the land and because this fresh water and the vegetation serve as a dam to hold the salt water out.   A small-scale illustration of this nature may be seen on the Gulf of St. Lawrence between the mouth of the Mingan River and Eskimo Point. One type of the littoral environment is where mangroves are advancing into the sea.   A particular facies is the coral reef.   A littoral bordered by extremely shallow waters into which numerous streams are flowing may be bathed by waters which are fresh most of the time.   Such seem to be rare at the present time, as most of the littorals are bordered by fairly deep waters, but may have been frequent in some of the shallow epicontinental seas of the Paleozoic.

A bare rock shore receives no littoral deposits.   The mud and muddy sand shore is inhabited by many mud- and sand-eating organisms which live within the sediments and leave their shells therein on death.   The solid rock shore may be covered with cemented forms or those attached by byssal threads.   The shores of sand, gravel, and boulders usually are without macroscopic organisms, other than vagrant benthos.

Sedimentary Processes in the Littoral Environment

The sedimentary processes of the littoral environment are mainly mechanical.   The sediments in considerable if not largest part are derived from the shore through rock breaking and grinding, aided by frost action and undermining. Organic matter is limited, although on some coasts the sediments are mainly organic. There is some work done by the wind, but it is indeterminate and probably small, but wind deposits of beach derivation may occur inland from the shore. The exposure to the atmosphere twice each day permits some evaporation, and mud cracks may develop during the exposures. The exposure also may assist in the cementation of some of the sediments.[128]

Characteristics, Thicknesses, and Associations of Littoral Sediments

The deposits made in the littoral environment are in large part the result of wave deposition. There is much variety, and the sediments range from boulders, gravels, sands, and muds to organic matter composed of shells, logs, and seaweeds. Some shores are composed of sands for long distances. In such cases the land adjacent to the shore usually is not high, and the shore is regular and uniform, thus permitting uniformity of wave action. The average shore is irregular, with a variety of relief to the adjacent land. The consequence is that the shore deposits show extremely great irregularity. Lenses of mud may be found lying in the midst of sand, gravel, or boulders. A walk of a mile along some shores ordinarily will show several types of shore environment and almost every kind of mechanical sediment. Lime muds, shell matter, and logs and seaweeds are more or less common littoral materials, and on many low shores these dominate. The shores of some of the Paleozoic epicontinental seas bordering lands which had been reduced to base level probably had uniformity of deposits, and it is considered likely that such extensive black shale formations as the Chattanooga represent a variety of littoral deposit made under such conditions in seas with weak tides.

In general, the deposits of the littoral environment consist of boulders, gravels, sands, muds, and shells and shell fragments, each grading into another alongshore and grading outward by more or less insensible stages into the deposits of the neritic environment. Shores bordering low lands may have the sediments largely calcareous or organic. The original colors of the mechanical sediments of the littoral environment are light to dark gray unless the composing rock particles are differently colored. Organic sediments range from white to black.

The deposits of the littoral environment may be mud cracked, but, except locally, the conditions are not particularly favorable for mud-crack development. Rain impressions and the markings of similar appearance may be present, as most of the agents responsible for such markings are in almost

[128] Andrée, K., Geologie des Meeresbodens, Bd. 2, 1920, pp. 30–118. A rather complete consideration of the processes and phenomena of the strand is given in this work.

daily operation in this environment. Ripple mark may form on every surface, and both symmetrical and asymmetrical types may be present, the latter the more common. The strong wave activity produces much cross lamination. The littoral environment is the feeding ground for many land animals, and these leave their tracks on the sands and muds, and marine organisms leave their burrows in the deposits, these being tubes of various kinds, from the U-shaped tubes made by *Arenicola* to the nearly vertical tubes made by *Mya*, some crabs, and certain of the worms. The draining of water from the sands and muds of the littoral following retreat of the waves and the tides produces dendritic rill markings and on some sands the series of diamond-shaped markings described on page 671. The expulsion of air from sands by incoming waves produces the numerous sand holes.

Littoral deposits for any single position of sea level cannot attain a great thickness, as such is limited by the tidal range. Rise of sea level may produce a greater thickness. The rise of sea level may move the littoral environment inland or build a new littoral deposit upon the old, the results depending upon the strength of the waves, which in turn depends upon the depth of water in the neritic zone. If shallow water exists for a long distance outward from the shore, little inland movement is likely, and a new littoral deposit may be superimposed directly on the old. If considerable depth of water exists adjacent to the shore, the previous littoral deposit is likely to be more or less reworked to form a part of the deposits of the neritic environment, and a new littoral deposit built inland from the old. The former condition has as an invariable accompaniment deposits of mud and sand, the muds not infrequently carrying considerable organic matter, and it is suggested that some of the black shales formed under such conditions. A great thickness is possible, depending upon the relations between rise of sea level and building up of the bottom. If a new littoral deposit is built inland from the old, the deposits consist mainly of sands and gravels. The thickness of the littoral deposits made under these conditions is small, and it seems probable that the combined thickness of coarse materials of the littoral and neritic environments is not likely to exceed 100 feet, and Barrell expressed the opinion that the possible thickness would be considerably less than 100 feet.[129]

Criteria for the Determination of Littoral Deposits

The stratigraphic positions of deposits of the littoral environment are at the base and the top of each marine deposit made between an advance and retreat of the sea. The deposits at the top have little chance of being pre-

[129] Barrell, J., Some distinctions between marine and terrestrial conglomerates, Bull. Geol. Soc. Am., vol. 20, 1909, p. 620; Criteria for the recognition of ancient delta deposits, Ibid., 23, 1912, p. 441.

served,[130] and those at the base may be partly or wholly reworked and more or less incorporated in the neritic deposits. Littoral deposits may be mud cracked and may contain "rain prints," rill marks, sand pits, ripple marks, and tracks of land and water animals. Coarse materials have irregular stratification and are likely to be cross-laminated. Shells of marine animals may be common, and some land animal remains are probable, both generally in a fragmentary condition. Fine sediments may be evenly laminated and may contain shells and other organic materials in an excellent state of preservation.

Relative Importance of Littoral Deposits

Quantitatively, littoral deposits made in waters with strong waves have little significance. They are not thick at any time of their existence, and as they are progressively buried, the thickness is decreased and in many instances reduced to nothing. Their importance lies in the fact that they record positions of the shorelines. Littoral deposits made in waters with weak wave action may, on the other hand, attain considerable thickness and cover extensive areas.

Littoral Deposits in the Geologic Column

Deposits which are either those of the littoral environment or the upper portion of the neritic are common in the upper Mississippi Valley and elsewhere at the base of the Cambrian. The different geologic systems have similar deposits on one or more levels, as that between the Beekmantown and Chazy of the northern Appalachians, the base of the Pennsylvanian west of the Mississippi River, the base of the Lower Cretaceous of Texas, etc. If some of the black shale and other formations were deposited in the littoral environment, it follows that the occurrences are more extensive than generally supposed. Scott[131] interprets the Woodbine sands of the Texas Cretaceous as due to a retiring sea, from which it follows that a part of them may be of littoral origin.

THE DELTA ENVIRONMENT AND ITS SEDIMENTS

Following Barrell,[132] a delta is defined "as a deposit partly subaerial built by a river into or against a body of permanent water." A delta results

---

[130] Scott, G., The Woodbine sand of Texas interpreted as a regressive phenomenon, Bull. Am. Assoc. Pet. Geol., vol. 10, 1926, pp. 613–624. Scott presents evidence supporting the view that the Woodbine sands were left by a retiring sea.

[131] Scott, G., op. cit., 1926.

[132] Barrell, J., Criteria for the determination of ancient delta deposits, Bull. Geol. Soc. Am., vol. 23, 1912, pp. 377–446. This article has been extensively used in the preparation of this topic. Studies of the sediments of the Mississippi delta have been made by Professor A. C. Trowbridge and his assistants. These studies have not been published.

when a stream supplies more material than can be handled by the waves and currents of the body of water into which it empties. Deltas may be built into lakes and rivers, and such are continental deposits. They resemble deltas built into the sea except as the latter are modified by the presence of marine factors.

The Components of Deltas

The deposits made in deltas are partly subaerial and partly below the surface of the permanent body of water into which a stream empties. The subaerial deposits are fluvial, lacustrine, and paludal. The subaqueous deposits are partly of stream deposition and partly of marine or lacustrine, depending on whether the permanent body of water is the sea or a lake.

Deposits are made on a delta's upper surface, in the channels which cross it, on its front, and over the bottom beyond its front. The deposits on its upper surface are known as the topset beds. These are essentially flat-lying, although they may slope gently from the drainage lines over the subaerial portions and seaward over those which are subaqueous. The deposits over the delta front are known as the foreset beds. These have a wide range in their inclinations, sloping at high angles in small bodies of water with weak wave and current action, and at low angles in large bodies with vigorous waves and currents. The deposits made beyond a delta's front are known as the bottomset beds. These are composed of fine materials and are essentially flat-lying. The three components are readily differentiable in deltas made in the laboratory and those of small lakes. In large deltas the conditions are so extremely complex that they may not be apparent. In a large way, however, they should be present.

The topset beds are either subaerial or subaqueous. The subaerial deposits are made on the subaerial delta plain, or that part of the delta which is exposed except when covered by stream flood waters or the waters of great sea waves and tides, and in the channels which are cut across this plain. The sediments on the surface of this plain are deposited by floods, by the stream in its channels, and in delta lakes and swamps. In dry regions wind may also assist in deposition. Near the outer margin of the subaerial plain waves may raise barriers which in turn create lagoons. The waters of these lagoons may be either fresh or salty, the more common occurrence being alternating conditions of longer or shorter duration. If waves are weak and shallow waters extend a long distance outward from the shore, barriers seem unlikely, and there arc no lagoons but a gradual passage of salt waters and a characteristic plant life into a fresh-water marsh environment.

The subaerial delta plain is the delta of the geographers, but from the point of view of the sedimentationist it is but one part of a connected deposit. It may be more or less separated from the subaqueous plain or submerged part of the topset beds by the shore face, and it grades upstream without break into the flood plain, from the deposits of which its own may differ in no important particulars.

The deposits of the subaerial plain are extremely variable, both horizontally and vertically. Fluvial, lacustrine, paludal, and lagoonal sediments may occur on many levels and in most vertical sections. Mud cracks and "rain print" markings may be present locally. Both are common on the subaerial plains of dry regions. Slumping of sediments due to settling, undermining, and other cases should be more or less common. There are great variations in the extents, thicknesses, colors, markings, materials, and structures of the sedimentary units.

The organic remains in the deposits of the subaerial plain are mostly of terrestrial origin, and root structures and plants in place may be present. Remains of marine animals may be carried in by birds and other land animals; an occasional large marine flood may sweep marine organisms for long distances over the surface of the subaerial plain; and marine organisms not uncommonly may be brought into tidal channels and delta lakes at times of high tides.

The shore face separating the subaerial from the subaqueous plain is a result of stream deposition or is formed by the waves. Its extent and shape largely depend upon the vigor of wave action. Where wave action is strong, the slope may be steep and relatively high, and in some cases there may be a barrier beach. Where the waves are weak with respect to the stream currents, the shore face is relatively insignificant and its position indeterminate, as the sea bottom may gradually pass into a swamp area. The shore face and associated intertidal zone have the characteristics of the littoral environment. The position of the shore face in a geologic section may be determined by the fact that it separates the sediments of stream deposition from those of standing water, and by the further fact that the organisms in the deposits of the landward side are dominantly terrestrial and those on the water side are partly marine or lacustrine. It is obvious that great difficulty would attend accurate determination of the position of the shore face.

The subaqueous plain slopes gently outward into deeper waters at inclinations determined by the conditions. The sediments upon it are laid down by waves and marine and stream currents, and they have the characteristics of sediments so deposited. The waters over this plain range from fresh to salt, the salt content varying seasonally with the tides, the direction and strength of the winds, and the positions and discharge of the distributaries on the subaerial portion of the delta.. The sedimentary units are more or less discontinuous, particularly on the landward margins. Inclinations and coarseness should decrease outward in directions radial to the mouths of the distributaries. The deposits may contain terrestrial and fresh-water organisms, but root structures and plants in natural position are not present, although stumps with roots attached may assume an upright position when they come to rest and thus appear to be in place.[133] Marine and brackish-water organisms are present to a greater or less degree, particularly in the deposits made between the distributaries.

The foreset slope receives the deposits known as the foreset beds. Both river and marine waters are concerned in their deposition, the former adjacent to the ends of the distributary currents and the latter over the intervening areas. The coarsest materials of a delta may be found here (channels in the subaerial plain excepted), and they may be deposited with considerable initial inclination. Streams flowing into quiet bodies of water and carrying coarse material usually have high angles of initial inclination in the foreset deposits. In large bodies of water the angles of initial inclination usually are low. The upper portions of the foreset beds are deposited above wave base; the lower portions may be below that level. The sediments are mostly muds and sands. Lime sediments are not common, and peat formed in place does not occur. The deposits contain remains of marine organisms, particularly between the distributaries. Terrestrial and fresh-water organic remains may occur in the deposits adjacent to the mouths of the distributaries. The areas of the subaqueous topset beds and foreset beds have great environmental instability. The mouths of the distributaries undergo considerable shifting, and the quantity of water discharged by the streams is subject to much variation. A shift of a distributary leads to the discharge of fresh water upon areas where previously the waters may have been salty. Great destruction of the marine organisms of these areas would necessarily follow. Floods like that of the Mississippi River in 1927 displace much salt water about the mouth of a stream, with much destruction of marine life. Denison[134] has called attention to such destruction on the coast of India during times of great discharge from rivers consequent to rainfall connected with the southwest monsoon.

The bottomset beds are deposited largely under marine conditions and for the greater part consist of fine suspended and colloidal materials which owe their precipitation largely to the action of electrolytes in solution or colloids of opposite sign. The beds range outward to extreme thinness and

[133] Johnston, W. A., Sedimentation of the Fraser River delta, Mem. 125, Geol. Surv., Canada, 1921, p. 38.

[134] Denison, W., Quart. Jour. Geol. Soc., vol. 18, 1862, p. 453.

are deposited in essentially horizontal position. They do not greatly differ from other fine deposits made in marine waters of similar depth and character.

As a delta advances, the subaerial plain is built over the subaqueous plain, the latter over the foreset beds, and the bottomset beds are progressively covered by sediments of foreset deposition. Thus, a vertical section through a delta deposit should have bottomset beds at the base succeeded upward by foreset beds, sediments of the subaqueous plain, and at the top sediments of the subaerial plain.

From what has been said it should not be inferred that the deposits of the different parts of deltas are sharply defined. It is possible for materials as coarse as those found anywhere in a delta to be deposited with the bottomset beds. The material precipitated by flocculation is deposited in the delta channels, in the bays between the distributaries, and during low-water stages over the foreset slopes as well as over the bottomset portion of a delta. Gravels do not seem to be common in large delta deposits, but they may be present. In the Los Angeles Basin section the Pliocene Pico formation strongly suggests the delta environment. Its total thickness exceeds 12,000 feet. It contains beds of gravels, the average diameters of which average about an inch, but dimensions range to a foot. The gravel beds are 5 or more feet thick; the rock particles are round to angular; and they are in a sand matrix. The beds are very lenticular, lens out from the source of supply, are characterized by cut-and-fill structure, are separated by cross-laminated sands and lignitic clay, and marine fossils occur in some of the beds.[135] The gravels probably are present because of nearness of deposition to distributive areas.

Streams emptying into bodies of water of which the waves and currents have energy sufficiently ample to dispose of all sediments which may be brought have no subaerial plain, as the sediments are distributed outward and alongshore to greater or less extents. These sediments are not greatly unlike those of the subaqueous portions of deltas with subaerial plains and foreset and bottomset beds, except, perhaps, in containing a greater abundance of marine fossils.

The Nile delta illustrates the topographic features of large deltas.[136] The subaerial plain is dotted with lakes and swamps, and about its seaward margin are many lagoons. Tortuous distributaries find their way through this plain to the Mediterranean. The shore face extends to depths of 6 to 10 meters, as shown by the closeness of these depths to the shore. The

---

[135] Cartwright, L. D., jr., Sedimentation of the Pico formation in the Ventura Quadrangle, California, Bull. Am. Assoc. Pet. Geol., vol. 12, 1928, pp. 235–270.

[136] Barrell, J., op. cit., pp. 387–389.

subaqueous plain extends outward to a depth of 200 meters. The depth of 50 meters is attained at a distance of 50 km. from the shore, and to this depth the slope is very gentle. The surface then descends rapidly to 200 meters and then still more rapidly to 1000 meters, the slope from 50 to 200 meters being in the nature of a transition zone between the subaqueous plain and the foreset slope. The latter is considered to extend from depths of 200 to 1000 meters and has an inclination of about 1.5°. The bottomset beds lie at depths of 1000 to 2000 meters and show their presence in outward convexity of the submarine contours. Studies made by Judd[137] of deposits in the subaerial portion of the delta indicate that the chief constituents are sands and silts. The sands are mostly quartz, but contain more or less feldspar, mica, and small percentages of rarer minerals. The silts contain little clay or kaolin, but the chief constituents are small particles of quartz, feldspar, mica, and other minerals. The mineral particles are dominantly fresh.

Within recent years the somewhat youthful delta of the Fraser River of British Columbia, Canada, has been studied in detail by Johnston, and much has been learned of the component parts of this delta and the characteristics of its deposits.[138] The following description is slightly modified after that of Johnston (1922, pp. 119–120).

The inclined foreset beds forming the subaqueous front are well developed and extend from the 3-fathom line to about the 30-fathom line and have an average dip of about 10 degrees. The dip, however, is irregular and in places the subaqueous front of the delta is nearly vertical for heights of 1 to 3 fathoms. Below the 30-fathom line the beds slope gradually seaward, the 100-fathom line being reached at from 1 to 2 miles from the outer edge of the sand banks. The horizontal bottom-set beds, consisting of very fine material, form a considerable part of the floor of the strait of Georgia off the entrance of the river. . . The horizontal top-set beds forming the upper part of the delta are thinnest and in most places are only a few feet thick. In some places, as in the deep abandoned channels of the river the thickness may attain more than 100 feet. The top-set beds are sandy to high tide level; above they are silty and the silty, fine-grained beds formed from deposition of flood waters overflowing the banks, become progressively thicker upstream. The shore face of the delta is feebly developed because wave action has little effect, owing to the shallowness of the water over the sand banks.

The subaqueous topset beds are composed of sand and silt, the latter evenly and thinly laminated, the laminations being due to tidal action. Banding interpreted as seasonal is indicated in places by layers of vegetable matter and by tidal laminations formed during the freshets when the sedi-

[137] Judd, J. W., Report on a series of specimens of the deposits of the Nile Delta, obtained by the recent boring operations, Proc. Roy. Soc. London, vol. 39, 1885, pp. 213–227.
[138] Johnston, W. A., Sedimentation of the Fraser River delta, Mem. 125, Geol. Surv. Canada, 1921; The character of the stratification of the sediments of the recent delta of the Fraser River, Jour. Geol., vol. 30, 1922, pp. 115–129.

ments are mostly silt and at low water when they are mostly fine sand.
The supposed seasonal layers average five to six to a foot.   The record is
not complete, as every section shows evidence of contemporaneous erosion.

The lower part of the top-set beds, exposed at low tide in the seaward part of the delta,
is dominantly sandy, but contains in places thick beds of silt and clay.   These beds are
not definitely laminated and are lenticular in outline.   They are usually compacted and
offer greater resistance to erosion than the sandy beds, which are in part horizontally
bedded and in part crossbedded and current ripple-marked.   In places shell beds or dead
shells of marine species occur embedded in the sand and silt.   They are most abundant at
about the contact of the upper silty beds and the underlying sandy beds.   They occur in
the bank of the river at Steveston and in the seaward part of the delta near the shore face.

The core samples from the subaqueous part of the delta in the strait of Georgia showed
that the foreset beds off the main mouth of the river are thinly but irregularly laminated.
The lamination is somewhat similar to that of the tidal flood-plain deposits, but is more
irregular and is in places markedly crossbedded.   This bedding is also tidal, but is the
result of the combined effects of flocculation, river and tidal currents, and slack water.

The core samples from depths of 50 to 100 fathoms in the strait of Georgia showed that
the bottom-set, fine-grained beds, occur in massive, thick beds, in which no definite
stratification is visible to a depth of at least 2 feet.

In this absence of lamination the bottomset beds differ from the fine-
grained sediments which are being deposited in the fresh waters of Pitt
Lake on the delta.   The color of the bottom sediments is uniformly gray.
Beds of black silt and clay occur in those parts of the topset beds in which
dead shells are abundant.   A well drilled on the delta shows the deposits to
have a thickness of at least 700 feet.

Development of the Components of Deltas

The development of the components of deltas varies with the size and
depth of the water, the character and abundance of sediments, the extent
of the delta front, the vigor of the waves and currents, the velocity and
volume of the water in the streams, and the movement of sea level.

Strong ocean currents and waves and fine waste give wide distribution of
sediments and extensive development of the bottomset beds as compared
to the other components.   These conditions obtain about the mouth of
the Mississippi, as the waste carried is fine and the waves and currents
about the delta front strong.   Streams emptying into bodies of water of
which the waves and currents have energy sufficiently ample to dispose of
all sediments brought may have no subaerial plain, as the sediments may
be entirely distributed.   Deep waters about a delta front with constant
sea level and weak wave and current action lead to the deposition of most of
the waste in the foreset beds.   The deltas of the Ganges and Brahmaputra
rivers illustrate these conditions except that waves and currents are by no

means weak. Strong wave action, moderate depth, great extent of delta front, and a slowly rising sea level favor the development of a wide sub-aqueous plain. These conditions are thought to obtain about the delta of the Nile. Weak waves, coarse and abundant sediments, stationary or falling sea level, and several rivers converging toward a shallow sea lead to the development of an extensive subaerial plain. The compound delta of the Rhine and adjacent rivers illustrates these conditions. Other combinations of the factors lead to other results.[139]

The Delta Cycle

The development of the three components of a delta is closely related to the physiographic age of the country drained by the forming stream. In physiographic youth a stream usually supplies more waste than the waves and currents of the stationary body of water can distribute. The excess is left at the mouth of the stream to form the delta. With extension of a stream into the region drained the excess of waste may increase to a maximum, and during this period of increase the delta continues to advance, but each advance widens its front and renders it more accessible to wave and current attack. Following the time of supply of maximum waste, a decline sets in, culminating in old age of the physiographic cycle when the waste supplied is so small in quantity as to be negligible. At some time in this decline, probably about late maturity of the physiographic cycle, the quantity of waste supplied is equal to that which can be handled by the waves and currents, and further decline leaves an excess to these abilities. This excess energy is devoted to removal of some parts of the delta to a level and profile determined by the conditions. Most, if not the whole of the deposits of the subaerial plain, large parts and perhaps the whole of the deposits of the subaqueous plain, and possibly the upper portions of the topset beds, particularly on the seaward margin, may be removed. A plain of erosion results. The time involved in the building and destruction of the delta to the extent described is the delta cycle (fig. 118).

The above statement of delta history assumes a stationary sea level. If sea level is not stationary, the results are different. If sea level slowly rises with respect to the delta surface and there is no increase in the supply of waste, the subaerial plain attains slight development, and there is a great development of the subaqueous plain whose topset beds attain a thickness proportionate to the rise of sea level. If the rise of sea level is accompanied by elevation of the region from which the stream derives its sediments, the distributive area, sufficient waste may be supplied to enable the stream to

[139] See Barrell, J., op. cit.

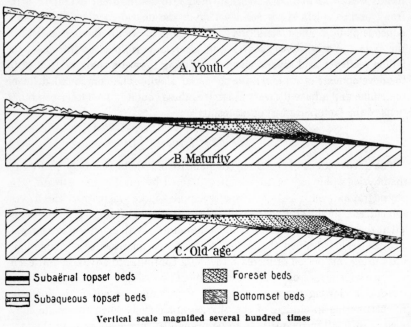

Subaërial topset beds
Subaqueous topset beds
Foreset beds
Bottomset beds

Vertical scale magnified several hundred times

FIG. 118. ILLUSTRATING THE DELTA CYCLE
After Barrell

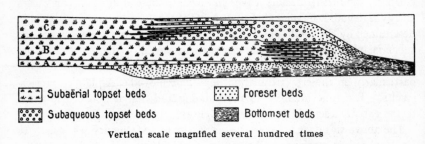

Subaërial topset beds
Subaqueous topset beds
Foreset beds
Bottomset beds

Vertical scale magnified several hundred times

FIG. 119. RELATION BETWEEN DELTA BUILDING AND SUBSIDENCE

A. First stage: Delta built out into water of constant level; basin deeper than base level of deposition. No subsidence. Shows initial dominance of foreset beds, increasing importance of topset beds, shallowing of the basin, and decreasing importance of foreset beds.

B. Second stage: Intermittent subsidence balanced by deposition. Delta built upward rather than outward with dominance of topset beds.

C. Third stage: Subsidence at a faster rate, maintaining a larger ratio of subaqueous topset beds. After Barrell.

build a subaerial plain. The progressive but intermittent rise of sea level will repeatedly extend the sea over the subaerial plain and lead to marine deposits thereon, over which there will then be deposited the sediments of the three components of the delta as it advances during the period of stability. The result is a dovetailing of marine and delta sediments, the extent of each varying with the conditions. Each marine and each delta unit may be bounded by unconformities (fig. 119). If the movement of sea level is oscillating, each rise brings in the sea; each fall moves it outward, extends the foreset beds, and erodes the subaerial and subaqueous plains. A section from a boring made in the subaerial plain of the Mississippi delta between the river and Lake Borgne at a distance of 15,000 feet from the river shows what may be expected and is as follows:

	feet
Soft dark brown mud, many fresh-water and a few marine shells	10
Fine blue clay, fresh-water origin	14
Coarse gray sand, fresh-water origin, except possibly base	16
Sand and clay mixed, probably fresh-water origin	10
Blue clay, contains marine shells	14
Sands, contain chips from a log and marine shells	9
Blue clay with marine shells	7
Sand and blue clay with marine shells	11
Blue clay	9 [140]

It is not known to what depth the bottom materials extend.

Summary of Delta Deposits

Deposits are of four classes: the topset deposits of the subaerial plain, the topset deposits of the subaqueous plain, the deposits of the foreset slope, and the bottomset beds beyond the foreset slope.[141] The deposits of the subaerial plain are of continental origin, are decidedly lenticular, show much channel cutting, are locally mud cracked and marked with "rain prints," locally contain the tracks of land animals, and have in greater or less abundance the remains of land and fresh-water animals and plants, some of the latter occurring in places where they grew. They exhibit various degrees of oxidation and reduction and hence have colors related to the quantity of organic matter they contain and the degree of oxidation. The color in some cases is black, in others gray, yellow, and red. Sorting and stratification tend to be poor and irregular, although each may be locally excellent. Many strata are cross laminated, and contemporaneous deformation may

[140] Hilgard, E. W., and Hopkins, F. V., Ann. Rept. Chief Eng., War Dept., App. W 2, 1878, pp. 855–890.
[141] Trowbridge, A. C., Personal communication, suggests that undue emphasis has been placed on these distinctions. The present writer agrees with Trowbridge, but the distinctions, as made, serve to emphasize the differences in environmental conditions.

be not uncommon. The sediments consist of sand, silt, clay, and vegetable matter. Beds of lime sediments are not likely to be present, although much lime may occur throughout the sediments. Gravel seems to be uncommon, but may be present. Marine fossils may be present to a greater or lesser extent.

The sediments of the subaqueous plain are deposited by the waters of the distributaries and waves and currents of varying direction and vigor. The units are usually lenticular and have uneven stratification, although regularity of stratification may obtain over extensive areas. Both land and fresh-water organisms may be present, but no land plants will be found in the places of growth, although stumps with attached roots may come to rest so as to appear in place. The sediments consist of clay, silt, sand, and occasional accumulations of vegetable matter. Beds of calcareous material are rare, and such seems also to be the case for gravels. Contemporaneous deformation may be common. The most common colors are gray and blue.

The sediments of the foreset slope are deposited by waves and currents and the waters of the distributaries. Some of the depositing water may be salty, or at least brackish, leading to flocculation of the fine sediments. The sediments may be poorly sorted and stratified, and the beds may have considerable initial inclination. Marine or lake fossils are commonly present, and organic matter of land or stream origin is not uncommon. Gray and blue colors dominate. The bedding is inclined fan-shaped from the distributary mouths, and considerable contemporaneous deformation may be associated with strata of high angles of initial inclination. The materials consist of clays, silts, sands, and some lime sediments.

The bottomset beds are deposited under marine conditions, although the materials are of stream derivation. The materials range from fine sands to silts and clays.

The deposits of the delta environment may attain thicknesses of many thousands of feet, dependent upon the depth of the body of water in which they are made and the extent of settling of the base upon which deposition takes place. Andrée[142] following Credner[143] seems to incline to the view that delta deposits attain slight thickness, but this statement seems to apply only to that part of delta deposits which are of subaerial deposition and even then it seems of doubtful validity.

Subaqueous delta sediments dovetail with each other, and no sharp distinctions exist. Studies of sediments carried into the Gulf of Mexico by the Mississippi through Southwest Pass indicate: (1) That the largest

[142] Andrée, K., Geologie des Meeresbodens, vol. 2, 1920, pp. 121–122.
[143] Credner, G. R., Die Deltas, Ergänzungheft, no. 56, Petermann's Mitth., 1878.

particles range from $\frac{1}{4}$ to $\frac{1}{2}$ mm. in diameter and that these are deposited on the crest of an offshore bar or in the beaches on the sides of the Pass lands and that few particles exceeding $\frac{1}{8}$ to $\frac{1}{4}$ mm. in diameter are carried outward farther than 5 miles.   (2) That the sediments of the offshore bar are coarser than those of any of the beaches and that the finest sediments are in the deepest water southwest of the Pass mouth.   (3) That 22 miles straight out from the Pass mouth there is an area over which the water is 32 fathoms deep (water nearer the Pass mouth having a depth of 50 fathoms), over which the sediments are coarser than on bar or beach and do not seem to have been contributed by the present river.   (4) That the particles are angular, are of varied mineral content, and contain glauconite on the outer steep slope.   (5) That except for shell fragments an area about the mouth of about 3 miles radius appears to be without life and organic remains, a zone 3 to 8 miles out contains agglutinate and chitinous foraminifera, beyond this there are calcareous foraminifera, and beyond 10 miles pelagic forms constitute a part of the bottom sediments.[144]

No one single characteristic can be relied upon to determine that a deposit was formed in the delta environment, as each of the characteristics to which reference has been made may develop in any one of several other environments.   The aggregate of characteristics coupled with the relations of the components of a deposit to each other and to the deposits of adjacent environments is essential.   Many marine deposits may show every feature which is found in the sediments of the bottomset, foreset, and subaqueous topset beds.   Marine deposits may be similarly cross laminated, contain the same fossils, and have the same mineralogical and lithological constituents.

Deposits of Ancient and Modern Deltas

Due to the various movements of Pleistocene and Recent time, existing streams seem to be more or less out of adjustment to sea level, and, in general, conditions do not seem to be particularly favorable for the extensive development of the subaerial parts of deltas.   Many large rivers, as the St. Lawrence, Amazon, and Congo, have this component lacking or feebly developed. Nevertheless, subaerial delta plains constitute extensive areas of the present land surface.   The subaerial plain of the delta of the Ganges and Brahmaputra rivers has an area approximating 50,000 square miles; that of the Nile is about as large; that of the Hoang Ho is of greater extent; and other large delta plains are those of the Rhine, Mississippi, Orinoco, Colorado, Indus, and Yukon.   In addition there are scores of smaller delta plains, and it is not improbable that over a half million square miles of the present land

[144] Trowbridge, A. C., Disposal of sediments carried to the Gulf of Mexico by Southwest Pass, Mississippi River Abstract Bull. Geol. Soc. Am. vol. 38, 1927 p. 148.

surface are underlain by the subaerial deposits of deltas.   As the submerged portions of deltas are as large, and probably larger than the exposed portions, the total present area receiving deposits of the delta environment may aggregate around 2,000,000 square miles.

During those times of the geologic past when shallow seas covered vast areas of the continents and highland regions bordered the seas, ideal conditions existed for the development of large deltas.   If the regions of supply of sediments were being elevated and the sites of delta deposition were sinking, great thickness of delta deposits would be possible.   That this has occurred during several periods of geologic time is certain.

Barrell[145] has shown that the lower portions of the Cretaceous formations of the Atlantic coast are best interpreted as of delta origin, and Barton[146] has presented evidence to the effect that the materials forming the coastal portions of southeast Texas were deposited in a coalescent delta of probably late Pleistocene time formed by the Trinity and Brazos rivers.   The Catskill formation of New York and along the Appalachians to the south is the delta deposit of a late Devonian river,[147] apparently accumulated under conditions of a slowly rising sea level.   The Coal Measures of Indiana and Illinois are best interpreted as deposits made in the delta environment under conditions of progressive, but intermittent, rises and occasional falls of sea level, many streams probably contributing to form the deposits.   The sediments consist largely of lenticular yellow sandstones, some of which are micaceous, and shales of different colors, but with yellow, gray, and blue dominating.   Coal beds occur at several horizons, and mud cracks are common.   Few strata persist for long distances.   At several levels are widespread layers with marine fossils.   These marine beds commonly are limestones and record a rise of sea level with wide invasion of marine waters over a flat delta surface.   The Coal Measure deposits of southwestern Indiana appear to be largely those of the subaerial plain.   True foreset beds seem to be rare.

The Coal Measures of Kansas, Missouri, and Oklahoma were also largely deposited under the condition of a delta environment, but they differ from those of Indiana and Illinois in that the sea made many invasions, and thus considerable parts of the sequence are marine.   The rise of sea level was intermittent and unequal, as shown by the variations in thickness of the deltaic and typically marine formations.   This is illustrated by the Weston

[145] Barrell, J., Criteria for the recognition of ancient delta deposits, Bull. Geol. Soc. Am., vol. 23, 1912, pp. 406–411.

[146] Barton, D. C., Surface geology of coastal southeast Texas, Bull. Am. Assoc. Pet. Geol., vol. 14, 1930, pp. 1301–1320.

[147] Barrell, J., The Upper Devonian delta and the Appalachian geosyncline, Am. Jour Sci., vol. 36, 1913, pp. 429–472; vol. 37, pp. 87–109 and 225–253.

shale, Iatan limestone, Lawrence shale, and Oread limestone formations. Each of the two shale formations consists of sandstones and shales and has a thickness of 150 feet or more. The Oread limestone, consisting of three limestone members separated by shale members, has a thickness approximating 50 feet. The Iatan limestone in most places is under 10 feet thick. The Weston and Lawrence formations appear to be largely of topset deposition, as they are without marine fossils, contain an abundance of plant remains, and have local lenses of coal. The Weston formation appears to have been built into a shallow sea. A rapid rise of sea level flooded the surface of the Weston delta and led to the deposition of the Iatan limestone. The Lawrence shales were deposited as a delta over this limestone. Another rise of sea level led to the deposition of the Oread formation.

The great pile of Pennsylvanian sediments north of the old land of Llanoria in Texas and Louisiana seems best interpreted as partly deposited in the delta environment with the subaerial phase dominating. The Pennsylvanian deposits of north-central Texas are referred to the same environment, but with a greater development of subaqueous deposition.[148]

Great thicknesses of the Pennsylvanian of the Appalachian geosyncline seem to have accumulated in the delta environment, and delta building was in progress in the Appalachian geosyncline at one place or another throughout the entire period. Schuchert states that three fresh-water deltas formed in this trough, one in the vicinity of Pottsville, Pennsylvania, a second in the Kanawha valley of West Virginia, and a third in the Cahaba valley of Alabama.[149] Branson[150] has described a delta deposit from the Mississippian of Virginia.

Considerable portions of the Cretaceous strata of Montana, Wyoming, and Alberta along the western borders are best interpreted as ancient delta deposits made by streams flowing into the Cretaceous sea from land areas to the west. The sediments consist mostly of muds, silts, and sands, and it is thought that every component part of deltas may be identified, fine dark muds with marine fossils representing the bottomset beds, foreset cross-laminated sandstones containing marine and terrestrial fossils, and shales and sandstones with coal beds and terrestrial plants representing the deposits of the subaerial and subaqueous plains.[151] Berry[152] has called

[148] Honess, C. W., Geology of southern Le Flore and northwestern McCurtain counties, Oklahoma, Oklahoma Bureau of Geology, cir. no. 3, 1924; Miser, H. D., Llanoria, the Paleozoic land area in Louisiana and eastern Texas, Am. Jour. Sci., vol. 2, 1921, pp. 61–89.

[149] Schuchert, C., Text book of geology, pt. ii, Historical geology, 2nd ed., 1924, p. 354.

[150] Branson, E. B., A Mississippian delta, Bull. Geol. Soc. Am., vol. 23, 1912, pp. 447–452.

[151] Bowen, C. F., Gradation from continental to marine conditions of deposition in central Montana during the Eagle and Judith River epochs, Prof. Paper 125–B, U. S. Geol. Surv., 1919.

[152] Berry, E. W., The delta character of the Tuscaloosa formation, Johns Hopkins Univ., Cont. to Geology, 1917, pp. 18–24.

attention to the probability that the sediments of the Tuscaloosa formation of Misssissippi, Alabama, and parts of some adjacent states were deposited in the delta environment.

The Huronian and Keewatin deposits of the Lake Superior region in part appear to have developed in the delta environment, and some parts of the Keweenawan may have had this origin.

The Tertiary Ione formation of the Great Valley of California, consisting of quartz sands and gravels, clays, and beds of lignite, was assigned by Allen[153] to an environment about the mouths of many streams flowing from land to the east, that is, it is a compound delta deposit. The Pico formation of the Los Angeles Basin seems to be of delta origin.

Strata of delta origin seem to be equally abundant on other continents. The Weald of the Cretaceous of southeast England and the Estuarine series of the Jurassic of Yorkshire[154] have been referred to an origin in this environment. The Estuarine series is said to show filled channels, washouts, deposits of lagoons, and the topset and foreset deposits of a delta. The Millstone Grit[155] is referred to delta origin, the delta having been made by a large river draining from the north with tributaries flowing over different kinds of rocks. Parts of the Molasse and Flysch of the Cretaceous and Tertiary of the Alpine region and some of the Tertiary of the London and Paris basins seem to be of deltaic origin.

The Tertiary of the Irrawaddy Basin of Burma seems to be composed of delta deposits that filled an ancient Burmese gulf under conditions of fluctuating sea level.[156]

THE MARGINAL LAGOON ENVIRONMENT AND ITS SEDIMENTS

The marginal lagoon is a small body of water which has been partially separated from a larger body by the building of a bar or barrier beach, connection with the parent body being maintained by one or more openings. The lagoon differs from the shore lake in its more intimate connection with the parent body. Along parts of the southern coast of the Gulf of St. Lawrence a lagoon is known as a *barachois* and the opening as a *tickle*. In the

---

[153] Allen, V. T., The Ione formation of California, Univ. California Publ. Geol. Sci., vol. 18, 1929–30, pp. 347–419 (402–406), pls. 24–37.

[154] Black, M., Drifted plant beds of the upper Estuarine series of Yorkshire, Qu'art. Jour. Geol. Soc., vol. 85, 1929, pp. 389–439.

[155] Gilligan, A., The petrography of the Millstone grit of Yorkshire, Quart. Jour. Geol. Soc., vol. 75, 1919, pp. 251–294.

[156] Stamp, L. D., An outline of Tertiary geology of Burma, Geol. Mag., vol. 59, 1922, pp. 481–501; Geology of the oil fields of Burma, Bull. Am. Assoc. Pet. Geol., vol. 11, 1927, pp. 557–579; Cotter, G. de P., The geotectonics of the Tertiary Irrawaddy Basin, Jour. Asiatic Soc. Bengal, vol. 14, 1918, pp. 409–420. Stamp refers to other papers relating to these delta deposits.

old-age stage of the lagoon cycle the lagoon may become a marsh, or the bar may be removed by wave erosion, and complete connection with the parent body be reestablished. Consideration of the lagoon environment is limited to those connected with marine waters.

The waters of a lagoon range from fresh to salt, and the concentration in places may exceed that of the adjacent sea. Normally fresh water is brought by streams, and the quantity at times may be so large as to exclude the entrance of much salt water. Certain areas may be overlain by salt water at all times, and other areas by fresh water. As salt waters are heavier than fresh, the former may enter a lagoon as subsurface currents, and the fresh waters contributed by streams may be confined entirely to the surface over some parts of a lagoon. The different concentrations influence the temperatures of the waters.

The variations in salinity, both laterally and vertically, and those in temperature determined by salinity and other factors may control and certainly do influence the distribution of organisms, leading to considerable variation in the organic assemblages over different parts of a lagoon. In places of repeated and decided changes in salinity, organisms may be altogether excluded, and in other places too great or too little concentration may dwarf many forms. As noted later, there are other conditions in certain lagoons which may result in dwarfing. Over some areas the bottoms may be densely populated with marine forms, and over others the organisms may be those of the fresh water. Some places may support a marine fauna in the lower waters and possibly fresh-water organisms in the upper levels. The quiet waters encourage the growth of considerable bottom and floating vegetation, the presence of which will bring in organisms adapted to the plants concerned.

The sediments may exhibit considerable range. Terrigenous sediments are brought by the streams and winds and carried in by currents from the sea, and materials of organic derivation and chemical precipitation are produced *in situ*. The terrigenous sediments range from clay to sand and perhaps particles of larger dimension. The currents from the sea may bring in some shell and plant matter and particularly planktonic organisms, the latter perhaps being killed on contact with fresh water, and thus becoming buried in the deposits of an environment to which the organisms were not adapted. Calcium carbonate is precipitated by green plants, by invertebrates, and probably by other agents. As the waters in the deeper parts of the bottom may become stagnant, such places are likely to become filled with black muds containing abundant anaërobic bacteria, among which the so-called sulphur bacteria are likely to be common. Formation of hydrogen sulphide is apt to occur on a considerable scale, resulting in the precipitation of ferrous monosulphide and the formation of sulphuric acid, the latter assisting in dissolving any calcium or other carbonates which may enter the environment of the black mud deposits. Carbonate fossils in such muds either disappear altogether or are replaced by iron sulphide. The hydrogen sulphide in the waters may affect neighboring areas, and dwarfed organisms result from its presence. Some lagoons, in whole or in part, particularly those associated with coral reefs, may have deposits consisting largely of calcium carbonate.

The stratification of lagoonal deposits should be regular and even, with little or no cross lamination due to currents, except near openings in the bar and about the mouths of inflowing streams. The shallowness of the water makes it possible for waves to leave their characteristic markings on the bottoms, so that every surface may contain ripple mark. Tracks, trails, "rain prints," and other markings may be common. The colors range from gray where the vegetable matter is scanty to dark and even black where it is abundant.

Lagoonal Deposits in the Geologic Column

Little seems to be known relating to lagoonal deposits in the geologic column. The Solenhofen lithographic stone has been interpreted as the lagoonal deposits of a coral reef, and a lagoonal origin has been suggested for the Birdseye limestone of New York. The shallow epicontinental Paleozoic and later seas should have been margined by many lagoons, and there should be deposits of this environment in every system. Few have been recognized, however, which probably indicates that some misinterpretations with relation to the stratigraphy exist.

THE ESTUARINE ENVIRONMENT AND ITS SEDIMENTS

An estuary is defined as that region in and adjacent to the mouth of a river in which the stream current is periodically barred from flowing into the sea by rise of tides, the water level in the stream being raised so that portions of the banks exposed at low tide are inundated at high. At high tide an under current of salt water flows upstream beneath fresh water. At low tide fresh water extends to a greater depth, and the salt water is partially replaced by fresh. An estuary to be important requires a considerable tidal range, with an enlargement of the river about its mouth due to coastal submergence. The environment passes upstream into the fluvial and seaward into the shallow neritic. The intervening area between the typical fluvial and typical neritic environment is the estuarine. Its limits are fluctuating. Its shore margins are like those of the littoral except for the more or less decided variations in the salinity of the water. Important existing estuaries are the upper part of the Gulf of St. Lawrence, the upper part of the Bay of Fundy, Chesapeake and Delaware bays, and the estuaries of the La Plata, Thames, and Severn. Estuaries do not exist in tideless seas.

The salinity of different parts of an estuary has considerable range. Those into which there is a rather steady discharge of fresh water, as the St. Lawrence, have a somewhat constant salinity for any given place. Those in which the discharge of fresh water is subject to much variation may have considerable range in salinity for a given place. Variations in tidal range also have important effects. Some places have salt water over the bottom and fresh water above, and some parts of the bottom are alternately bathed by fresh and salt water. An estuary may have salt water flowing upstream at the same time that fresh water is flowing seaward on top.[157]

Due to the funnel-like shape of many estuaries, the tides tend to be high compared to the shores of the open sea. This leads to strong tidal currents, resulting in much scouring of the bottom.[158] The tides also restrict the areas of the estuaries through the building of marine and brackish-water marshes and mud flats. These features are well shown about parts of the Bay of Fundy.

Twice daily the tidal currents contend with the waters of the stream, following which the two work together to produce strong currents out of the estuary. Where the opposing currents conflict, there may be deposition of material held in suspension in either current, resulting in the formation of mud and sand banks on the bottom. In course of time these may become mud or sand flats or islands. This deposition leads to the concentration of the ebb and flow waters in the deeper channels, which are thus kept open. The tides may extend for long distances upstream, 600 miles in the Amazon, making the tidal bores. These concern only fresh water, and while a river to the extent of the influence of its bore is an estuary, the influence on the sediments is negligible except that current ripple mark and cross lamination may become reversed in direction.

The estuary of the Severn has been studied in detail.[159] Here the tidal currents flow at velocities of 6 to 12 miles per hour.

[157] Johnston, W. A., Sedimentation of the Fraser River delta, Mem. 125, Geol. Ser. no. 107, Geol. Surv. Canada, 1921, pp. 17–18.

[158] Hunter, J. F., Erosion and sedimentation in Chesapeake around the mouth of Choptank River, Prof. Paper, 90-B, U. S. Geol. Surv., 1914.

[159] Sollas, W. J., The estuaries of the Severn and its tributaries; an inquiry into the nature and origin of their tidal sediment and alluvial flats, Quart. Jour. Geol. Soc. London, vol. 39, 1883, pp. 611–626.

At high tide the tidal channel of the river is filled with a sea of turbid water, thick and opaque with tawny-coloured sediments; as the tide ebbs a broad expanse of shining mud flats is revealed fringing the coast; but so like is the water to the mud that, seen from a distance, it is hard to tell where the sea ends and the shore begins.

The mud appears to be partly derived from the rivers flowing into the estuary, partly from the erosion of the shores, and partly from the sea. This mud wanders back and forth, now carried inland by the tidal currents, now outward by the stream currents, withdrawals constantly being made for deposition in the sea, and accessions as constantly being made by the streams, and possibly by inflowing marine currents.

Due to variations in salinity, turbidity, and strong currents, the bottoms of those parts of estuaries subject to such variations do not have a large population of marine organisms. Estuarine faunas also may be composed of smaller individuals than the same forms in the open sea, as is illustrated by the fauna of the Baltic Sea, where such shells as *Mytilus* and *Mya* are not more than half as large as the same forms on shores of the Atlantic. The organisms of different parts of an estuary may be much unlike. Above the salt-water influence they are those of fresh water; seaward they are adapted to normal sea water. There should, therefore, be more or less mingling of marine and fresh-water organisms.

There is considerable range in the sediments of estuaries, and the units have somewhat lenticular deposition. Cross lamination and current ripple mark should show considerable variation in direction. The sediments on the bottom of the tidal portion of the Severn consist of

a variable quantity of fine argillaceous granules, small angular fragments of colorless transparent quartz containing numerous minute included cavities, a few similar fragments of flint, siliceous fragments of a glauconitic green colour, minute crystals of quartz of the ordinary form, minute crystals of tourmaline, highly pleochroic and similar in form to the microscopic prisms of schorl, and minute rhombohedra of calcite.

The Severn muds contain siliceous and calcareous organic matter in the form of coccoliths and coccospheres similar to those in the adjacent Atlantic, the tests of several species of foraminifera, spicules of Alcyonaria, minute spines and fragments of echinoderms, spicules of calcareous and siliceous sponges, tests of diatoms, and shells of other invertebrates. The foraminiferal shells are generally empty, but a few were found filled with brownish material, and one was found practically replaced by pyrite. Above the limits of tidal action the muds appear to be of similar character, but the contained organic matter is of fresh-water origin.

A section of older deposits of the Severn estuary is as follows:

3. Upper clay which at the top through a thickness of 5 to 7 feet is more sandy than the 7 to 8 feet below. Below the clay are 1 to 2.5 feet of peat which is formed of aquatic plants at the base and has branches and other parts of trees on the top.

2. Lower clay with 1 to 4 feet of peat at the base.

1. Sand and mud underlain by gravel, the last resting on Triassic sandstone. The gravel contains pebbles and boulders of glacial origin.

Organic matter in the form of shells occurs in some of the layers,[160] and the thickness is about 50 feet.

Estuarine deposits are not likely to contain thick or extensive beds of carbonate sediments, though lenses of local extent may be not uncommon. The colors of estuarine deposits usually are gray or blue, and they may be black.

The general outline of an estuarine deposit should be rudely triangular, and it should grade outward into typical marine sediments and landward into those of fluvial origin. On the lateral margins there should be peats and dark muds or mud-cracked clays and silts.

There is no single criterion by which an estuarine deposit may be distinguished, but the aggregate of characters which have been stated and the general geologic relationships to fluvial and marine deposits may serve to differentiate them.

That estuarine deposits exist in the geologic column must be accepted as certain. Grabau has advanced the view that the black graptolite shales of the Utica type were deposited under estuarine conditions and the present writer is more or less in harmony with this view.[161] This carries with it the correlate that the graptolites are found in these shales not because the waters of deposition were the natural environments of life, but because they were the environments of death, and that, too, under conditions favorable for rapid burial and consequent preservation. The fluctuating and unstable conditions on the bottom repelled the benthos and hence the bottom muds after deposition did not make frequent passages through intestinal tracts with consequent disappearance of organic matter.

MARINE ENVIRONMENTS

The marine environments are those of the shallow water (neritic), the bottom intermediate to the deep sea (bathyal), and the deep sea (abyssal).

[160] Sollas, W. J., op. cit.

[161] Grabau, A. W., and O'Connell, M., Were the graptolite shales, as a rule, deep or shallow water deposits?, Bull. Geol. Soc. Am., vol. 28, 1917, pp. 959–964; Grabau, A. W., Origin, distribution, and mode of preservation of the graptolites, Mem. Inst. Geol., Nat. Res. Inst. China, no. 7, 1929, pp. 1–52.

To a considerable extent the littoral, delta, marginal lagoon, and estuarine sediments have marine characteristics. The sediments brought to marine environments are derived from all sources, but the greater portions are of terrigenous and pelagic origins.[162]

Bottom waters as a whole may be placed in four classes: (1) bottom waters carrying little mud or sand, and deposition of mud or sand on the bottom of slight quantity; (2) bottom waters very muddy, and deposition of mud large; (3) bottom waters carrying much sand, and bottom deposits composed of sand; (4) bottom waters more or less periodically carrying much sand or mud.

Under the conditions of clean waters over the bottom and small deposition of clastics, bottoms, other conditions being favorable, are likely to be densely populated, and such will also be the case in the waters above. There will also be an abundance of scavengers adapted to the food supply and the chances are that most of the organic materials will be broken and ground to pieces as a consequence of many passages through the digestive tracts of scavenger and bottom-eating organisms. The conditions for preservation of organic remains are poor, and rocks formed under these conditions are not likely to contain many well preserved shells.

The conditions of very muddy bottom waters and deposition of much mud are not congenial to many organisms, and the bottom population is small and of few species. The rapid deposition of mud, however, favors preservation of organic remains, and the fossil record may suggest a larger population than was the case. Contributions of organic matter may be made from outside, as the presence of muddy waters indicates presence of currents. These, however, are of low competency, and hence introduced organic matter would consist of small shells.

The conditions of bottom waters carrying much sand and bottom deposits composed of sand are also not favorable to many organisms, and such conditions seem usually to be accompanied by small bottom populations. The transportation of sand implies considerable competency, and there is likelihood of extensive introduction of shell materials from other bottoms. Here again a section of sediments formed under these conditions may suggest a greater abundance of life on the bottom than actually existed.

Bottoms irregularly or periodically subjected to the deposition of considerable mud, if the times of deposition are sufficiently far apart to permit

[162] Important works dealing with marine deposits are: Murray, J., and Renard, A. F., Deep sea deposits, in Challenger Repts.; Collet, L. W., Les dépôts marins; Murray, J., and Hjort, J., The depths of the ocean; and Andrée, K., Geologie des Meeresbodens, Leipzig, 1920. Reports of the different marine exploring expeditions should also be consulted.

colonization by organisms, offer the greatest possibilities for preservation of organic matter, as the influx of mud may bury and smother both the scavengers and predatory benthos and the organisms upon which they feed, producing a sedimentary deposit of calcareous shales and thin limestones abundantly filled with fossil shells.

It seems obvious that the marine deposits may not give a true picture of the abundance of marine life at the time of deposition. Differentiation needs to be made as to whether the organic remains in the sediments are of animals living where the remains are found, or whether the remains were transported from some other environment. Sediments, particularly limestones, with few fossil remains do not prove a small bottom population, as these sediments may represent a bottom that was abundantly populated and conclusion must be deferred until the rocks are examined in thin section to determine whether or not they are abundantly filled with fragments.

THE NERITIC OR MARINE SHALLOW-WATER ENVIRONMENT

The neritic environment of the sea is that portion of the bottom extending from the low-tide level to the depth of around 100 fathoms. It embraces the greater portion of the sea bottom known as the continental shelf, together with such epicontinental seas as Hudson Bay.

At the present time the neritic bottom of the sea is estimated to have an area between 10,000,000 and 15,000,000 square miles. About oceanic islands and some shores of the continents the neritic zone is narrow; about shores which have not been uplifted for a long time and those which have recently been submerged it may attain widths which in some cases exceed 100 miles. The distribution, extent, and depths of the most important areas of the neritic environment are shown in table 91.[163] Those parts of the continental shelf having depths exceeding 100 fathoms are arbitrarily assigned to the bathyal environment.

Were sea level to rise materially, the outer and deeper portions of the neritic zone would be added to the bathyal, but there would be an increase on the landward side through the overflooding of the lower lands of the continents. During those times of the geologic past when the lands were reduced to low peneplains, slight raises of sea level extended the neritic environment far into the hearts of the continents and added hundreds of thousands of square miles to its area. At times during the Cambrian, Ordovician, Silurian, Devonian, and Cretaceous the extent of sea bottom of neritic depths must have been fully twice as great as at present, and, if Walther's opinion that there was no deep sea until after the close of the

[163] Krümmel, O., Handbuch der Ozeanographie, Bd. 1, 1897, p. 113.

TABLE 91

LOCATION	AREA	DEPTH
	sq. km.	*meters*
Atlantic Ocean:		
America:		
Newfoundland shelf..........................	345,000	150–200
Florida-Texas shelf..........................	385,000	Mostly less than 50
Campeche shelf.............................	170,000	Mostly less than 50
Guiana shelf...............................	485,000	Mostly less than 50
South Brazil shelf..........................	370,000	Mostly less than 50
Patagonian shelf...........................	960,000	Mostly less than 50
Africa:		
Agulhas shelf..............................	75,000	Mostly over 100
Europe:		
British shelf...............................	1,050,000	Mostly under 100
Arctic Ocean:		
Norwegian shelf............................	93,000	200–300
Iceland-Faroe shelf.........................	115,000	200–300
Barents shelf..............................	830,000	200–300
North Siberian shelf (Nova Zembla to 155° W. long)..	1,330,000	One-half under 50
Indian Ocean:		
Africa:		
Zambesi shelf..............................	55,000	Mostly under 50
Asia:		
Bombay shelf..............................	230,000	50–100
Burma shelf...............................	290,000	Mostly under 100
Australia:		
N. W. Australia shelf......................	590,000	50–100
S. Australia shelf..........................	320,000	50–100
Pacific Ocean:		
Australia:		
Tasmania shelf............................	160,000	50–100
Queensland shelf...........................	190,000	Mostly under 100
Arafura shelf..............................	930,000	50–100
Borneo-Java shelf..........................	1,850,000	50–100
Asia:		
Tonkin-Hongkong shelf.....................	435,000	Mostly under 100
Tunghai shelf (Strait of Formosa to Strait of Korea)...................................	915,000	Mostly under 100
Okhotsk-Sakhalin shelf.....................	715,000	50–100
Behring shelf..............................	1,120,000	One-half under 50

Paleozoic be correct, the extent of the neritic environment during the Paleozoic may have been many times the present area.[164]

[164] Walther, J., The origin and peopling of the deep sea, Naturwiss. Wochenschr., 1904, transl. by LeVene, C. M., Am. Jour. Sci., vol. 31, 1911, pp. 55–64.

The seas between continents, as the Mediterranean, Caribbean, and Gulf of Mexico, which do not lie on the continental shelf, but are isolated parts of the deep sea, have been designated mediterraneans. These have neritic margins, but their bottoms descend to the depths of the bathyal and abyssal environments.

The neritic environment has different expressions depending upon whether it margins the shores of the open sea, an epicontinental sea, a coral island or barrier, a submerged bank, or a volcanic island.

The neritic environment on the shores of the open sea commonly has strong waves and currents to great depths. Tides and tidal currents are invariable. The faunas are normal and tend to have cosmopolitan characteristics and wide distribution. This is the typical neritic environment.

About coral islands and reefs there is great variety to the sediments and the faunas. In the lagoon of a coral atoll or the lagoon between a reef and the land the sediments commonly are extremely fine muds which may be almost wholly calcareous. Channels between the reefs may contain limestone gravel and sand. One fauna may dwell on the reef, another in the channels, a third in the lagoon, and a fourth in the deeper waters outward from the reef. The stratification ranges from none at all in the coral masses to the finest of laminations in the lime muds of the lagoons. The strata have inclinations ranging from essentially horizontal within the lagoons to an approximation to the angle of repose about the reefs. The neritic environment may embrace the whole of an epicontinental or epeiric sea. The waters may range from nearly fresh in such seas to high salinity. The tides may be much smaller than in the open sea or they may have a greater range. The Baltic Sea illustrates an epicontinental sea with brackish waters in its eastern areas, and its tides are small. Hudson Bay has strong tides. The faunas tend to be more or less provincial.

The neritic environment about volcanic islands is characterized by an abundance of volcanic matter in the sediments and the probable occurrence of high initial inclinations.

Processes of the Neritic Environment

PHYSICAL PROCESSES. Essentially the whole of the neritic environment is within the range of wave and current action, this being particularly true of the shoreward portions where the sediments may attain only temporary deposition. Near the shore the variations in wave and current trend are extremely great. Ripple and current mark have equally great variation in trend and development, and the strata commonly are cross-laminated to some extent. The shells which enter this portion of the neritic environment not infrequently are broken, and entire shells may have one or more healed places. Due to the fact that the bottom of the neritic zone is subject to wave activity, it is near the critical point of deposition and erosion, and over large areas the sediments are only temporarily deposited. As a consequence, local unconformities or diastems are common. If sea level remains stationary sufficiently long, a base level of deposition may be reached, with cessation of deposition until a change of conditions produces a new base level above the original one. This must have occurred many times in the neritic environment of the geologic past, and there must be many stratigraphic breaks which are due to this cause. In nearly enclosed epicontinental seas the attainment of a base level of deposition is somewhat different from what it is in the open sea, as it is possible for an epicontinental sea to be filled up. A great volume of sediments may be deposited upon the landward margins of an epicontinental sea which later may be moved into the central deeper portions. This would give stratigraphic breaks about the margins.

Epicontinental seas may have weak tidal action and tidal currents. This condition leads to the presence of quiet bays and sounds of which the bottoms may become covered with black muds rich in hydrogen sulphide. This is illustrated by the limans of the east Baltic. Deep places in the bottom may contain similar muds. The shoreward waters of epicontinental seas with low tidal range may be so shallow as to destroy the effectiveness of waves for eroding at distances of many miles from the shore, and thus a vast stretch of shallow water may be given over to the deposition of muds and marine and fresh-water plant life with black muds as a result. It is thought that some black shales formed under such conditions. The waters of epicontinental seas may be abnormally salty or brackish, and dwarfed and provincial faunas are not unlikely. The shallowness of epicontinental seas may lead to the stirring up of previous deposits by storm waves. Lenticularity of units is the probable result.

It is to the neritic environment that streams bring the major portions of their waters with their burdens of suspended sediments, and it is upon neritic bottoms that great portions of these sediments come to rest. This deposition is permanent or temporary, depending upon the position of the bottom with respect to a base level of deposition. If the bottom is at or above this level, any deposits which are made will later be shifted outward to bathyal depths. The initial deposition is brought about by the checking of velocity and the electrolytes in solution in the sea water and the presence of colloids of opposite sign. If deposition is rapid, there is little differential settling.[165] Convection currents may form in the muds which settle rapidly, giving rise

[165] Johnston, W. A., Sedimentation of the Fraser River delta, Mem. 125, Geol. Ser. no. 107, Geol. Surv. Canada, 1921, p. 37.

to pit and mound structures. "Rain prints" formed by bubbles arising from the decay of organic matter are not improbable on the surfaces of the muds. Rates of deposition probably have an extremely high range, no doubt from a rate of a foot in a few days to the same thickness in many thousand years.

CHEMICAL PROCESSES. It is in the neritic environment where there is the greatest mingling of waters of different character, where there are immense quantities of decaying organic matter, where the waters are in rather general circulation from bottom to top, where there are great variations in temperature with consequent variations in carbon dioxide content, where there is much evaporation, where flourishes the greatest number of green plants, and where there is probably the densest population of marine invertebrates. As these conditions and processes are thought to be mainly responsible for the deposition of calcium carbonate, it follows that it is in the neritic environments that the greatest thickness of calcareous sediments has been deposited and deposition of calcareous sediments per unit area is now most rapid. The conditions quite generally are those of reduction.

ORGANIC PROCESSES. The neritic bottoms support a greater abundance of life than any other part of the ocean bottom of equal area. Bottoms which are sufficiently solid for long enough times to permit organisms to obtain and retain footholds are densely carpeted with both plants and animals, and the waters above such bottoms are equally abundantly filled with planktonic and nectonic life. It is on neritic bottoms that live the most mollusks, the most brachiopods, and other animals with thick and strong shells. Here also live the reef-building corals. Bottoms composed of gravel, sand, mud, and shells have each their own particular grouping of organisms, although many organisms thrive on several types of bottom. Black mud bottoms, because of limited quantity of oxygen and abundance of hydrogen sulphide, are not inhabited by a large variety of plants and animals. Bottoms composed of shifting sands also are scantily populated. There is possibility of sudden and vast destruction of life in neritic waters, such as the recent great destruction of the tile fish. Heavy rains in shallow waters may so change the salinity as to eliminate the bottom life almost totally. On the coast of Dorset, England, 1000 lobsters in boxes were killed in one night in 1863 by a heavy rain, and in 1865 on the same coast a sudden thaw in late January and early February produced so much melt water as to kill immense numbers of *Octopus vulgaris*;[166] similar great destruction of fish and other marine animals off the coast of India at the time of the abundant rainfall of the southwest monsoon has been described by Denison.[167]

[166] Geol. Mag., vol. 2, 1865, pp. 141–142.

[167] Denison, W., On the death of fishes during the monsoon off the coast of India, Quart. Jour. Geol. Soc., vol. 18, 1862, p. 453.

A great storm in 1918 over the Great Barrier Reef of Australia caused so much water to fall that all animals were killed locally to a depth of 10 feet below mean tide level.[168]

Stratification of Deposits in the Neritic Environment

Deposits adjacent to the shores are usually lenticular, with much cross lamination and great range in dimensions or particles. This is particularly true with respect to the deposits about coral reefs and in the separating channels and on shoreward bottoms with steep slopes. Bottoms with steep slopes have sediments deposited with high initial inclinations, and slumping should be not uncommon. In deeper waters the units are better defined, and there is less irregularity. The experiments of Kindle[169] suggest that laminations in marine sediments are sharply defined.

Distribution of Sediments on Neritic Bottoms

In general, the coarser sediments are adjacent to the shore and grade into finer deposits seaward, but the exceptions to this generalization are many. Bottoms adjacent to low shores without streams are apt to receive fine sediments, although some bottoms near such shores may have currents sufficiently strong to bring coarse sediments. On many existing bottoms muds and calcareous sediments are being deposited as far up the beach as the waters reach. Bottoms adjacent to high shores undergoing erosion commonly receive much coarse material derived from rocks of the shore. In greater depths of neritic waters the sediments tend to be more uniform in character and to consist very largely of calcareous matter and mud. About coral reefs, as shown in the ancient reefs of Gotland, Anticosti, and elsewhere in the Silurian and other systems, the distribution of sediments is extremely irregular. Any bottom of sufficient depth to permit strong waves and not so deep but that waves and currents reach bottom with sufficient competency to move sands and muds, should show considerable variation in its sediments and correspondingly in its faunas. Such vertical variations in sediments as are exhibited in the Ordovician about the Cincinnati Arch, in the Ordovician and Silurian of the Anticosti region, and in the Pennsylvanian of the Mid-Continent region imply variations of equal extent in the lateral, and variations as great should be expected in the faunas.

Sediments of the Neritic Environment and Their Colors

The sediments of the neritic environment are mainly terrigenous and pelagic. Cosmic and volcanic materials are present, the former constituting

[168] Yonge, C. M., A year on the Great Barrier Reef, 1930, pp. 79–80.
[169] Kindle, E. M., Diagnostic characteristics of marine clastics, Bull. Geol. Soc. Am., vol. 28, 1917, p. 908.

only a very small and inconspicuous part of the whole and the latter being only locally important.

The terrigenous sediments consist of gravels, sands, and muds. The gravels and sands tend to be well sorted; most are long travelled; and quartz is the most common substance. Excellent rounding seems to be the rule in the larger dimensions. The small particles are angular. The muds have gray, blue, green, red, and black colors. The red muds occur about the mouths of some tropical rivers like the Amazon. The black muds have limited distribution and are confined both to deep and shallow bottoms with poor circulation. The blue, gray, and green muds are found at all depths. The green color appears to be due to glauconite, which in the earlier geologic periods was abundantly developed over shallow portions of the neritic environment, but at the present time it does not appear to be so common in shallow waters.

The pelagic sediments consist of shell, coral and algal materials, and matter precipitated from solution. Most consists of calcareous matter, but some silica, iron carbonate, and iron oxide are deposited in this environment, and it is probable that the extent of such deposition has been greater in past ages than at present, as the Lake Superior and some of the other silica and iron sediments seem to have been deposited in waters of depths not greater than those of the neritic environment, although it is not known that the waters were salty or the sediments pelagic. A magmatic source has been postulated in some cases for the iron and silica. Before the pelagic foraminifera became of importance in the precipitation of calcium carbonate and thus increased its deposition on the deeper bottoms, it is suggested that there was an extremely great concentration of this sediment in the neritic environment. Foraminifera do not seem to have become abundant prior to the late Mesozoic or Tertiary, since which time there has been large and abundant deposition of lime over deep bottoms. Deposits of carbonaceous matter of pelagic origin are occasionally made, but the quantity is small and of local distribution. It seems improbable that peat deposits could originate in this environment.

The Marine Cycle

The marine cycle affects littoral, estuarine, neritic, and locally other sediments. In the early stages of the cycle the shores are irregular; they may be high; and the bottoms may descend rather abruptly from the shore (exceptions are where low, flat lands have been submerged). Under these conditions the sediments supplied are apt to be in quantities larger than can be disposed of by the marine waves and currents. The bottom is then built up, and the building continues until the sea's ability to dispose of material is adequate for the quantity contributed. The shore by that time will have acquired less irregular outlines—the headlands having been more or less cut away and the indentations filled. As the cycle continues, the quantity of sediments contributed gradually grows less, and any energy of the marine agents of transportation in excess of that necessary for disposing of the sediments contributed will be utilized to remove part of that previously deposited. Ultimately the old age of the cycle is attained, by which time the shore is far inland from its place of beginning, and an eroded surface has been cut across the neritic deposits of the earlier portion of the cycle and also across any lagoonal, estuarine, littoral, and other deposits which may have been present. Further progress carries this erosion surface to greater depths, the rate of erosion becoming progressively slower as the base level of erosion or wave base (about 600 feet below sea level) is approached.[170] The sediments removed in this erosion are moved outward into deeper waters (fig. 3).

Criteria for the Determination of Neritic Deposits

Neritic deposits may be composed of gravels, sands, muds, calcareous matter, glauconite, flint and chert, various minerals of iron, and rarer substances. An abundance of shells may or may not be present, depending upon the facies of the environment, the rates of deposition, and the abundance of scavenger organisms. Occasional layers contain shells and tests in excellent preservation. Usually they are more or less broken. Trails of marine animals and marks made by floating objects may occur, and ripple and current marks are generally common. There is a somewhat sharp delimitation of laminations and strata, and the continuity of bedding seems to increase with depth and distance from shore. These are positive characteristics. Negative characteristics are the absence of mud cracks and the tracks of land animals. The occurrence of thick conglomerates suggests a continental origin. The thickness of neritic sediments is limited only by the distance of the bottoms to a base level of deposition plus the distance of rise of sea level.

Neritic Deposits of the Past

It seems probable that the marine sediments of the known geologic column were almost wholly deposited in the neritic environment. A few may have originated in the shallower depths of the bathyal environment. The estimated average thickness of sediments on the continents is placed at one mile for the 45,000,000 square miles which are underlain by sedimentary rocks. The estimate probably is high. This gives 45,000,000 cubic miles of sedi-

---

[170] Johnson, D. W., Shore processes and shoreline development, 1919.

mentary materials on the continental areas. Probably 80 per cent, or 36,000,000 cubic miles, is of neritic origin, most of the rest being of continental origin or mixed continental and marine. Neritic sediments over the existing neritic environment are estimated to have an average thickness of 3 miles, giving an additional volume of 30,000,000 cubic miles.

THE BATHYAL ENVIRONMENT AND ITS SEDIMENTS

The bathyal environment of the sea bottom is that portion between depths of 100 and 1000 fathoms. Its shallower depths receive more or less light, and some plant life is present. The area is around 15,000,000 square miles, some of which is upon the deeper parts of the continental shelf and the rest upon the continental slopes. The sediments by slow transitions grade on the seaward side into those of the abyssal depths and by equally slow transitions on the landward side into those of the neritic bottoms.

Processes of the Bathyal Environment

PHYSICAL PROCESSES. Only the occasionally strong waves and currents are thought to make any impression on the bottoms, so that wave and current markings should be of limited occurrence. Sediments once deposited are thus rarely removed. Deposition takes place through settling from suspension, through a slow drift over the bottom from the neritic district, and through slumping. About many oceanic islands and the younger continental margins are steep slopes down which materials are readily moved to the deeper waters of the bathyal environment. Such steep slopes lead to inclined deposition and favor slumping, particularly if the steep slopes are the loci of seismic movement. The rate of deposition is thought to be slow, and not subject to serious interruptions.

CHEMICAL PROCESSES. The same processes noted in connection with the neritic environment are operative in the waters and sediments of the bathyal, but probably with less intensity for most of them. As sediments are precipitated from solution, they must sink a considerable distance before reaching bottom, and there is thus opportunity for return to solution. The conditions seem almost entirely to be those of reduction.

Some of the epicontinental seas of great depths are connected with the main body by shallow passages of neritic depths. This is the case in the Black Sea. Such conditions may lead to poor circulation and the development over the deep bottom of mud rich in hydrogen sulphide and the dark monosulphide and disulphide of iron. Such waters may be unfit for life. The muds are dark when wet, but the dark color tends to disappear on drying unless there is sufficient organic matter present for its maintenance.

ORGANIC PROCESSES. Bathyal bottoms are covered with numerous marine organisms where conditions permit. As light adequate for green plant growth does not penetrate to any great extent in bathyal depths, green plant material is absent unless brought in from shallower waters, and animal life is limited in accordance. In general, life seems to be prolific on bathyal bottoms, but there probably is not the abundance characteristic of neritic bottoms. Scavenger action is probably as intense as on shallow bottoms.

Structures and Continuity of Strata in Bathyal Deposits

The strata should be continuous over large areas. The exceptions are on the steep slopes about oceanic and coral islands and along the younger margins of the continents. Under such conditions nearness to the distributive areas may develop lenticularity of units, but these should be on a larger scale than occurs in neritic waters. The strata have an initial inclination determined by the surface and rapidity of deposition. This probably is gentle in most instances. Where it is sufficiently steep, slumping may take place. The sediments may be cross-laminated in the shallower portions of the environment, and both types of aqueous ripple marks may be present, but each probably is not common.

Sediments of the Bathyal Environment

The sediments of the bathyal environment are red, green, gray, and black muds, glauconite, calcareous materials, volcanic muds and sands, and rarer substances. Sands of terrigenous origin may also be present. The calcareous sediments consist of coral muds and sands, various oozes, and shell matter. According to the "Challenger" report, the coral muds and sands cover an area of 2,236,800 square miles, with the former having a mean depth of 740 fathoms and extending to a depth of 1820 fathoms, and the latter a mean depth of 176 fathoms. The volcanic muds and sands cover an area of 600,000 square miles, with the muds having a mean depth of 1033 fathoms and a range from 260 to 2800 fathoms, and the sands a mean depth of 243 fathoms and a range from 100 to 420 fathoms. The green muds and sands cover an area of 850,000 square miles, with the former having an average depth of 513 fathoms and a range from 100 to 1270 fathoms, and the latter an average depth of 449 fathoms with none collected from depths greater than 900 fathoms. The red muds cover an area of 400,000 square miles, with an average depth of 623 fathoms and a range from 120 to 1200 fathoms. The blue muds extend over 14,500,000 square miles at an average depth of 1421 fathoms and a range from 125 to 2800 fathoms.[171]

[171] Murray, J., and Renard, A. F., Deep sea deposits, Challenger Rept., 1891.

Bathyal Deposits in the Geologic Column

It is not certain that sediments deposited in the bathyal environment are present in the exposed geologic column, but it is not unlikely that some parts of the shallower parts of this environment have been elevated above sea level. It seems probable that the total quantity of sediments deposited in the bathyal environment is extremely great, as sediments once deposited are permanent and do not experience the frequent erosion which is the common fate of neritic sediments. The volume, of course, is unknown, but it is thought probable that 40,000,000 to 50,000,000 or more cubic miles of sediments must lie beneath bathyal bottoms.

THE DEEP-SEA ENVIRONMENT

In the deep abyss of the ocean there is no light other than that emitted by the phosphorescent organs of some of the animals living there. The pressure is tremendous, rising with depth at the rate of a little over a ton per square inch per mile, so that at a depth of 4 to 6 miles the weight on each square inch is 5 to 7 tons. The temperature is around 40° F. at all times. Currents and waves in the ordinary sense do not exist, and there is no appreciable motion of the water except in narrow channels and at times of earthquakes.

In the deep-sea environment may be included all that portion of the sea bottom which lies below the depth of about 1,000 fathoms. This gives an area of about 115,000,000 square miles. The shallower portions of the environment have deposits which are like those of the bathyal.

The absence of light eliminates green plants and any plants requiring light. Animals requiring green plants for food are thus not likely to be present. The darkness makes eyes unnecessary or leads to their development to an immense size in order to catch the feeble gleams emitted by animals with phosphorescent organs. The generally unfavorable conditions are responsible for the much smaller variety of organisms in the deep sea and for fewer individuals than exist in shallower waters.

The absence of currents and the little density of population coupled with the great pressure have made supporting and protecting structures more or less unnecessary in organisms, and such are very thin and fragile.

The sediments which reach the deep abyss are of cosmic, volcanic, terrigenous, and pelagic origin. The cosmic particles are not important from the quantitative point of view. They probably fall in approximately equal quantities over the entire surface of the earth, but because of the slowness of deposition over the bottom of the deep sea they have a greater relative importance there than in any other environment. The sediments of volcanic origin consist of volcanic ash and pumice. In many instances these are little decayed, but more frequently the pumice is considerably altered and its soluble parts removed; also in many instances the pumice is deeply impregnated with manganese oxide. The sediments of terrigenous origin have been carried by wind, water, or ice. The particles carried by ice may be of large size, and their occurrence in deepsea sediments introduces components which are abnormal to the environment. Similar large particles may be floated to the deep sea in the roots of trees or the holdfasts of marine plants. According to Murray and Hjort, these fragments should settle into the muds of the bottom with the longer axes in vertical position,[172] but it is by no means certain that the assumption of this position is the rule. The sediments carried by wind and water are very fine and settle with extreme slowness, and by the time they have reached the bottom all matter soluble in the sea water or alterable to a soluble state has been dissolved, so that little remains other than ferric oxide and aluminum silicate. The general assumption is that the quantity of terrigenous sediments in the deep abyss is not large, but it does not seem that this assumption is warranted. The writer has presented evidence suggesting that the total volume of inorganic sediments over the deep abyss is of the order of magnitude of 80,000,000 cubic miles, or nearly twice the volume of all the sediments on the land.[173] Parts of this are of volcanic origin, but it seems probable that the major portions are of terrigenous derivation. The pelagic sediments consist of the hard parts of organisms which lived in the upper lighted waters, or on the bottom. The contributions from the latter source appear to be slight, as the population is small, and the shells are thin and fragile. In the shallower portions of the deep sea the contributions from the lighted waters are extremely important. As the shells from the lighted waters sink, those most fragile and delicate are dissolved, and only the very resistant, compact, and large reach the bottom, in whose deposits their relative importance is great because of the small quantities of other constituents. Those which reach the bottom are corroded by solution to some degree, but none shows abrasion and fracturing from wave and current action. Some may have been crushed by predaceous animals. The actual importance is also extremely great, and it is estimated that the total quantity approximates 40,000,000 to 60,000,000 cubic miles.

Deep-sea deposits thus consist largely of the insoluble residue of materials which have settled through many feet of water, volcanic and cosmic matter, and the shells of pelagic organisms, the last decreasing in importance with

[172] Murray, J., and Hjort, J., Depths of the ocean, 1912, p. 207.
[173] Twenhofel, W. H., Magnitude of the sediments beneath the deep sea, Bull. Geol. Soc. Am., vol. 40, 1929, pp. 385–402.

depth. The samples collected by the "Challenger" Expedition show a progressive decrease of calcium carbonate in the sediments with depth. This is shown in the table which follows:[174]

	Per cent
Samples under 500 fathoms average $CaCO_3$	86.04
Samples between 500 and 1000 fathoms average $CaCO_3$	66.86
Samples between 1000 and 1500 fathoms average $CaCO_3$	70.87
Samples between 1500 and 2000 fathoms average $CaCO_3$	69.55
Samples between 2000 and 2500 fathoms average $CaCO_3$	46.73
Samples between 2500 and 3000 fathoms average $CaCO_3$	17.36
Samples between 3000 and 3500 fathoms average $CaCO_3$	0.88
Samples between 3500 and 4000 fathoms average $CaCO_3$	0.00
Samples over 4000 fathoms average $CaCO_3$	trace

This progressive decrease in calcium carbonate with depth may be largely assigned to the high carbon dioxide content of the deep waters, but the small production of shell matter on the bottom and the great depth through which shells from the lighted waters must sink are also responsible. The writer has suggested that earlier deep-sea sediments may not have had as high a content of lime carbonate as those of the present, and that this sediment did not become important in deep-sea deposits until the abundant development of pelagic foraminifera toward the end of Mesozoic time. Since the advent of these organisms there has been a continuous withdrawal of lime from sedimentary circulation, and it is possible that future ages may see a poverty of this salt due to its permanent burial beneath the deep sea.

The deposits of the deep sea contain many secondary products of which crystals of phillipsite and nodules of phosphate and manganese are the most abundant. The manganese nodules are confined mostly to the red clays, but also occur in the globigerina oozes. The occurrence of the resistant parts of upper-water animals is also a distinctive feature of the deposits of deep waters. A single dredge made by the "Challenger" in the central Pacific from a bottom of dark chocolate clay at a depth of 2385 fathoms yielded between 2 and 3 bushels of manganese nodules of which the diameters were between 1 and 2.5 mm. In addition there were over 1500 specimens of shark teeth and fragments, about 50 ear bones of whales, 12 rounded pieces of pumice of which the largest was about the size of a hen's egg, and 6 rounded pebbles or cobbles of which one of basaltic rock was over 3 inches in diameter; others were of gneiss and granite. The rock fragments probably were ice borne.[175]

The rate of deposition of deep-sea sediments must be extremely slow, as attested by the abundance of shark teeth and other uncommon substances.

[174] Murray, J., and Renard, A. F., Deep sea deposits, Challenger Rept., 1891, p. 279.
[175] Murray, J., and Renard, A. F., op. cit., pp. 359–360.

A minimum rate of one foot in 87,100 years has been suggested.[176]   Except in volcanic regions and regions of recent faulting, the strata must be deposited on nearly level surfaces, with each layer extending in essentially uniform character for immense distances.

Summary of Characteristics of Deep-sea Sediments[177]

(1) Deep-sea sediments usually contain no large fragments of quartz or other continental rocks except as such may be dropped by floating ice or plants.   Exceptions are where deep sea is close to land.   (2) They contain no plant residues which are brown or black in color.   (3) They are piled in horizontal layers and are spread over marvelous distances.   (4) They contain no or few remains of shallow-water animals or plant eaters.   (5) By very slow and gradual transitions they are connected with the shallower water sediments of another origin.   (6) There are no features due to wave and current action.   (7) The deepest deposits contain an abundance of the resistant parts of swimming organisms and many things which are not common in other environments.   (8) The shell matter either is more or less corroded by solution or is fragile and thin, the former having settled from above, the latter being derived from organisms living in the environment.

These characters are not always present.   An earthquake wave may move the waters to the greatest depths and thus produce current marks in the deepest deposits.

The Sediments of the Deep Sea

The sediments of the deep sea consist of red clay covering 51,500,000 square miles on bottoms ranging in depth from 2225 fathoms to the deepest known, and having an estimated volume of 75,000,000 cubic miles; globigerina ooze covering 49,520,000 square miles at a mean depth of about 2000 fathoms, but occurring as deep as 2925 fathoms and as shallow as 400 fathoms, and having a volume estimated to range from 50,000,000 to 100,000,000 cubic miles; diatom ooze covering 10,880,000 square miles with a mean depth of 1477 fathoms, but present in depths of 600 to 1975 fathoms, and with an estimated volume of 3,900,000 cubic miles; radiolarian ooze extending over 2,290,000 square miles with a mean depth of 2894 fathoms, found in depths from 2350 to 4475 fathoms, and estimated to have a volume of 19,-900,000 cubic miles,[178] and pteropod ooze over 400,000 square miles at an average depth of 1044 fathoms.[179]

[176] Twenhofel, W. H., op. cit.

[177] Walther, J., The origin and peopling of the deep sea, Naturwissen. Wochenschr., 1904, Transl. by LeVene, C. M., Am. Jour. Sci., vol. 31, 1911, pp. 55–64.

[178] The figures of volume are taken from Twenhofel, W. H., op. cit.

[179] Murray, J., and Renard, A. F., op. cit., p. 248.

Deep-sea Sediments in the Geologic Column

Walther[180] expressed the opinion that no deep sea existed until the Mesozoic, as the expression of the present deep-sea faunas is Mesozoic, and Paleozoic elements are lacking. If this opinion is correct, no Paleozoic deep-sea deposits ever existed. At any rate, none has been identified. Clarke and others have referred certain black shales to a deep-sea origin under conditions similar to those of the Black Sea, but these shales are best interpreted as having originated in other environments.[181] Formerly the Cretaceous Chalk was referred to a deep-sea environment, but this view has very generally been abandoned. Grabau has suggested that some of the massive limestones of the eastern Alps and some of the Alpine Jurassic beds may be of comparatively deep-sea origin, as some of them contain few or no organic remains other than the opercula of ammonites.[182] Malta, Barbados, and Christmas Island in the East Indies are said to possess true deep-sea oozes of Tertiary age, the occurrences being assigned to local upheavals from the bottom of the deep sea.[183] Mesozoic deposits which appear to have developed in the deep-sea environment have been described by Molengraaff and Brouwer from the islands of Borneo, Timor, and Rotti of the East Indies. The deposits have been designated the Danau formation and cover some 40,000 sq. km.; the age is pre-Cretaceous and perhaps Jurassic. The sediments are said to contain no constituents suggestive of terrigenous sources. Manganese is common, occurring as grains in red shales; nodules in red shales, hornstone, and chert; and slabs in siliceous clay shales and radiolarian cherts. The strata consist of radiolarian hornstone or flint, which is composed of closely packed tests of radiolaria, and bright red argillaceous chert or siliceous clay shale. The latter differs from the radiolarian chert in containing fewer radiolaria, more iron and clay, and less silica. The two types, however, gradually pass into each other. The radiolarian chert is interpreted as indurated radiolarian ooze and the siliceous red clay shale as indurated red clay. The facts suggest that the Danau formation represents a true deep-sea deposit, and, if so, it is the most important occurrence known.[184]

[180] Walther, J., op. cit.

[181] Clarke, J. M., The Naples fauna, Mem. 6, New York State Mus., pt. ii, 1904, pp. 199–254.

[182] Grabau, A. W., Principles of stratigraphy, 1913, p. 678.

[183] Walther, J., op. cit., p. 60; Schuchert, C., Science, vol. 69, 1929, p. 142.

[184] Molengraaff, G. A. F., On the oceanic deep-sea deposits of central Borneo; Kon. Akad. van Wetens. Amsterdam, Sec. of Sciences, vol. 12, 1909–1910, pp. 141–147; On the occurrence of manganese nodules in Mesozoic deep sea deposits from Borneo, Timor, and Rotti; their significance and mode of formation, Ibid., vol. 18, pt. i, 1916, pp. 415–430.

CHAPTER VIII

FIELD AND LABORATORY STUDIES OF SEDIMENTS

The study of sediments is concerned with the solution of five problems: what the sediments are and their characteristics, the changes occurring between their deposition and lithification, the environments in which they were deposited, the processes responsible for their transportation and deposition, and the sources from which they were derived. The economic products derived from sediments are by-products of the study. In some cases the solution of all of these problems may be attained, but in the present state of investigation and knowledge results are more or less incomplete, as geologists have not yet acquired the ability to recognize and evaluate all characters of sediments and to appreciate their importance and relations. Studies are made both in the field and laboratory, the former yielding the broader information and a certain amount of detail, the latter giving exact information with respect to detail.

FIELD STUDIES OF SEDIMENTS

Field studies of sediments should yield an adequate description of the dimensions of the rock units, their colors, their larger sedimentary structures, their megascopic composition in organic and inorganic constituents, and the broader relations of the sedimentary units, and should suggest the provenance and distributive areas of the detritals of the sediments. In the study of a rock section the largest units recognized should be described first and then in order to the smallest. Measurements are best expressed in the metric system and should be sufficiently precise, but ordinarily absolute accuracy is not essential. Statements should be definite and not ambiguous, and when doubt exists as to the meanings of terms used, they should be defined. It is better that descriptions be profuse than scanty. Photographs and diagrams should be made wherever possible.

So far as possible, hypotheses relating to the problems of sedimentation should be thoroughly tested in the field, and the problems should be studied in accordance with the "method of multiple working hypotheses."[1] Many hypotheses suggest many lines of attack and lead to keener and more exact study and observation than might otherwise be made. Every sedimentary

[1] Chamberlin, T. C., The method of multiple working hypotheses, Jour. Geol., vol. 5, 1897, pp. 837–848.

rock contains an immense quantity of data, and it is virtually impossible to state in advance which facts are the most important and which will lead most directly to the solution of the problems. The history of science has too often demonstrated that characters considered trivial were of the greatest importance in that they and their relations contained the clue to a particular problem. One needs but to recall former disregard of cross lamination, ripple mark, positions of fossil shells, flow and fracture cleavage, drag folds, etc., by geologists who were attempting the unraveling of the structure and stratigraphy of formations containing these structures. It is, therefore, vital that every character within one's knowledge, so far as each relates to the problem of interest, should receive careful observation and study. The relations of the characters to each other are of equal, if not of greater importance than the characters themselves, and their larger aspects are seen to best advantage in the field.

Geologists, in general, and sedimentationists, in particular, should follow a precept taught by the late Professors John Duer Irving and Joseph Barrell, which holds that "a geologist working in any region should go on the assumption that he is never to see the region again and that it is up to him to get all the information available." The precept, of course, is an ideal, as points of view developed after a visit will show that information might have been obtained had this point of view been realized when the rocks of the region were seen. Most geologists will recall having failed to observe certain characters of sedimentary or other rocks due to oversight, and in order to avoid this failure experience has demonstrated that it is wise to carry a schedule for field observation and description. The schedule which follows is slightly modified from one organized through the Committee on Sedimentation of the National Research Council.[2]

SCHEDULE FOR FIELD DESCRIPTIONS

A. 1. External form of rock unit. Lenticular, persistent, regularity in thickness, etc.; dimensions.

2. Relations to other rock units; conformable, unconformable. Type of unconformity, origin, and environment of origin of the dividing surface. Relief of an unconformity, nature of lower surface, character and sequence of materials in basal and immediately succeeding units of overlying formation.

B. Color. Color of the unit as a whole; rock wet or dry, in shade or sunlight. This should follow Goldman and Merwin's or some other recog-

[2] Modified after Goldman, M. I., and Hewett, D. F., Schedule for field description of sedimentary rocks, Nat. Research Council, published by the U. S. Geol. Surv. See also Tieje, A. J., Suggestions as to the description and naming of sedimentary rocks, Jour. Geol., vol. 29, 1921, pp. 650–666.

nized color chart and not be left to impressions which are apt to vary from day to day.

C. Sedimentary structures.

1. Bedding.

a. How manifested: sharp; by shale or other partings; by difference in texture, color, etc.; transitional, shaly, banded, without parting.

b. Shape of bedding surfaces: even, undulating, ripple-marked, wave- and current-marked, etc.; irregular. If bedding surfaces are not even, give details of form and dimensions of features. Presence of stylolites should be noted.

c. Cross lamination: inclinations and directions of inclinations of foresets; nature of bounding planes of cross-laminated units; position of truncation of the cross laminations.

d. Thickness of beds: comparative thicknesses. Relations of thickness; random, rhythmic. If thickness is variable, relation between thickness and composition, bedding, etc. Factors responsible for the conditions.

e. Attitude and direction of bedding surfaces: horizontal, inclined, curved. Relation to each other: parallel, intersecting, extent; angles between different attitudes and directions; dips, strikes; relations of size, composition, shape, etc., to attitude and direction; relation of composition to different types of bedding. Are the attitudes primary or secondary?

f. Markings on bedding surfaces: mud cracks, ripple marks, rain prints, bubble impressions, ice crystal impressions, trails, footprints, etc. Details and dimensions of each feature.

g. Contemporaneous deformation: indicated by edgewise or other con- glomerates, folding or crumpling of individual beds, etc. Is the deformation due to settling, gliding, or other causes? If due to gliding, the causes for such taking place and the place of origin of the materials.

2. Concretions.

a. Form, size, color, composition, variations in each respect.

b. Internal structure: nucleus organic or inorganic; center hollow; homogeneous; banded horizontally, concentrically, etc.; radial; compact; vesicular.

c. Boundary against country rock: sharp, transitional.

d. Relation of bedding to concretions: continuous through concretions or ending abruptly against them; deflected above, below, both; thinned above, below, etc.

e. Distribution: random; regular; if regular, intervals between groups (layers); differences between characters of concretions in different groups (layers). Relation of distribution to other characters, as composition, jointing, fissuring, folding, etc., of country rock; topography; surface; ground-water level; etc.

f. Fossils in concretions: random, surface, in bands, etc.

g. Relation of composition of concretions to containing rock.

h. Other structures: stylolites, cone-in-cone, septaria, etc.

D. Composition.

1. Inorganic constituents.

a. Mineralogy or lithology of principal constituents.   Rare constituents. Parts authigenic and allothogenic or detrital.

b. Size: prevailing size if fairly uniform; range in sizes if not; proportions of different sizes as determined by preliminary sieving where feasible; distribution of sizes with relation to other features; vertical and lateral variations in sizes.

c. Shape: crystalline (automorphic), angular, subangular, subrounded, rounded; relation of shape to size, material, position in beds, etc. For quantitative results on pebbles, etc., estimate or measure radius of curvature of sharpest edge, radius of curvature in the most convex direction on the flattest portion of the surface, mean radius, and maximum and minimum diameters.[3]

d. Character of surface of particles: glossy, smooth, mat (ground glass surface), pitted, chatter-marked, etc.

e. Orientation: if not equidimensional, direction of different dimensions with respect to bedding, to each other, etc.

f. Chemical and internal physical condition: fresh, decomposed, cracked, etc. Age relations of these features.

g. Packing: closeness and manner.

h. Pore space.

i. Cement: present or absent; proportion; composition; variations in composition vertically and laterally and in relation to other characters; disposition with respect to bedding, fracturing, fossils, etc.

2. Organic constituents.

a. Kinds and proportions to each other and the inorganic constituents of the rock.

b. Size: does the distribution of sizes show mechanical deposition?

c. Condition: entire, fragmental, partly dissolved, healed shells, etc. Relations to kinds.

d. Distribution: with respect to character of beds, kind of organisms,

[3] Wentworth, C. K., Method of measuring and plotting the shapes of pebbles, Abstract, Bull. Geol. Soc. Am., vol. 32, 1921, p. 89; Bull. 730, U. S. Geol. Surv., 1922, pp. 91–102; A field study of the shapes of river pebbles, Ibid., pp. 103–114.

bedding, evidence of burrowing, etc.   Have the shells been transported, or
are they in the places where their builders lived?

e. Orientation: with respect to bedding; with respect to life habits.
Possible manner of death, etc.

f. Positions of the shells: concave upward, downward.

COLLECTION AND PRESERVATION OF SAMPLES

The field study of sedimentary rocks is usually not adequate to acquire
all the desired information, and laboratory studies are necessary for attain-
ments of certain lines of information, to supplement the field observations,
and to test further explanations entertained in the field.

Specimens may be collected:

(a) To form part of a complete series representing every bed or what appears to the
collector to be a distinct type of rock.

(b) To represent some peculiar type of rock which the collector cannot sufficiently
identify in the field, or which he recognizes to be new.

(c) To help in the testing of hypotheses formed in the field as to the origin of the
characters of any rock.[4]

As a general proposition, it is usually best to collect a complete series of
rocks.   Such is the method of students of igneous and metamorphic rocks,
and sedimentationists may do well to follow their method.   It needs to
be emphasized that in the collection of material for laboratory study the
solutions of the problems are not attained through collection of specimens at
random or collection of peculiar and curious specimens; the problems may
be solved, rather, through study of complete suites of specimens from the
terrane that is being investigated.

The collection of material from sedimentary deposits is governed by the
same general rules and should receive the same care as the collection of samples of ores and other products of nature which are taken for commercial
purposes.   It is important that the material representing a given horizon
should be taken from points widely enough distributed to give the various
phases of the deposit.   Beds of a generally uniform character may be
"sampled."   Samples from consolidated deposits should be unweathered.
Samples may be acquired from surface exposures; they may be cuttings
of rotary or cable drilling; or the more or less complete core of diamond drilling.

All samples should be guarded against contamination through entrance
of foreign materials, should be adequately labelled as to locality, horizon, and
facies of collection, and the complete history of collection should be given
together with reasons for collecting.   The object is to have all necessary in-

[4] Goldman and Hewett, op. cit.

formation accompany the sample or specimen. Samples and specimens derived from unknown localities and horizons usually are valueless. To avoid the transportation of unduly large quantities, the first stage of "sampling down" should be carried out in the field so far as conditions permit, but it is much better to ship large quantities to the laboratory than to attempt imperfect sampling where facilities are inadequate for performing such work properly. The actual "sampling down" is accomplished by the well known "quartering" method or by the aid of one of the various devices now on the market. Muds and other finely divided sediments which it is inadvisable to dry for fear of change in the colloidal constitution or chemical change should have sufficient water added so that the mixture will easily flow, following which the sample may be reduced with a "cross grid" sampler.

One of the first and most important lessons a student of sediments should learn is that like materials tend to become segregated, and in splitting samples to reduce the material to be transported one must be constantly on guard to see that the part of a sample intended for study is representative.[5]

Collection of samples from unconsolidated materials is done either upon the surface or beneath a water cover. The former may be done with the hands or some form of small shovel or scoop. Care should be taken to see that the materials collected adequately represent the deposit from which they are taken. Collection of materials from beneath a water cover of such shallow depth as to be accessible to the hands involves nothing greatly different from surface sampling. Materials collected from depths not so accessible involve some form of mechanical instrument, several of which have been devised. Some merely sample the materials on or near the surface, whereas others obtain a core of the bottom to depths of several feet. As bottom samplers and sounders are more or less constantly being perfected, it does not seem worth while to attempt description of any, and the reader should refer to works appropriate to the subject or to the institutions interested in oceanography or limnology.

Most bottom sediments contain organic matter of animal and vegetable origin, and if a preservative is not used, decomposition is soon initiated and the organic components changed or dissipated, and concomitantly the decomposition and the resulting products may alter the character of the inorganic constituents. Grain alcohol is very satisfactory for preservation of the physical form of animal life or for samples intended for mechanical study only, but this preservative is rarely satisfactory for determination of the chemical character of the organic matter. The U. S. Bureau of Fisheries used a 2 per cent solution of sodium hydroxide to preserve samples collected

[5] Wentworth, C. K., Methods of mechanical analysis of sediments, Univ. Iowa Studies, vol. 11, no. 11, 1926, pp. 18–20.

in the Gulf of Maine.   Mercuric bichloride may be used to advantage in some cases.   Sediments, particularly finely divided sediments and those containing organic matter, should be studied as soon as possible after collection.   Before the collection of bottom sediments is undertaken the various problems should be carefully studied, and contact should be made with oceanographic and other institutions to learn the best methods of preservation.

Wet material and material containing volatile matter should be shipped in airtight containers.   If these are not available, the samples should be wrapped in oil or paraffin paper.   Samples that cannot be delivered promptly should have a plain geometrical figure carved from the material, its edge accurately measured, and these data and the specimens thus carved sent to the laboratory.

Laboratory studies of sediments include the determination and detailed study of the physical (mechanical), mineralogical, chemical, and organic constituents to the end that the sediments may be made to yield their history and their provenance or distributive areas, and assist in the development of their commercial possibilities.   The objectives are somewhat different depending on whether the sediments are those of some past geologic period or are those of the present.   In the latter case the environment, provenance, distributive areas, and processes of deposition are usually known, and the main objectives are the character of the sediments, their structures, and distribution.   In the case of sediments of some past geologic period the objectives are larger in that in addition there must be learned the environments and processes of deposition and the provenance and distributive areas.

The diagram given below, slightly modified after one by Milner, illustrates the various tasks involved in a study of sedimentary materials and is in the nature of a flow sheet.   It is self-explanatory and should be followed without difficulty.   Any analysis which is intended to be recorded should have a part of the original sample retained for reference, and this should be ample to permit any checking necessary.   The various divisions of the study are more or less briefly considered, and for detail the reader should consult standard works dealing with particular phases.   It needs to be stated, however, that the various parts of the study should be carried on more or less simultaneously.

GRAVITY AND POROSITY DETERMINATIONS

Methods for the determination of gravity and porosity are given in various works on mineralogy, and a method was outlined in the first edition of this book.[6]

[6] Milner, H. B., Sedimentary petrography, 1929, pp. 111–112, 114; Leith, C. K., and Mead, W. J., Metamorphic geology, 1915, pp. 285–286.

SAMPLE
MACROSCOPICAL DATA

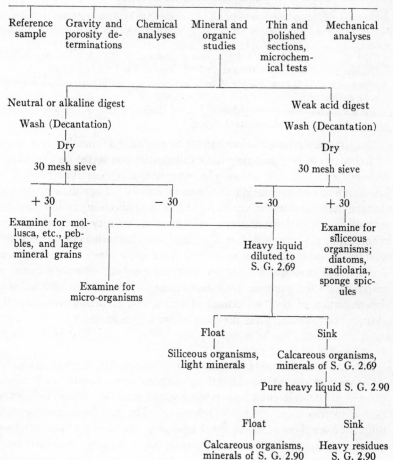

CHEMICAL ANALYSIS

Methods found in "The analysis of silicate and carbonate rocks" by Hille-brand[7] were selected or devised with special reference to their applicability to the ultimate analysis of both igneous and sedimentary rocks, and these methods may be applied without change to the chemical analysis of practically all sediments. Other works on general inorganic analysis will give additional or supplementary detail.

It has been suggested that certain inferences may be drawn from ultimate

[7] Hillebrand, W. F., Bull. 700, U. S. Geol. Surv., 1919.

analyses of sediments which are applicable to the interpretation of rocks that have undergone anamorphism. Bastin[8] states:

> That a sedimentary origin is to be suspected when the analysis of a fresh foliate shows Al_2O_3 in excess of 5 per cent over the 1:1 ratio necessary to satisfy the K_2O, Na_2O and CaO present.
>
> That when the excess exceeds 10 per cent a sedimentary origin is extremely probable.
>
> Dominance of MgO over CaO is strongly indicative of sedimentary origin.
>
> Dominance of K_2O over Na_2O is of lesser critical value, but is nevertheless suggestive of sedimentary origin.
>
> The double relationship of dominance both of MgO over CaO and of K_2O over Na_2O affords strong evidence of sedimentary origin.

That Bastin's generalizations cannot be generally applied has been shown by Leith and Mead,[9] and they have called attention to the fact that many igneous rocks and their anamorphic equivalents possess the chemical relations postulated by Bastin for sedimentary rocks. They show by analyses that the chemical compositions are of uncertain applicability in differentiating sedimentary from igneous rocks and that "in the very cases where other criteria fail, the chemical data also fail" and that "chemical criteria may warrant decisive classification only in those cases where other criteria are decisive and chemical criteria are thus not needed." Perhaps future research may show methods by which chemical criteria will have value for differentiation of the two classes of rocks, but at present it seems that chemical composition gives little aid where it is most needed.

MINERAL STUDIES

The outline or flow sheet for the study of sediments shows the procedure for studies of composing mineral and organic constituents. The characteristics of the different minerals are given in works on sedimentary petrography, to which the reader is referred.[10] The problems are somewhat different from those of the study of igneous rocks, in that in studies of sedimentary materials it is desired to learn the provenance and distributive areas from which the minerals were derived as well as their characteristics and meaning in terms of processes and environments of deposition. The minerals also fall into the two classes of allothogenic or detrital and authigenic, and discrimination is required for their differentiation. The minerals also give information relating to the environments and processes to which some of them owe their deposition, and some of them may tell something

[8] Bastin, E. S., Chemical composition as a criterion in identifying metamorphosed sediments, Jour. Geol., vol. 17, 1909, pp. 445–472.

[9] Leith, C. K., and Mead, W. J., Metamorphic geology, 1915, pp. 226–240.

[10] Milner, H. B., Sedimentary petrography, 1929; Introduction to sedimentary petrography, 1922; Supplement to sedimentary petrography, 1926; Edson, F. C., Criteria for the recognition of heavy minerals occurring in the mid-continent field, Bull. 31, Oklahoma Geol. Surv., 1925; Raeburn, C., and Milner, H. B., Alluvial prospecting, 1927, Tickell, F. G., The examination of fragmental rocks, 1931.

of their history since deposition. The detritals may aid in correlation and assist in unraveling the paleogeography of the region of occurrence.

The minerals may serve to differentiate anamorphosed sediments from other anamorphic rocks of igneous ancestry. It has been suggested that rounded zircon grains with dull and pitted surfaces indicate a sedimentary origin for the containing rocks,[11] the same writer stating that the zircon particles of igneous rocks have clear, fresh, and glassy surfaces and are not generally rounded. It was pointed out, however, that rounded zircons may be found in igneous rocks, particularly those of basic composition. This method of differentiation was first suggested by Derby.[12] It has later been shown that rounded zircon particles may also be present in acid igneous rocks, and that many of the zircons of igneous rocks have pitted and corroded surfaces to such an extent as to resemble the particles found in sediments.[13] Unworn zircon particles also occur in some sediments, and on the whole it seems that too great reliance must not be placed on zircons as a means of differentiating anamorphic rocks of sedimentary ancestry from those of igneous ancestry. Rounded particles of monazite and zenotime have the same significance as zircon.

Carlson[14] has presented evidence suggesting that a wide variety of feldspars in an anamorphic rock indicates a sedimentary origin.

The preparation of sediments for mineral study varies with the character of the materials and the method of study. Materials may be studied in thin and polished sections or by means of heavy liquids and mineral grains. Thin sections are most easily prepared of consolidated materials. As methods of preparation are so generally known, it does not seem worth while to give details; those not familiar with their preparation should consult standard works in which details are given.[15] Thin sections of incoherent materials may be made after cementation by means of Canada balsam, kollolith, or bakelite varnish.[16]

Study by means of heavy liquids requires that the sedimentary materials be composed of discrete particles. The method is not generally applicable to particles of dimensions less than 0.01 mm. in diameter. Some sediments

[11] Trueman, J. D., The value of certain criteria for the determination of the origin of the foliated crystalline rocks, Jour. Geol., vol. 20, 1912, pp. 244–257.

[12] Derby, O. A., On the separation and study of the heavy accessories of rocks, Proc. Rochester Acad. Sci., vol. 1, 1891, pp. 198–206.

[13] Armstrong, P., Zircon as a criterion of origin of igneous or sedimentary metamorphics, Am. Jour. Sci., vol. 4, 1922, pp. 391–395; Rawles, Wm., Unpublished thesis, Univ. Wisconsin, 1930.

[14] Carlson, C. J., A test of the feldspar method for the determination of the origin of metamorphic rocks, Jour. Geol., vol. 28, 1920, pp. 632–644.

[15] Milner, H. B., Sedimentary petrography, 1929, pp. 29–37; Milner, H. B., and Part, G. M., Method in practical petrology, 1916.

[16] For details see Ross, C. S., Methods of preparation of sedimentary materials for study, Econ. Geol., vol. 21, 1926, pp. 454–468.

are already so completely separated that no treatment for separation into constituent particles is necessary. If the material is thoroughly consolidated, it should be broken into particles with dimensions of about 5 mm. These should then be placed on a flat steel plate and crushed by rolling with a steel roller. Many sandstones are so poorly cemented as to crush readily on application of slight pressure, but examination shows the separated materials to be composed of aggregates. These may be reduced to their individual particles by rolling on a steel or glass plate, using an ordinary wooden rolling pin.

In cases of sediments cemented by carbonate the cement may be removed by boiling until effervescence stops in a dilute solution of hydrochloric acid, followed by filtration, thorough washing, and drying to constant weight. The variety of carbonate should be determined by standard methods.

Some sediments are cemented by pyrite. This may be removed by boiling in a 12 to 15 per cent solution of nitric acid, but the material should be checked before treatment, as some other minerals may be removed.

In many cases sediments, particularly sand grains, are coated with a film of iron oxide. This may be removed by boiling in a dilute hydrochloric acid to which has been added stannous chloride to form a 10 to 15 per cent solution.

In some cases it is desired to remove prolific minerals from a sample. Carbonates, pyrite, and iron oxide may be removed as outlined above. Pyrrhotite may be removed by boiling in hydrochloric acid, and this treatment will also remove anhydrite. Gypsum may also be removed by this treatment, but digesting in a strong ammoniacal solution of ammonium sulphate is more effective. Barite can be removed by treatment with hot concentrated sulphuric acid. Other minerals are affected in some of the above treatments, so that mounts of the original materials should be made before treatment. Magnetite, glauconite, and other iron-bearing and magnetic minerals may be removed by means of an electro- or other magnet.

Heavy liquids serve little purpose in the study of the very fine particles of clays, silts, and shales. The coarse particles of these sediments may be determined after separation. The materials should first be crushed and then treated in distilled water with some deflocculant, as sodium carbonate or ammonia, and so thoroughly shaken as to place the clay and finer silt particles in suspension. The clay and silt particles may then be decanted and the minerals of the residue determined. Methods of crushing and deflocculation are given in standard works.[17]

[17] Milner, H. B., op. cit., 1929, p. 51; Goldman, M. I., The petrography and genesis of the sediments of the Upper Cretaceous of Maryland, Maryland Geol. Surv., Upper Cretaceous, 1916, pp. 115–119; Wentworth, C. K., Methods of mechanical analysis of sediments, Univ. Iowa Studies, vol. 11, no. 11, 1926, pp. 42–43.

The heavy liquids used in the study of mineral particles are bromoform, methylene iodide, tetrabromoethane, and the Clerici solution.   Bromoform and tetrabromoethane are probably the cheapest.   The specific gravity of each when pure is about 2.9, but it may be decreased by use of benzol in the case of bromoform and of nitrobenzene (specific gravity 1.2) in tetrabromoethane.   The specific gravity of each should be determined before use. Methylene iodide is most satisfactory for minerals whose specific gravity is above that of 3.33.   Clerici solution[18] has the specific gravity of 4.25 at ordinary room temperature, and the gravity may be varied by changing the temperature.   It is a mixture of thallium malonate ($CH_2(COOTh)_2$) and thallium formate (HCOOTh).

Procedure and apparatus for use of heavy liquids are given by Milner[19] and others to whom the reader is referred.

After the separations by means of heavy liquids and accessory apparatus have been made the organic and mineral components are identified and evaluated by methods well known to every user of a microscope.   The specimens are suitably mounted, either in Canada balsam on slides or in slide containers.[20]   Each slide should be properly labeled and contain sufficient information or references to records to make the materials of use to others than the collector.

MECHANICAL ANALYSIS

The determination of the physical constitution of any sedimentary aggregate involves the separation of the sedimentary particles into fractions of definite sizes or characters in the cases of unconsolidated sediments.   Disregarding the methods of electrostatic separation, dielectric separation and separation by vibration, there are three methods of general applicability.[21] These are panning, sieving, and elutriation.[22]   Panning is useful at times

---

[18] Vassar, H. E., Clerici solution for mineral separation by gravity, Am. Min., vol. 10, 1925, pp. 123–125.

[19] Milner, H. B., Sedimentary petrography, 1929, pp. 46–55; Holmes, A., Petrographic methods and calculations, 1921.

[20] Milner, H. B., op. cit., 1929, pp. 44, et al.; Slocum, A. W., and Thomas, E. T., Bull. Am. Assoc. Pet. Geol., vol. 9, 1925, pp. 667–669; Hanna, G. D., and Driver, H. L., 10th Ann. Rept. California State Min. Bureau, vol. 10, 1924, pp. 5–26.

[21] Another method is that of Mitscherlich (Mitscherlich, E. A., Bodenkunde für Lande-und Festschutte, Berlin, 1905, pp. 49–70) which is based on the determination of the relative internal surface of a soil.   The method does not appear to have much application to the study of sediments.

[22] Udden, J. A., Mechanical composition of wind deposits, Augustana Library Publ. no. 1, 1898; Udden, J. A., Mechanical composition of clastic sediments, Bull. Geol. Soc. Am., vol. 25, 1914, pp. 655–744; Goldman, M. I., The petrography and genesis of the sediments of the Upper Cretaceous of Maryland, Maryland Geol. Surv., Upper Cretaceous, 1916, pp. 113–123; Thoulet, J., Précis d'analyse des fonds sous-marins actuels et anciens,

in forming a concentrate of the larger and heavier minerals, but is of little value for exact quantitative work. Sieving has little application to silts, clays, and shales, but is useful in the study of sediments composed of sands and particles of larger dimension. In the method of sieving the material to be studied is first washed to remove the fine materials (which are separately treated), and the residue is passed through sieves of progressively finer mesh. The use of sieves of more than 200 mesh to the inch is not practicable, and the use of sieves with openings of less than 1/16 mm. diameter is not recommended. The sieves employed are made either of woven wire or bolting cloth. Each is open to objection. In the former it is extremely difficult to maintain the openings to accurate dimension, and after short usage they will be found to possess material differences. Furthermore, in the finer mesh so much material is held in the wires as often to vitiate results. In some cases removal of the particles thus held leads to spoiling the sieve. Much the same difficulties obtain in the use of bolting cloth except that this is somewhat easier to clean. Bolting cloth, however, does not give as good sizing as wire screens. Another difficulty existing in grading by sieves arises from the fact that the three diameters of particles are rarely equal, there usually being a greatest, a smallest, and a mean, and the dimension of the last ordinarily determines whether or not a particle passes through a sieve, but the large dimension may determine that it is held. For particles of dimension of 1/4 mm. or larger, wire screens are quite satisfactory, and their use has the advantage of speed.

After a sample has been separated into its various fractions it is often well to study each of these by means of heavy liquids and subject each to magnetic separation, and treatment for removal of carbonates, as in this way it may be learned that certain substances are confined to definite fractions.

The elutriation method is based on the rate of subsidence of particles in liquids. When grains are permitted to settle freely in a liquid, they do so under the influence of gravity, the rate of subsidence of a particle being controlled by its size, density, shape, and the density and viscosity of the liquid used, the two characters of the liquid varying inversely with the temperature.[23]

Paris, 1907; Instructions pratiques pour l'établissement d'une carte bathymétrique-lithologique sous-marin, Bull. de l'Inst. Océanograph., no. 169, Monaco, 1910, pp. 1–29. Milner, H. B., Sedimentary petrography, 1929, pp. 108–111, 468–470; Baker, H. A., On the investigation of the mechanical composition of loose arenaceous sediments by the method of elutriation with special reference to the Thanet beds on the southern side of the London Basin, Geol. Mag., vol. 57, 1920, pp. 321–332, 363–370 411–420, 463–467; Wentworth, C. K., Methods of mechanical analyses of sediments, Univ. Iowa Studies, vol. 11, no. 11, 1926; Ross, C. S., Methods of preparation of sedimentary materials for study, Econ. Geol., vol. 21, 1926, pp. 455–468.

[23] Atterberg, A., Die mechanische Bodenanalyse und die Klassification der Mineralboden Schwedens, Intern. Mitt. f. Bodenkunde, Bd. 2, 1912.

If a settling particle encounters an upward current in the liquid, the rate of settling is retarded, and the speed of the upward current may be so regulated that the particle maintains a stationary position.   If velocities in a given liquid are graded in proportion to dimensions of particles, a given sediment may be separated into fractions based on dimensions without the disadvantages arising from the use of sieves, so long as the particles do not become too large or too small; in the former case the specific gravity dominates in the settling as viscosity is negligible, and in the case of very small particles viscosity dominates and settling is so slow that separation of particles is hardly possible.   The upper limit in elutriation is about 1/2 mm., and for this and larger dimensions the use of sieves is better.   The small particles may be separated in the centrifugal elutriator of Yoder.[24]

The method given by Steiger[25] for fine sediments is as follows:

The procedure of the mechanical analyses of the finer grained sediments is like that of soils for which methods have been very carefully worked out in the many laboratories devoted to their study.   The following is a brief description of the method used in the Bureau of Soils, United States Department of Agriculture.[26]

The specimen as received is sieved through a screen having meshes 2 mm. in diameter.[27] Lumps are broken apart by rubbing between the fingers or by gentle abrasion with a rolling-pin.   The extent of crushing rests with the investigator; after examination of the material with the hand lens or microscope he must use his judgment to determine how far the material may be crushed and at the same time not break up the particles which should be preserved intact.   The larger material is studied with the hand lens and in any other way desirable.   The material passing the 2 mm. mesh is dealt with as follows.

Five grams of the material passing the 2 mm. mesh, previously air-dried, are put in an 8-ounce sterilizer bottle with 2 ounces of water and 2 to 3 cc. of ammonia.   A much smaller quantity of ammonia will serve to flocculate the material, but the quantity stated is sufficient to keep the clay-colloid and silt deflocculated until the end of the operation. A determination of water at 110°C. must be made in another portion and due allowance made in the 5-gram sample.

Tests are usually carried out in batteries of eight to ten.

When the required number of bottles has been filled they are securely closed with rubber stoppers and all are placed in a mechanical shaker which gives them a very gentle motion, just sufficient to keep the contents agitated; violent shaking is unnecessary.   The bottles are shaken for six or seven hours—a longer period of shaking will do no harm provided the stoppers are not eroded to such an extent that particles become detached and contaminate the contents of the bottles.   At the end of the shaking period the bottles are placed upright in a rack and unstoppered, any of the material adhering to the stoppers being washed

---

[24] Yoder, P. A., Bull. 89, Utah Experiment Station, 1904.

[25] Steiger, G., Treatise of sedimentation, 1st ed., 1925, pp. 630–632.

[26] Bull. 84, Bureau of Soils, U. S. Dept. Agriculture.

[27] In applying this method to the examination of some material from the Gulf of Maine the sieving of the material in the Geological Survey laboratory was carried out through a 2 mm. sieve under water.   The results were most satisfactory, the material not having been brought near to the air-dried condition and the danger of affecting the irreversible colloids was thus avoided.

back into the bottles. The bottles are then carefully filled with a jet of water under pressure, which serves to thoroughly stir the contents and bring the solid particles into suspension.

After standing for a length of time which will vary with different sediments, a sample is taken an inch from the bottom and examined with a microscope. If it shows sand particles it is allowed to settle for an additional period. When the sample so taken is free from sand, the liquid in the bottle is either decanted or siphoned off to the level from which the sample was taken. The decanted liquid is received in a centrifugal tube; when the number of tubes required to fill the centrifuge has been filled they are put into position and the centrifugal machine run for five or ten minutes, after which samples are taken in the same manner as in the sterilizer bottle, the cycle is again run in a similar manner, water under pressure being employed to stir the various residues. This process is repeated until the separations are considered complete.

Here again it must be left to the judgment of the operator when to stop. The separations are not absolute; if the washing is continued until the sand is entirely free from silt, some of the finer sand will be washed into the silt portion and in a similar manner silt will contaminate the clay-colloid portion.

When these operations are completed, the sand will be in the sterilizer bottle, the silt in the centrifugal tubes, and the clay colloid in the vessels used to receive the last washings. The sand is transferred from the bottles to small dishes, dried at 110°C. and weighed. After its weight has been determined it is placed in the top of a set of four sieves and separated into grades. The silt is determined by drying at 110°C. and weighing. The determination of the clay-colloid is accomplished by evaporating the liquid decanted from the silt in dishes, drying at 110°C. and weighing. The bulk of this liquid being large, the evaporation is tedious and in many laboratories the dust collecting during the long evaporation introduces considerable uncertainty in the results. The clay-colloid may be calculated by difference, and for most purposes this is sufficiently accurate. In one hundred analyses taken at random from the files of the Bureau of Soils the difference between the percentages of the clay-colloid as directly determined and those obtained by difference only eleven exceeded 1 per cent and the greatest difference was only 2.28 per cent.

In the English method the material is given a preliminary treatment with very dilute hydrochloric acid after which it is deflocculated with ammonia. The Sudan[28] method depends on a dilute solution of sodium carbonate for deflocculation. Both of these methods differ from the Bureau of Soils procedure in that they depend on settling by gravity for separating silt from clay-colloid. It is claimed that sodium carbonate is superior to ammonia for deflocculation; on the other hand, it will certainly take varying amounts of colloidal silica into solution: the quantity of silica dissolved by ammonia will be negligible. These methods have the advantage of requiring very simple apparatus and require less actual attention, although the work is spread over a greater period of time.

Trask has used the centrifuge to advantage in the analysis of fine sediments.[29]

After a sediment has been separated into its fractions based on dimensions, these should be graphically expressed and the degree of sorting and other

[28] Beam, W., Cairo Sci. Jour., 1911, p. 107.
[29] Trask, P. D., Mechanical analyses of fine sediments, Econ. Geol., vol. 25, 1930, pp. 581–699.

characteristics determined. Various methods of graphical representation have been devised, among which are the pyramidal graph, known as histogram, used by Udden,[30] Goldman, Wentworth, Trowbridge, and others[31] (fig. 16), the cumulative curve used by Dake[32] and others, the simple curve, and equivalent grade diagram of Baker[33] (fig. 120). Baker's method expresses the mechanical constitution of a sandy or coarser sediment by two

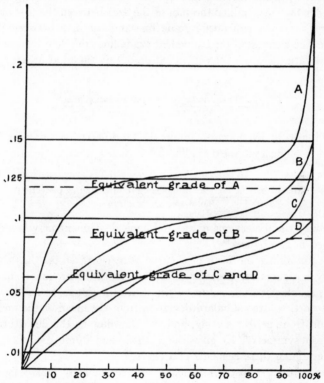

FIG. 120. ELUTRIATION CURVES TO SHOW EQUIVALENT GRADE
After Baker, op. cit.

figures which he designates the "equivalent grade" and the "grading factor." The area bounded by the cumulative curve of a sediment, the first and last ordinates, and the x-axis gives the grade of that sediment. The equivalent

[30] Udden, op. cit.

[31] Goldman, op. cit.; Trowbridge, A. C., and Mortimore, M. E., Correlation of soil sands by sedimentary analyses, Econ. Geol., vol. 20, 1925, pp. 409–423.

[32] Dake, C. L., The problem of the St. Peter sandstone, Bull. Missouri School of Mines, vol. 6, no. 1, 1921.

[33] Baker, op. cit.

grade is represented by a rectangle whose length is the distance between the bounding ordinates of the curve and whose height is the mean ordinate. The equivalent grade, hence, represents a sediment of equi-dimensional particles whose curve is a straight line parallel to the x-axis to 100 per cent and at a distance above the x-axis equal to the length of the mean ordinate. Sediments of widely different characters may have the same equivalent grade. The grading factor is the quotient obtained by dividing the total area under the curve minus the sum of the area between the first ordinate, the curve, and the equivalent grade line and the area between the last ordinate, the curve, and the equivalent grade line (this sum expressing the the total variation from the equivalent grade) by the total area under the curve, or:

$$\frac{\text{Total area under curve-total variation area}}{\text{Total area under curve}}$$

The total area under the curve minus the total variation area expresses the measure of tendency toward grading perfection, so that the fraction may be written:

$$\frac{\text{Area expressing measure of tendency toward grading perfection}}{\text{Total area under curve}}$$

In this way the dimensions of any mechanical sediment may be definitely expressed in two figures.[34]

For determining the form of a curve Wentworth states that three elementary measures are necessary. These are the approximate mean size of the particles or the position of the center of the curve on the scale of sizes of particles, the standard deviation from the mean or the measure of deviation from perfect sorting, and the skewness or the departure of the curve from symmetry. He gives the methods and formulæ of computation for determining these elements of a curve.[35]

Three factors were used in the many analyses made by Trask: the median diameter, the coefficient of sorting, and the skewness. The median diameter separates the size distribution into two equal halves, one having diameters less than the median and the other greater. The first and third quartiles divide the halves into quarters. The coefficient of sorting equals the square

[34] The method of elutriation used by Baker is described in his paper, and further details may be found in Crook, T., Appendix to Hatch, F. H., and Rastall, R. H., Sedimentary rocks, London, 1913, p. 349; Boswell, P. G. H., British resources of sands and rocks used in glass-making, 2nd ed., 1918; Stadler, Grading analyses by elutriation, Trans. Inst. Min. and Metal., vol. 12, 1912–1913, p. 686; Ries, H., Clays, their occurrence, properties, and uses, 3rd ed., 1927.

[35] Wentworth, C. K., Methods of computing mechanical composition types of sediments, Bull. Geol. Soc. Am., vol. 40, 1929, pp. 771–790.

root of the first quartile divided by the third quartile.   The skewness equals the product of the first and third quartiles divided by the square of the median.   For details Trask's paper should be consulted.[36]

In plotting the curves of sediments their form will depend to a very large extent on the scale used, and the same sediment plotted on different scales will give graphs or curves impossible of recognition as representing the same sediment.   The results are that comparison becomes essentially impossible. It is recommended that all sediments be plotted to the same scale, and because of its simplicity, the form card devised by Wentworth is recommended.   The card is based on the ratio of 2 and is shown in figure 121.

The origin of the sediments, the environments in which they were deposited and the agents of deposition to some extent may be determined from the

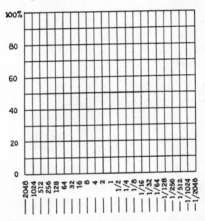

Fig. 121. Form Card to the 1–2–4–8 mm. Scale Recommended for Use in Plotting Histograms

characters of the curves made by their fractions; and the variations in grading factors, equivalent grades, and other elements of the curve also state something with respect to the environments of deposition.

Organic Studies

The examination of sediments for the organic constituents involves the actual picking out of the organic matter from the sample used for study and from the fractions made in the mechanical analyses.   When sediments are consolidated, a thin section is made and the organic particles counted and identified if such is possible.   In some consolidated sediments the fossils

[36] Trask, P. D., Studies of recent marine sediments conducted by the American Petroleum Institute, Rept. Comm. Sedimentation, Nat. Research Council, in press.

are silicified and when such is the case the materials should be treated with hydrochloric acid to remove the carbonates and free the organic matter.

In every case the determination of the kind of organisms is desirable, and the final result should show the part that each variety of organism takes in a sediment's composition. The organic matter should also be carefully studied to determine the physical condition with respect to wear, breaking, distribution in the sediments, habits of life, and the light it throws on the environment.

LIST OF AUTHORS CITED

This list covers both volumes of the work. Volume One contains pages 1 through 460. Volume Two contains pages 461 through 890.

Berg, G., 443
Bergeat, A., 762
Berkey, C. P., 464, 787
Berkheimer, F., 301
Berry, E. W., 161, 375, 849
Bertololy, E., 645
Bertrand, C. E., 361, 391, 397
Bertrand, P., 365
Bevan, A., 680
Biglow, H. W., 462
Birge, E. A., 820
Birse, D. J., 335
Bischof, G., 335
Black, M., 850
Blackwelder, E., 6, 9, 24, 69, 72, 97, 99, 126, 138, 146, 201, 207, 238, 309, 551, 554, 561, 626, 745, 776, 782, 789, 798
Blackwell, T. E., 40
Blair, T. A., 680
Blanford, W. T., 553, 790
Blasius, H., 635, 639, 654
Blayac, M., 561
Blegvad, H., 150
Blum, H. F., 154
Bode, C., 390
Böggild, O. B., 292, 296, 336
Bogue, R. H., 510
Bolton, H. C., 14
Bonine, C. A., 268, 270
Bonney, T. G., 105, 192, 557, 733
Boswell, P. G. H., 14, 62, 125, 189, 195, 224, 227, 888
Bourne, C. O., 707
Bouyoucos, C. J., 24
Bowen, C. F., 849
Brackett, R. N., 519
Bradley, F. H., 105
Bradley, W. H., 271, 311, 402, 598, 766, 767
Bradley, W. M., 331, 410
Bramlette, M. N., 270, 307
Brammall, A., 14, 192
Branner, J. C., 17, 104, 112, 323, 334, 672
Branson, C. C., 548
Branson, E. B., 276, 279, 502, 606, 695, 849
Brazier, J. S., 253, 258
Breazeale, J. F., 327
Breger, C. E., 554
Bridenstine, I. J., 438

Bridge, J., 606
Brinkmann, R., 708
Broadhead, G. C., 733
Brock, R. W., 102
Brongniart, A., 599
Brouwer, H. A., 871
Brown, A. P., 668
Brown, B. E., 23
Brown, L. S., 602
Brown, T. C., 217, 744, 758
Bruce, R. J., 155
Bryan, K., 76, 207, 238, 786, 789
Brydone, A., 534, 708
Bryson, A., 683
Buchanan, J. Y., 151, 289, 459, 575, 576
Bucher, W. H., 16, 303, 634, 635, 637, 638, 640, 641, 644, 648, 649, 653, 654, 662, 665, 761, 762, 767
Buckland, W., 682
Buckley, E. R., 750
Buckman, H. O., 22, 23, 63
Bullen, R. A., 303
Bunker, H. J., 15
Burchard, E. F., 443, 566
Burgess, 420, 421
Burgess, P. A., 598
Burnett, J. B., 583
Burt, F. A., 702
Burton, T. H., 192
Butkevich, E. S., 564
Butler, G. M., 569
Butschli, O., 586
Butters, R. M., 279
Buttram, F., 265

Cady, G. H., 762
Cagniard-Latour, C., 417
Calvin, S., 335
Cameron, F. K., 16, 507
Campbell, J. M., 247
Campbell, M. R., 15, 492
Cana, F. B., 785
Cangully, P. B., 434
Cantrill, T. C., 444
Capps, S. R., Jr., 27, 100, 238, 266
Carlson, A. J., 419
Carlson, C. J., 881
Carnot, M. A., 561
Carthaus, E., 365

INDEX

This comprehensive index covers both volumes of the work. Volume One contains pages 1 through 460. Volume Two contains pages 461 through 890.

Catalogue of Dover
SCIENCE BOOKS

BOOKS THAT EXPLAIN SCIENCE

THE NATURE OF LIGHT AND COLOUR IN THE OPEN AIR, M. Minnaert. Why is falling snow sometimes black? What causes mirages, the fata morgana, multiple suns and moons in the sky; how are shadows formed? Prof. Minnaert of U. of Utrecht answers these and similar questions in optics, light, colour, for non-specialists. Particularly valuable to nature, science students, painters, photographers. "Can best be described in one word—fascinating!" Physics Today. Translated by H. M. Kremer-Priest, K. Jay. 202 illustrations, including 42 photos. xvi + 362pp. 5⅜ x 8.　　　　　　　　　　　　　　　　　**T196 Paperbound $1.95**

THE RESTLESS UNIVERSE, Max Born. New enlarged version of this remarkably readable account by a Nobel laureate. Moving from sub-atomic particles to universe, the author explains in very simple terms the latest theories of wave mechanics. Partial contents: air and its relatives, electrons and ions, waves and particles, electronic structure of the atom, nuclear physics. Nearly 1000 illustrations, including 7 animated sequences. 325pp. 6 x 9.　　　　　　　　　　　　　　　　　　　　　　　　　**T412 Paperbound $2.00**

MATTER AND LIGHT, THE NEW PHYSICS, L. de Broglie. Non-technical papers by a Nobel laureate explain electromagnetic theory, relativity, matter, light, radiation, wave mechanics, quantum physics, philosophy of science. Einstein, Planck, Bohr, others explained so easily that no mathematical training is needed for all but 2 of the 21 chapters. "Easy simplicity and lucidity . . . should make this source-book of modern physcis available to a wide public," Saturday Review. Unabridged. 300pp. 5⅜ x 8.　　　　**T35 Paperbound $1.60**

THE COMMON SENSE OF THE EXACT SCIENCES, W. K. Clifford. Introduction by James Newman, edited by Karl Pearson. For 70 years this has been a guide to classical scientific, mathematical thought. Explains with unusual clarity basic concepts such as extension of meaning of symbols, characteristics of surface boundaries, properties of plane figures, vectors, Cartesian method of determining position, etc. Long preface by Bertrand Russell. Bibliography of Clifford. Corrected. 130 diagrams redrawn. 249pp. 5⅜ x 8.
　　　　　　　　　　　　　　　　　　　　　　　　　　　T61 Paperbound $1.60

THE EVOLUTION OF SCIENTIFIC THOUGHT FROM NEWTON TO EINSTEIN, A. d'Abro. Einstein's special, general theories of relativity, with historical implications, analyzed in non-technical terms. Excellent accounts of contributions of Newton, Riemann, Weyl, Planck, Eddington, Maxwell, Lorentz, etc., are treated in terms of space, time, equations of electromagnetics, finiteness of universe, methodology of science. "Has become a standard work," Nature. 21 diagrams. 482pp. 5⅜ x 8.　　　　　　　　　　　　　　　　**T2 Paperbound $2.00**

BRIDGES AND THEIR BUILDERS, D. Steinman, S. R. Watson. Engineers, historians, everyone ever fascinated by great spans will find this an endless source of information and interest. Dr. Steinman, recent recipient of Louis Levy Medal, is one of the great bridge architects, engineers of all time. His analysis of great bridges of history is both authoritative and easily followed. Greek, Roman, medieval, oriental bridges; modern works such as Brooklyn Bridge, Golden Gate Bridge, etc. described in terms of history, constructional principles, artistry, function. Most comprehensive, accurate semi-popular history of bridges in print in English. New, greatly revised, enlarged edition. 23 photographs, 26 line drawings. xvii + 401pp. 5⅜ x 8.　　　　　　　　　　　　　　　　　　**T431 Paperbound $1.95**

CONCERNING THE NATURE OF THINGS, Sir William Bragg. Christmas lectures at Royal Society by Nobel laureate, dealing with atoms, gases, liquids, and various types of crystals. No scientific background is needed to understand this remarkably clear introduction to basic processes and aspects of modern science. "More interesting than any bestseller," London Morning Post. 32pp. of photos. 57 figures. xii + 232pp. 5⅜ x 8.   T31 Paperbound **$1.35**

THE RISE OF THE NEW PHYSICS, A. d'Abro. Half million word exposition, formerly titled "The Decline of Mechanism," for readers not versed in higher mathematics. Only thorough explanation in everyday language of core of modern mathematical physical theory, treating both classical, modern views. Scientifically impeccable coverage of thought from Newtonian system through theories of Dirac, Heisenberg, Fermi's statistics. Combines history, exposition; broad but unified, detailed view, with constant comparison of classical, modern views. "A must for anyone doing serious study in the physical sciences," J. of the Franklin Inst. "Extraordinary faculty . . . to explain ideas and theories . . . in language of everyday life," Isis. Part I of set: philosophy of science, from practice of Newton, Maxwell, Poincaré, Einstein, etc. Modes of thought, experiment, causality, etc. Part II: 100 pp. on grammar, vocabulary of mathematics, discussions of functions, groups, series, Fourier series, etc. Remainder treats concrete, detailed coverage of both classical, quantum physics: analytic mechanics, Hamilton's principle, electromagnetic waves, thermodynamics, Brownian movement, special relativity, Bohr's atom, de Broglie's wave mechanics, Heisenberg's uncertainty, scores of other important topics. Covers discoveries, theories of d'Alembert, Born, Cantor, Debye, Euler, Foucault, Galois, Gauss, Hadamard, Kelvin, Kepler Laplace, Maxwell, Pauli, Rayleigh Volterra, Weyl, more than 180 others. 97 illustrations. ix + 982pp. 5⅜ x 8.
T3 Vol. 1 Paperbound **$2.00**
T4 Vol. II Paperbound **$2.00**

SPINNING TOPS AND GYROSCOPIC MOTION, John Perry. Well-known classic of science still unsurpassed for lucid, accurate, delightful exposition. How quasi-rigidity is induced in flexible, fluid bodies by rapid motions; why gyrostat falls, top rises; nature, effect of internal fluidity on rotating bodies; etc. Appendixes describe practical use of gyroscopes in ships, compasses, monorail transportation. 62 figures. 128pp. 5⅜ x 8.
T416 Paperbound **$1.00**

FOUNDATIONS OF PHYSICS, R. B. Lindsay, H. Margenau. Excellent bridge between semi-popular and technical writings. Discussion of methods of physical description, construction of theory; valuable to physicist with elementary calculus. Gives meaning to data, tools of modern physics. Contents: symbolism, mathematical equations; space and time; foundations of mechanics; probability; physics, continua; electron theory; relativity; quantum mechanics; causality; etc. "Thorough and yet not overdetailed. Unreservedly recommended," Nature. Unabridged corrected edition. 35 illustrations. xi + 537pp. 5⅜ x 8.   S377 Paperbound **$2.45**

FADS AND FALLACIES IN THE NAME OF SCIENCE, Martin Gardner. Formerly entitled "In the Name of Science," the standard account of various cults, quack systems, delusions which have masqueraded as science: hollow earth fanatics, orgone sex energy, dianetics, Atlantis, Forteanism, flying saucers, medical fallacies like zone therapy, etc. New chapter on Bridey Murphy, psionics, other recent manifestations. A fair reasoned appraisal of eccentric theory which provides excellent innoculation. "Should be read by everyone, scientist or non-scientist alike," R. T. Birge, Prof. Emeritus of Physics, Univ. of Calif; Former Pres., Amer. Physical Soc. x + 365pp. 5⅜ x 8.   T394 Paperbound **$1.50**

ON MATHEMATICS AND MATHEMATICIANS, R. E. Moritz. A 10 year labor of love by discerning, discriminating Prof. Moritz, this collection conveys the full sense of mathematics and personalities of great mathematicians. Anecdotes, aphorisms, reminiscences, philosophies, definitions, speculations, biographical insights, etc. by great mathematicians, writers: Descartes, Mill, Locke, Kant, Coleridge, Whitehead, etc. Glimpses into lives of great mathematicians, from Archimedes to Euler, Gauss, Weierstrass. To mathematicians, a superb browsing-book. To laymen, exciting revelation of fullness of mathematics. Extensive cross index. 410pp. 5⅜ x 8.   T489 Paperbound **$1.95**

GUIDE TO THE LITERATURE OF MATHEMATICS AND PHYSICS, N. G. Parke III. Over 5000 entries under approximately 120 major subject headings, of selected most important books, monographs, periodicals, articles in English, plus important works in German, French, Italian, Spanish, Russian (many recently available works). Covers every branch of physics, math, related engineering. Includes author, title, edition, publisher, place, date, number of volumes, number of pages. 40 page introduction on basic problems of research, study provides useful information on organization, use of libraries, psychology of learning, etc. Will save you hours of time. 2nd revised edition. Indices of authors, subjects. 464pp. 5⅜ x 8.   S447 Paperbound **$2.49**

THE STRANGE STORY OF THE QUANTUM, An Account for the General Reader of the Growth of Ideas Underlying Our Present Atomic Knowledge, B. Hoffmann. Presents lucidly, expertly, with barest amount of mathematics, problems and theories which led to modern quantum physics. Begins with late 1800's when discrepancies were noticed; with illuminating analogies, examples, goes through concepts of Planck, Einstein, Pauli, Schroedinger, Dirac, Sommerfield, Feynman, etc. New postscript through 1958. "Of the books attempting an account of the history and contents of modern atomic physics which have come to my attention, this is the best," H. Margenau, Yale U., in Amer. J. of Physics. 2nd edition. 32 tables, illustrations. 275pp. 5⅜ x 8.   T518 Paperbound **$1.45**

HISTORY OF SCIENCE
AND PHILOSOPHY OF SCIENCE

THE VALUE OF SCIENCE, Henri Poincaré. Many of most mature ideas of "last scientific universalist" for both beginning, advanced workers. Nature of scientific truth, whether order is innate in universe or imposed by man, logical thought vs. intuition (relating to Weierstrass, Lie, Riemann, etc), time and space (relativity, psychological time, simultaneity), Herz's concept of force, values within disciplines of Maxwell, Carnot, Mayer, Newton, Lorentz, etc. iii + 147pp. 5⅜ x 8. S469 Paperbound **$1.35**

PHILOSOPHY AND THE PHYSICISTS, L. S. Stebbing. Philosophical aspects of modern science examined in terms of lively critical attack on ideas of Jeans, Eddington. Tasks of science, causality, determinism, probability, relation of world physics to that of everyday experience, philosophical significance of Planck-Bohr concept of discontinuous energy levels, inferences to be drawn from Uncertainty Principle, implications of "becoming" involved in 2nd law of thermodynamics, other problems posed by discarding of Laplacean determinism. 285pp. 5⅜ x 8. T480 Paperbound **$1.65**

THE PRINCIPLES OF SCIENCE, A TREATISE ON LOGIC AND THE SCIENTIFIC METHOD, W. S. Jevons. Milestone in development of symbolic logic remains stimulating contribution to investigation of inferential validity in sciences. Treats inductive, deductive logic, theory of number, probability, limits of scientific method; significantly advances Boole's logic, contains detailed introduction to nature and methods of probability in physics, astronomy, everyday affairs, etc. In introduction, Ernest Nagel of Columbia U. says,"[Jevons] continues to be of interest as an attempt to articulate the logic of scientific inquiry." liii + 786pp. 5⅜ x 8. S446 Paperbound **$2.98**

A HISTORY OF ASTRONOMY FROM THALES TO KEPLER, J. L. E. Dreyer. Only work in English to give complete history of cosmological views from prehistoric times to Kepler. Partial contents: Near Eastern astronomical systems, Early Greeks, Homocentric spheres of Euxodus, Epicycles, Ptolemaic system, Medieval cosmology, Copernicus, Kepler, much more. "Especially useful to teachers and students of the history of science . . . unsurpassed in its field," Isis. Formerly "A History of Planetary Systems from Thales to Kepler." Revised foreword by W. H. Stahl. xvii + 430pp. 5⅜ x 8. S79 Paperbound **$1.98**

A CONCISE HISTORY OF MATHEMATICS, D. Struik. Lucid study of development of ideas, techniques, from Ancient Near East, Greece, Islamic science, Middle Ages, Renaissance, modern times. Important mathematicians described in detail. Treatment not anecdotal, but analytical development of ideas. Non-technical—no math training needed. "Rich in content, thoughtful in interpretations," U.S. Quarterly Booklist. 60 illustrations including Greek, Egyptian manuscripts, portraits of 31 mathematicians. 2nd edition. xix + 299pp. 5⅜ x 8. S255 Paperbound **$1.75**

THE PHILOSOPHICAL WRITINGS OF PEIRCE, edited by Justus Buchler. A carefully balanced expositon of Peirce's complete system, written by Peirce himself. It covers such matters as scientific method, pure chance vs. law, symbolic logic, theory of signs, pragmatism, experiment, and other topics. "Excellent selection . . . gives more than adequate evidence of the range and greatness," Personalist. Formerly entitled "The Philosophy of Peirce." xvi + 368pp. T217 Paperbound **$1.95**

SCIENCE AND METHOD, Henri Poincaré. Procedure of scientific discovery, methodology, experiment, idea-germination—processes by which discoveries come into being. Most significant and interesting aspects of development, application of ideas. Chapters cover selection of facts, chance, mathematical reasoning, mathematics and logic; Whitehead, Russell, Cantor, the new mechanics, etc. 288pp. 5⅜ x 8. S222 Paperbound **$1.35**

SCIENCE AND HYPOTHESIS, Henri Poincaré. Creative psychology in science. How such concepts as number, magnitude, space, force, classical mechanics developed, how modern scientist uses them in his thought. Hypothesis in physics, theories of modern physics. Introduction by Sir James Larmor. "Few mathematicians have had the breadth of vision of Poincaré, and none is his superior in the gift of clear exposition," E. T. Bell. 272pp. 5⅜ x 8. S221 Paperbound **$1.35**

ESSAYS IN EXPERIMENTAL LOGIC, John Dewey. Stimulating series of essays by one of most influential minds in American philosophy presents some of his most mature thoughts on wide range of subjects. Partial contents: Relationship between inquiry and experience; dependence of knowledge upon thought; character logic; judgments of practice, data, and meanings; stimuli of thought, etc. viii + 444pp. 5⅜ x 8. T73 Paperbound **$1.95**

WHAT IS SCIENCE, Norman Campbell. Excellent introduction explains scientific method, role of mathematics, types of scientific laws. Contents: 2 aspects of science, science and nature, laws of chance, discovery of laws, explanation of laws, measurement and numerical laws, applications of science. 192pp. 5⅜ x 8. S43 Paperbound **$1.25**

FROM EUCLID TO EDDINGTON: A STUDY OF THE CONCEPTIONS OF THE EXTERNAL WORLD, Sir Edmund Whittaker. Foremost British scientist traces development of theories of natural philosophy from western rediscovery of Euclid to Eddington, Einstein, Dirac, etc. 5 major divisions: Space, Time and Movement; Concepts of Classical Physics; Concepts of Quantum Mechanics; Eddington Universe. Contrasts inadequacy of classical physics to understand physical world with present day attempts of relativity, non-Euclidean geometry, space curvature, etc. 212pp. 5⅜ x 8.   T491 Paperbound **$1.35**

THE ANALYSIS OF MATTER, Bertrand Russell. How do our senses accord with the new physics? This volume covers such topics as logical analysis of physics, prerelativity physics, causality, scientific inference, physics and perception, special and general relativity, Weyl's theory, tensors, invariants and their physical interpretation, periodicity and qualitative series. "The most thorough treatment of the subject that has yet been published," The Nation. Introduction by L. E. Denonn. 422pp. 5⅜ x 8.   T231 Paperbound **$1.95**

LANGUAGE, TRUTH, AND LOGIC, A. Ayer. A clear introduction to the Vienna and Cambridge schools of Logical Positivism. Specific tests to evaluate validity of ideas, etc. Contents: function of philosophy, elimination of metaphysics, nature of analysis, a priori, truth and probability, etc. 10th printing. "I should like to have written it myself," Bertrand Russell. 160pp. 5⅜ x 8.   T10 Paperbound **$1.25**

THE PSYCHOLOGY OF INVENTION IN THE MATHEMATICAL FIELD, J. Hadamard. Where do ideas come from? What role does the unconscious play? Are ideas best developed by mathematical reasoning, word reasoning, visualization? What are the methods used by Einstein, Poincaré, Galton, Riemann? How can these techniques be applied by others? One of the world's leading mathematicians discusses these and other questions. xiii + 145pp. 5⅜ x 8.
                                                                         T107 Paperbound **$1.25**

GUIDE TO PHILOSOPHY, C. E. M. Joad. By one of the ablest expositors of all time, this is not simply a history or a typological survey, but an examination of central problems in terms of answers afforded by the greatest thinkers: Plato, Aristotle, Scholastics, Leibniz, Kant, Whitehead, Russell, and many others. Especially valuable to persons in the physical sciences; over 100 pages devoted to Jeans, Eddington, and others, the philosophy of modern physics, scientific materialism, pragmatism, etc. Classified bibliography. 592pp. 5⅜ x 8.   T50 Paperbound **$2.00**

SUBSTANCE AND FUNCTION, and EINSTEIN'S THEORY OF RELATIVITY, Ernst Cassirer. Two books bound as one. Cassirer establishes a philosophy of the exact sciences that takes into consideration new developments in mathematics, shows historical connections. Partial contents: Aristotelian logic, Mill's analysis, Helmholtz and Kronecker, Russell and cardinal numbers, Euclidean vs. non-Euclidean geometry, Einstein's relativity. Bibliography. Index. xxi + 464pp. 5⅜ x 8.   T50 Paperbound **$2.00**

FOUNDATIONS OF GEOMETRY, Bertrand Russell. Nobel laureate analyzes basic problems in the overlap area between mathematics and philosophy: the nature of geometrical knowledge, the nature of geometry, and the applications of geometry to space. Covers history of non-Euclidean geometry, philosophic interpretations of geometry, especially Kant, projective and metrical geometry. Most interesting as the solution offered in 1897 by a great mind to a problem still current. New introduction by Prof. Morris Kline, N.Y. University. "Admirably clear, precise, and elegantly reasoned analysis," International Math. News. xii + 201pp. 5⅜ x 8.   S233 Paperbound **$1.60**

THE NATURE OF PHYSICAL THEORY, P. W. Bridgman. How modern physics looks to a highly unorthodox physicist—a Nobel laureate. Pointing out many absurdities of science, demonstrating inadequacies of various physical theories, weighs and analyzes contributions of Einstein, Bohr, Heisenberg, many others. A non-technical consideration of correlation of science and reality. xi + 138pp. 5⅜ x 8.   S33 Paperbound **$1.25**

EXPERIMENT AND THEORY IN PHYSICS, Max Born. A Nobel laureate examines the nature and value of the counterclaims of experiment and theory in physics. Synthetic versus analytical scientific advances are analyzed in works of Einstein, Bohr, Heisenberg, Planck, Eddington, Milne, others, by a fellow scientist. 44pp. 5⅜ x 8.   S308 Paperbound **60¢**

A SHORT HISTORY OF ANATOMY AND PHYSIOLOGY FROM THE GREEKS TO HARVEY, Charles Singer. Corrected edition of "The Evolution of Anatomy." Classic traces anatomy, physiology from prescientific times through Greek, Roman periods, dark ages, Renaissance, to beginning of modern concepts. Centers on individuals, movements, that definitely advanced anatomical knowledge. Plato, Diocles, Erasistratus, Galen, da Vinci, etc. Special section on Vesalius. 20 plates. 270 extremely interesting illustrations of ancient, Medieval, Renaissance, Oriental origin. xii + 209pp. 5⅜ x 8.   T389 Paperbound **$1.75**

SPACE - TIME - MATTER, Hermann Weyl. "The standard treatise on the general theory of relativity," (Nature), by world renowned scientist. Deep, clear discussion of logical coherence of general theory, introducing all needed tools: Maxwell, analytical geometry, non-Euclidean geometry, tensor calculus, etc. Basis is classical space-time, before absorption of relativity. Contents: Euclidean space, mathematical form, metrical continuum, general theory, etc. 15 diagrams. xviii + 330pp. 5⅜ x 8.   S267 Paperbound **$1.75**

4

MATTER AND MOTION, James Clerk Maxwell. Excellent exposition begins with simple particles, proceeds gradually to physical systems beyond complete analysis; motion, force, properties of centre of mass of material system; work, energy, gravitation, etc. Written with all Maxwell's original insights and clarity. Notes by E. Larmor. 17 diagrams. 178pp. 5⅜ x 8.
S188 Paperbound **$1.25**

PRINCIPLES OF MECHANICS, Heinrich Hertz. Last work by the great 19th century physicist is not only a classic, but of great interest in the logic of science. Creating a new system of mechanics based upon space, time, and mass, it returns to axiomatic analysis, understanding of the formal or structural aspects of science, taking into account logic, observation, a priori elements. Of great historical importance to Poincaré, Carnap, Einstein, Milne. A 20 page introduction by R. S. Cohen, Wesleyan University, analyzes the implications of Hertz's thought and the logic of science. 13 page introduction by Helmholtz. xlii + 274pp. 5⅜ x 8.
S316 Clothbound **$3.50**
S317 Paperbound **$1.75**

FROM MAGIC TO SCIENCE, Charles Singer. A great historian examines aspects of science from Roman Empire through Renaissance. Includes perhaps best discussion of early herbals, penetrating physiological interpretation of "The Visions of Hildegarde of Bingen." Also examines Arabian, Galenic influences; Pythagoras' sphere, Paracelsus; reawakening of science under Leonardo da Vinci, Vesalius; Lorica of Gildas the Briton; etc. Frequent quotations with translations from contemporary manuscripts. Unabridged, corrected edition. 158 unusual illustrations from Classical, Medieval sources. xxvii + 365pp. 5⅜ x 8.
T390 Paperbound **$2.00**

A HISTORY OF THE CALCULUS, AND ITS CONCEPTUAL DEVELOPMENT, Carl B. Boyer. Provides laymen, mathematicians a detailed history of the development of the calculus, from beginnings in antiquity to final elaboration as mathematical abstraction. Gives a sense of mathematics not as technique, but as habit of mind, in progression of ideas of Zeno, Plato, Pythagoras, Eudoxus, Arabic and Scholastic mathematicians, Newton, Leibniz, Taylor, Descartes, Euler, Lagrange, Cantor, Weierstrass, and others. This first comprehensive, critical history of the calculus was originally entitled "The Concepts of the Calculus." Foreword by R. Courant. 22 figures. 25 page bibliography. v + 364pp. 5⅜ x 8.
S509 Paperbound **$2.00**

A DIDEROT PICTORIAL ENCYCLOPEDIA OF TRADES AND INDUSTRY, Manufacturing and the Technical Arts in Plates Selected from "L'Encyclopédie ou Dictionnaire Raisonné des Sciences, des Arts, et des Métiers" of Denis Diderot. Edited with text by C. Gillispie. First modern selection of plates from high-point of 18th century French engraving. Storehouse of technological information to historian of arts and science. Over 2,000 illustrations on 485 full page plates, most of them original size, show trades, industries of fascinating era in such great detail that modern reconstructions might be made of them. Plates teem with men, women, children performing thousands of operations; show sequence, general operations, closeups, details of machinery. Illustrates such important, interesting trades, industries as sowing, harvesting, beekeeping, tobacco processing, fishing, arts of war, mining, smelting, casting iron, extracting mercury, making gunpowder, cannons, bells, shoeing horses, tanning, papermaking, printing, dying, over 45 more categories. Professor Gillispie of Princeton supplies full commentary on all plates, identifies operations, tools, processes, etc. Material is presented in lively, lucid fashion. Of great interest to all studying history of science, technology. Heavy library cloth. 920pp. 9 x 12.
T421 2 volume set **$18.50**

DE MAGNETE, William Gilbert. Classic work on magnetism, founded new science. Gilbert was first to use word "electricity," to recognize mass as distinct from weight, to discover effect of heat on magnetic bodies; invented an electroscope, differentiated between static electricity and magnetism, conceived of earth as magnet. This lively work, by first great experimental scientist, is not only a valuable historical landmark, but a delightfully easy to follow record of a searching, ingenious mind. Translated by P. F. Mottelay. 25 page biographical memoir. 90 figures. lix + 368pp. 5⅜ x 8.
S470 Paperbound **$2.00**

HISTORY OF MATHEMATICS, D. E. Smith. Most comprehensive, non-technical history of math in English. Discusses lives and works of over a thousand major, minor figures, with footnotes giving technical information outside book's scheme, and indicating disputed matters. Vol. I: A chronological examination, from primitive concepts through Egypt, Babylonia, Greece, the Orient, Rome, the Middle Ages, The Renaissance, and to 1900. Vol. II: The development of ideas in specific fields and problems, up through elementary calculus. "Marks an epoch . . . will modify the entire teaching of the history of science," George Sarton. 2 volumes, total of 510 illustrations, 1355pp. 5⅜ x 8. Set boxed in attractive container.
T429, 430 Paperbound, the set **$5.00**

THE PHILOSOPHY OF SPACE AND TIME, H. Reichenbach. An important landmark in development of empiricist conception of geometry, covering foundations of geometry, time theory, consequences of Einstein's relativity, including: relations between theory and observations; coordinate definitions; relations between topological and metrical properties of space; psychological problem of visual intuition of non-Euclidean structures; many more topics important to modern science and philosophy. Majority of ideas require only knowledge of intermediate math. "Still the best book in the field," Rudolf Carnap. Introduction by R. Carnap. 49 figures. xviii + 296pp. 5⅜ x 8.
S443 Paperbound **$2.00**

FOUNDATIONS OF SCIENCE: THE PHILOSOPHY OF THEORY AND EXPERIMENT, N. Campbell. A critique of the most fundamental concepts of science, particularly physics. Examines why certain propositions are accepted without question, demarcates science from philosophy, etc. Part I analyzes presuppositions of scientific thought: existence of material world, nature of laws, probability, etc; part 2 covers nature of experiment and applications of mathematics: conditions for measurement, relations between numerical laws and theories, error, etc. An appendix covers problems arising from relativity, force, motion, space, time. A classic in its field. "A real grasp of what science is," Higher Educational Journal. xiii + 565pp. 5⅝ x 8⅜.   S372 Paperbound **$2.95**

THE STUDY OF THE HISTORY OF MATHEMATICS and **THE STUDY OF THE HISTORY OF SCIENCE, G. Sarton.** Excellent introductions, orientation, for beginning or mature worker. Describes duty of mathematical historian, incessant efforts and genius of previous generations. Explains how today's discipline differs from previous methods. 200 item bibliography with critical evaluations, best available biographies of modern mathematicians, best treatises on historical methods is especially valuable. 10 illustrations. 2 volumes bound as one. 113pp. + 75pp. 5⅜ x 8.   T240 Paperbound **$1.25**

MATHEMATICAL PUZZLES

MATHEMATICAL PUZZLES OF SAM LOYD, selected and edited by **Martin Gardner.** 117 choice puzzles by greatest American puzzle creator and innovator, from his famous "Cyclopedia of Puzzles." All unique style, historical flavor of originals. Based on arithmetic, algebra, probability, game theory, route tracing, topology, sliding block, operations research, geometrical dissection. Includes famous "14-15" puzzle which was national craze, "Horse of a Different Color" which sold millions of copies. 120 line drawings, diagrams. Solutions. xx + 167pp. 5⅜ x 8.   T498 Paperbound **$1.00**

SYMBOLIC LOGIC and THE GAME OF LOGIC, Lewis Carroll. "Symbolic Logic" is not concerned with modern symbolic logic, but is instead a collection of over 380 problems posed with charm and imagination, using the syllogism, and a fascinating diagrammatic method of drawing conclusions. In "The Game of Logic" Carroll's whimsical imagination devises a logical game played with 2 diagrams and counters (included) to manipulate hundreds of tricky syllogisms. The final section, "Hit or Miss" is a lagniappe of 101 additional puzzles in the delightful Carroll manner. Until this reprint edition, both of these books were rarities costing up to $15 each. Symbolic Logic: Index. xxxi + 199pp. The Game of Logic: 96pp. 2 vols. bound as one. 5⅜ x 8.   T492 Paperbound **$1.50**

PILLOW PROBLEMS and A TANGLED TALE, Lewis Carroll. One of the rarest of all Carroll's works, "Pillow Problems" contains 72 original math puzzles, all typically ingenious. Particularly fascinating are Carroll's answers which remain exactly as he thought them out, reflecting his actual mental process. The problems in "A Tangled Tale" are in story form, originally appearing as a monthly magazine serial. Carroll not only gives the solutions, but uses answers sent in by readers to discuss wrong approaches and misleading paths, and grades them for insight. Both of these books were rarities until this edition, "Pillow Problems" costing up to $25, and "A Tangled Tale" $15. Pillow Problems: Preface and Introduction by Lewis Carroll. xx + 109pp. A Tangled Tale: 6 illustrations. 152pp. Two vols. bound as one. 5⅜ x 8.   T493 Paperbound **$1.50**

NEW WORD PUZZLES, G. L. Kaufman. 100 brand new challenging puzzles on words, combinations, never before published. Most are new types invented by author, for beginners and experts both. Squares of letters follow chess moves to build words; symmetrical designs made of synonyms; rhymed crostics; double word squares; syllable puzzles where you fill in missing syllables instead of missing letter; many other types, all new. Solutions. "Excellent," Recreation. 100 puzzles. 196 figures. vi + 122pp. 5⅜ x 8.   T344 Paperbound **$1.00**

MATHEMATICAL EXCURSIONS, H. A. Merrill. Fun, recreation, insights into elementary problem solving. Math expert guides you on by-paths not generally travelled in elementary math courses—divide by inspection, Russian peasant multiplication; memory systems for pi; odd, even magic squares; dyadic systems; square roots by geometry; Tchebichev's machine; dozens more. Solutions to more difficult ones. "Brain stirring stuff . . . a classic," Genie. 50 illustrations. 145pp. 5⅜ x 8.   T350 Paperbound **$1.00**

THE BOOK OF MODERN PUZZLES, G. L. Kaufman. Over 150 puzzles, absolutely all new material based on same appeal as crosswords, deduction puzzles, but with different principles, techniques. 2-minute teasers, word labyrinths, design, pattern, logic, observation puzzles, puzzles testing ability to apply general knowledge to peculiar situations, many others. Solutions. 116 illustrations. 192pp. 5⅜ x 8.   T143 Paperbound **$1.00**

MATHEMAGIC, MAGIC PUZZLES, AND GAMES WITH NUMBERS, R. V. Heath. Over 60 puzzles, stunts, on properties of numbers. Easy techniques for multiplying large numbers mentally, identifying unknown numbers, finding date of any day in any year. Includes The Lost Digit, 3 Acrobats, Psychic Bridge, magic squares, triangles, cubes, others not easily found elsewhere. Edited by J. S. Meyer. 76 illustrations. 128pp. 5⅜ x 8.   T110 Paperbound **$1.00**

PUZZLE QUIZ AND STUNT FUN, J. Meyer. 238 high-priority puzzles, stunts, tricks—math puzzles like The Clever Carpenter, Atom Bomb, Please Help Alice; mysteries, deductions like The Bridge of Sighs, Secret Code; observation puzzlers like The American Flag, Playing Cards, Telephone Dial; over 200 others with magic squares, tongue twisters, puns, anagrams. Solutions. Revised, enlarged edition of "Fun-To-Do." Over 100 illustrations. 238 puzzles, stunts, tricks. 256pp. 5⅜ x 8.   T337 Paperbound **$1.00**

101 PUZZLES IN THOUGHT AND LOGIC, C. R. Wylie, Jr. For readers who enjoy challenge, stimulation of logical puzzles without specialized math or scientific knowledge. Problems entirely new, range from relatively easy to brainteasers for hours of subtle entertainment. Detective puzzles, find the lying fisherman, how a blind man identifies color by logic, many more. Easy-to-understand introduction to logic of puzzle solving and general scientific method. 128pp. 5⅜ x 8.   T367 Paperbound **$1.00**

CRYPTANALYSIS, H. F. Gaines. Standard elementary, intermediate text for serious students. Not just old material, but much not generally known, except to experts. Concealment, Transposition, Substitution ciphers; Vigenere, Kasiski, Playfair, multafid, dozens of other techniques. Formerly "Elementary Cryptanalysis." Appendix with sequence charts, letter frequencies in English, 5 other languages, English word frequencies. Bibliography. 167 codes. New to this edition: solutions to codes. vi + 230pp. 5⅜ x 8⅜.   T97 Paperbound **$1.95**

CRYPTOGRAPHY, L. D. Smith. Excellent elementary introduction to enciphering, deciphering secret writing. Explains transposition, substitution ciphers; codes; solutions; geometrical patterns, route transcription, columnar transposition, other methods. Mixed cipher systems; single, polyalphabetical substitutions; mechanical devices; Vigenere; etc. Enciphering Japanese; explanation of Baconian biliteral cipher; frequency tables. Over 150 problems. Bibliography. Index. 164pp. 5⅜ x 8.   T247 Paperbound **$1.00**

MATHEMATICS, MAGIC AND MYSTERY, M. Gardner. Card tricks, metal mathematics, stage mind-reading, other "magic" explained as applications of probability, sets, number theory, etc. Creative examination of laws, applications. Scores of new tricks, insights. 115 sections on cards, dice, coins; vanishing tricks, many others. No sleight of hand—math guarantees success. "Could hardly get more entertainment . . . easy to follow," Mathematics Teacher. 115 illustrations. xii + 174pp. 5⅜ x 8.   T335 Paperbound **$1.00**

AMUSEMENTS IN MATHEMATICS, H. E. Dudeney. Foremost British originator of math puzzles, always witty, intriguing, paradoxical in this classic. One of largest collections. More than 430 puzzles, problems, paradoxes. Mazes, games, problems on number manipulations, unicursal, other route problems, puzzles on measuring, weighing, packing, age, kinship, chessboards, joiners', crossing river, plane figure dissection, many others. Solutions. More than 450 illustrations. viii + 258pp. 5⅜ x 8.   T473 Paperbound **$1.25**

THE CANTERBURY PUZZLES H. E. Dudeney. Chaucer's pilgrims set one another problems in story form. Also Adventures of the Puzzle Club, the Strange Escape of the King's Jester, the Monks of Riddlewell, the Squire's Christmas Puzzle Party, others. All puzzles are original, based on dissecting plane figures, arithmetic, algebra, elementary calculus, other branches of mathematics, and purely logical ingenuity. "The limit of ingenuity and intricacy," The Observer. Over 110 puzzles, full solutions. 150 illustrations. viii + 225 pp. 5⅜ x 8.   T474 Paperbound **$1.25**

MATHEMATICAL PUZZLES FOR BEGINNERS AND ENTHUSIASTS, G. Mott-Smith. 188 puzzles to test mental agility. Inference, interpretation, algebra, dissection of plane figures, geometry, properties of numbers, decimation, permutations, probability, all are in these delightful problems. Includes the Odic Force, How to Draw an Ellipse, Spider's Cousin, more than 180 others. Detailed solutions. Appendix with square roots, triangular numbers, primes, etc. 135 illustrations. 2nd revised edition. 248pp. 5⅜ x 8.   T198 Paperbound **$1.00**

MATHEMATICAL RECREATIONS, M. Kraitchik. Some 250 puzzles, problems, demonstrations of recreation mathematics on relatively advanced level. Unusual historical problems from Greek, Medieval, Arabic, Hindu sources; modern problems on "mathematics without numbers," geometry, topology, arithmetic, etc. Pastimes derived from figurative, Mersenne, Fermat numbers: fairy chess; latruncles: reversi; etc. Full solutions. Excellent insights into special fields of math. "Strongly recommended to all who are interested in the lighter side of mathematics," Mathematical Gaz. 181 illustrations. 330pp. 5⅜ x 8.   T163 Paperbound **$1.75**

FICTION

FLATLAND, E. A. Abbott. A perennially popular science-fiction classic about life in a 2-dimensional world, and the impingement of higher dimensions. Political, satiric, humorous, moral overtones. This land where women are straight lines and the lowest and most dangerous classes are isosceles triangles with 3° vertices conveys brilliantly a feeling for many concepts of modern science. 7th edition. New introduction by Banesh Hoffmann. 128pp. 5⅜ x 8.   T1 Paperbound **$1.00**

SEVEN SCIENCE FICTION NOVELS OF H. G. WELLS. Complete texts, unabridged, of seven of Wells' greatest novels: The War of the Worlds, The Invisible Man, The Island of Dr. Moreau, The Food of the Gods, First Men in the Moon, In the Days of the Comet, The Time Machine. Still considered by many experts to be the best science-fiction ever written, they will offer amusements and instruction to the scientific minded reader. "The great master," Sky and Telescope. 1051pp. 5⅜ x 8. T264 Clothbound **$3.95**

28 SCIENCE FICTION STORIES OF H. G. WELLS. Unabridged! This enormous omnibus contains 2 full length novels—Men Like Gods, Star Begotten—plus 26 short stories of space, time, invention, biology, etc. The Crystal Egg, The Country of the Blind, Empire of the Ants, The Man Who Could Work Miracles, Aepyornis Island, A Story of the Days to Come, and 20 others "A master . . . not surpassed by . . . writers of today," The English Journal. 915pp. 5⅜ x 8. T265 Clothbound **$3.95**

FIVE ADVENTURE NOVELS OF H. RIDER HAGGARD. All the mystery and adventure of darkest Africa captured accurately by a man who lived among Zulus for years, who knew African ethnology, folkways as did few of his contemporaries. They have been regarded as examples of the very best high adventure by such critics as Orwell, Andrew Lang, Kipling. Contents: She, King Solomon's Mines, Allan Quatermain, Allan's Wife, Maiwa's Revenge. "Could spin a yarn so full of suspense and color that you couldn't put the story down," Sat. Review. 821pp. 5⅜ x 8. T108 Clothbound **$3.95**

CHESS AND CHECKERS

LEARN CHESS FROM THE MASTERS, Fred Reinfeld. Easiest, most instructive way to improve your game—play 10 games against such masters as Marshall, Znosko-Borovsky, Bronstein, Najdorf, etc., with each move graded by easy system. Includes ratings for alternate moves possible. Games selected for interest, clarity, easily isolated principles. Covers Ruy Lopez, Dutch Defense, Vienna Game openings; subtle, intricate middle game variations; all-important end game. Full annotations. Formerly "Chess by Yourself." 91 diagrams. viii + 144pp. 5⅜ x 8. T362 Paperbound **$1.00**

REINFELD ON THE END GAME IN CHESS, Fred Reinfeld. Analyzes 62 end games by Alekhine, Flohr, Tarrasch, Morphy, Capablanca, Rubinstein, Lasker, Reshevsky, other masters. Only 1st rate book with extensive coverage of error—tell exactly what is wrong with each move you might have made. Centers around transitions from middle play to end play. King and pawn, minor pieces, queen endings; blockage, weak, passed pawns, etc. "Excellent . . . a boon," Chess Life. Formerly "Practical End Play." 62 figures. vi + 177pp. 5⅜ x 8. T417 Paperbound **$1.25**

HYPERMODERN CHESS as developed in the games of its greatest exponent, ARON NIMZO-VICH, edited by Fred Reinfeld. An intensely original player, analyst, Nimzovich's approaches startled, often angered the chess world. This volume, designed for the average player, shows how his iconoclastic methods won him victories over Alekhine, Lasker, Marshall, Rubinstein, Spielmann, others, and infused new life into the game. Use his methods to startle opponents, invigorate play. "Annotations and introductions to each game . . . are excellent," Times (London). 180 diagrams. viii + 220pp. 5⅜ x 8. T448 Paperbound **$1.35**

THE ADVENTURE OF CHESS, Edward Lasker. Lively reader, by one of America's finest chess masters, including: history of chess, from ancient Indian 4-handed game of Chaturanga to great players of today; such delights and oddities as Maelzel's chess-playing automaton that beat Napoleon 3 times; etc. One of most valuable features is author's personal recollections of men he has played against—Nimzovich, Emanuel Lasker, Capablanca, Alekhine, etc. Discussion of chess-playing machines (newly revised). 5 page chess primer. 11 illustrations. 53 diagrams. 296pp. 5⅜ x 8. S510 Paperbound **$1.45**

THE ART OF CHESS, James Mason. Unabridged reprinting of latest revised edition of most famous general study ever written. Mason, early 20th century master, teaches beginning, intermediate player over 90 openings; middle game, end game, to see more moves ahead, to plan purposefully, attack, sacrifice, defend, exchange, govern general strategy. "Classic . . . one of the clearest and best developed studies," Publishers Weekly. Also included, a complete supplement by F. Reinfeld, "How Do You Play Chess?", invaluable to beginners for its lively question-and-answer method. 448 diagrams. 1947 Reinfeld-Bernstein text. Bibliography. xvi + 340pp. 5⅜ x 8. T463 Paperbound **$1.85**

MORPHY'S GAMES OF CHESS, edited by P. W. Sergeant. Put boldness into your game by flowing brilliant, forceful moves of the greatest chess player of all time. 300 of Morphy's best games, carefully annotated to reveal principles. 54 classics against masters like Anderssen, Harrwitz, Bird, Paulsen, and others. 52 games at odds; 54 blindfold games; plus over 100 others. Follow his interpretation of Dutch Defense, Evans Gambit, Giuoco Piano, Ruy Lopez, many more. Unabridged reissue of latest revised edition. New introduction by F. Reinfeld. Annotations, introduction by Sergeant. 235 diagrams. x + 352pp. 5⅜ x 8. T386 Paperbound **$1.75**

DOVER SCIENCE BOOKS

WIN AT CHECKERS, M. Hopper. (Formerly "Checkers.") Former World's Unrestricted Checker Champion discusses principles of game, expert's shots, traps, problems for beginner, standard openings, locating best move, end game, opening "blitzkrieg" moves to draw when behind, etc. Over 100 detailed questions, answers anticipate problems. Appendix. 75 problems with solutions, diagrams. 79 figures. xi + 107pp. 5⅜ x 8.　　T363 Paperbound **$1.00**

HOW TO FORCE CHECKMATE, Fred Reinfeld. If you have trouble finishing off your opponent, here is a collection of lightning strokes and combinations from actual tournament play. Starts with 1-move checkmates, works up to 3-move mates. Develops ability to lock ahead, gain new insights into combinations, complex or deceptive positions; ways to estimate weaknesses, strengths of you and your opponent. "A good deal of amusement and instruction," Times, (London). 300 diagrams. Solutions to all positions. Formerly "Challenge to Chess Players." 111pp. 5⅜ x 8.　　T417 Paperbound **$1.25**

A TREASURY OF CHESS LORE, edited by Fred Reinfeld. Delightful collection of anecdotes, short stories, aphorisms by, about masters; poems, accounts of games, tournaments, photographs; hundreds of humorous, pithy, satirical, wise, historical episodes, comments, word portraits. Fascinating "must" for chess players; revealing and perhaps seductive to those who wonder what their friends see in game. 49 photographs (14 full page plates). 12 diagrams. xi + 306pp. 5⅜ x 8.　　T458 Paperbound **$1.75**

WIN AT CHESS, Fred Reinfeld. 300 practical chess situations, to sharpen your eye, test skill against masters. Start with simple examples, progress at own pace to complexities. This selected series of crucial moments in chess will stimulate imagination, develop stronger, more versatile game. Simple grading system enables you to judge progress. "Extensive use of diagrams is a great attraction," Chess. 300 diagrams. Notes, solutions to every situation. Formerly "Chess Quiz." vi + 120pp. 5⅜ x 8.　　T433 Paperbound **$1.00**

MATHEMATICS:
ELEMENTARY TO INTERMEDIATE

HOW TO CALCULATE QUICKLY, H. Sticker. Tried and true method to help mathematics of everyday life. Awakens "number sense"—ability to see relationships between numbers as whole quantities. A serious course of over 9000 problems and their solutions through techniques not taught in schools: left-to-right multiplications, new fast division, etc. 10 minutes a day will double or triple calculation speed. Excellent for scientist at home in higher math, but dissatisfied with speed and accuracy in lower math. 256pp. 5 x 7¼.
Paperbound **$1.00**

FAMOUS PROBLEMS OF ELEMENTARY GEOMETRY, Felix Klein. Expanded version of 1894 Easter lectures at Göttingen. 3 problems of classical geometry: squaring the circle, trisecting angle, doubling cube, considered with full modern implications: transcendental numbers, pi, etc. "A modern classic . . . no knowledge of higher mathematics is required," Scientia. Notes by R. Archibald. 16 figures. xi + 92pp. 5⅜ x 8.　　T298 Paperbound **$1.00**

HIGHER MATHEMATICS FOR STUDENTS OF CHEMISTRY AND PHYSICS, J. W. Mellor. Practical, not abstract, building problems out of familiar laboratory material. Covers differential calculus, coordinate, analytical geometry, functions, integral calculus, infinite series, numerical equations, differential equations, Fourier's theorem probability, theory of errors, calculus of variations, determinants. "If the reader is not familiar with this book, it will repay him to examine it," Chem. and Engineering News. 800 problems. 189 figures. xxi + 641pp. 5⅜ x 8.　　S193 Paperbound **$2.25**

TRIGONOMETRY REFRESHER FOR TECHNICAL MEN, A. A. Klaf. 913 detailed questions, answers cover most important aspects of plane, spherical trigonometry—particularly useful in clearing up difficulties in special areas. Part I: plane trig, angles, quadrants, functions, graphical representation, interpolation, equations, logs, solution of triangle, use of slide rule, etc. Next 188 pages discuss applications to navigation, surveying, elasticity, architecture, other special fields. Part 3: spherical trig, applications to terrestrial, astronomical problems. Methods of time-saving, simplification of principal angles, make book most useful. 913 questions answered. 1738 problems, answers to odd numbers. 494 figures. 24 pages of formulas, functions. x + 629pp. 5⅜ x 8.　　T371 Paperbound **$2.00**

CALCULUS REFRESHER FOR TECHNICAL MEN, A. A. Klaf. 756 questions examine most important aspects of integral, differential calculus. Part I: simple differential calculus, constants, variables, functions, increments, logs, curves, etc. Part 2: fundamental ideas of integrations, inspection, substitution, areas, volumes, mean value, double, triple integration, etc. Practical aspects stressed. 50 pages illustrate applications to specific problems of civil, nautical engineering, electricity, stress, strain, elasticity, similar fields. 756 questions answered. 566 problems, mostly answered. 36pp. of useful constants, formulas. v + 431pp. 5⅜ x 8.　　T370 Paperbound **$2.00**

9

MONOGRAPHS ON TOPICS OF MODERN MATHEMATICS, edited by J. W. A. Young. Advanced mathematics for persons who have forgotten, or not gone beyond, high school algebra. 9 monographs on foundation of geometry, modern pure geometry, non-Euclidean geometry, fundamental propositions of algebra, algebraic equations, functions, calculus, theory of numbers, etc. Each monograph gives proofs of important results, and descriptions of leading methods, to provide wide coverage. "Of high merit," Scientific American. New introduction by Prof. M. Kline, N.Y. Univ. 100 diagrams. xvi + 416pp. 6⅛ x 9¼.
S289 Paperbound **$2.00**

MATHEMATICS IN ACTION, O. G. Sutton. Excellent middle level application of mathematics to study of universe, demonstrates how math is applied to ballistics, theory of computing machines, waves, wave-like phenomena, theory of fluid flow, meteorological problems, statistics, flight, similar phenomena. No knowledge of advanced math required. Differential equations, Fourier series, group concepts, Eigenfunctions, Planck's constant, airfoil theory, and similar topics explained so clearly in everyday language that almost anyone can derive benefit from reading this even if much of high-school math is forgotten. 2nd edition. 88 figures. viii + 236pp. 5⅜ x 8.
T450 Clothbound **$3.50**

ELEMENTARY MATHEMATICS FROM AN ADVANCED STANDPOINT, Felix Klein. Classic text, an outgrowth of Klein's famous integration and survey course at Göttingen. Using one field to interpret, adjust another, it covers basic topics in each area, with extensive analysis. Especially valuable in areas of modern mathematics. "A great mathematician, inspiring teacher, . . . deep insight," Bul., Amer. Math Soc.

Vol. I. ARITHMETIC, ALGEBRA, ANALYSIS. Introduces concept of function immediately, enlivens discussion with graphical, geometric methods. Partial contents: natural numbers, special properties, complex numbers. Real equations with real unknowns, complex quantities. Logarithmic, exponential functions, infinitesimal calculus. Transcendence of e and pi, theory of assemblages. Index. 125 figures. ix + 274pp. 5⅜ x 8.
S151 Paperbound **$1.75**

Vol. II. GEOMETRY. Comprehensive view, accompanies space perception inherent in geometry with analytic formulas which facilitate precise formulation. Partial contents: Simplest geometric manifold; line segments, Grassman determinant principles, classication of configurations of space. Geometric transformations: affine, projective, higher point transformations, theory of the imaginary. Systematic discussion of geometry and its foundations. 141 illustrations. ix + 214pp. 5⅜ x 8.
S151 Paperbound **$1.75**

A TREATISE ON PLANE AND ADVANCED TRIGONOMETRY, E. W. Hobson. Extraordinarily wide coverage, going beyond usual college level, one of few works covering advanced trig in full detail. By a great expositor with unerring anticipation of potentially difficult points. Includes circular functions; expansion of functions of multiple angle; trig tables; relations between sides, angles of triangles; complex numbers; etc. Many problems fully solved. "The best work on the subject," Nature. Formerly entitled "A Treatise on Plane Trigonometry." 689 examples. 66 figures. xvi + 383pp. 5⅜ x 8.
S353 Paperbound **$1.95**

NON-EUCLIDEAN GEOMETRY, Roberto Bonola. The standard coverage of non-Euclidean geometry. Examines from both a historical and mathematical point of view geometries which have arisen from a study of Euclid's 5th postulate on parallel lines. Also included are complete texts, translated, of Bolyai's "Theory of Absolute Space," Lobachevsky's "Theory of Parallels." 180 diagrams. 431pp. 5⅜ x 8.
S27 Paperbound **$1.95**

GEOMETRY OF FOUR DIMENSIONS, H. P. Manning. Unique in English as a clear, concise introduction. Treatment is synthetic, mostly Euclidean, though in hyperplanes and hyperspheres at infinity, non-Euclidean geometry is used. Historical introduction. Foundations of 4-dimensional geometry. Perpendicularity, simple angles. Angles of planes, higher order. Symmetry, order, motion; hyperpyramids, hypercones, hyperspheres; figures with parallel elements; volume, hypervolume in space; regular polyhedroids. Glossary. 78 figures. ix + 348pp. 5⅜ x 8.
S182 Paperbound **$1.95**

MATHEMATICS: INTERMEDIATE TO ADVANCED

GEOMETRY (EUCLIDEAN AND NON-EUCLIDEAN)

THE GEOMETRY OF RENÉ DESCARTES. With this book, Descartes founded analytical geometry. Original French text, with Descartes's own diagrams, and excellent Smith-Latham translation. Contains: Problems the Construction of Which Requires only Straight Lines and Circles; On the Nature of Curved Lines; On the Construction of Solid or Supersolid Problems. Diagrams. 258pp. 5⅜ x 8.
S68 Paperbound **$1.50**

DOVER SCIENCE BOOKS

THE WORKS OF ARCHIMEDES, edited by T. L. Heath. All the known works of the great Greek mathematician, including the recently discovered Method of Archimedes. Contains: On Sphere and Cylinder, Measurement of a Circle, Spirals, Conoids, Spheroids, etc. Definitive edition of greatest mathematical intellect of ancient world. 186 page study by Heath discusses Archimedes and history of Greek mathematics. 563pp. 5⅜ x 8.   S9 Paperbound **$2.00**

COLLECTED WORKS OF BERNARD RIEMANN. Important sourcebook, first to contain complete text of 1892 "Werke" and the 1902 supplement, unabridged. 31 monographs, 3 complete lecture courses, 15 miscellaneous papers which have been of enormous importance in relativity, topology, theory of complex variables, other areas of mathematics. Edited by R. Dedekind, H. Weber, M. Noether, W. Wirtinger. German text; English introduction by Hans Lewy. 690pp. 5⅜ x 8.   S226 Paperbound **$2.85**

THE THIRTEEN BOOKS OF EUCLID'S ELEMENTS, edited by Sir Thomas Heath. Definitive edition of one of very greatest classics of Western world. Complete translation of Heiberg text, plus spurious Book XIV. 150 page introduction on Greek, Medieval mathematics, Euclid, texts, commentators, etc. Elaborate critical apparatus parallels text, analyzing each definition, postulate, proposition, covering textual matters, refutations, supports, extrapolations, etc. This is the full Euclid. Unabridged reproduction of Cambridge U. 2nd edition. 3 volumes. 995 figures. 1426pp. 5⅜ x 8.   S88, 89, 90, 3 volume set, paperbound **$6.00**

AN INTRODUCTION TO GEOMETRY OF N DIMENSIONS, D. M. Y. Sommerville. Presupposes no previous knowledge of field. Only book in English devoted exclusively to higher dimensional geometry. Discusses fundamental ideas of incidence, parallelism, perpendicularity, angles between linear space, enumerative geometry, analytical geometry from projective and metric views, polytopes, elementary ideas in analysis situs, content of hyperspacial figures. 60 diagrams. 196pp. 5⅜ x 8.   S494 Paperbound **$1.50**

ELEMENTS OF NON-EUCLIDEAN GEOMETRY, D. M. Y. Sommerville. Unique in proceeding step-by-step. Requires only good knowledge of high-school geometry and algebra, to grasp elementary hyperbolic, elliptic, analytic non-Euclidean Geometries; space curvature and its implications; radical axes; homopethic centres and systems of circles; parataxy and parallelism; Gauss' proof of defect area theorem; much more, with exceptional clarity. 126 problems at chapter ends. 133 figures. xvi + 274pp. 5⅜ x 8.   S460 Paperbound **$1.50**

THE FOUNDATIONS OF EUCLIDEAN GEOMETRY, H. G. Forder. First connected, rigorous account in light of modern analysis, establishing propositions without recourse to empiricism, without multiplying hypotheses. Based on tools of 19th and 20th century mathematicians, who made it possible to remedy gaps and complexities, recognize problems not earlier discerned. Begins with important relationship of number systems in geometrical figures. Considers classes, relations, linear order, natural numbers, axioms for magnitudes, groups, quasi-fields, fields, non-Archimedian systems, the axiom system (at length), particular axioms (two chapters on the Parallel Axioms), constructions, congruence, similarity, etc. Lists: axioms employed, constructions, symbols in frequent use. 295pp. 5⅜ x 8.
S481 Paperbound **$2.00**

CALCULUS, FUNCTION THEORY (REAL AND COMPLEX), FOURIER THEORY

FIVE VOLUME "THEORY OF FUNCTIONS" SET BY KONRAD KNOPP. Provides complete, readily followed account of theory of functions. Proofs given concisely, yet without sacrifice of completeness or rigor. These volumes used as texts by such universities as M.I.T., Chicago, N.Y. City College, many others. "Excellent introduction . . . remarkably readable, concise, clear, rigorous," J. of the American Statistical Association.

ELEMENTS OF THE THEORY OF FUNCTIONS, Konrad Knopp. Provides background for further volumes in this set, or texts on similar level. Partial contents: Foundations, system of complex numbers and Gaussian plane of numbers, Riemann sphere of numbers, mapping by linear functions, normal forms, the logarithm, cyclometric functions, binomial series. "Not only for the young student, but also for the student who knows all about what is in it," Mathematical Journal. 140pp. 5⅜ x 8.   S154 Paperbound **$1.35**

THEORY OF FUNCTIONS, PART I, Konrad Knopp. With volume II, provides coverage of basic concepts and theorems. Partial contents: numbers and points, functions of a complex variable, integral of a continuous function, Cauchy's intergral theorem, Cauchy's integral formulae, series with variable terms, expansion and analytic function in a power series, analytic continuation and complete definition of analytic functions, Laurent expansion, types of singularities. vii + 146pp. 5⅜ x 8.   S156 Paperbound **$1.35**

THEORY OF FUNCTIONS, PART II, Konrad Knopp. Application and further development of general theory, special topics. Single valued functions, entire, Weierstrass. Meromorphic functions: Mittag-Leffler. Periodic functions. Multiple valued functions. Riemann surfaces. Algebraic functions. Analytical configurations, Riemann surface. x + 150pp. 5⅜ x 8.
S157 Paperbound **$1.35**

PROBLEM BOOK IN THE THEORY OF FUNCTIONS, VOLUME I, Konrad Knopp. Problems in elementary theory, for use with Knopp's "Theory of Functions," or any other text. Arranged according to increasing difficulty. Fundamental concepts, sequences of numbers and infinite series, complex variable, integral theorems, development in series, conformal mapping. Answers. viii + 126pp. 5⅜ x 8.   S 158 **Paperbound $1.35**

PROBLEM BOOK IN THE THEORY OF FUNCTIONS, VOLUME II, Konrad Knopp. Advanced theory of functions, to be used with Knopp's "Theory of Functions," or comparable text. Singularities, entire and meromorphic functions, periodic, analytic, continuation, multiple-valued functions, Riemann surfaces, conformal mapping. Includes section of elementary problems. "The difficult task of selecting . . . problems just within the reach of the beginner is here masterfully accomplished," AM. MATH. SOC. Answers. 138pp. 5⅜ x 8.
                                                                    S159 Paperbound **$1.35**

ADVANCED CALCULUS, E. B. Wilson. Still recognized as one of most comprehensive, useful texts. Immense amount of well-represented, fundamental material, including chapters on vector functions, ordinary differential equations, special functions, calculus of variations, etc., which are excellent introductions to these areas. Requires only one year of calculus. Over 1300 exercises cover both pure math and applications to engineering and physical problems. Ideal reference, refresher. 54 page introductory review. ix + 566pp. 5⅜ x 8.
                                                                    S504 Paperbound **$2.45**

LECTURES ON THE THEORY OF ELLIPTIC FUNCTIONS, H. Hancock. Reissue of only book in English with so extensive a coverage, especially of Abel, Jacobi, Legendre, Weierstrass, Hermite, Liouville, and Riemann. Unusual fullness of treatment, plus applications as well as theory in discussing universe of elliptic integrals, originating in works of Abel and Jacobi. Use is made of Riemann to provide most general theory. 40-page table of formulas. 76 figures. xxiii + 498pp. 5⅜ x 8.   S483 Paperbound **$2.55**

THEORY OF FUNCTIONALS AND OF INTEGRAL AND INTEGRO-DIFFERENTIAL EQUATIONS, Vito Volterra. Unabridged republication of only English translation. General theory of functions depending on continuous set of values of another function. Based on author's concept of transition from finite number of variables to a continually infinite number. Includes much material on calculus of variations. Begins with fundamentals, examines generalization of analytic functions, functional derivative equations, applications, other directions of theory, etc. New introduction by G. C. Evans. Biography, criticism of Volterra's work by E. Whittaker. xxxx + 226pp. 5⅜ x 8.   S502 Paperbound **$1.75**

AN INTRODUCTION TO FOURIER METHODS AND THE LAPLACE TRANSFORMATION, Philip Franklin. Concentrates on essentials, gives broad view, suitable for most applications. Requires only knowledge of calculus. Covers complex qualities with methods of computing elementary functions for complex values of argument and finding approximations by charts; Fourier series; harmonic anaylsis; much more. Methods are related to physical problems of heat flow, vibrations, electrical transmission, electromagnetic radiation, etc. 828 problems, answers. Formerly entitled "Fourier Methods." x + 289pp. 5⅜ x 8.
                                                                    S452 Paperbound **$1.75**

THE ANALYTICAL THEORY OF HEAT, Joseph Fourier. This book, which revolutionized mathematical physics, has been used by generations of mathematicians and physicists interested in heat or application of Fourier integral. Covers cause and reflection of rays of heat, radiant heating, heating of closed spaces, use of trigonometric series in theory of heat, Fourier integral, etc. Translated by Alexander Freeman. 20 figures. xxii + 466pp. 5⅜ x 8.
                                                                    S93 Paperbound **$2.00**

ELLIPTIC INTEGRALS, H. Hancock. Invaluable in work involving differential equations with cubics, quatrics under root sign, where elementary calculus methods are inadequate. Practical solutions to problems in mathematics, engineering, physics; differential equations requiring integration of Lamé's, Briot's, or Bouquet's equations; determination of arc of ellipse, hyperbola, lemiscate; solutions of problems in elastics; motion of a projectile under resistance varying as the cube of the velocity; pendulums; more. Exposition in accordance with Legendre-Jacobi theory. Rigorous discussion of Legendre transformations. 20 figures. 5 place table. 104pp. 5⅜ x 8.   S484 Paperbound **$1.25**

THE TAYLOR SERIES, AN INTRODUCTION TO THE THEORY OF FUNCTIONS OF A COMPLEX VARIABLE, P. Dienes. Uses Taylor series to approach theory of functions, using ordinary calculus only, except in last 2 chapters. Starts with introduction to real variable and complex algebra, derives properties of infinite series, complex differentiation, integration, etc. Covers biuniform mapping, overconvergence and gap theorems, Taylor series on its circle of convergence, etc. Unabridged corrected reissue of first edition. 186 examples, many fully worked out. 67 figures. xii + 555pp. 5⅜ x 8.   S391 Paperbound **$2.75**

LINEAR INTEGRAL EQUATIONS, W. V. Lovitt. Systematic survey of general theory, with some application to differential equations, calculus of variations, problems of math, physics. Includes: integral equation of 2nd kind by successive substitutions; Fredholm's equation as ratio of 2 integral series in lambda, applications of the Fredholm theory, Hilbert-Schmidt theory of symmetric kernels, application, etc. Neumann, Dirichlet, vibratory problems. ix + 253pp. 5⅜ x 8.   S175 Clothbound **$3.50**
                                                                    S176 Paperbound **$1.60**

DOVER SCIENCE BOOKS

DICTIONARY OF CONFORMAL REPRESENTATIONS, H. Kober. Developed by British Admiralty to solve Laplace's equation in 2 dimensions. Scores of geometrical forms and transformations for electrical engineers, Joukowski aerofoil for aerodynamics, Schwartz-Christoffel transformations for hydro-dynamics, transcendental functions. Contents classified according to analytical functions describing transformations with corresponding regions. Glossary. Topological index. 447 diagrams. 6⅛ x 9¼. .S160 Paperbound **$2.00**

ELEMENTS OF THE THEORY OF REAL FUNCTIONS, J. E. Littlewood. Based on lectures at Trinity College, Cambridge, this book has proved extremely successful in introducing graduate students to modern theory of functions. Offers full and concise coverage of classes and cardinal numbers, well ordered series, other types of series, and elements of the theory of sets of points. 3rd revised edition. vii + 71pp. 5⅜ x 8. S171 Clothbound **$2.85**
S172 Paperbound **$1.25**

INFINITE SEQUENCES AND SERIES, Konrad Knopp. 1st publication in any language. Excellent introduction to 2 topics of modern mathematics, designed to give student background to penetrate further alone. Sequences and sets, real and complex numbers, etc. Functions of a real and complex variable. Sequences and series. Infinite series. Convergent power series. Expansion of elementary functions. Numerical evaluation of series. v + 186pp. 5⅜ x 8. S152 Clothbound **$3.50**
S153 Paperbound **$1.75**

THE THEORY AND FUNCTIONS OF A REAL VARIABLE AND THE THEORY OF FOURIER'S SERIES, E. W .Hobson. One of the best introductions to set theory and various aspects of functions and Fourier's series. Requires only a good background in calculus. Exhaustive coverage of: metric and descriptive properties of sets of points; transfinite numbers and order types; functions of a real variable; the Riemann and Lebesgue integrals; sequences and series of numbers; power-series; functions representable by series sequences of continuous functions; trigonometrical series; representation of functions by Fourier's series; and much more. "The best possible guide," Nature. Vol. I: 88 detailed examples, 10 figures. Index. xv + 736pp. Vol. II: 117 detailed examples, 13 figures. x + 780pp. 6⅛ x 9¼.
Vol. I: S387 Paperbound **$3.00**
Vol. II: S388 Paperbound **$3.00**

ALMOST PERIODIC FUNCTIONS, A. S. Besicovitch. Unique and important summary by a well known mathematician covers in detail the two stages of development in Bohr's theory of almost periodic functions: (1) as a generalization of pure periodicity, with results and proofs; (2) the work done by Stepanof, Wiener, Weyl, and Bohr in generalizing the theory. xi + 180pp. 5⅜ x 8. S18 Paperbound **$1.75**

INTRODUCTION TO THE THEORY OF FOURIER'S SERIES AND INTEGRALS, H. S. Carslaw. 3rd revised edition, an outgrowth of author's courses at Cambridge. Historical introduction, rational, irrational numbers, infinite sequences and series, functions of a single variable, definite integral, Fourier series, and similar topics. Appendices discuss practical harmonic analysis, periodogram analysis, Lebesgue's theory. 84 examples. xiii + 368pp. 5⅜ x 8. S48 Paperbound **$2.00**

SYMBOLIC LOGIC

THE ELEMENTS OF MATHEMATICAL LOGIC, Paul Rosenbloom. First publication in any language. For mathematically mature readers with no training in symbolic . logic. Development of lectures given at Lund Univ., Sweden, 1948. Partial contents: Logic of classes, fundamental theorems, Boolean algebra, logic of propositions, of propositional functions, expressive languages, combinatory logics, development of math within an object language, paradoxes, theorems of Post, Goedel, Church, and similar topics. iv + 214pp. 5⅜ x 8. S227 Paperbound **$1.45**

INTRODUCTION TO SYMBOLIC LOGIC AND ITS APPLICATION, R. Carnap. Clear, comprehensive, rigorous, by perhaps greatest living master. Symbolic languages analyzed, one constructed. Applications to math (axiom systems for set theory, real, natural numbers), topology (Dedekind, Cantor continuity explanations), physics (general analysis of determination, causality, space-time topology), biology (axiom system for basic concepts). "A masterpiece," Zentralblatt für Mathematik und Ihre Grenzgebiete. Over 300 exercises. 5 figures. xvi + 241pp. 5⅜ x 8. S453 Paperbound **$1.85**

AN INTRODUCTION TO SYMBOLIC LOGIC, Susanne K. Langer. Probably clearest book for the philosopher, scientist, layman—no special knowledge of math required. Starts with simplest symbols, goes on to give remarkable grasp of Boole-Schroeder, Russell-Whitehead systems, clearly, quickly. Partial Contents: Forms, Generalization, Classes, Deductive System of Classes, Algebra of Logic, Assumptions of Principia Mathematica, Logistics, Proofs of Theorems, etc. "Clearest . . . simplest introduction . . . the intelligent non-mathematician should have no difficulty," MATHEMATICS GAZETTE. Revised, expanded 2nd edition. Truth-value tables. 368pp. 5⅜ 8. S164 Paperbound **$1.75**

13

TRIGONOMETRICAL SERIES, Antoni Zygmund. On modern advanced level. Contains carefully organized analyses of trigonometric, orthogonal, Fourier systems of functions, with clear adequate descriptions of summability of Fourier series, proximation theory, conjugate series, convergence, divergence of Fourier series. Especially valuable for Russian, Eastern European coverage. 329pp. 5⅜ x 8.   S290 Paperbound **$1.50**

THE LAWS OF THOUGHT, George Boole. This book founded symbolic logic some 100 years ago. It is the 1st significant attempt to apply logic to all aspects of human endeavour. Partial contents: derivation of laws, signs and laws, interpretations, eliminations, conditions of a perfect method, analysis, Aristotelian logic, probability, and similar topics. xvii + 424pp. 5⅜ x 8.   S28 Paperbound **$2.00**

SYMBOLIC LOGIC, C. I. Lewis, C. H. Langford. 2nd revised edition of probably most cited book in symbolic logic. Wide coverage of entire field; one of fullest treatments of paradoxes; plus much material not available elsewhere. Basic to volume is distinction between logic of extensions and intensions. Considerable emphasis on converse substitution, while matrix system presents supposition of variety of non-Aristotelian logics. Especially valuable sections on strict limitations, existence theorems. Partial contents: Boole-Schroeder algebra; truth value systems, the matrix method; implication and deductibility; general theory of propositions; etc. "Most valuable," Times, London. 506pp. 5⅜ x 8.   S170 Paperbound **$2.00**

GROUP THEORY AND LINEAR ALGEBRA, SETS, ETC.

LECTURES ON THE ICOSAHEDRON AND THE SOLUTION OF EQUATIONS OF THE FIFTH DEGREE, Felix Klein. Solution of quintics in terms of rotations of regular icosahedron around its axes of symmetry. A classic, indispensable source for those interested in higher algebra, geometry, crystallography. Considerable explanatory material included. 230 footnotes, mostly bibliography. "Classical monograph . . . detailed, readable book," Math. Gazette. 2nd edition. xvi + 289pp. 5⅜ x 8.   S314 Paperbound **$1.85**

INTRODUCTION TO THE THEORY OF GROUPS OF FINITE ORDER, R. Carmichael. Examines fundamental theorems and their applications. Beginning with sets, systems, permutations, etc., progresses in easy stages through important types of groups: Abelian, prime power, permutation, etc. Except 1 chapter where matrices are desirable, no higher math is needed. 783 exercises, problems. xvi + 447pp. 5⅜ x 8.   S299 Clothbound **$3.95**
                                                                                                                    S300 Paperbound **$2.00**

THEORY OF GROUPS OF FINITE ORDER, W. Burnside. First published some 40 years ago, still one of clearest introductions. Partial contents: permutations, groups independent of representation, composition series of a group, isomorphism of a group with itself, Abelian groups, prime power groups, permutation groups, invariants of groups of linear substitution, graphical representation, etc. "Clear and detailed discussion . . . numerous problems which are instructive," Design News. xxiv + 512pp. 5⅜ x 8.   S38 Paperbound **$2.45**

COMPUTATIONAL METHODS OF LINEAR ALGEBRA, V. N. Faddeeva, translated by C. D. Benster. 1st English translation of unique, valuable work, only one in English presenting systematic exposition of most important methods of linear algebra—classical, contemporary. Details of deriving numerical solutions of problems in mathematical physics. Theory and practice. Includes survey of necessary background, most important methods of solution, for exact, iterative groups. One of most valuable features is 23 tables, triple checked for accuracy, unavailable elsewhere. Translator's note. x + 252pp. 5⅜ x 8.   S424 Paperbound **$1.95**

THE CONTINUUM AND OTHER TYPES OF SERIAL ORDER, E. V. Huntington. This famous book gives a systematic elementary account of the modern theory of the continuum as a type of serial order. Based on the Cantor-Dedekind ordinal theory, which requires no technical knowledge of higher mathematics, it offers an easily followed analysis of ordered classes, discrete and dense series, continuous series, Cantor's transfinite numbers. "Admirable introduction to the rigorous theory of the continuum . . . reading easy," Science Progress. 2nd edition. viii + 82pp. 5⅜ x 8.   S129 Clothbound **$2.75**
                                                                                                                    S130 Paperbound **$1.00**

THEORY OF SETS, E. Kamke. Clearest, amplest introduction in English, well suited for independent study. Subdivisions of main theory, such as theory of sets of points, are discussed, but emphasis is on general theory. Partial contents: rudiments of set theory, arbitrary sets, their cardinal numbers, ordered sets, their order types, well-ordered sets, their cardinal numbers. vii + 144pp. 5⅜ x 8.   S141 Paperbound **$1.35**

CONTRIBUTIONS TO THE FOUNDING OF THE THEORY OF TRANSFINITE NUMBERS, Georg Cantor. These papers founded a new branch of mathematics. The famous articles of 1895-7 are translated, with an 82-page introduction by P. E. B. Jourdain dealing with Cantor, the background of his discoveries, their results, future possibiilties. ix + 211pp. 5⅜ x 8.
                                                                                                                    S45 Paperbound **$1.25**

14

DOVER SCIENCE BOOKS

NUMERICAL AND GRAPHICAL METHODS, TABLES

JACOBIAN ELLIPTIC FUNCTION TABLES, L. M. Milne-Thomson. Easy-to-follow, practical, not only useful numerical tables, but complete elementary sketch of application of elliptic functions. Covers description of principle properties; complete elliptic integrals; Fourier series, expansions; periods, zeros, poles, residues, formulas for special values of argument; cubic, quartic polynomials; pendulum problem; etc. Tables, graphs form body of book: Graph, 5 figure table of elliptic function sn (u m); cn (u m); dn (u m). 8 figure table of complete elliptic integrals K, K′, E, E′, nome q. 7 figure table of Jacobian zeta-function Z(u). 3 figures. xi + 123pp. 5⅜ x 8.   S194 Paperbound **$1.35**

TABLES OF FUNCTIONS WITH FORMULAE AND CURVES, E. Jahnke, F. Emde. Most comprehensive 1-volume English text collection of tables, formulae, curves of transcendent functions. 4th corrected edition, new 76-page section giving tables, formulae for elementary functions not in other English editions. Partial contents: sine, cosine, logarithmic integral; error integral; elliptic integrals; theta functions; Legendre, Bessel, Riemann, Mathieu, hypergeometric functions; etc. "Out-of-the-way functions for which we know no other source." Scientific Computing Service, Ltd. 212 figures. 400pp. 5⅝ x 8⅜.   S133 Paperbound **$2.00**

MATHEMATICAL TABLES, H. B. Dwight. Covers in one volume almost every function of importance in applied mathematics, engineering, physical sciences. Three extremely fine tables of the three trig functions, inverses, to 1000th of radian; natural, common logs; squares, cubes; hyperbolic functions, inverses; $(a^2 + b^2)$ exp. ½a; complete elliptical integrals of 1st, 2nd kind; sine, cosine integrals; exponential integrals; $Ei(x)$ and $Ei(-x)$; binomial coefficients; factorials to 250; surface zonal harmonics, first derivatives; Bernoulli, Euler numbers, their logs to base of 10; Gamma function; normal probability integral; over 60pp. Bessel functions; Riemann zeta function. Each table with formulae generally used, sources of more extensive tables, interpolation data, etc. Over half have columns of differences, to facilitate interpolation. viii + 231pp. 5⅜ x 8.   S445 Paperbound **$1.75**

PRACTICAL ANALYSIS, GRAPHICAL AND NUMERICAL METHODS, F. A. Willers. Immensely practical hand-book for engineers. How to interpolate, use various methods of numerical differentiation and integration, determine roots of a single algebraic equation, system of linear equations, use empirical formulas, integrate differential equations, etc. Hundreds of short-cuts for arriving at numerical solutions. Special section on American calculating machines, by T. W. Simpson. Translation by R. T. Beyer. 132 illustrations. 422pp. 5⅜ x 8.
          S273 Paperbound **$2.00**

NUMERICAL SOLUTIONS OF DIFFERENTIAL EQUATIONS, H. Levy, E. A. Baggott. Comprehensive collection of methods for solving ordinary differential equations of first and higher order. 2 requirements: practical, easy to grasp; more rapid than school methods. Partial contents: graphical integration of differential equations, graphical methods for detailed solution. Numerical solution. Simultaneous equations and equations of 2nd and higher orders. "Should be in the hands of all in research and applied mathematics, teaching," Nature. 21 figures. viii + 238pp. 5⅜ x 8.   S168 Paperbound **$1.75**

NUMERICAL INTEGRATION OF DIFFERENTIAL EQUATIONS, Bennet, Milne, Bateman. Unabridged republication of original prepared for National Research Council. New methods of integration by 3 leading mathematicians: "The Interpolational Polynomial," "Successive Approximation," A. A. Bennett, "Step-by-step Methods of Integration," W. W. Milne. "Methods for Partial Differential Equations," H. Bateman. Methods for partial differential equations, solution of differential equations to non-integral values of a parameter will interest mathematicians, physicists. 288 footnotes, mostly bibliographical. 235 item classified bibliography. 108pp. 5⅜ x 8.   S305 Paperbound **$1.35**

Write for free catalogs!
Indicate your field of interest. Dover publishes books on physics, earth sciences, mathematics, engineering, chemistry, astronomy, anthropology, biology, psychology, philosophy, religion, history, literature, mathematical recreations, languages, crafts, art, graphic arts, etc.

Write to Dept. catr
Dover Publications, Inc.
Science A   *180 Varick St., N. Y. 14, N. Y.*

15